Haynes
THE BOOK ®

Rover 25 & MG ZR Series
Service and Repair Manual

Mike Edge

(4145 - 320 - 9AN2)

Models covered
Rover 25 and MG ZR Hatchback models with petrol and turbo-diesel engines,
including special/limited editions

Petrol engines: 1.1 litre (1120 cc), 1.4 litre (1396 cc), 1.6 litre (1589 cc) & 1.8 litre (1796 cc)
Turbo-diesel engines: 2.0 litre (1994 cc)

*Does not cover 1.1 litre SOHC engine or 1.8 litre DOHC 'VVC' (GTi & ZR160) petrol engine
or 'Stepspeed'/'Steptronic' automatic transmission
Does not cover 'Streetwise' range*

© Haynes Publishing 2010

ABCDE
FGH

A book in the **Haynes Service and Repair Manual Series**

ISBN 978 1 78521 314 4

British Library Cataloguing in Publication Data
A catalogue record for this book is available from the British Library.

Printed in the USA

Haynes Publishing
Sparkford, Yeovil, Somerset BA22 7JJ, England

Haynes North America, Inc
861 Lawrence Drive, Newbury Park, California 91320, USA

Haynes Publishing Nordiska AB
Box 1504, 751 45 UPPSALA, Sverige

*Printed using 33-lb Resolute Book 65 4.0 from Resolute Forest Products Calhoun, TN mill. Resolute is a member of World Wildlife Fund's
Climate Savers programme committed to significantly reducing GHG emissions. This paper uses 50% less wood fibre than traditional offset. The
Calhoun Mill is certified to the following sustainable forest management and chain of custody standards: SFI, PEFC and FSC Controlled Wood.*

Contents

LIVING WITH YOUR ROVER/MG

Roadside Repairs

Weekly Checks

Lubricants and Fluids

Capacities

Tyre Pressures

MAINTENANCE

Routine Maintenance and Servicing

Contents

Launched in November 1999, the Rover 25 and MG ZR 'super-mini' models covered by this manual are a further development based on the Rover 200 three- and five-door hatchback series.

The engine/transmission unit is mounted transversely across the front of the car.

Designed to meet EU3 emission requirements, the four-cylinder petrol engines feature belt-driven double overhead camshafts (DOHC) with four valves per cylinder (16V), and multipoint fuel injection.

Early petrol engines retained the distributor-based ignition system, whilst later engines have a 'distributorless' ignition system with two ignition coils.

Engine operation, including fuelling and ignition, is electronically controlled by a Modular Engine Management System (MEMS) version 3.

Engine emissions are controlled by a comprehensive range of features including – exhaust gas catalytic converter with oxygen sensors, crankcase gas recirculation, and fuel evaporation control.

The four-cylinder diesel engine has a single, belt-driven, overhead camshaft, with two valves per cylinder (8V).

Engine performance is enhanced by use of a turbocharger and intercooler.

Engine operation, including fuel injection timing and quantity, is controlled by an Electronic Diesel Control (EDC) system. The high pressure rotary fuel injection pump is electronically controlled by the EDC, and has no mechanical connection to the throttle pedal.

Engine emissions are controlled by a comprehensive range of features including an exhaust gas catalytic converter, crankcase gas recirculation, and exhaust gas recirculation (EGR).

The gearbox and differential is an integral unit in a common housing attached to the left-hand side of the engine. Drive from the differential to the front wheels is via unequal length solid driveshafts, with constant velocity joints and dynamic dampers.

Suspension is fully independent all round. Each front wheel is carried on a coil-over-damper Macpherson strut, located longitudinally by a tie-bar, and laterally by a transverse lower arm. An anti-roll bar provides roll stiffness.

The rear suspension main components are an H-frame beam axle assembly, and a coil-over-damper strut assembly. The H-frame is attached to the body via brackets forward of the rear wheels. The frame is located in the brackets by an angled pivot bush secured by a through-bolt. The bushes are constructed from a combination of interleaved rubber and steel, and space chambers. This construction causes the bush to react in a predetermined manner according to the direction of applied force. The result is that, during hard cornering, the rear wheels start to turn slightly in phase with the front wheels.

Attached to each side of the H-frame are a stub axle, which carries the hub and wheel assembly, and a coil spring/damper assembly, which controls vertical suspension movement.

A hydraulic, dual circuit brake system, with servo assistance, operates front disc brakes and rear drum brakes on Rover 25 models.

An Anti-lock Brake System (ABS) with Electronic Brake force Distribution (EBD) is standard on 1.6 models, and optional on all other models.

MG ZR

The MG ZR models covered by this manual are 'sports' versions derived from the Rover 25 range.

Sports modifications include stiffer and lowered suspension, and higher geared steering.

ZR 105 and ZR TD have front disc brakes and drum rear brakes. ZR 120 and ZR TD 115 have disc brakes all round.

An Anti-lock Brake System (ABS) with Electronic Brake force Distribution (EBD) is standard on ZR 120 and ZR TD 115 models, and optional on all other models.

Your Rover Manual

The aim of this manual is to help you get the best value from your vehicle. It can do so in several ways. It can help you decide what work must be done (even should you choose

to get it done by a garage), provide information on routine maintenance and servicing, and give a logical course of action and diagnosis when random faults occur. However, it is hoped that you will use the manual by tackling the work yourself. On simpler jobs, it may even be quicker than booking the car into a garage and going there twice, to leave and collect it. Perhaps most important, a lot of money can be saved by avoiding the costs a garage must charge to cover its labour and overheads.

The manual has drawings and descriptions to show the function of the various components, so that their layout can be understood. Then the tasks are described and photographed in a clear step-by-step sequence.

References to the 'left' or 'right' of the vehicle are in the sense of a person in the driver's seat facing forward.

Acknowledgements

Thanks are due to Draper Tools Limited, who supplied some of the workshop tools,

and to all those people at Sparkford who helped in the production of this Manual.

We take great pride in the accuracy of information given in this manual, but vehicle manufacturers make alterations and design changes during the production run of a particular vehicle of which they do not inform us. No liability can be accepted by the authors or publishers for loss, damage or injury caused by any errors in, or omissions from the information given.

Illegal Copying

It is the policy of Haynes Publishing to actively protect its Copyrights and Trade Marks. Legal action will be taken against anyone who unlawfully copies the cover or contents of this Manual. This includes all forms of unauthorised copying including digital, mechanical, and electronic in any form. Authorisation from Haynes Publishing will only be provided expressly and in writing. Illegal copying will also be reported to the appropriate statutory authorities.

Working on your car can be dangerous. This page shows just some of the potential risks and hazards, with the aim of creating a safety-conscious attitude.

General hazards

Scalding

• Don't remove the radiator or expansion tank cap while the engine is hot.
• Engine oil, automatic transmission fluid or power steering fluid may also be dangerously hot if the engine has recently been running.

Burning

• Beware of burns from the exhaust system and from any part of the engine. Brake discs and drums can also be extremely hot immediately after use.

Crushing

• When working under or near a raised vehicle, always supplement the jack with axle stands, or use drive-on ramps. *Never venture under a car which is only supported by a jack.*
• Take care if loosening or tightening high-torque nuts when the vehicle is on stands. Initial loosening and final tightening should be done with the wheels on the ground.

Fire

• Fuel is highly flammable; fuel vapour is explosive.
• Don't let fuel spill onto a hot engine.
• Do not smoke or allow naked lights (including pilot lights) anywhere near a vehicle being worked on. Also beware of creating sparks (electrically or by use of tools).
• Fuel vapour is heavier than air, so don't work on the fuel system with the vehicle over an inspection pit.
• Another cause of fire is an electrical overload or short-circuit. Take care when repairing or modifying the vehicle wiring.
• Keep a fire extinguisher handy, of a type suitable for use on fuel and electrical fires.

Electric shock

• Ignition HT voltage can be dangerous, especially to people with heart problems or a pacemaker. Don't work on or near the ignition system with the engine running or the ignition switched on.

• Mains voltage is also dangerous. Make sure that any mains-operated equipment is correctly earthed. Mains power points should be protected by a residual current device (RCD) circuit breaker.

Fume or gas intoxication

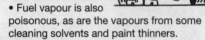

• Exhaust fumes are poisonous; they often contain carbon monoxide, which is rapidly fatal if inhaled. Never run the engine in a confined space such as a garage with the doors shut.
• Fuel vapour is also poisonous, as are the vapours from some cleaning solvents and paint thinners.

Poisonous or irritant substances

• Avoid skin contact with battery acid and with any fuel, fluid or lubricant, especially antifreeze, brake hydraulic fluid and Diesel fuel. Don't syphon them by mouth. If such a substance is swallowed or gets into the eyes, seek medical advice.
• Prolonged contact with used engine oil can cause skin cancer. Wear gloves or use a barrier cream if necessary. Change out of oil-soaked clothes and do not keep oily rags in your pocket.
• Air conditioning refrigerant forms a poisonous gas if exposed to a naked flame (including a cigarette). It can also cause skin burns on contact.

Asbestos

• Asbestos dust can cause cancer if inhaled or swallowed. Asbestos may be found in gaskets and in brake and clutch linings. When dealing with such components it is safest to assume that they contain asbestos.

Special hazards

Hydrofluoric acid

• This extremely corrosive acid is formed when certain types of synthetic rubber, found in some O-rings, oil seals, fuel hoses etc, are exposed to temperatures above 400ºC. The rubber changes into a charred or sticky substance containing the acid. *Once formed, the acid remains dangerous for years. If it gets onto the skin, it may be necessary to amputate the limb concerned.*
• When dealing with a vehicle which has suffered a fire, or with components salvaged from such a vehicle, wear protective gloves and discard them after use.

The battery

• Batteries contain sulphuric acid, which attacks clothing, eyes and skin. Take care when topping-up or carrying the battery.
• The hydrogen gas given off by the battery is highly explosive. Never cause a spark or allow a naked light nearby. Be careful when connecting and disconnecting battery chargers or jump leads.

Air bags

• Air bags can cause injury if they go off accidentally. Take care when removing the steering wheel and/or facia. Special storage instructions may apply.

Diesel injection equipment

• Diesel injection pumps supply fuel at very high pressure. Take care when working on the fuel injectors and fuel pipes.

⚠ *Warning: Never expose the hands, face or any other part of the body to injector spray; the fuel can penetrate the skin with potentially fatal results.*

Remember...

DO

• Do use eye protection when using power tools, and when working under the vehicle.

• Do wear gloves or use barrier cream to protect your hands when necessary.

• Do get someone to check periodically that all is well when working alone on the vehicle.

• Do keep loose clothing and long hair well out of the way of moving mechanical parts.

• Do remove rings, wristwatch etc, before working on the vehicle – especially the electrical system.

• Do ensure that any lifting or jacking equipment has a safe working load rating adequate for the job.

DON'T

• Don't attempt to lift a heavy component which may be beyond your capability – get assistance.

• Don't rush to finish a job, or take unverified short cuts.

• Don't use ill-fitting tools which may slip and cause injury.

• Don't leave tools or parts lying around where someone can trip over them. Mop up oil and fuel spills at once.

• Don't allow children or pets to play in or near a vehicle being worked on.

The following pages are intended to help in dealing with common roadside emergencies and breakdowns. You will find more detailed fault finding information at the back of the manual, and repair information in the main chapters.

If your car won't start and the starter motor doesn't turn

☐ Open the bonnet and make sure that the battery terminals are clean and tight.
☐ Switch on the headlights and try to start the engine. If the headlights go very dim when you're trying to start, the battery is probably flat. Get out of trouble by jump starting (see next page) using another car.

If your car won't start even though the starter motor turns as normal

☐ Is there fuel in the tank?
☐ Is there moisture on electrical components under the bonnet? Switch off the ignition, then wipe off any obvious dampness with a dry cloth. Spray a water-repellent aerosol product (WD-40 or equivalent) on ignition and fuel system electrical connectors like those shown in the photos. Pay special attention to the ignition coils wiring connector. (Note that diesel engines don't normally suffer from damp.)

A A poor earth connection can cause intermittent faults in more than one circuit.

B If the automatic fuel cut-off switch has been triggered, reset it by pressing the rubber disc on top of the switch.

C Check the security and condition of the battery connections.

Check (with the ignition switched off) that all electrical connections are secure and spray them with a water-dispersant spray (such as WD40) if you suspect a problem due to damp.

D Visually check engine harness connections/multi-plugs, including the Engine Control Unit (ECU) connector.

Early engines with distributor – check that the distributor cap connections are clean and secure.

Jump starting

When jump-starting a car using a booster battery, observe the following precautions:

✔ Before connecting the booster battery, make sure that the ignition is switched off.

✔ Ensure that all electrical equipment (lights, heater, wipers, etc) is switched off.

✔ Take note of any special precautions printed on the battery case.

✔ Make sure that the booster battery is the same voltage as the discharged one in the vehicle.

✔ If the battery is being jump-started from the battery in another vehicle, the two vehicles MUST NOT TOUCH each other.

✔ Make sure that the transmission is in neutral (or PARK, in the case of automatic transmission).

HAYNES HiNT *Jump starting will get you out of trouble, but you must correct whatever made the battery go flat in the first place. There are three possibilities:*

1 *The battery has been drained by repeated attempts to start, or by leaving the lights on.*

2 *The charging system is not working properly (alternator drivebelt slack or broken, alternator wiring fault or alternator itself faulty).*

3 *The battery itself is at fault (electrolyte low, or battery worn out).*

1 Connect one end of the red jump lead to the positive (+) terminal of the flat battery

2 Connect the other end of the red lead to the positive (+) terminal of the booster battery.

3 Connect one end of the black jump lead to the negative (-) terminal of the booster battery

4 Connect the other end of the black jump lead to a bolt or bracket on the engine block, well away from the battery, on the vehicle to be started.

5 Make sure that the jump leads will not come into contact with the fan, drive-belts or other moving parts of the engine.

6 Start the engine using the booster battery and run it at idle speed. Switch on the lights, rear window demister and heater blower motor, then disconnect the jump leads in the reverse order of connection. Turn off the lights etc.

Identifying leaks

Puddles on the garage floor or drive, or obvious wetness under the bonnet or underneath the car, suggest a leak that needs investigating. It can sometimes be difficult to decide where the leak is coming from, especially if the engine bay is very dirty already. Leaking oil or fluid can also be blown rearwards by the passage of air under the car, giving a false impression of where the problem lies.

 Warning: Most automotive oils and fluids are poisonous. Wash them off skin, and change out of contaminated clothing, without delay.

HAYNES HiNT *The smell of a fluid leaking from the car may provide a clue to what's leaking. Some fluids are distinctively coloured. It may help to clean the car carefully and to park it over some clean paper overnight as an aid to locating the source of the leak.*
Remember that some leaks may only occur while the engine is running.

Sump oil

Engine oil may leak from the drain plug...

Oil from filter

...or from the base of the oil filter.

Gearbox oil

Gearbox oil can leak from the seals at the inboard ends of the driveshafts.

Antifreeze

Leaking antifreeze often leaves a crystalline deposit like this.

Brake fluid

A leak occurring at a wheel is almost certainly brake fluid.

Power steering fluid

Power steering fluid may leak from the pipe connectors on the steering rack.

Towing

☐ The Rover 25/MG ZR is not fitted with towing eyelets. The lashing eyelets fitted to the front and rear of the car are intended for use by emergency services during vehicle recovery and should not be used for any other purpose.

Wheel changing

 Warning: Do not change a wheel in a situation where you risk being hit by another vehicle. On busy roads, try to stop in a lay-by or a gateway. Be wary of passing traffic while changing the wheel - it is easy to become distracted by the job in hand.

Preparation

☐ When a puncture occurs, stop as soon as it is safe to do so.
☐ Park on firm level ground, if possible, and well out of the way of other traffic.
☐ Use hazard warning lights if necessary.

☐ If you have one, use a warning triangle to alert other drivers of your presence.
☐ Apply the handbrake and engage first or reverse gear.
☐ Chock the wheel diagonally opposite the

one being removed – a couple of large stones will do for this.
☐ If the ground is soft, use a flat piece of wood to spread the load under the foot of the jack.

Changing the wheel

1 Lift up the floor carpet in the boot space and remove the wheel changing toolkit.

2 Unscrew the spare wheel retaining cap.

3 Use the end of the wheel brace to lever off the wheel trim on the flat tyre.

4 Slacken each of the wheel nuts in turn slightly, using the wheel brace.

5 Locate the jack head under the correct jacking point – this is the area between the two protrusions on the sill. Turn the jack handle until the wheel is clear of the ground.

6 Remove the flat wheel and slide it under the sill in front of the jack; this is a safety measure in case the jack collapses.

7 Fit the spare wheel into position.

8 Fit the wheel nuts onto the studs, lower the car to the ground and tighten the wheel nuts securely using the wheel brace.

Finally...

☐ Remove the wheel chocks.
☐ Stow the jack and tools in the correct locations in the car.
☐ Check the tyre pressure on the wheel just fitted. If it is low, or if you don't have a pressure gauge with you, drive slowly to the next garage and inflate the tyre to the correct pressure.
☐ Have the damaged tyre or wheel repaired as soon as possible, or another puncture will leave you stranded.

Introduction

There are some very simple checks which need only take a few minutes to carry out, but which could save you a lot of inconvenience and expense.

These *Weekly checks* require no great skill or special tools, and the small amount of time they take to perform could prove to be very well spent, for example;

☐ Keeping an eye on tyre condition and pressures, will not only help to stop them wearing out prematurely, but could also save your life.

☐ Many breakdowns are caused by electrical problems. Battery-related faults are particularly common, and a quick check on a regular basis will often prevent the majority of these.

☐ If your car develops a brake fluid leak, the first time you might know about it is when your brakes don't work properly. Checking the level regularly will give advance warning of this kind of problem.

☐ If the oil or coolant levels run low, the cost of repairing any engine damage will be far greater than fixing the leak, for example.

Underbonnet check points

◀ Petrol engine

A Brake fluid reservoir

B Engine oil filler cap

C Engine oil level dipstick

D Power steering fluid reservoir

E Windscreen washer fluid reservoir filler cap

F Coolant expansion tank

G Battery

Engine oil level

Before you start
✔ Make sure that your car is on level ground.
✔ Check the oil level before the car is driven, or at least 5 minutes after the engine has been switched off.

 HAYNES HiNT *If the oil is checked immediately after driving the vehicle, some of the oil will remain in the upper engine components, resulting in an inaccurate reading on the dipstick.*

The correct oil
Modern engines place great demands on their oil. It is very important that the correct oil for your car is used (See *Lubricants and fluids*).

Car Care
● If you have to add oil frequently, you should check whether you have any oil leaks. Place some clean paper under the car overnight, and check for stains in the morning. If there are no leaks, the engine may be burning oil.

● Always maintain the level between the upper and lower dipstick marks (see photo 3). If the level is too low severe engine damage may occur. Oil seal failure may result if the engine is overfilled by adding too much oil.

1 The dipstick is located at the right-hand end of the engine (see *Underbonnet check points*). Withdraw the dipstick.

2 Using a clean rag or paper towel, wipe all the oil from the dipstick. Insert the clean dipstick into the tube as far as it will go, then withdraw it again.

3 Note the oil level on the end of the dipstick, which should be between the upper HI mark and the lower LO mark. Approximately 1.0 litre of oil will raise the level from the lower mark to the upper mark.

4 Oil is added through the filler cap. Rotate the cap through a quarter-turn anti-clockwise and withdraw it. Top-up the level. A funnel may help to reduce spillage. Add the oil slowly, checking the level on the dipstick often. Do not overfill.

Power steering fluid level

Before you start
✔ Park the vehicle on level ground.
✔ Set the front roadwheels in the straight-ahead position.
✔ The engine should be turned off.
✔ Do not operate the steering once the engine is stopped.

Safety First!
● If the reservoir requires repeated topping-up, there is a fluid leak somewhere in the system which should be investigated immediately.
● If a leak is suspected, the car should not be driven until the power steering system has been checked.

1 The power steering fluid reservoir is located on the right-hand side of the engine compartment. MAX and MIN level marks are indicated on the side of the reservoir and the fluid level should be maintained between these marks at all times.

2 If topping-up is necessary, first wipe the area around the filler cap with a clean rag before removing the cap. When adding fluid, pour it carefully into the reservoir to avoid spillage – be sure to use only the specified fluid. After filling the reservoir to the proper level, make sure that the cap is refitted securely to avoid leaks and the entry of foreign matter into the reservoir.

Brake fluid level

Warning:
● **Brake fluid can harm your eyes and damage painted surfaces, so use extreme caution when handling and pouring it.**
● **Do not use fluid that has been standing open for some time, as it absorbs moisture from the air, which can cause a dangerous loss of braking effectiveness.**

Before you start

✔ Make sure that your car is on level ground.
✔ Cleanliness is of great importance when dealing with the braking system, so take care to clean around the reservoir cap before topping-up. Use only clean brake fluid from a container which has stood for at least 24 hours (to allow air bubbles to separate out).

Safety First!

● If the reservoir requires repeated topping-up this is an indication of a fluid leak somewhere in the system, which should be investigated immediately.
● If a leak is suspected, the car should not be driven until the braking system has been checked. Never take any risks where brakes are concerned.

1 The brake master cylinder and fluid reservoir is located at the rear right-hand end of the engine compartment. The MAX and MIN level marks are indicated on the side of the reservoir and the fluid level should be maintained between these marks at all times.

3 Before adding fluid it is a good idea to inspect the reservoir. The system should be drained and refilled if deposits, dirt particles or contamination are seen in the fluid.

2 If topping-up is necessary, unplug the electrical connector before removing the cap. Pour fluid carefully into the reservoir to avoid spilling it on surrounding painted surfaces. Be sure to use only the specified brake fluid since mixing different types of fluid can cause damage to the system.

4 After filling the reservoir to the proper level, make sure that the cap is refitted securely to avoid leaks and the entry of foreign matter. Ensure that the fluid level switch plunger is free to move.

Coolant level

Warning: DO NOT attempt to remove the expansion tank pressure cap when the engine is hot, as there is a very great risk of scalding. Do not leave open containers of coolant about, as it is poisonous.

Car Care

● With a sealed-type cooling system, adding coolant should not be necessary on a regular basis. If frequent topping-up is required, it is likely there is a leak. Check the radiator, all hoses and joint faces for signs of staining or wetness, and rectify as necessary.

● It is important that antifreeze is used in the cooling system all year round, not just during the winter months. Don't top-up with water alone, as the antifreeze will become too diluted.

1 The coolant level varies with the temperature of the engine. When the engine is cold, the coolant level should be between the MAX and MIN markings on the side of the reservoir. When the engine is hot, the level may rise slightly.

2 If topping-up is necessary, wait until the engine is cold, then cover the expansion tank with a rag and unscrew the filler cap anti-clockwise. Wait until the hissing ceases, indicating that all pressure is released, then unscrew and remove the filler cap.

3 Add a mixture of water and antifreeze through the expansion tank filler neck, until the coolant is up to the MAX level. Refit the cap, turning it clockwise as far as it will go until it is secure.

Tyre condition and pressure

It is very important that tyres are in good condition, and at the correct pressure - having a tyre failure at any speed is highly dangerous. Tyre wear is influenced by driving style - harsh braking and acceleration, or fast cornering, will all produce more rapid tyre wear. As a general rule, the front tyres wear out faster than the rears. Interchanging the tyres from front to rear ("rotating" the tyres) may result in more even wear. However, if this is completely effective, you may have the expense of replacing all four tyres at once! Remove any nails or stones embedded in the tread before they penetrate the tyre to cause deflation. If removal of a nail does reveal that the tyre has been punctured, refit the nail so that its point of penetration is marked. Then immediately change the wheel, and have the tyre repaired by a tyre dealer.

Regularly check the tyres for damage in the form of cuts or bulges, especially in the sidewalls. Periodically remove the wheels, and clean any dirt or mud from the inside and outside surfaces. Examine the wheel rims for signs of rusting, corrosion or other damage. Light alloy wheels are easily damaged by "kerbing" whilst parking; steel wheels may also become dented or buckled. A new wheel is very often the only way to overcome severe damage.

New tyres should be balanced when they are fitted, but it may become necessary to re-balance them as they wear, or if the balance weights fitted to the wheel rim should fall off. Unbalanced tyres will wear more quickly, as will the steering and suspension components. Wheel imbalance is normally signified by vibration, particularly at a certain speed (typically around 50 mph). If this vibration is felt only through the steering, then it is likely that just the front wheels need balancing. If, however, the vibration is felt through the whole car, the rear wheels could be out of balance. Wheel balancing should be carried out by a tyre dealer or garage.

1 Tread Depth - visual check
The original tyres have tread wear safety bands (B), which will appear when the tread depth reaches approximately 1.6 mm. The band positions are indicated by a triangular mark on the tyre sidewall (A).

2 Tread Depth - manual check
Alternatively, tread wear can be monitored with a simple, inexpensive device known as a tread depth indicator gauge.

3 Tyre Pressure Check
Check the tyre pressures regularly with the tyres cold. Do not adjust the tyre pressures immediately after the vehicle has been used, or an inaccurate setting will result.

Tyre tread wear patterns

Shoulder Wear

Underinflation (wear on both sides)
Under-inflation will cause overheating of the tyre, because the tyre will flex too much, and the tread will not sit correctly on the road surface. This will cause a loss of grip and excessive wear, not to mention the danger of sudden tyre failure due to heat build-up.
Check and adjust pressures
Incorrect wheel camber (wear on one side)
Repair or renew suspension parts
Hard cornering
Reduce speed!

Centre Wear

Overinflation
Over-inflation will cause rapid wear of the centre part of the tyre tread, coupled with reduced grip, harsher ride, and the danger of shock damage occurring in the tyre casing.
Check and adjust pressures

If you sometimes have to inflate your car's tyres to the higher pressures specified for maximum load or sustained high speed, don't forget to reduce the pressures to normal afterwards.

Uneven Wear

Front tyres may wear unevenly as a result of wheel misalignment. Most tyre dealers and garages can check and adjust the wheel alignment (or "tracking") for a modest charge.
Incorrect camber or castor
Repair or renew suspension parts
Malfunctioning suspension
Repair or renew suspension parts
Unbalanced wheel
Balance tyres
Incorrect toe setting
Adjust front wheel alignment
Note: *The feathered edge of the tread which typifies toe wear is best checked by feel.*

Screen washer fluid level

● Screenwash additives not only keep the windscreen clean during bad weather, they also prevent the washer system freezing in cold weather – which is when you are likely to need it most. Don't top up using plain water, as the screenwash will become diluted and will freeze in cold weather.

● Check the operation of the windscreen and rear window washers. Adjust the nozzles using a pin if necessary, aiming the spray to a point slightly above the centre of the swept area.

 Warning: On no account use coolant antifreeze in the washer system - this could discolour or damage paintwork.

1 The reservoir for the windscreen and rear window washer systems is located at the front right-hand side of the engine compartment. When topping-up the reservoir, a screenwash additive should be added in the quantities recommended on the bottle.

Wiper blades

1 Check the condition of the wiper blades. If they are cracked or show any signs of deterioration, or if the glass swept area is smeared, renew them. For maximum clarity of vision, wiper blades should be renewed annually, as a matter of course.

2 To remove a wiper blade, pull the arm fully away from the glass until it locks. Swivel the blade through 90°, press the locking tab with a finger nail and slide the blade out of the arm's hooked end. On refitting, ensure that the blade locks securely into the arm.

Battery

Caution: Before carrying out any work on the vehicle battery, read the precautions given in 'Safety first!' at the start of this manual.

✔ Make sure that the battery tray is in good condition, and that the clamp is tight. Corrosion on the tray, retaining clamp and the battery itself can be removed with a solution of water and baking soda. Thoroughly rinse all cleaned areas with water. Any metal parts damaged by corrosion should be covered with a zinc-based primer, then painted.

✔ Periodically (approximately every three months), check the charge condition of the battery, as described in Chapter 5A.

✔ If the battery is flat, and you need to jump start your vehicle, see *Jump starting*.

1 The battery is located on the left-hand side of the engine compartment. The exterior of the battery should be inspected periodically for damage such as a cracked case or cover.

2 Check the tightness of the battery cable clamps to ensure good electrical connections. You should not be able to move them. Also check each cable for cracks and frayed conductors.

HAYNES HiNT

Battery corrosion can be kept to a minimum by applying a layer of petroleum jelly to the clamps and terminals after they are reconnected.

3 If corrosion (white, fluffy deposits) is evident, remove the cables from the battery terminals, clean them with a small wire brush, then refit them. Automotive stores sell a tool for cleaning the battery post . . .

4 . . . as well as the battery cable clamps.

Electrical systems

HAYNES HiNT *If you need to check your brake lights and indicators unaided, back up to a wall or garage door and operate the lights. The reflected light should show if they are working properly.*

✔ Check all external lights and the horn. Refer to the appropriate Sections of Chapter 12 for details if any of the circuits are found to be inoperative, and replace the fuse if necessary. Most fuses are located behind a panel at the lower right-hand side of the facia. Other fuses are located in the fusebox on the left-hand side of the engine compartment. To replace a blown fuse, pull it from position, using the plastic tool provided. Fit a new fuse of the same rating. If a second fuse blows, it is important that you find the reason – do not use a fuse with a higher rating.

✔ Visually check all accessible wiring connectors, harnesses and retaining clips for security, and for signs of chafing or damage.

1 If a single indicator light, stop-light, sidelight or headlight has failed, it is likely that a bulb has blown, and will need to be renewed. Refer to Chapter 12 for details. If both stop-lights have failed, it is possible that the switch has failed (see Chapter 9).

2 If more than one indicator or tail light has failed, it is likely that either a fuse has blown or that there is a fault in the circuit. Fuses are located behind a cover in the glovebox. Open the glovebox, rotate the screw fastener anti-clockwise to lower the cover. Additional fuses and relays are located in the left-hand side of the engine compartment fusebox.

Lubricants and fluids

Engine	
Petrol	Multigrade engine oil, viscosity SAE 10W/40 to ACEA A2 or A3
Diesel	Multigrade engine oil, viscosity SAE 10W/40 to ACEA A3 and ACEA B3
Cooling system	Ethylene glycol based (with no methanol) with Organic Acid Technology (OAT) corrosion inhibitors. Mixture 50% by volume
Manual transmission	
R65 transmission	Gear oil viscosity SAE 75W-80W to API GL5
PG1 transmission	Special gearbox oil – refer to your Rover dealer
Braking system	Hydraulic fluid to spec. SAE J 1703 or DOT 4, but note that Rover specify brake fluids produced by approved manufacturers only – refer to your Rover dealer
Power steering system	Automatic transmission fluid (ATF) to Dexron II D specification
General greasing	Multi-purpose lithium-based grease to NLGI consistency No 2

Choosing your engine oil

Engines need oil, not only to lubricate moving parts and minimise wear, but also to maximise power output and to improve fuel economy.

HOW ENGINE OIL WORKS

• Beating friction

Without oil, the moving surfaces inside your engine will rub together, heat up and melt, quickly causing the engine to seize. Engine oil creates a film which separates these moving parts, preventing wear and heat build-up.

• Cooling hot-spots

Temperatures inside the engine can exceed 1000° C. The engine oil circulates and acts as a coolant, transferring heat from the hot-spots to the sump.

• Cleaning the engine internally

Good quality engine oils clean the inside of your engine, collecting and dispersing combustion deposits and controlling them until they are trapped by the oil filter or flushed out at oil change.

OIL CARE - FOLLOW THE CODE

To handle and dispose of used engine oil safely, always:

- **Avoid skin contact with used engine oil. Repeated or prolonged contact can be harmful.**
- **Dispose of used oil and empty packs in a responsible manner in an authorised disposal site. Call 0800 663366 to find the one nearest to you. Never tip oil down drains or onto the ground.**

Capacities

Engine oil	4.5 litres – including filter
Cooling system	
Petrol engines	5.5 litres (from dry)
Diesel engines	7.0 litres (from dry)
Manual transmission	
R65	2.0 litres (from dry)/1.8 litres (drain and refill)
PG1	2.2 litres (from dry)/2.0 litres (drain and refill)
Power steering reservoir	0.3 litres
Fuel tank	50 litres
Washer system reservoir	6.5 litres

Tyre pressures (cold)

Note: *This is a selection of typical tyre pressures – refer to your handbook, service station wallchart or Rover dealer for greater detail.*

Petrol models

Normal driving conditions	Bar	lbf/in²
175/65 R14:		
Front & rear	2.1	30
185/65 R14:		
Front & rear	1.9	28
185/55 R15:		
Front & rear	2.1	30
205/50 R16:		
Front & rear	1.9	<u>28</u>
205/45 R14:		
Front & rear	1.9	28

Speeds above 100 mph (160 km/h)		
175/65 R14:		
Front & rear	2.3	33
185/65 R14:		
Front & rear	2.1	30
185/55 R15:		
Front & rear	2.4	35
205/50 R16:		
Front & rear	1.9	28
205/45 R14:		
Front & rear	1.9	28

Diesel models

Normal driving conditions		
185/65 R14:		
Front & rear	2.1	30
185/55 R15:		
Front	2.3	33
Rear	2.1	30
205/50 R16 and 205/45 R17:		
Front	2.2	32
Rear	1.9	28

Speeds above 100 mph (160 km/h)		
185/65 R14:		
Front & rear	2.1	30
185/55 R15:		
Front	2.4	35
Rear	2.2	32
205/50 R16 and 205/45 R17:		
Front	2.2	32
Rear	1.9	28

Note: *Pressures apply only to original equipment tyres and may vary if any other make or type is fitted. Check with the tyre manufacturer or supplier for correct pressures if necessary. Pressures also vary for increased loads or towing – refer to your car's handbook or Rover dealer .*

Chapter 1 Part A:
Routine maintenance and servicing – petrol models

Contents

Degrees of difficulty

Easy, suitable for novice with little experience

Fairly easy, suitable for beginner with some experience

Fairly difficult, suitable for competent DIY mechanic

Difficult, suitable for experienced DIY mechanic

Very difficult, suitable for expert DIY or professional

Lubricants, fluids and capacities .... Refer to the end of *Weekly Checks* on page 0•17

Cooling system

Antifreeze properties – 50% antifreeze (by volume):
Commences freezing	- 36°C
Frozen solid	- 48°C

Fuel system

Idle speed	825 ± 50 rpm (Controlled by MEMS)
Idle mixture (CO content) – engine at normal operating temperature ..	Less than 0.5 %
Recommended fuel	95 RON premium unleaded

Ignition system

Firing order	1-3-4-2 (No 1 cylinder at timing belt end of engine)
Crankshaft rotation	Clockwise (viewed from timing belt end of engine)
Distributor rotor arm rotation	Anti-clockwise (viewed from flywheel end of engine)
Ignition timing	Controlled by engine management system – no adjustment possible

Spark plugs:

	Type	Electrode gap
1.1 litre	No Bosch recommendation	
1.4 litre:		
Up to chassis number YD471564:		
MG models	Bosch FR 7 D+X	1.1 mm
Non-MG models	Bosch FR 7 D+	0.9 mm
From chassis number YD471565	Bosch FR 7 DPP 22 U	1.0 mm
1.6 litre:		
Up to chassis number YD471564	Bosch FR 7 D+	0.9 mm
From chassis number YD471565	Bosch FR 7 DPP 22 U	1.0 mm
1.8 litre	Bosch FR 7 DPP 22 U	1.0 mm

Braking system

Front and rear brake pad friction material minimum thickness	3.0 mm
Rear brake shoe friction material minimum thickness	2.0 mm
Handbrake lever travel:	
Models with rear drum brakes	8 to 12 clicks
Models with rear disc brakes	10 to 14 clicks

Suspension and steering

Power steering pump drivebelt deflection:
Used belt	7.5 to 8.5 mm
New belt	5.5 to 8.5 mm

Tyre pressures .... Refer to the end of *Weekly checks* on page 0•18

Electrical system

Alternator/air conditioning compressor drivebelt deflection:
With air conditioning	9 to 10 mm
Without air conditioning	6 to 8 mm

Torque wrench settings

	Nm	lbf ft
Alternator mounting bolts	25	18
Alternator/air conditioning compressor drivebelt tensioner pulley bolt .	25	18
Brake caliper bleed screws	10	7
Engine oil drain plug	28	21
Front/rear brake caliper guide pin bolts	27	20
Fuel pipe to filter unions	28	21
Manual transmission filler/level plug:		
R65-type transmission	25	18
PG1-type transmission	40	30
Plug top coils to camshaft cover	9	7
Power steering drivebelt tensioner pulley bolt	25	18
Rear brake drum retaining screws	7	5
Roadwheel nuts	See Chapter 10	
Spark plug coil cover to camshaft cover	9	7
Spark plugs	25	18
Wheel cylinder bleed screws	7	5

The maintenance intervals in this manual are provided with the assumption that you will be carrying out the work yourself. These are based on the minimum maintenance intervals recommended by the manufacturer for vehicles driven daily. If you wish to keep your vehicle in peak condition at all times, you may wish to perform some of these procedures more often. We encourage frequent maintenance because it enhances the efficiency, performance and resale value of your vehicle.

If the vehicle is driven in dusty areas, used to tow a trailer, or driven frequently at slow speeds (idling in traffic) or on short journeys, more frequent maintenance intervals are recommended.

When the vehicle is new, it should be serviced by a factory-authorised dealer service department, in order to preserve the factory warranty.

Every 250 miles (400 km) or weekly

☐ Refer to *Weekly Checks*

Every 7500 miles (12 000 km) or 6 months – whichever comes first

☐ Engine oil and filter – renew (Section 3)
Note: *Frequent oil and filter changes are good for the engine. We recommend renewing the oil and filter at these intervals, or at least twice a year.*

Every 15 000 miles (24 000 km) or 12 months whichever comes first

☐ Bodywork corrosion check (Section 4)
☐ Alarm remote keypad batteries – renew (Section 5)
☐ Coolant specific gravity – check (Section 6)
☐ Manual transmission – check oil level (Section 7)
☐ Vacuum hose – check condition (Section 8)
☐ Underbonnet and underbody hoses and pipes – check condition (Section 9)
☐ Air conditioning system check and heater/ventilation intake filter renewal (Section 10)
☐ Auxiliary drivebelt – check condition and tension (Section 11)
☐ Exhaust system check (Section 12)
☐ Front brake check (Section 13)
☐ Rear brake check (Section 14)
☐ Driveshaft and gaiter check (Section 15)
☐ Suspension and steering check (Section 16)
☐ Handbrake check (Section 17)
☐ Lock and hinge lubrication (Section 18)
☐ Windscreen and number plate check (Section 19)
☐ Seat belt check (Section 20)
☐ SRS system component check (Section 21)
☐ Road test (Section 22)

Every 30 000 miles (48 000 km) or 2 years – whichever comes first

☐ Brake fluid – renew (Section 23)

Every 45 000 miles (72 000 km) or 3 years – whichever comes first

☐ Air filter element – renew (Section 24)

Every 60 000 miles (96 000 km) or 4 years – whichever comes first

☐ Spark plugs – renew (Section 25)
☐ Coolant – renew (Section 26)
☐ Fuel filter – renew (Section 27)

Every 90 000 miles (144 000 km) or 6 years – whichever comes first

☐ Camshaft drivebelt – renew (Section 28)
Note: *This is the MG Rover recommendation. However, because of the serious and extensive damage which will occur to the engine if the belt breaks, we strongly recommend that belts are renewed more frequently – eg, every 45 000 miles (72 000 km) or 3 years.*

Every 105 000 miles (168 000 km) or 7 years – whichever comes first

☐ Manual transmission oil – renew (Section 29)

Every 15 years, regardless of mileage

☐ SRS components – renew (Section 30)

Underbonnet view of a Rover 25 with K series petrol engine

1 Engine oil dipstick
2 Engine oil filler cap
3 Spark plugs
4 Alternator
5 Washer fluid reservoir cap
6 Power steering fluid
   reservoir cap
7 Windscreen wiper motor
8 Brake fluid
   reservoir/master cylinder
9 Fuel filter
10 Coolant expansion tank
11 Throttle body
12 Air filter housing
13 Battery
14 Engine compartment
   fusebox

Front underbody view of a Rover 25 with K series petrol engine

1 Brake caliper
2 Tie bar
3 Suspension lower arm
4 Track rod
5 Power steering gear
6 Anti-roll bar
7 Exhaust system front pipe
8 Suspension front beam
9 Radiator
10 Engine oil filter
11 Sump drain plug
12 Driveshaft

Rear underbody view of a Rover 25 with K series petrol engine

1 Handbrake cables
2 Beam axle assembly
3 Beam axle pivot mountings
4 Fuel tank
5 Suspension strut lower mountings
6 Exhaust system tailbox
7 Brake backplates

Maintenance procedures – petrol models

1 Introduction

This Chapter is designed to help the home mechanic maintain his/her vehicle for safety, economy, long life and peak performance.

The Chapter contains a master maintenance schedule, referring to Sections dealing specifically with each task in the schedule, or other Chapters. Visual checks, adjustments, component renewal and other helpful items are included. Refer to the accompanying illustrations of the engine compartment and the underside of the vehicle for the locations of the various components.

Servicing your vehicle in accordance with the mileage/time maintenance schedule and the following Sections will provide a planned maintenance programme, which should result in a long and reliable service life. This is a comprehensive plan, so maintaining some items but not others at the specified service intervals will not produce the same results.

As you service your vehicle, you will discover that many of the procedures can be grouped together, because of the particular procedure being performed, or because of the close proximity of two otherwise-unrelated components to one another. For example, if the vehicle is raised for any reason, the exhaust can be inspected at the same time as the suspension and steering components.

The first step in this maintenance programme is to prepare yourself before the actual work begins. Read through all the Sections relevant to the work to be carried out, then make a list and gather together all the parts and tools required. If a problem is encountered, seek advice from a parts specialist, or a dealer service department.

2 Maintenance

1 If, from the time the vehicle is new, the routine maintenance schedule is followed closely and frequent checks are made of fluid levels and high-wear items, as suggested throughout this Manual, the engine will be kept in relatively good running condition and the need for additional work will be minimised.
2 It is possible that there will be times when the engine is running poorly due to the lack of regular maintenance. This is even more likely if a used vehicle, which has not received regular and frequent maintenance checks, is purchased. In such cases, additional work may need to be carried out, outside of the regular maintenance intervals.
3 If engine wear is suspected, a compression test will provide valuable information regarding the overall performance of the main internal components. Such a test can be used as a basis to decide on the extent of the work to be carried out. If, for example, a compression test indicates serious internal engine wear, conventional maintenance as described in this Chapter will not greatly improve the performance of the engine, and may prove a waste of time and money, unless extensive overhaul work is carried out first.
4 The following series of operations are those most often required to improve the performance of a generally poor-running engine:

Primary operations

a) Clean, inspect and test the battery.
b) Check all the engine-related fluids.
c) Check the condition and tension of the auxiliary drivebelt(s).
d) Renew the spark plugs.
e) Early engines – inspect the distributor cap, coil and HT leads. Later engines – inspect the twin coils and HT leads (under spark plug cover).
f) Check the condition of the air cleaner filter element, and renew if necessary.
g) Renew the fuel filter (if fitted).
h) Check the condition of all hoses, and check for fluid leaks.
i) Check the idle speed and mixture settings – as applicable.

5 If the above operations do not prove fully effective, carry out the following operations:

Secondary operations

a) Check the charging system.
b) Check the ignition system.
c) Check the fuel system.
d) Early engines – renew the distributor cap/ rotor arm/coil/HT leads as applicable. Later engines – renew the twin coils/HT leads as applicable (under spark plug cover).
e) Renew the ignition HT leads – as applicable.

3.5 Slackening the engine oil drain plug

3.8 Oil filter location

Every 7500 miles (12 000 km) or 6 months

3 Engine oil and filter renewal

Note: *An oil filter removal tool and a new oil drain plug sealing washer will be required for this operation.*

1 Frequent oil and filter changes are the most important preventative maintenance procedures which can be undertaken by the DIY owner. As engine oil ages, it becomes diluted and contaminated, which leads to premature engine wear.

2 Before starting this procedure, gather together all the necessary tools and materials. Also make sure that you have plenty of clean rags and newspapers handy, to mop up any spills. Ideally, the engine oil should be warm, as it will drain more easily, and more built-up sludge will be removed with it. Take care not to touch the exhaust or any other hot parts of the engine when working under the vehicle. To avoid any possibility of scalding, and to protect yourself from possible skin irritants and other harmful contaminants in used engine oils, it is advisable to wear gloves when carrying out this work.

3.10 Slackening the filter using an oil filter removal tool

3 Access to the underside of the vehicle will be greatly improved if it can be raised on a lift, driven onto ramps, or jacked up and supported on axle stands (see *Jacking and Vehicle Support*). Whichever method is chosen, make sure that the vehicle remains level, or if it is at an angle, that the drain plug is at the lowest point. The drain plug is located at the front of the sump.

4 Remove the oil filler cap from the cylinder head cover.

5 Using a spanner, or preferably a suitable socket and bar, slacken the drain plug about half a turn **(see illustration)**. Position the draining container under the drain plug, then remove the plug completely. If possible, try to keep the plug pressed into the sump while unscrewing it by hand the last couple of turns.

> **HAYNES HINT** *As the plug releases from the threads, move it away sharply, so that the stream of oil from the sump runs into the container, not up your sleeve.*

6 Allow some time for the oil to drain, noting that it may be necessary to reposition the container as the oil flow slows to a trickle.

7 After all the oil has drained, wipe the drain plug and the sealing washer with a clean rag. The sealing washer should be renewed as a matter of course. Clean the area around the drain plug opening, and refit the plug complete with the new sealing washer. Tighten the plug securely, preferably to the specified torque, using a torque wrench.

8 The oil filter is located at the right-hand front corner of the engine. Access is most easily obtained by jacking up the front of the vehicle (see *Jacking and Vehicle Support*) **(see illustration)**.

9 Move the container into position under the oil filter.

10 Use an oil filter removal tool to slacken the filter initially, then unscrew it by hand the rest of the way **(see illustration)**. Empty the oil from the old filter into the container.

11 Use a clean rag to remove all oil, dirt and sludge from the filter sealing area on the engine. Check the old filter to make sure that the rubber sealing ring has not stuck to the engine. If it has, carefully remove it.

12 Apply a light coating of clean engine oil to the sealing ring on the new filter, then screw the filter into position on the engine. Tighten the filter firmly by hand only – **do not** use any tools.

13 Remove the old oil and all tools from under the vehicle then, if applicable, lower the vehicle to the ground.

14 Fill the engine through the filler hole in the cylinder head cover, using the correct grade and type of oil (see *Lubricants and fluids*). Pour in half the specified quantity of oil first, then wait a few minutes for the oil to drain into the sump. Continue to add oil, a small quantity at a time, until the level is up to the lower mark on the dipstick. Adding approximately 1.0 litre will bring the level up to the upper mark on the dipstick.

15 Start the engine and run it for a few minutes, while checking for leaks around the oil filter seal and the sump drain plug. Note that there may be a delay of a few seconds before the low oil pressure warning light goes out when the engine is first started, as the oil circulates through the new oil filter and the engine oil galleries before the pressure builds-up.

16 Stop the engine, and wait a few minutes for the oil to settle in the sump once more. With the new oil circulated and the filter now completely full, recheck the level on the dipstick, and add more oil as necessary.

17 Dispose of the used engine oil safely.

5.1a Using a flat-bladed screwdriver, carefully prise the two halves of the keypad apart . . .

5.1b . . . to expose the battery

5.3 Fit the new battery, handling it with a piece of tissue paper to avoid touching the battery contact surfaces

Every 15 000 miles (24 000 km) or 12 months

4 Bodywork corrosion check

1 Start at the front of the car and work along each body panel in turn, look for any signs of paintwork damage. It may be possible to repair small scratches with a touch-up pen. These should be purchased from a Rover dealer, to get an accurate colour match.

2 Larger scratches that have penetrated the primer or exposed the bare metal beneath should be repaired professionally. The Rover 25 has an extensive Anti-Corrosion Warranty, the terms of which specify how bodywork repairs must be carried out; failure to adhere to the guidelines may invalidate the Warranty. Have the damage assessed by a Rover Dealer or automotive bodywork specialist at the earliest opportunity.

3 Check each body panel for evidence of corrosion, such as raised blisters behind the paintwork and rust-coloured staining. Pay particular attention to vulnerable areas, including the wheel arches, the front edge of the bonnet , the front valence (under the front bumper) and the lower edges of the doors. Corrosion can quickly destroy bodywork, so have any dubious-looking areas examined by a professional.

4 Jack up the front/rear car and support it securely on axle stands (see *Jacking and Vehicle Support*).

5 Examine the underside of the car for signs of corrosion. Look for cracking or flaking of the metal floorpan. Pay particular attention to the areas around the suspension and steering components mountings. Look for damage that may have been caused by attempting to jack up the car at incorrect jacking points.

6 Check for corrosion along the length of the side sills, which run between the front and rear wheel arches.

7 The underside of the vehicle is coated with a protective sealant, which helps to prevent corrosion. If this coating has been scraped off at any point, due to an impact or repair work, it must be re-applied as soon as possible, to protect the bodywork beneath.

5 Alarm remote keypad battery renewal

1 Place the keypad on a work surface and using a flat-bladed screwdriver, carefully prise the two halves of the keypad apart (see illustrations). Take care to avoid damaging the rubber seal and internal components with the screwdriver blade.

2 Remove the battery from the terminal clips, noting which way up it is. Press each keypad button in turn and hold it down for a few seconds, to fully discharge the electronic components inside.

3 Obtain a new battery of the correct type and insert it between the terminal clips, ensuring that it is fitted the correct way around (the positive '+' side faces upwards). Avoid touching the contact surfaces of the battery as you do this, by handling it with a piece of tissue paper; moisture from fingertips can cause the battery surfaces to corrode (see illustration).

4 Press the two halves of the keypad back together, ensuring that the rubber seal is correctly located, then check the operation of the keypad.

6.3 Using a hydrometer to measure the specific gravity of the coolant

6 Coolant specific gravity check

1 Ensure that the engine has cooled completely before starting work.

2 Slowly unscrew the coolant expansion tank cap by about half a turn, allowing any residual pressure in the cooling system to reduce gradually – use a cloth to protect your hands from any escaping steam.

3 Insert a hydrometer into the expansion tank filler neck and measure the specific gravity of the coolant (see illustration).

4 The hydrometer shown in the photo incorporates an integral syringe, which allows a 'sample' of the coolant to be collected. The coloured indicator balls inside the hydrometer float or sink in the coolant sample, depending on the specific gravity.

5 If the specific gravity is too low, do not try to correct it by adding neat antifreeze, as it may not mix completely with the existing coolant and could lead to 'hot spots' in the cooling system. With reference to Section 26, partially drain the cooling system, then refill it with antifreeze and water mixed in the correct proportions.

6 If the specific gravity is too high, refer to Section 26 and partially drain the cooling system, then top up with clean water.

7 Manual transmission oil level check

1 Ensure that the vehicle is parked on level ground then, where applicable, remove the engine/transmission undershield to gain access to the transmission filler/level plug.

2 Remove all traces of dirt from around the filler/level plug which is located on the left-hand side of the transmission, behind the driveshaft inboard joint. Place a suitable container beneath the plug to catch any

7.2a Transmission filler/level plug (arrowed) – R65-type transmission

7.2b Transmission filler/level plug (arrowed) – PG1-type transmission

7.5 Topping up the transmission oil level – PG1-type transmission

escaping oil, then unscrew the plug and recover the sealing washer **(see illustrations)**.

3 Check that the oil is level with the bottom of the filler/level plug hole. Note that oil which has collected behind the filler/level plug will probably trickle out when the plug is removed, which can give a false impression that the level is correct.

4 If necessary, top up using the specified type of oil (see *Lubricants and fluids*). Refilling the transmission is an awkward operation. Allow plenty of time for the oil level to settle properly before checking it. Note that the car must be parked on flat level ground when checking the oil level.

5 Using a tube inserted through the filler/level plug hole, slowly top up the level until the oil reaches the bottom of the filler/level plug hole **(see illustration)**. Allow plenty of time for the level to stabilise.

6 When the level is correct, refit the filler/level plug, using a new sealing washer, and tighten it to the specified torque.

8 Vacuum hose condition check

1 Open the bonnet and check the condition of the vacuum hose that connects the brake servo to the inlet manifold **(see illustration)**. Look for damage in the form of chafing, melting or cracking. Check that the union nuts and T-joints (where applicable) are secure. Also examine the vacuum hoses serving the

evaporative loss emission control and fuel pressure regulation systems.

2 A leak in a vacuum hose means that air is being drawn into the hose (rather than escaping from it) and this makes leakage very difficult to detect. If you suspect that a vacuum hose may be leaking, the following method may help you to pinpoint it. Start the engine and allow it to idle. Hold one end of a length of narrow bore tubing close to your ear, then run the other end along the vacuum hose. If a leak exists, you should be able to hear a hissing noise through the tubing as the air 'escapes' into the hose at the suspected leak.

9 Underbonnet and underbody hose and pipe condition check

Coolant

⚠ **Warning: Refer to the safety information given in 'Safety First!' and Chapter 3, before disturbing any of the cooling system components.**

1 Carefully check the radiator and heater coolant hoses along their entire length. Renew any hose which is cracked, swollen or which shows signs of deterioration. Cracks will show up better if the hose is squeezed **(see illustration)**. Pay close attention to the clips that secure the hoses to the cooling system components. Hose clips that have been over-tightened can pinch and puncture hoses, resulting in leakage.

2 Inspect all the cooling system components (hoses, joint faces, etc) for leaks. Where any problems of this nature are found on system components, renew the component or gasket with reference to Chapter 3.

3 A leak from the cooling system will usually show up as white or rust-coloured deposits, on the area surrounding the leak **(see Haynes Hint)**.

Fuel

⚠ **Warning: Refer to the safety information given in 'Safety First!' and the relevant part of Chapter 4, before disturbing any of the fuel system components.**

4 Petrol leaks are difficult to pinpoint, unless the leakage is significant and hence easily visible. Fuel tends to evaporate quickly once it comes into contact with air, especially in a hot engine bay. Small drips can disappear before you get a chance to identify the point of leakage. If you suspect that there is a fuel leak from the area of the engine bay, leave the vehicle overnight then start the engine from cold, with the bonnet open. Metal components tend to shrink when they are cold, and rubber seals and hoses tend to harden, so any leaks may be more apparent whilst the engine is warming up from a cold start.

5 Check all fuel lines at their connections to the fuel rail, fuel pressure regulator and fuel filter **(see illustration)**. Examine each rubber

8.1 Check the condition of the brake servo vacuum hose

9.1 Checking the condition of a coolant hose

HAYNES HINT

Leaks in the cooling system will usually show up as white or rust coloured deposits around the point of leakage.

9.5 Check for fuel leaks at the fuel filter unions (arrowed)

9.9 Checking a power steering fluid hose for damage

9.15 Checking a master cylinder brake pipe union for leakage

fuel hose along its length for splits or cracks. Check for leakage from the crimped joints between rubber and metal fuel lines. Examine the unions between the metal fuel lines and the fuel filter housing. Also check the area around the fuel injectors for signs of O-ring leakage.

6 To identify fuel leaks between the fuel tank and the engine bay, the vehicle should be raised and securely supported on axle stands (see *Jacking and Vehicle Support*). Inspect the petrol tank and filler neck for punctures, cracks and other damage. The connection between the filler neck and tank is especially critical. Sometimes a rubber filler neck or connecting hose will leak due to loose retaining clamps or deteriorated rubber.

7 Carefully check all rubber hoses and metal fuel lines leading away from the petrol tank. Check for loose connections, deteriorated hoses, kinked lines, and other damage. Pay particular attention to the vent pipes and hoses, which often loop up around the filler neck and can become blocked or kinked, making tank filling difficult. Follow the fuel supply and return lines to the front of the vehicle, carefully inspecting them all the way for signs of damage or corrosion. Renew damaged sections as necessary.

Power assisted steering fluid

8 Examine the hose running between the fluid reservoir and the power steering pump, and the return hose running from the steering rack to the fluid reservoir. Also examine the high pressure supply hose between the pump and the steering rack **(see illustration)**.

9 Pay particular attention to crimped unions, and the area surrounding the hoses that are secured with adjustable worm drive clips. PAS fluid is a thin oil, and is usually red in colour.

Air conditioning refrigerant

⚠️ *Warning: Refer to the safety information given in 'Safety First!' and Chapter 3, regarding the dangers of disturbing any of the air conditioning system components.*

10 The air conditioning system is filled with a liquid refrigerant, which is retained under high pressure. If the air conditioning system is opened and depressurised without the aid of

specialised equipment, the refrigerant will immediately turn into gas and escape into the atmosphere. If the liquid comes into contact with your skin, it can cause severe frostbite. In addition, the refrigerant may contain substances which are environmentally damaging; for this reason, it should not be allowed to escape into the atmosphere.

11 Any suspected air conditioning system leaks should be immediately referred to a Rover dealer or air conditioning specialist. Leakage will be shown up as a steady drop in the level of refrigerant in the system – refer to Section 10 for details.

12 Note that water may drip from the condenser drain pipe, underneath the car, immediately after the air conditioning system has been in use. This is normal, and should not be cause for concern.

Brake fluid

⚠️ *Warning: Refer to the safety information given in 'Safety First!' and Chapter 9, regarding the dangers of handling brake fluid.*

13 With reference to Chapter 9, examine the following items and their connections for signs of fluid leaks – master cylinder, proportioning valve, ABS hydraulic unit, and fluid reservoir **(see illustration)**. Brake fluid is an effective paint stripper, so if cracked or bubbling paintwork on or around any of the braking system components is found, suspect fluid leakage.

14 If fluid loss is evident, but the leak cannot be pinpointed in the engine bay, the brake calipers and underbody brakelines should be carefully checked with the vehicle raised and supported on axle stands (see *Jacking and Vehicle Support*). Leakage of fluid from the braking system is a serious fault that must be rectified immediately.

15 Brake hydraulic fluid is a toxic substance with a watery consistency. New fluid is almost colourless, but it becomes darker with age and use.

Unidentified fluid leaks

16 If there are signs that a fluid of some description is leaking from the vehicle, but you cannot identify the type of fluid or its exact origin, park the vehicle overnight and slide a large piece of card underneath it. Providing that

the card is positioned in roughly in the right location, even the smallest leak will show up on the card. Not only will this help you to pinpoint the exact location of the leak, it should be easier to identify the fluid from its colour. Bear in mind, though, that the leak may only be occurring when the engine is running!

Vacuum hoses

17 Refer to Section 8.

10 Air conditioning system check and heater/ventilation intake filter renewal

1 The refrigerant condition and level is checked via the sightglass on the top of the receiver/drier. The receiver/drier is situated in the engine compartment, just to the left of the radiator.

2 Start the engine then switch on the air conditioning system and allow the engine to idle for a couple of minutes whilst observing the sightglass. If the air conditioning system is operating normally then occasional bubbles should be visible through the sightglass.

3 If a constant stream of bubbles is visible, the refrigerant level is low and must be topped up. If the sightglass has become clouded or streaked, there is a fault in the system. If either condition is present, the vehicle must be taken to a Rover dealer or suitable professional refrigeration specialist for the air conditioning system to be checked further and overhauled.

4 It is recommended that the heater/ventilation intake filter (pollen filter) is renewed at this service interval. Refer to the procedures contained in Chapter 3, Section 10.

11 Auxiliary drivebelt tension and condition check

General information

1 Two micro-V drivebelts are fitted; both are driven from the crankshaft pulley.

The outer belt drives the power steering pump, and is automatically tensioned by a spring-loaded roller.

The inner belt drives the alternator, and has

11.6a Slacken the alternator upper pivot mounting bolts (arrowed) . . .

11.6b . . . and lower adjusting arm bolt (A) then rotate adjuster bolt (located in the end of the arm) – models without air conditioning

H44811

11.10 Alternator drivebelt adjustment – models with air conditioning

a manual tensioner at the base of the alternator. When air conditioning is fitted, this belt also drives the refrigerant compressor. In this configuration, a spring-loaded roller automatically controls belt tension.

Checking condition

2 Check the belts for cracks, splitting, fraying, glazing (shiny patches) or other damage. Use a socket and extension bar on the crankshaft bolt to turn the crankshaft, so that the whole length of both belts can be examined. Renew any worn or damaged belt – see Chapter 5A or 10.

Checking/adjusting tension

Alternator with no air conditioning

3 Disconnect the battery earth lead.
4 Apply the handbrake, chock the rear roadwheels, then jack up the front of the car and support it on axle stands (see *Jacking and Vehicle Support*). Remove the right hand front roadwheel.
5 Check tension by applying a force of 10 kg to the belt upper run, midway between the crankshaft pulley and alternator pulley. If belt deflection is more or less than that specified, adjust the belt tension.
6 Slacken upper and lower alternator mounting bolts. Slacken adjusting link bolt. Increase tension by turning the tension adjusting bolt clockwise **(see illustrations)**. *Caution: Do not apply excessive torque to the adjusting bolt. If it is seized, apply anti-seize fluid.*

7 Tighten the mounting bolts to the specified torque. Recheck the belt tension.
8 Fit the roadwheel, and tighten the nuts to secure the wheel. Remove the stands and lower the vehicle to the ground. Use a torque wrench to tighten the roadwheel nuts to the specified torque.
9 Connect the battery earth lead.

Alternator with air conditioning

10 The spring-loaded roller automatically controls belt tension. Check the position of the tension indicator in the slot. The belt must be renewed before the indicator reaches the right hand end of the slot **(see illustration)**.
11 For belt renewal see Chapter 10.

Power steering belt

12 The spring-loaded roller automatically controls belt tension. Check the position of the tension indicator in the slot. The belt must be renewed before the indicator reaches the left the recess in the tensioner backplate.
13 For belt renewal see Chapter 10.

12 Exhaust system check

1 With the engine cold (at least an hour after the vehicle has been driven), check the complete exhaust system from the engine to the end of the tailpipe. The exhaust system is most easily checked with the vehicle raised on a hoist, or suitably supported on axle stands,

so that the exhaust components are readily visible and accessible.
2 Check the exhaust pipes and connections for evidence of leaks, severe corrosion and damage. Make sure that all brackets and mountings are in good condition, and that all relevant nuts and bolts are tight **(see illustration)**. Leakage at any of the joints or in other parts of the system will usually show up as a black sooty stain in the vicinity of the leak.
3 Rattles and other noises can often be traced to the exhaust system, especially the brackets and mountings. Try to move the pipes and silencers. If the components are able to come into contact with the body or suspension parts, secure the system with new mountings. Otherwise separate the joints (if possible) and twist the pipes as necessary to provide additional clearance.

13 Front brake check

1 Firmly apply the handbrake then jack up the front of the vehicle and support it securely on axle stands (see *Jacking and Vehicle Support*). Remove the front roadwheels.
2 For a quick check, the thickness of friction material remaining on each brake pad can be measured through the inspection aperture in the front of the caliper body **(see illustration)**. If any pad's friction material is worn to the specified thickness or less, all four pads must be renewed as a set.
3 For a comprehensive check, the brake pads should be removed and cleaned. This will permit the operation of the caliper to be checked and the condition of the brake disc itself to be fully examined on both sides. Refer to Chapter 9 for further information.

12.2 Make sure that the exhaust mountings are in good condition

13.2 Front brake pad friction material (arrowed) can be measured through the inspection aperture in caliper body

14 Rear brake check

Models with drum brakes

1 Chock the front wheels then jack up the rear of the vehicle and support it on axle stands (see *Jacking and Vehicle Support*).

2 For a quick check the thickness of friction material remaining on one of the brake shoes can be measured through the slot in the brake backplate that is exposed by prising out its sealing grommet **(see illustration)**. If a rod of the same diameter as the specified minimum thickness is placed against the shoe friction material, the amount of wear can quickly be assessed. If any shoe's friction material is worn to the specified thickness or less, all four shoes must be renewed.

3 For a comprehensive check, the brake drums should be removed and cleaned. This will permit the wheel cylinders to be checked and the condition of the brake drum itself to be fully examined. Refer to Chapter 9 for further information.

Models with disc brakes

4 Chock the front wheels then jack up the rear of the vehicle and support it on axle stands (see *Jacking and Vehicle Support*).

5 For a quick check, the thickness of friction material remaining on each brake pad can be measured through the inspection aperture in the caliper body. If any pad's friction material is worn to the specified thicknessor less, all four pads must be renewed as a set.

6 For a comprehensive check, the brake pads should be removed and cleaned. This will permit the operation of the caliper to be checked and the condition of the brake disc itself to be fully examined on both sides. Refer to Chapter 9 for further information.

15 Driveshaft and gaiter check

1 With the vehicle raised and securely supported on axle stands (see *Jacking and Vehicle Support*), turn the steering onto full lock then slowly rotate the roadwheel. Inspect the condition of the outer constant velocity (CV) joint rubber gaiters while squeezing the gaiters to open out the folds **(see illustration)**. Check for signs of cracking, splits or deterioration of the rubber which may allow the grease to escape and lead to the entry of water and grit into the joint. Also check the security and condition of the gaiter retaining clips. Repeat these checks on the inner CV joints. If any damage or deterioration is found, then renew the gaiters.

2 Check the general condition of the CV joints by first holding the driveshaft and attempting to rotate the roadwheel. Repeat this check by

14.2 Remove grommet to check rear brake shoe friction material thickness

holding the inner joint and attempting to rotate the driveshaft. Any appreciable movement indicates wear in the joints or driveshaft splines, or a loose driveshaft nut.

16 Suspension and steering check

Front suspension and steering

1 Raise the front of the vehicle and securely support it on axle stands (see *Jacking and Vehicle Support*).

2 Inspect the balljoint dust covers and the steering gear rubber gaiters for splits, chafing or deterioration **(see illustration)**. Any wear of these components will cause loss of lubricant, together with dirt and water entry, resulting in rapid deterioration of the balljoints or steering gear.

3 On vehicles equipped with power steering, check the fluid hoses for chafing or deterioration and the pipe and hose unions for fluid leakage. Also check for signs of fluid leakage under pressure from the steering gear rubber gaiters which would indicate failed fluid seals within the steering gear.

4 Grasp the roadwheel at the 12 o'clock and 6 o'clock positions and try to rock it **(see illustration)**. Very slight free play may be felt but if the movement is appreciable then further investigation is necessary to determine the source. Continue rocking the wheel while an assistant depresses the brake pedal. If the movement is now eliminated or significantly

16.2 Checking the condition of a steering gear rubber gaiter

15.1 Inspecting a driveshaft joint rubber gaiter

reduced, it is likely that the hub bearings are at fault. If the free play is still evident with the brake pedal depressed, then there is wear in the suspension joints or mountings.

5 Now grasp the roadwheel at the 9 o'clock and 3 o'clock positions and try to rock it as before. Any movement felt now may again be caused by wear in the hub bearings, or in the track rod balljoints. If a balljoint is worn the visual movement will be obvious. If the inner joint is suspect it can be felt by placing a hand over the steering gear rubber gaiter and gripping the track rod. If the wheel is now rocked, movement will be felt at the inner joint if wear has taken place.

6 Using a large screwdriver or flat bar check for wear in the suspension mounting bushes by levering between the relevant suspension component and its attachment point. Some movement is to be expected as the mountings are made of rubber, but excessive wear should be obvious. Also check the condition of any visible rubber bushes, looking for splits, cracks or contamination of the rubber.

7 With the vehicle standing on its wheels, have an assistant turn the steering wheel back-and-forth about an eighth of a turn each way. There should be very little, if any, lost movement between the steering wheel and the roadwheels. If this is not the case, closely observe the joints and mountings previously described but in addition, check for wear of the steering column universal joint and the steering gear itself.

Rear suspension

8 Chock the front wheels then jack up the

16.4 Checking the condition of the steering and suspension components by rocking a roadwheel

17.5a Remove the ashtray from the rear of the centre console . . .

rear of the vehicle and support it on axle stands (see *Jacking and Vehicle Support*).

9 Working as described for the front suspension, check the rear hub bearings and the trailing arm and lateral link bushes for wear.

17 Handbrake check and adjustment

Checking

1 The handbrake should be capable of holding the parked vehicle stationary, even on steep slopes, when applied with moderate force. Equally, the handbrake must release properly, or the brakes will bind and overheat when the car is driven.

2 The mechanism should be firm and positive in feel with no trace of stiffness or sponginess from the cables and should release immediately the handbrake lever is released. If the mechanism is faulty in any of these respects then it must be checked immediately.

3 To check the handbrake setting, first apply the footbrake firmly several times to establish correct shoe-to-drum clearance. Applying normal, moderate pressure, pull the handbrake lever to the fully-applied position whilst

counting the number of 'clicks' produced by the handbrake ratchet mechanism. Check that the number of clicks produced is as listed in the Specifications. If this is not the case, then adjustment is required.

Adjustment

4 To adjust the handbrake, chock the front wheels then jack up the rear of the vehicle and support it on axle stands (see *Jacking and Vehicle Support*).

5 Lift out the ashtray from the rear of the centre console to gain access to the handbrake adjusting nut **(see illustrations)**.

6 Apply the handbrake and check that the equaliser and cables move freely and smoothly, then set the lever on the first notch of the ratchet mechanism. With the lever in this position, rotate the handbrake lever adjusting nut until only a slight drag can be felt when the rear wheels are turned by hand. Once this is the case, fully release the handbrake lever and check that the wheels rotate freely. Check adjustment by applying the handbrake fully whilst counting the clicks emitted from the handbrake ratchet. Carry out the adjustment procedure again, if necessary.

7 Once adjustment is correct, refit the ashtray and lower the vehicle to the ground.

18 Lock and hinge lubrication

1 Lubricate the hinges of the bonnet, doors and tailgate with a light duty oil.

2 Lightly grease the bonnet release mechanism and cable.

3 The door and tailgate latches, strikers and locks must be lubricated using only the special Rover Door Lock and Latch Lubricant supplied in small sachets. Inject 1 gram into each lock and wipe off any surplus, then apply a thin film to the latches and strikers.

4 Do not lubricate the steering lock mechanism with oil or any other lubricant

17.5b . . . to gain access to the handbrake cable adjuster nut (arrowed) and equaliser mechanism

which might foul the ignition switch contacts. If the lock is stiff, try the effect of a proprietary electrical contact lubricant, rather than conventional lubricant.

5 If a sunroof is fitted, lubricate very sparingly the seal lip with Rover supplied non-staining seal grease.

19 Windscreen and number plate condition check

Refer to the MOT pre-test checks described in the *Reference* Chapter, at the end of this manual.

20 Seat belt check

1 Check the webbing of each seat belt for signs of fraying, cuts or other damage, pulling the belt out to its full extent to check its entire length **(see illustration)**.

2 Check the operation of the belt buckles by fitting the belt tongue plate and pulling hard to ensure that it remains locked in position.

3 Check the retractor mechanism (inertia reel only) by pulling out the belt to the halfway point and jerking it downwards **(see illustration)**.

20.1 Check the webbing of each seat belt for signs of fraying, cuts or other damage

20.3 Checking the operation of the inertia reel locking mechanism

The mechanism must lock immediately to prevent any further unreeling but must allow free movement during normal driving.

4 Ensure that all belt mounting bolts are securely tightened. Note that the bolts are shouldered so that the belt anchor points are free to rotate.

5 If there is any sign of damage, or any doubt about a belt's condition, then it must be renewed. If the vehicle has been involved in a collision, then any belt in use at the time must be renewed as a matter of course and all other belts checked carefully.

6 Use only warm water and non-detergent soap to clean the belts.

Caution: Never use any chemical cleaners, strong detergents, dyes or bleaches. Keep the belts fully extended until they have dried naturally and do not apply heat to dry them.

21 SRS system component check

1 Checking of the SRS/airbag system by the home mechanic is limited to a visual inspection of the outer surface of the driver and passenger airbag modules (as applicable). If the surface of the casing has sustained any damage (such as that caused by an impact, or fluid spillage for example) then the airbag system should be checked by a Rover dealer at the earliest opportunity.

2 Sit in the driver's seat and release the steering column lock. Start the engine and allow it to idle. Turn the steering wheel from lock-to-lock, whilst listening to the rotary coupler at the steering wheel hub. Any noise or roughness in operation could indicate a worn rotary coupler – refer to a Rover dealer for further advice.

3 The SRS warning lamp on the instrument panel should illuminate for about six seconds when the ignition key is turned to the 'II' position and then extinguish. If the lamp fails to extinguish, or does not illuminate at all, there may be a fault with the SRS system; the advice of a Rover dealer should be sought.

22 Road test

Instruments and electrical equipment

1 Check the operation of all instruments and electrical equipment.

2 Make sure that all instruments read correctly, and switch on all electrical equipment in turn, to check that it functions properly.

Steering and suspension

3 Check for any abnormalities in the steering, suspension, handling or road 'feel'.

4 Drive the vehicle, and check that there are no unusual vibrations or noises.

5 Check that the steering feels positive, with no excessive 'sloppiness', or roughness, and check for any suspension noises when cornering and driving over bumps.

Drivetrain

6 Check the performance of the engine, clutch, transmission and driveshafts.

7 Listen for any unusual noises from the engine, clutch and transmission.

8 Make sure that the engine runs smoothly when idling, and that there is no hesitation when accelerating.

9 Check that the clutch action is smooth and progressive, that the drive is taken up smoothly, and that the pedal travel is not excessive. Also listen for any noises when the clutch pedal is depressed.

10 Check that all gears can be engaged smoothly without noise, and that the gear lever action is smooth and not abnormally vague or 'notchy'.

11 Listen for a metallic clicking sound from the front of the vehicle, as the vehicle is driven slowly in a circle with the steering on full-lock. Carry out this check in both directions. If a clicking noise is heard, this indicates wear in a driveshaft joint (see Chapter 8).

Braking system

12 Make sure that the vehicle does not pull to one side when braking, and that the wheels do not lock when braking hard.

13 Check that there is no vibration through the steering when braking.

14 Check that the handbrake operates correctly, and that it holds the vehicle stationary on a slope.

Every 30 000 miles (48 000 km) or 2 years

23 Brake fluid renewal

1 This procedure is similar to that described for the bleeding of the hydraulic system, as described in Chapter 9, except that the brake fluid reservoir should be emptied by syphoning and allowance should be made for all old fluid to be expelled when bleeding a section of the circuit.

2 Working as described in Chapter 9, open the first bleed nipple in the sequence and pump the brake pedal gently until nearly all the old fluid has been emptied from the master cylinder reservoir. Top up to the MAX level on the reservoir with new fluid and continue pumping until only new fluid remains in the reservoir and new fluid can be seen emerging from the bleed nipple. Old hydraulic fluid is much darker in colour than new fluid, making it easy to distinguish between them.

3 Tighten the nipple and top the reservoir level up to the MAX level line.

4 Work through all the remaining nipples in the sequence until new fluid can be seen emerging from all of them. Be careful to keep the master cylinder reservoir topped up to above the MIN level at all times, or air may enter the system and greatly increase the length of the task.

5 When the operation is complete, check that all nipples are securely tightened and that their dust caps are refitted. Wash off all traces of spilt fluid and recheck the master cylinder reservoir fluid level.

6 Check the operation of the brakes before taking the vehicle on the road.

24.1 Lifting off the air cleaner cover

24.2a Wiping out the air cleaner casing

24.2b Fitting a new air cleaner element

Every 45 000 miles (72 000 km) or 3 years

24 Air cleaner filter element renewal

1 Release the four securing clips, lift off the cover and remove the filter element (**see illustration**).
2 Wipe out the filter housing, and fit a new element (**see illustration**).

3 Fit the cover, and secure with four clips (**see illustration**).

Every 60 000 miles (96 000 km) or 4 years

25 Spark plug renewal

Removal

1 Disconnect battery earth lead.
2 Remove three bolts securing coil/plug cover to camshaft cover, and remove the cover.
3 Note the position and clipping of the HT leads and cables running to the coils and camshaft position sensor. Release the HT leads, and pull the tubular connectors from the spark plugs next to the two coils.
4 Remove the two bolts attaching each coil to the camshaft cover, and pull the coils from the spark plugs.

Early engine with distributor

5 Disconnect the battery negative lead.
6 Release two clips and disconnect two breather hoses from the camshaft cover. Remove the two bolts attaching the plug cover to the camshaft cover, and remove the cover. Disconnect the HT lead tubular connectors from the spark plugs, and withdraw the connectors from the cylinder head, with the clip plate and grommet from the left-hand end of the camshaft cover.

All engines

7 Use a 16 mm deep socket and extension bar to unscrew the plugs (**see illustration**). To avoid risk of breaking the plug insulator, ensure that the socket and extension are kept vertical whilst the plug is unscrewed.

Plug condition

8 The electronic engine management system will normally maintain the fuel/air mixture at exactly the correct ratio, and this will result in a light coating of grey/brown deposit on the insulator and electrodes. Deposits other than this could indicate a fault, eg, pale/white deposits indicate a weak petrol/air mixture – sooty/black deposits indicate a rich petrol/air mixture – any oily traces indicate that the engine is burning oil, due to worn bores/piston rings, or valve guides.

Plug specification

9 It is essential that only plugs specified for the engine type are used. In addition to differing size and thread, plugs have different 'temperature grades' – a 'hot' plug transfers heat from the electrode slowly – a 'cold' plug transfers heat more slowly.
10 Ensuring that the correct plugs have been selected, use feeler gauges to check the gap between the centre and side electrodes. If the gap is not as specified, bend the side electrode closer to or away from the centre electrode. **Note**: *Never attempt to bend the centre electrode. A special spark plug tool is available, and this can be used to check the gap, and bend the side electrode.*

Refitting

11 When the plug gaps are correct, fit terminals to the new plugs, and screw them into the cylinder head by hand (**see Haynes Hint**). Use a torque wrench to tighten them to the specified torque.

25.7 Unscrewing a spark plug

25.10a Measuring a spark plug gap using a feeler blade

25.10b Adjusting the spark plug gap using a special tool

Later engines

12 In the positions noted before removal – fit the coils and securing bolts. Use a torque wrench to tighten the bolts to the specified torque. Fit the HT lead tubular connectors to the plugs next to the coils – position the HT leads and cables in the grooves and clips.

13 Fit the coil cover, and securing bolts. Use a torque wrench to tighten the bolts to the specified torque.

All engines

14 Connect the battery earth lead.

26 Coolant renewal

Warning: Wait until the engine is completely cold before starting the coolant renewal procedure. Do not allow antifreeze to come into contact with your skin or painted surfaces of the vehicle. Rinse off spills immediately with plenty of water. Never leave antifreeze lying around in an open container or in a puddle in the driveway or on the garage floor. Children and pets are attracted by its sweet smell; and antifreeze can be fatal if ingested.

Antifreeze mixture

1 Antifreeze should always be renewed at the specified intervals. This is necessary not only to maintain the anti-freezing properties of the coolant but also to prevent corrosion which would otherwise occur, as the corrosion inhibitors in the coolant become progressively less effective.

2 Always use an ethylene glycol based antifreeze which is suitable for use in mixed-metal cooling systems.

3 The type of antifreeze and levels of protection afforded are indicated in *Lubricants and fluids)* and Specifications. To achieve the recommended 50% concentration, equal quantities of antifreeze and clean, soft water must be mixed together. It is best to make up slightly more than is actually needed to refill the cooling system, so that a supply is available for subsequent topping-up.

Caution: Always pre-mix the antifreeze and water in a suitable container before refilling the cooling system. If the antifreeze and water are poured into the cooling system separately, they may not mix correctly and could cause localised overheating, which may lead to engine damage.

Draining

4 To drain the cooling system, remove the expansion tank filler cap then move the heater air temperature control to the maximum heat position.

5 Place a large drain tray beneath the bottom hose connection, at the bottom left-hand corner of the radiator. Release the hose clip and carefully pull the bottom hose off the

It is often difficult to insert spark plugs into their holes without cross-threading them. To avoid this possibility, fit a short length of suitable internal diameter rubber hose over the end of the spark plug. The flexible hose acts as a universal joint to help align the plug with the plug hole. Should the plug begin to cross-thread, the hose will slip on the spark plug, preventing thread damage to the cylinder head.

radiator stub, allowing the coolant to drain into the container below. Once the system has drained completely, reconnect the bottom hose and secure with the hose clip.

Flushing

6 With time, the cooling system may gradually lose its efficiency due to the radiator core having become choked with rust, scale deposits and other sediment. To minimise this, the system should be flushed as described in the following paragraphs, whenever the coolant is renewed.

7 With the coolant drained, refill the system with fresh water. Refit the expansion tank filler cap, start the engine and warm it up to normal operating temperature, then stop it and (after allowing it to cool down completely) drain the system again. Repeat as necessary until only clean water can be seen to emerge, then refill finally with the specified coolant mixture.

8 If the specified coolant mixture has been used and has been renewed at the specified intervals, the above procedure will be sufficient to keep clean the system for a considerable length of time. If, however, the system has been neglected, a more thorough operation will be required, as follows.

26.15 Slackening the cooling system bleed screw, to allow trapped air to escape during refilling

9 First drain the coolant, then disconnect the radiator top and bottom hoses from the radiator. Insert a garden hose into the radiator top hose outlet and allow water (under LOW pressure only) to circulate through the radiator until it runs clean from the bottom outlet. *Caution: Do not flush with water under high pressure, as this may damage the radiator.*

10 To flush the engine, insert the garden hose into the top hose and allow water to circulate until it runs clear from the bottom hose. If, after a reasonable period, the water still does not run clear, the cooling system should be flushed with a good proprietary cleaning agent. Bear in mind, however, that any leaks sealed in the past using a cooling system sealant additive may be weakened by this course of action, and could start to leak again.

11 In severe cases of contamination, reverse-flushing of the radiator may be necessary. To do this, remove the radiator, invert it and insert a garden hose into the bottom outlet. Continue flushing (again, using water under LOW pressure only) until clear water runs from the top hose outlet. If necessary, a similar procedure can be used to flush the heater matrix.

12 The use of chemical cleaners should be necessary only as a last resort as regular renewal of the coolant will prevent excessive contamination of the system.

Filling

13 With the cooling system drained and flushed, ensure that all radiator hoses are securely reconnected. Check all hose unions for security and all hoses for condition. Fresh antifreeze has a searching action which will rapidly find any weaknesses in the system.

14 Prepare a sufficient quantity of the specified coolant mixture, allowing for a surplus so as to have a reserve supply for topping-up (see *Antifreeze Mixture* above).

15 Remove the air cleaner assembly (see Chapter 4A) to gain access to the cooling system bleed screw, in the coolant rail underneath the ignition distributor. Slacken the bleed screw fully, to allow trapped air to escape during refilling **(see illustration)**.

16 Remove the expansion tank filler cap, then fill the system slowly through the filler neck **(see illustration)**. When coolant can be

26.16 Remove the expansion tank filler cap, then fill the system slowly through the filler neck

26.18 Top up the expansion tank to the MAX level

seen emerging from the bleed screw in a steady stream, tighten the bleed screw securely. Continue filling until the coolant level reaches the MAX mark on the side of the expansion tank. Refit the filler cap and tighten it securely.

17 Start the engine and run it at no more than idle speed until it has warmed-up to normal operating temperature and the radiator electric cooling fan has cut in once. Watch the temperature gauge to check for signs of overheating.

18 Stop the engine and allow it to cool down completely, then remove the expansion tank filler cap carefully and top up the tank to the MAX level **(see illustration)**. Refit the filler cap and wash off any spilt coolant from the engine compartment and bodywork with plenty of clean water.

19 After refilling, check carefully all system components for signs of coolant leaks. A label should now be attached to the radiator or expansion tank stating the type and concentration of antifreeze used and the date installed. Any subsequent topping-up should be made with the same type and concentration of antifreeze.

20 If, after draining and refilling the system, symptoms of overheating are found which did not occur previously, then the fault is almost certainly due to trapped air at some point in the system causing an airlock and restricting the flow of coolant. Usually air is trapped because the system was refilled too quickly. In some cases, airlocks can be released by tapping or squeezing the appropriate coolant hose. If the problem persists, stop the engine and allow it to cool down completely before unscrewing the bleed screw and expansion tank filler cap, to allow the trapped air to escape.

27 Fuel filter renewal

⚠ **Warning: Petrol is extremely flammable – great care must be taken during this procedure. Before carrying out any operation on the fuel system, refer to the precautions given in 'Safety first!', and follow them implicitly. Petrol is a highly-dangerous and volatile liquid, and the precautions necessary when handling it cannot be overstressed.**

1 The fuel filter is located on the bulkhead at the rear of the engine compartment **(see illustration)**.

2 Disconnect the battery negative lead.

3 Release the charcoal canister from its mounting bracket, and move it to one side, to improve access to the fuel filter **(see illustration)**.

4 Position a wad of absorbent cloth beneath the inlet pipe union on the bottom of the fuel filter.

5 Counterhold the union on the fuel filter, and **slowly** slacken the fuel pipe union nut using a second spanner **(see illustration)**.

⚠ **Warning: Be prepared for the escape of some fuel. Take adequate fire precautions.**

6 Allow the fuel pressure to dissipate, then fully unscrew the union nut, and disconnect the fuel inlet pipe. If the new filter is not going to be fitted immediately, cover the open end of the fuel pipe union to prevent dirt entry.

7 Repeat the procedure to disconnect the fuel outlet pipe from the top of the fuel filter **(see illustration)**.

8 Slacken the filter clamp bolt, then withdraw

27.1 Fuel filter location (arrowed)

27.3 Move the charcoal canister to one side

27.5 Slackening the fuel inlet pipe union

27.7 Disconnect the fuel outlet pipe . . .

27.8a ... then slacken the filter clamp bolt ...

27.8b ... and withdraw the filter from the mounting bracket

27.10 Ensure that the flow direction arrow on the side of the filter is pointing upwards

the filter from the mounting bracket **(see illustrations)**.

9 Collect the fuel from the filter, then dispose of the filter safely.

10 Fit the new filter using a reversal of the removal procedure, but ensure that the flow direction arrow on the side of the filter is pointing upwards, and tighten the fuel unions securely **(see illustration)**.

Every 90 000 miles (144 000 km) or 6 years

28 Camshaft timing belt renewal

The procedure is described in Chapter 2A.

Every 15 years, regardless of mileage

29 SRS system component renewal

1 The supplementary Restraint System (SRS), which includes the airbag(s), and seat belt pretensioners, has components which contain pyrotechnic materials. Because these materials degrade with age, MG Rover specify that the following components must be renewed every 15 years:

Driver airbag module.
Passenger airbag module.
Seat belt pretensioners.
Rotary coupler.

2 Remove and refit information is given in Chapter 12. However, because of the safety critical nature of these components, and the need for special equipment to test their operation, we strongly recommend that renewal is done by an MG Rover dealer.

Notes

Chapter 1 Part B:
Routine maintenance and servicing – diesel models

Contents

Degrees of difficulty

Easy, suitable for novice with little experience

Fairly easy, suitable for beginner with some experience

Fairly difficult, suitable for competent DIY mechanic

Difficult, suitable for experienced DIY mechanic

Very difficult, suitable for expert DIY or professional

Lubricants and fluids

Refer to the end of *Weekly Checks* on page 0•17

Cooling system

Antifreeze properties – 50% antifreeze (by volume):
Commences freezing .... - 36°C
Frozen solid .... - 48°C

Fuel system

Idle speed (for reference only) .... 805 ± 50 rpm

Braking system

Front and rear brake pad friction material minimum thickness .... 3.0 mm
Rear brake shoe friction material minimum thickness .... 2.0 mm
Handbrake lever travel:
Models with rear drum brakes .... 8 to 12 clicks
Models with rear disc brakes .... 10 to 14 clicks

Tyre pressures

Refer to the end of *Weekly checks* on page 0•18

Torque wrench settings	Nm	lbf ft
Engine		
Engine oil drain plug	25	18
Manual transmission		
Filler/level plug	40	30
Drain plug	45	33
Brake system		
Caliper bleed screws	10	7
Front/rear brake caliper guide pin bolts	27	20
Rear brake drum retaining screws	7	5
Wheel cylinder bleed screws	7	5
Suspension and steering		
Roadwheel nuts	See Chapter 10	

The maintenance intervals in this manual are provided with the assumption that you will be carrying out the work yourself. These are based on the minimum maintenance intervals recommended by the manufacturer for vehicles driven daily. If you wish to keep your vehicle in peak condition at all times, you may wish to perform some of these procedures more often. We encourage frequent maintenance because it enhances the efficiency, performance and resale value of your vehicle.

If the vehicle is driven in dusty areas, used to tow a trailer, or driven frequently at slow speeds (idling in traffic) or on short journeys, more frequent maintenance intervals are recommended.

When the vehicle is new, it should be serviced by a factory-authorised dealer service department, in order to preserve the factory warranty.

Every 250 miles (400 km) or weekly
☐ Refer to *Weekly Checks*

Every 6000 miles (10 000 km) or 6 months – whichever comes first
☐ Engine oil and filter – renew (Section 3)
Note: *Frequent oil and filter changes are good for the engine. We recommend renewing the oil and filter at these intervals, or at least twice a year.*

Every 12 000 miles (20 000 km) or 12 months – whichever comes first
☐ Bodywork corrosion check (Section 4)
☐ Alarm remote keypad batteries – renew (Section 5)
☐ Fuel filter – renew (Section 6)
☐ Coolant specific gravity – check (Section 7)
☐ Manual transmission oil level – check (Section 8)
☐ Vacuum hose – check condition (Section 9)
☐ Underbonnet and underbody hoses and pipes – check condition (Section 10)
☐ Air conditioning system check and heater/ventilation intake filter renewal (Section 11)
☐ Auxiliary drivebelt – check condition and tension (Section 12)
☐ Exhaust system – check (Section 13)
☐ Front brake – check (Section 14)
☐ Rear brake – check (Section 15)
☐ Driveshaft and gaiter – check (Section 16)
☐ Suspension and steering – check (Section 17)
☐ Handbrake – check (Section 18)
☐ Lock and hinge lubrication (Section 19)
☐ Windscreen and number plate – check (Section 20)
☐ Seat belt – check (Section 21)
☐ SRS system component – check (Section 22)
☐ Road test (Section 23)

Every 24 000 miles (40 000 km) or 2 years – whichever comes first
☐ Air cleaner – renew (Section 24)
☐ Brake fluid – renew (Section 25)

Every 48 000 miles (80 000 km) or 4 years – whichever comes first
☐ Coolant – renew (Section 26)
☐ Camshaft drivebelt – renew (with manual tensioner for fuel injection pump drivebelt) (Section 27)
☐ Fuel injection pump drivebelt – renew (with manual tensioner for fuel injection pump drivebelt) (Section 28)

Every 84 000 miles (140 000 km) or 7 years – whichever comes first
☐ Camshaft drivebelt – renew (with auto tensioner for injection pump drivebelt) (Section 27)
☐ Fuel injection pump drivebelt – renew (with auto tensioner for pump drivebelt) (Section 28)
Note: *This is the MG Rover recommendation. However, because of the serious and extensive damage, which will occur to the engine if the belt breaks, we strongly recommend that belts are renewed more frequently – eg, every 48 000 miles (80 000 km) or 4 years.*

Every 108 000 miles (180 000 km) or 9 years – whichever comes first
☐ Manual transmission oil – renew (Section 29)

Every 15 years, regardless of mileage
☐ SRS components – renew (Section 30)

Underbonnet view of Rover 25 with L series diesel engine

1 Engine oil level dipstick
2 Engine oil filler cap
3 Fuel system priming bulb
4 Fuel filter
5 Coolant expansion tank
6 Engine compartment fusebox
7 Battery
8 Air cleaner
9 Air mass meter
10 Alternator/vacuum pump
11 Washer fluid reservoir cap
12 Power steering fluid reservoir
13 Windscreen wiper motor
14 Brake fluid reservoir/master cylinder

Front underbody view of Rover 25 with L series diesel engine

1 Engine oil sump drain plug
2 Engine oil filter
3 Tie bar
4 Brake caliper
5 Suspension lower arm
6 Track rod
7 Driveshaft
8 Exhaust system front pipe
9 Anti-roll bar
10 Power steering gear

Rear underbody view of Rover 25 with L series diesel engine

1 Brake backplate
2 Suspension strut lower
   mounting
3 Exhaust system tailbox
4 Beam axle assembly
5 Fuel tank
6 Handbrake cables
7 Beam axle pivot
   mountings

Maintenance procedures – diesel models

1 Introduction

This Chapter is designed to help the home mechanic maintain his/her vehicle for safety, economy, long life and peak performance.

The Chapter contains a master maintenance schedule, referring to Sections dealing specifically with each task in the schedule, or other Chapters. Visual checks, adjustments, component renewal and other helpful items are included. Refer to the accompanying illustrations of the engine compartment and the underside of the vehicle for the locations of the various components.

Servicing your vehicle in accordance with the mileage/time maintenance schedule and the following Sections will provide a planned maintenance programme, which should result in a long and reliable service life. This is a comprehensive plan, so maintaining some items but not others at the specified service intervals will not produce the same results.

As you service your vehicle, you will discover that many of the procedures can be grouped together, because of the particular procedure being performed, or because of the close proximity of two otherwise-unrelated components to one another. For example, if the vehicle is raised for any reason, the exhaust can be inspected at the same time as the suspension and steering components.

The first step in this maintenance programme is to prepare yourself before the actual work begins. Read through all the Sections relevant to the work to be carried out, then make a list and gather together all the parts and tools required. If a problem is encountered, seek advice from a parts specialist, or a dealer service department.

2 Maintenance

1 If, from the time the vehicle is new, the routine maintenance schedule is followed closely and frequent checks are made of fluid levels and high-wear items, as suggested throughout this Manual, the engine will be kept in relatively good running condition and the need for additional work will be minimised.
2 It is possible that there will be times when the engine is running poorly due to the lack of regular maintenance. This is even more likely if a used vehicle, which has not received regular and frequent maintenance checks, is purchased. In such cases, additional work may need to be carried out, outside of the regular maintenance intervals.
3 If engine wear is suspected, a compression test will provide valuable information regarding the overall performance of the main internal components. Such a test can be used as a basis to decide on the extent of the work

to be carried out. If, for example, a compression test indicates serious internal engine wear, conventional maintenance as described in this Chapter will not greatly improve the performance of the engine, and may prove a waste of time and money, unless extensive overhaul work is carried out first.
4 The following series of operations are those most often required to improve the performance of a generally poor-running engine:

Primary operations

a) Clean, inspect and test the battery.
b) Check all the engine-related fluids.
c) Check the condition and tension of the auxiliary drivebelt(s).
d) Check the condition of the air filter, and renew if necessary.
e) Check the fuel filter and drain off all water.
f) Check the condition of all hoses, and check for fluid leaks.

5 If the above operations do not prove fully effective, carry out the following secondary operations:

Secondary operations

a) Check the charging system (see relevant Part of Chapter 5).
b) Check the fuel system (see relevant Part of Chapter 4).
c) Check the preheating system (see relevant Part of Chapter 5).

3.5 Slackening the engine oil drain plug

3.7 Refit the drain plug using a new sealing washer

Every 6000 miles (10 000 km) or 6 months

3 Engine oil and filter renewal

Note: *An oil filter removal tool and a new oil drain plug sealing washer will be required for this operation.*

1 Frequent oil and filter changes are the most important preventative maintenance procedures which can be undertaken by the DIY owner. As engine oil ages, it becomes diluted and contaminated, which leads to premature engine wear.

2 Before starting this procedure, gather together all the necessary tools and materials. Also make sure that you have plenty of clean rags and newspapers handy, to mop up any spills. Ideally, the engine oil should be warm, as it will drain more easily, and more built-up sludge will be removed with it. Take care not to touch the exhaust or any other hot parts of the engine when working under the vehicle. To avoid any possibility of scalding, and to protect yourself from possible skin irritants and other harmful contaminants in used engine oils, it is advisable to wear gloves when carrying out this work.

3 Access to the underside of the vehicle will be greatly improved if it can be raised on a lift, driven onto ramps, or jacked up and supported on axle stands (see *Jacking and Vehicle Support*). Whichever method is

chosen, make sure that the vehicle remains level, or if it is at an angle, that the drain plug is at the lowest point. Where applicable, remove the engine/transmission undershield for access to the drain plug. The drain plug is located at the rear of the sump.

4 Remove the oil filler cap from the cylinder head cover.

5 Using a spanner, or preferably a suitable socket and bar, slacken the drain plug about half a turn **(see illustration)**. Position the draining container under the drain plug, then remove the plug completely. If possible, try to keep the plug pressed into the sump while unscrewing it by hand the last couple of turns.

> **HAYNES HiNT**
>
> *As the plug releases from the threads, move it away sharply, so that the stream of oil from the sump runs into the container, not up your sleeve.*

6 Allow some time for the oil to drain, noting that it may be necessary to reposition the container as the oil flow slows to a trickle.

7 After all the oil has drained, wipe the drain plug and the sealing washer with a clean rag. The sealing washer should be renewed as a matter of course. Clean the area around the drain plug opening, and refit the plug complete with the new sealing washer **(see illustration)**. Tighten the plug securely, preferably to the specified torque, using a torque wrench.

8 The oil filter is located at the right-hand rear corner of the engine. Access is most easily obtained by jacking up the front of the vehicle (see *Jacking and Vehicle Support*) **(see illustration)**.

9 Move the container into position under the oil filter.

10 Use an oil filter removal tool to slacken the filter initially, then unscrew it by hand the rest of the way **(see illustration)**. Empty the oil from the old filter into the container.

11 Use a clean rag to remove all oil, dirt and sludge from the filter sealing area on the engine. Check the old filter to make sure that the rubber sealing ring has not stuck to the engine. If it has, carefully remove it.

12 Apply a light coating of clean engine oil to the sealing ring on the new filter, then screw the filter into position on the engine. Tighten the filter firmly by hand only – **do not** use any tools.

13 Remove the old oil and all tools from under the vehicle then, if applicable, lower the vehicle to the ground.

14 Fill the engine through the filler hole in the cylinder head cover, using the correct grade and type of oil (see *Lubricants and fluids*). Pour in half the specified quantity of oil first, then wait a few minutes for the oil to drain into the sump. Continue to add oil, a small quantity at a time, until the level is up to the lower mark on the dipstick. Adding approximately 1.0 litre will bring the level up to the upper mark on the dipstick.

15 Start the engine and run it for a few minutes, while checking for leaks around the oil filter seal and the sump drain plug. Note that there may be a delay of a few seconds before the low oil pressure warning light goes out when the engine is first started, as the oil circulates through the new oil filter and the engine oil galleries before the pressure builds-up.

16 Stop the engine, and wait a few minutes for the oil to settle in the sump once more. With the new oil circulated and the filter now completely full, recheck the level on the dipstick, and add more oil as necessary.

17 Dispose of the used engine oil safely.

3.8 Oil filter location (arrowed)

3.10 Loosening the oil filter using an oil filter removal tool

5.1a Using a flat-bladed screwdriver, carefully prise the two halves of the keypad apart . . .

5.1b . . . to expose the battery

5.3 Fit the new battery, handling it with a piece of tissue paper to avoid touching the battery contact surfaces

Every 12 000 miles (20 000 km) or 12 months

4 Bodywork corrosion check

1 Start at the front of the car and work along each body panel in turn, look for any signs of paintwork damage. It may be possible to repair small scratches with a touch-up pen. These should be purchased from a Rover dealer, to get an accurate colour match.

2 Larger scratches that have penetrated the primer or exposed the bare metal beneath should be repaired professionally. The Rover 25 has an extensive Anti-Corrosion Warranty, the terms of which specify how bodywork repairs must be carried out; failure to adhere to the guidelines may invalidate the Warranty. Have the damage assessed by a Rover Dealer or automotive bodywork specialist at the earliest opportunity.

3 Check each body panel for evidence of corrosion, such as raised blisters behind the paintwork and rust-coloured staining. Pay particular attention to vulnerable areas, including the wheel arches, the front edge of the bonnet, the front valence (under the front bumper) and the lower edges of the doors. Corrosion can quickly destroy bodywork, so have any dubious-looking areas examined by a professional.

4 Jack up the front/rear car and support it securely on axle stands (see *Jacking and Vehicle Support*).

5 Examine the underside of the car for signs of corrosion. Look for cracking or flaking of the metal floorpan. Pay particular attention to the areas around the suspension and steering components mountings. Look for damage that may have been caused by attempting to jack up the car at incorrect jacking points.

6 Check for corrosion along the length of the side sills, which run between the front and rear wheel arches.

7 The underside of the vehicle is coated with a protective sealant, which helps to prevent corrosion. If this coating has been scraped off at any point, due to an impact or repair work, it must be re-applied as soon as possible, to protect the bodywork beneath.

5 Alarm remote keypad battery renewal

1 Place the keypad on a work surface and using a flat-bladed screwdriver, carefully prise the two halves of the keypad apart. Take care to avoid damaging the rubber seal with the screwdriver blade (**see illustrations**).

2 Remove the battery from the terminal clips, noting which way up it is. Press each keypad button in turn and hold them down for a few seconds, to fully discharge the electronic components inside.

3 Obtain a new battery of the correct type and insert it between the terminal clips, ensuring that it is fitted the correct way around (the positive '+' side faces the keypad backplate). Avoid touching the contact surfaces of the battery as you do this, by handling it with a piece of tissue paper; moisture from fingertips can cause the battery surfaces to corrode (**see illustration**).

4 Press the two halves of the keypad back together, ensuring that the rubber seal is correctly located, then check the operation of the keypad.

6 Fuel filter renewal

⚠️ *Warning: Fuel is extremely flammable – great care must be taken during this procedure. Before carrying out any operation on the fuel system, refer to the precautions given in 'Safety first!', and follow them implicitly. Fuel is a highly-dangerous and volatile liquid, and the precautions necessary when handling it cannot be overstressed.*

1 The fuel filter is located on the bulkhead at the rear of the engine compartment.

2 Position a wad of absorbent cloth beneath the fuel filter.

3 Release the hose clip, and disconnect the fuel inlet hose from the top of the fuel filter (**see illustration**). If the new filter is not going to be fitted immediately, clamp or cover the open end of the fuel hose to prevent dirt entry and fuel loss.

4 Repeat the procedure to disconnect the fuel outlet hose from the top of the filter (**see illustration**).

5 Slacken the fuel filter clamp bolt, and withdraw the filter from the clamp bracket (**see illustrations**).

6 Collect the fuel from the filter, then dispose of the filter safely.

6.3 Disconnect the fuel inlet hose . . .

6.4 . . . and the fuel outlet hose . . .

6.5a . . . then slacken the clamp bolt . . .

6.5b . . . and withdraw the fuel filter

6.7 Note the fuel flow arrows stamped into the top of the filter

7 Fit the new filter using a reversal of the removal procedure, but ensure that the hoses are correctly reconnected – fuel flow direction arrows are stamped into the filter adjacent to the fuel pipes **(see illustration)**. Ensure that the hose clips are tight and, on completion, prime the fuel system as described in Chapter 4B.

7 Coolant specific gravity check

1 Ensure that the engine has cooled completely before starting work.
2 Slowly unscrew the coolant expansion tank cap by about half a turn, allowing any residual pressure in the cooling system to reduce gradually – use a cloth to protect your hands from any escaping steam.

3 Insert a hydrometer into the expansion tank filler neck and measure the specific gravity of the coolant **(see illustration)**.
4 The hydrometer shown in the photo incorporates an integral syringe, which allows a 'sample' of the coolant to be collected. The coloured indicator balls inside the hydrometer float or sink in the coolant sample, depending on the specific gravity.
5 If the specific gravity is too low, do not try to correct it by adding neat antifreeze, as it may not mix completely with the existing coolant and could lead to 'hot spots' in the cooling system. With reference to Section 26, partially drain the cooling system, then refill it with antifreeze and water mixed in the correct proportions.
6 If the specific gravity is too high, refer to Section 26 and partially drain the cooling system, then top up with clean water.

7.3 Using a hydrometer to measure the specific gravity of the coolant

8.2 Transmission filler/level plug (arrowed) – PG1-type transmission

8.5 Topping-up the transmission oil level – PG1-type transmission

9.1 Check the condition of the brake servo vacuum hose

8 Manual transmission oil level check

1 Ensure that the vehicle is parked on level ground then, where applicable, remove the engine/transmission undershield to gain access to the transmission filler/level plug.
2 Remove all traces of dirt from around the filler/level plug which is located on the left-hand side of the transmission, behind the driveshaft inboard joint **(see illustration)**. Place a suitable container beneath the plug to catch any escaping oil, then unscrew the plug and recover the sealing washer.
3 Check that the oil is level with the bottom of the filler/level plug hole. Note that oil which has collected behind the filler/level plug will probably trickle out when the plug is removed, which can give a false impression that the level is correct.
4 If necessary, top-up using the specified type of oil (see *Lubricants and fluids*). Refilling the transmission is an awkward operation. Allow plenty of time for the oil level to settle properly before checking it. Note that the car must be parked on flat level ground when checking the oil level.
5 Using a tube inserted through the filler/level plug hole, slowly top up the level until the oil reaches the bottom of the filler/level plug hole **(see illustration)**. Allow plenty of time for the level to stabilise.
6 When the level is correct, refit the filler/level plug, using a new sealing washer, and tighten it to the specified torque.

9 Vacuum hose condition check

1 Open the bonnet and check the condition of the vacuum hose that connects the brake servo to the vacuum pump **(see illustration)**. Look for damage in the form of chafing, melting or cracking. Check that the union nuts and T-joints (where applicable) are secure. Also examine the vacuum hoses serving the evaporative loss emission control and fuel pressure regulation systems.

2 Locate the engine management system ECU at the left-hand side of the engine compartment. Inspect the vacuum hose that runs from the ECU to the inlet manifold, ensuring that it is secure and free from damage. Remove it from the engine compartment and clean it out using compressed air, to expel any fuel or oil which may have collected inside it. Do not use cleaning fluids, as these may contaminate the ECU pressure sensor.

3 A leak in a vacuum hose means that air is being drawn into the hose (rather than escaping from it) and this makes leakage very difficult to detect. If you suspect that a vacuum hose may be leaking, the following method may help you to pinpoint it. Start the engine and allow it to idle. Hold one end of a length of narrow bore tubing close to your ear, then run the other end along the vacuum hose. If a leak exists, you should be able to hear a hissing noise through the tubing as the air 'escapes' into the hose at the suspected leak.

10 Underbonnet and underbody hose and pipe condition check

Coolant

10.1 Checking the condition of a coolant hose

> ⚠ **Warning: Refer to the safety information given in 'Safety First!' and Chapter 3, before disturbing any of the cooling system components.**

1 Carefully check the radiator and heater coolant hoses along their entire length. Renew any hose which is cracked, swollen or which shows signs of deterioration. Cracks will show up better if the hose is squeezed **(see illustration)**. Pay close attention to the clips that secure the hoses to the cooling system components. Hose clips that have been over-tightened can pinch and puncture hoses, resulting in leakage.

2 Inspect all the cooling system components (hoses, joint faces, etc) for leaks. Where any problems of this nature are found on system components, renew the component or gasket with reference to Chapter 3.

3 A leak from the cooling system will usually show up as white or rust-coloured deposits, on the area surrounding the leak **(see Haynes Hint)**.

Fuel

> ⚠ **Warning: Refer to the safety information given in 'Safety First!' and the relevant part of Chapter 4, before disturbing any of the fuel system components.**

4 Unlike petrol leaks, diesel leaks are fairly easy to pinpoint; diesel fuel tends to settle on the surface around the point of leakage collecting dirt, rather than evaporate. If you suspect that there is a fuel leak from the area of the engine bay, leave the vehicle overnight

then start the engine from cold, and allow it to idle with the bonnet open. Metal components tend to shrink when they are cold, and rubber seals and hoses tend to harden, so any leaks may be more apparent whilst the engine is warming-up from a cold start.

5 Check all fuel lines at their connections to the fuel injection pump and fuel filter **(see illustration)**. Examine each rubber fuel hose along its length for splits or cracks. Check for leakage from the crimped joints between rubber and metal fuel lines. Examine the unions between the metal fuel lines and the fuel filter housing. Also check the area around the fuel injectors for signs of leakage.

6 To identify fuel leaks between the fuel tank and the engine bay, the vehicle should be raised and securely supported on axle stands (see *Jacking and Vehicle Support*). Inspect the fuel tank and filler neck for punctures, cracks and other damage. The connection between the filler neck and tank is especially critical. Sometimes a rubber filler neck or connecting hose will leak due to loose retaining clamps or deteriorated rubber.

7 Carefully check all rubber hoses and metal fuel lines leading away from the fuel tank. Check for loose connections, deteriorated hoses, kinked lines, and other damage. Pay particular attention to the vent pipes and hoses, which often loop up around the filler neck and can become blocked or kinked, making tank filling difficult. Follow the fuel supply and return lines to the front of the vehicle, carefully inspecting them all the way for signs of damage or corrosion. Renew damaged sections as necessary.

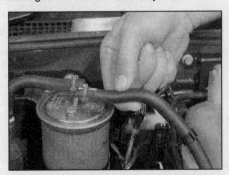

10.5 Check for fuel leaks at the fuel filter unions

Leaks in the cooling system will usually show up as white or rust coloured deposits around the point of leakage.

Engine oil

8 Check the hoses leading to the engine oil cooler at the front of the engine bay for leakage. Look for deterioration caused by corrosion and damage from grounding, or debris thrown up from the road surface.

Power assisted steering fluid

9 Examine the hose running between the fluid reservoir and the power steering pump, and the return hose running from the steering rack to the fluid reservoir. Also examine the high pressure supply hose between the pump and the steering rack **(see illustration)**.

10 Where applicable, check the hoses leading to the PAS fluid cooler at the front of the engine bay. Look for deterioration caused by corrosion and damage from grounding, or debris thrown up from the road surface.

11 Pay particular attention to crimped unions, and the area surrounding the hoses that are secured with adjustable worm drive clips. PAS fluid is a thin oil, and is usually red in colour.

Air conditioning refrigerant

> ⚠ **Warning: Refer to the safety information given in 'Safety First!' and Chapter 3, regarding the dangers of disturbing any of the air conditioning system components.**

12 The air conditioning system Is filled with a liquid refrigerant, which is retained under high pressure. If the air conditioning system is

10.9 Checking a power steering fluid hose for damage

10.15 Checking a master cylinder brake pipe union for leakage

opened and depressurised without the aid of specialised equipment, the refrigerant will immediately turn into gas and escape into the atmosphere. If the liquid comes into contact with your skin, it can cause severe frostbite. In addition, the refrigerant may contain substances which are environmentally damaging; for this reason, it should not be allowed to escape into the atmosphere.

13 Any suspected air conditioning system leaks should be immediately referred to a Rover dealer or air conditioning specialist. Leakage will be shown up as a steady drop in the level of refrigerant in the system – refer to Section 11 for details.

14 Note that water may drip from the condenser drain pipe, underneath the car, immediately after the air conditioning system has been in use. This is normal, and should not be cause for concern.

Brake fluid

 Warning: Refer to the safety information given in 'Safety First!' and Chapter 9, regarding the dangers of handling brake fluid.

15 With reference to Chapter 9, examine the area surrounding the brake pipe unions at the master cylinder for signs of leakage **(see illustration)**. Check the area around the base

of fluid reservoir, for signs of leakage caused by seal failure. Also examine the brake pipe unions at the ABS hydraulic unit. Brake fluid is an effective paint stripper, so if cracked or bubbling paintwork on or around any of the braking system components is found, suspect fluid leakage.

16 If fluid loss is evident, but the leak cannot be pinpointed in the engine bay, the brake calipers and underbody brakelines and should be carefully checked with the vehicle raised and supported on axle stands (see *Jacking and Vehicle Support*). Leakage of fluid from the braking system is serious fault that must be rectified immediately.

17 Brake hydraulic fluid is a toxic substance with a watery consistency. New fluid is almost colourless, but it becomes darker with age and use.

Unidentified fluid leaks

18 If there are signs that a fluid of some description is leaking from the vehicle, but you cannot identify the type of fluid or its exact origin, park the vehicle overnight and slide a large piece of card underneath it. Providing that the card is positioned in roughly in the right location, even the smallest leak will show up on the card. Not only will this help you to pinpoint the exact location of the leak, it should be easier to identify the fluid from its colour. Bear in mind, though, that the leak may only be occurring when the engine is running!

Vacuum hoses

19 Refer to Section 9.

11 Air conditioning system check and heater/ventilation intake filter renewal

1 The refrigerant condition and level is checked via the sightglass on the top of the receiver/drier. The receiver/drier is situated in the engine compartment, just to the left of the radiator.

2 Start the engine then switch on the air conditioning system and allow the engine to idle for a couple of minutes whilst observing the sightglass. If the air conditioning system is operating normally then occasional bubbles should be visible through the sightglass.

3 If a constant stream of bubbles is visible,

12.4 Checking the condition of the auxiliary drivebelt

the refrigerant level is low and must be topped-up. If the sightglass has become clouded or streaked, there is a fault in the system. If either condition is present, the vehicle must be taken to a Rover dealer or suitable professional refrigeration specialist for the air conditioning system to be checked further and overhauled.

4 It is recommended that the heater/ventilation intake filter (pollen filter) is renewed at this service interval. Refer to the procedures contained in Chapter 3, Section 10.

12 Auxiliary drivebelt tension and condition check

General information

1 A single micro-V belt is driven from the crankshaft pulley. Belt tension is controlled automatically by a spring-loaded roller **(see illustration)**. The belt drives:

The power steering pump and the coolant pump, which are mounted in tandem in a common housing.

The alternator, and the vacuum pump which is integral with the alternator.

The compressor – when air conditioning is fitted. When air conditioning is not fitted an idler pulley, mounted on a bracket, takes the place of the compressor.

Checking condition

2 Apply the handbrake, chock the rear roadwheels, then jack up the front of the car and support it on axle stands (see *Jacking and Vehicle Support*). Remove the right hand roadwheel.

3 Remove the engine undertray – two nuts at rear and two bolts at front.

4 Check the belts for cracks, splitting, fraying, glazing (shiny patches) or other damage. Use a socket and extension bar on the crankshaft bolt to turn the crankshaft, so that the whole length of both belts can be examined **(see illustration)**.

5 Check the belt length – the belt must be renewed before the indicator reaches the right hand end of the slot.

6 Renew any worn or damaged belt – see Chapter 5A.

13 Exhaust system check

1 With the engine cold (at least an hour after the vehicle has been driven), check the complete exhaust system from the engine to the end of the tailpipe. The exhaust system is most easily checked with the vehicle raised on a hoist, or suitably supported on axle stands, so that the exhaust components are readily visible and accessible.

2 Check the exhaust pipes and connections for evidence of leaks, severe corrosion and

12.1 Auxiliary drivebelt and wear indicator

H44810

13.2 Check that the exhaust mountings are secure

damage. Make sure that all brackets and mountings are in good condition, and that all relevant nuts and bolts are tight **(see illustration)**. Leakage at any of the joints or in other parts of the system will usually show up as a black sooty stain in the vicinity of the leak.

3 Rattles and other noises can often be traced to the exhaust system, especially the brackets and mountings. Try to move the pipes and silencers. If the components are able to come into contact with the body or suspension parts, secure the system with new mountings. Otherwise separate the joints (if possible) and twist the pipes as necessary to provide additional clearance.

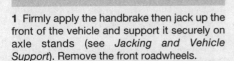

14 Front brake check

1 Firmly apply the handbrake then jack up the front of the vehicle and support it securely on axle stands (see *Jacking and Vehicle Support*). Remove the front roadwheels.

2 For a quick check, the thickness of friction material remaining on each brake pad can be measured through the inspection aperture in the front of the caliper body **(see illustration)**. If any pad's friction material is worn to the specified thickness or less, all four pads must be renewed as a set.

3 For a comprehensive check, the brake pads should be removed and cleaned. This will permit the operation of the caliper to be checked and the condition of the brake disc

15.2 Remove grommet to check rear brake shoe friction material thickness

14.2 Front brake pad friction material (arrowed) can be measured through the inspection aperture in caliper body

itself to be fully examined on both sides. Refer to Chapter 9 for further information.

15 Rear brake check

Models with drum brakes

1 Chock the front wheels then jack up the rear of the vehicle and support it on axle stands (see *Jacking and Vehicle Support*).

2 For a quick check, the thickness of friction material remaining on one of the brake shoes can be measured through the slot in the brake backplate that is exposed by prising out its sealing grommet **(see illustration)**. If a rod of the same diameter as the specified minimum thickness is placed against the shoe friction material, the amount of wear can quickly be assessed. If any shoe's friction material is worn to the specified thickness or less, all four shoes must be renewed.

3 For a comprehensive check, the brake drums should be removed and cleaned. This will permit the wheel cylinders to be checked and the condition of the brake drum itself to be fully examined. Refer to Chapter 9 for further information.

Models with disc brakes

4 Chock the front wheels then jack up the rear of the vehicle and support it on axle stands (see *Jacking and Vehicle Support*).

5 For a quick check, the thickness of friction material remaining on each brake pad can be

16.1 Inspecting a driveshaft joint rubber gaiter

measured through the inspection aperture in the caliper body. If any pad's friction material is worn to the specified thickness or less, all four pads must be renewed as a set.

6 For a comprehensive check, the brake pads should be removed and cleaned. This will permit the operation of the caliper to be checked and the condition of the brake disc itself to be fully examined on both sides. Refer to Chapter 9 for further information.

16 Driveshaft check

1 With the vehicle raised and securely supported on axle stands (see *Jacking and Vehicle Support*), turn the steering onto full lock then slowly rotate the roadwheel. Inspect the condition of the outer constant velocity (CV) joint rubber gaiters while squeezing the gaiters to open out the folds **(see illustration)**. Check for signs of cracking, splits or deterioration of the rubber which may allow the grease to escape and lead to the entry of water and grit into the joint. Also check the security and condition of the gaiter retaining clips. Repeat these checks on the inner CV joints. If any damage or deterioration is found, then renew the gaiters.

2 Check the general condition of the CV joints by first holding the driveshaft and attempting to rotate the roadwheel. Repeat this check by holding the inner joint and attempting to rotate the driveshaft. Any appreciable movement indicates wear in the joints or driveshaft splines, or a loose driveshaft nut.

17 Suspension and steering check

Front suspension and steering

1 Raise the front of the vehicle and securely support it on axle stands (see *Jacking and Vehicle Support*).

2 Inspect the balljoint dust covers and the steering gear rubber gaiters for splits, chafing or deterioration **(see illustration)**. Any wear of these components will cause loss of lubricant,

17.2 Checking the condition of a steering gear rubber gaiter

17.4 Checking the condition of the steering and suspension components by rocking a roadwheel

together with dirt and water entry, resulting in rapid deterioration of the balljoints or steering gear.

3 On vehicles equipped with power steering, check the fluid hoses for chafing or deterioration and the pipe and hose unions for fluid leakage. Also check for signs of fluid leakage under pressure from the steering gear rubber gaiters which would indicate failed fluid seals within the steering gear.

4 Grasp the roadwheel at the 12 o'clock and 6 o'clock positions and try to rock it **(see illustration)**. Very slight free play may be felt but if the movement is appreciable then further investigation is necessary to determine the source. Continue rocking the wheel while an assistant depresses the brake pedal. If the movement is now eliminated or significantly reduced, it is likely that the hub bearings are at fault. If the free play is still evident with the brake pedal depressed, then there is wear in the suspension joints or mountings.

5 Now grasp the roadwheel at the 9 o'clock and 3 o'clock positions and try to rock it as before. Any movement felt now may again be caused by wear in the hub bearings, or in the track rod balljoints. If a balljoint is worn the visual movement will be obvious. If the inner joint is suspect it can be felt by placing a hand over the steering gear rubber gaiter and gripping the track rod. If the wheel is now rocked, movement will be felt at the inner joint if wear has taken place.

6 Using a large screwdriver or flat bar, check

18.5a Remove the ashtray from the rear of the centre console . .

for wear in the suspension mounting bushes by levering between the relevant suspension component and its attachment point. Some movement is to be expected as the mountings are made of rubber, but excessive wear should be obvious. Also check the condition of any visible rubber bushes, looking for splits, cracks or contamination of the rubber.

7 With the vehicle standing on its wheels, have an assistant turn the steering wheel back-and-forth about an eighth of a turn each way. There should be very little, if any, lost movement between the steering wheel and the roadwheels. If this is not the case, closely observe the joints and mountings previously described but in addition, check for wear of the steering column universal joint and the steering gear itself.

Rear suspension

8 Chock the front wheels then jack up the rear of the vehicle and support it on axle stands (see *Jacking and Vehicle Support*).

9 Working as described for the front suspension, check the rear hub bearings and the trailing arm and lateral link bushes for wear.

18 Handbrake check and adjustment

Checking

1 The handbrake should be capable of holding the parked vehicle stationary, even on steep slopes, when applied with moderate force. Equally, the handbrake must release properly, or the brakes will bind and overheat when the car is driven.

2 The mechanism should be firm and positive in feel with no trace of stiffness or sponginess from the cables and should release immediately the handbrake lever is released. If the mechanism is faulty in any of these respects then it must be checked immediately.

3 To check the handbrake setting, first apply the footbrake firmly several times to establish

18.5b . . . to gain access to the handbrake cable adjuster nut (arrowed) and equaliser mechanism

correct shoe-to-drum clearance. Applying normal, moderate pressure, pull the handbrake lever to the fully-applied position whilst counting the number of 'clicks' produced by the handbrake ratchet mechanism. Check that the number of clicks produced is as listed in the Specifications. If this is not the case, then adjustment is required.

Adjustment

4 To adjust the handbrake, chock the front wheels then jack up the rear of the vehicle and support it on axle stands (see *Jacking and Vehicle Support*).

5 Lift out the ashtray from the rear of the centre console to gain access to the handbrake adjusting nut **(see illustrations)**.

6 Apply the handbrake and check that the equaliser and cables move freely and smoothly, then set the lever on the first notch of the ratchet mechanism. With the lever in this position, rotate the handbrake lever adjusting nut until only a slight drag can be felt when the rear wheels are turned by hand. Once this is the case, fully release the handbrake lever and check that the wheels rotate freely. Check adjustment by applying the handbrake fully whilst counting the clicks emitted from the handbrake ratchet. Carry out the adjustment procedure again, if necessary.

7 Once adjustment is correct, refit the ashtray and lower the vehicle to the ground.

19 Lock and hinge lubrication

1 Lubricate the hinges of the bonnet, doors and tailgate with a light duty oil.

2 Lightly grease the bonnet release mechanism and cable.

3 The door and tailgate latches, strikers and locks must be lubricated using only the special Rover Door Lock and Latch Lubricant supplied in small sachets. Inject 1 gram into each lock and wipe off any surplus, then apply a thin film to the latches and strikers.

4 Do not lubricate the steering lock mechanism with oil or any other lubricant which might foul the ignition switch contacts. If the lock is stiff, try the effect of a proprietary electrical contact lubricant, rather than conventional lubricant.

5 If a sunroof is fitted, lubricate very sparingly the seal lip with Rover supplied non-staining seal grease.

20 Windscreen and number plate condition check

Refer to the MOT pre-test checks described in the *Reference* Chapter, at the end of this manual.

21 Seat belt check

1 Check the webbing of each seat belt for signs of fraying, cuts or other damage, pulling the belt out to its full extent to check its entire length **(see illustration)**.

2 Check the operation of the belt buckles by fitting the belt tongue plate and pulling hard to ensure that it remains locked in position.

3 Check the retractor mechanism (inertia reel only) by pulling out the belt to the halfway point and jerking it downwards **(see illustration)**. The mechanism must lock immediately to prevent any further unreeling but must allow free movement during normal driving.

4 Ensure that all belt mounting bolts are securely tightened. Note that the bolts are shouldered so that the belt anchor points are free to rotate.

5 If there is any sign of damage, or any doubt about a belt's condition, then it must be renewed. If the vehicle has been involved in a collision, then any belt in use at the time must be renewed as a matter of course and all other belts checked carefully.

6 Use only warm water and non-detergent soap to clean the belts.

Caution: Never use any chemical cleaners, strong detergents, dyes or bleaches. Keep the belts fully extended until they have dried naturally and do not apply heat to dry them.

22 SRS system component check

1 Checking of the airbag system by the home mechanic is limited to a visual inspection of the outer surface of the driver and passenger airbag modules (as applicable). If the surface of the casing has sustained any damage (such as that caused by an impact, or fluid spillage for example) then the airbag system should be checked by a Rover dealer at the earliest opportunity.

2 Sit in the driver's seat and release the steering column lock. On models with power steering, start the engine and allow it to idle. Turn the steering wheel from lock-to-lock, whilst listening to the rotary coupler at the steering wheel hub. Any noise or roughness in operation could indicate a worn rotary coupler – refer to a Rover dealer for further advice.

3 The SRS warning lamp on the instrument panel should illuminate for about six seconds when the ignition key is turned to the 'II' position and then extinguish. If the lamp fails to extinguish, or does not illuminate at all, there may be a fault with the SRS system; the advice of a Rover dealer should be sought.

23 Road test

Instruments and electrical equipment

1 Check the operation of all instruments and electrical equipment.

2 Make sure that all instruments read correctly, and switch on all electrical equipment in turn, to check that it functions properly.

Steering and suspension

3 Check for any abnormalities in the steering, suspension, handling or road 'feel'.

4 Drive the vehicle, and check that there are no unusual vibrations or noises.

5 Check that the steering feels positive, with no excessive 'sloppiness', or roughness, and check for any suspension noises when cornering and driving over bumps.

Drivetrain

6 Check the performance of the engine, clutch, transmission and driveshafts.

7 Listen for any unusual noises from the engine, clutch and transmission.

8 Make sure that the engine runs smoothly when idling, and that there is no hesitation when accelerating.

9 Check that the clutch action is smooth and progressive, that the drive is taken up smoothly, and that the pedal travel is not excessive. Also listen for any noises when the clutch pedal is depressed.

10 Check that all gears can be engaged smoothly without noise, and that the gear lever action is smooth and not abnormally vague or 'notchy'.

11 Listen for a metallic clicking sound from the front of the vehicle, as the vehicle is driven slowly in a circle with the steering on full-lock. Carry out this check in both directions. If a clicking noise is heard, this indicates wear in a driveshaft joint (see Chapter 8).

Braking system

12 Make sure that the vehicle does not pull to one side when braking, and that the wheels do not lock when braking hard.

13 Check that there is no vibration through the steering when braking.

14 Check that the handbrake operates correctly, and that it holds the vehicle stationary on a slope.

21.1 Check the webbing of each seat belt for signs of fraying, cuts or other damage

21.3 Checking the operation of the inertia reel locking mechanism

24.2 Release the coolant pipe from the clips on the air cleaner

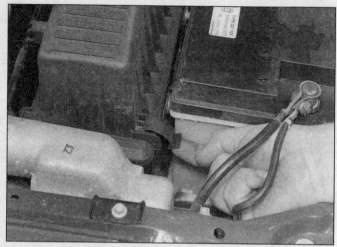

24.3a Release the air cleaner cover securing clips . . .

Every 24 000 miles (40 000 km) or 2 years

24 Air cleaner filter element renewal

1 The air cleaner is located at the left-hand side of the engine compartment, next to the battery.
2 Release the coolant pipe from the clips on the air cleaner **(see illustration)**.
3 Release the four securing clips, then lift up the air cleaner cover sufficiently to enable the element to be lifted out **(see illustrations)**.
4 Wipe out the air cleaner casing and the cover using a clean cloth.
5 Fit the new element, then refit the cover and secure with the clips, and clip the coolant pipe into position on the air cleaner.

25 Brake fluid renewal

1 This procedure is similar to that described for the bleeding of the hydraulic system, as described in Chapter 9, except that the brake fluid reservoir should be emptied by syphoning and allowance should be made for all old fluid to be expelled when bleeding a section of the circuit.
2 Working as described in Chapter 9, open the first bleed nipple in the sequence and pump the brake pedal gently until nearly all the old fluid has been emptied from the master cylinder reservoir. Top up to the MAX level on the reservoir with new fluid and continue pumping until only new fluid remains in the reservoir and new fluid can be seen emerging from the bleed nipple. Old hydraulic fluid is much darker in colour than new fluid, making it easy to distinguish between them.
3 Tighten the nipple and top the reservoir level up to the MAX level line.
4 Work through all the remaining nipples in the sequence until new fluid can be seen emerging from all of them. Be careful to keep the master cylinder reservoir topped-up to above the MIN level at all times, or air may

24.3b . . . then lift the cover and lift out the element

enter the system and greatly increase the length of the task.
5 When the operation is complete, check that all nipples are securely tightened and that their dust caps are refitted. Wash off all traces of spilt fluid and recheck the master cylinder reservoir fluid level.
6 Check the operation of the brakes before taking the vehicle on the road.

Every 48 000 miles (80 000 km) or 4 years

26 Coolant renewal

⚠️ **Warning: Wait until the engine is completely cold before starting the coolant renewal procedure. Do not allow antifreeze to come into contact with your skin or painted surfaces of the vehicle. Rinse off spills immediately with plenty of water. Never leave antifreeze lying around in an open container or in a puddle in the driveway or on the garage floor. Children and pets are attracted by its** sweet smell; and antifreeze can be fatal if ingested.

Antifreeze mixture

1 Antifreeze should always be renewed at the specified intervals. This is necessary not only to maintain the anti-freezing properties of the coolant but also to prevent corrosion which would otherwise occur, as the corrosion inhibitors in the coolant become progressively less effective.
2 Always use an ethylene glycol based antifreeze which is suitable for use in mixed-metal cooling systems.
3 The type of antifreeze and levels of protection afforded are indicated in *Lubricants and fluids* and Specifications. To achieve the recommended 50% concentration, equal quantities of antifreeze and clean, soft water must be mixed together. It is best to make up slightly more than is actually needed to refill the cooling system, so that a supply is available for subsequent topping-up.
Caution: Always pre-mix the antifreeze and water in a suitable container before refilling the cooling system. If the antifreeze and water are poured into the cooling system separately, they may not mix correctly and could cause localised overheating, which may lead to engine damage.

Draining

4 To drain the cooling system, remove the expansion tank filler cap then move the heater air temperature control to the maximum heat position.

5 Place a large drain tray beneath the bottom hose connection, at the bottom left-hand corner of the radiator. Release the hose clip and carefully pull the bottom hose off the radiator stub, allowing the coolant to drain into the container below. Once the system has drained completely, reconnect the bottom hose and secure with the hose clip.

Flushing

6 With time, the cooling system may gradually lose its efficiency due to the radiator core having become choked with rust, scale deposits and other sediment. To minimise this, the system should be flushed as described in the following paragraphs, whenever the coolant is renewed.

7 With the coolant drained, refill the system with fresh water. Refit the expansion tank filler cap, start the engine and warm it up to normal operating temperature, then stop it and (after allowing it to cool down completely) drain the system again. Repeat as necessary until only clean water can be seen to emerge, then refill finally with the specified coolant mixture.

8 If the specified coolant mixture has been used and has been renewed at the specified intervals, the above procedure will be sufficient to keep clean the system for a considerable length of time. If, however, the system has been neglected, a more thorough operation will be required, as follows.

9 First drain the coolant, then disconnect the radiator top and bottom hoses from the radiator. Insert a garden hose into the radiator top hose outlet and allow water (under LOW pressure only) to circulate through the radiator until it runs clean from the bottom outlet.

Caution: Do not flush with water under high pressure, as this may damage the radiator.

10 To flush the engine, insert the garden hose into the top hose and allow water to circulate until it runs clear from the bottom hose. If, after a reasonable period, the water still does not run clear, the cooling system should be flushed with a good proprietary cleaning agent. Bear in mind, however, that any leaks sealed in the past using a cooling system sealant additive may be weakened by this course of action, and could start to leak again.

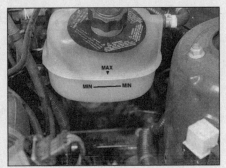

26.17a Remove the expansion tank filler cap and carefully top up the tank . . .

26.17b . . . to the MAX level

11 In severe cases of contamination, reverse-flushing of the radiator may be necessary. To do this, remove the radiator, invert it and insert a garden hose into the bottom outlet. Continue flushing (again, using water under LOW pressure only) until clear water runs from the top hose outlet. If necessary, a similar procedure can be used to flush the heater matrix.

12 The use of chemical cleaners should be necessary only as a last resort as regular renewal of the coolant will prevent excessive contamination of the system.

Filling

13 With the cooling system drained and flushed, ensure that all radiator hoses are securely reconnected. Check all hose unions for security and all hoses for condition. Fresh antifreeze has a searching action which will rapidly find any weaknesses in the system.

14 Prepare a sufficient quantity of the specified coolant mixture, allowing for a surplus so as to have a reserve supply for topping-up (see *Antifreeze Mixture* above).

15 Remove the expansion tank filler cap, then fill the system slowly through the filler neck. Continue filling until the coolant level reaches the MAX mark on the side of the expansion tank. Refit the filler cap and tighten it securely.

16 Start the engine and run it at no more than idle speed until it has warmed-up to normal operating temperature and the radiator electric cooling fan has cut in once. Watch the temperature gauge to check for signs of overheating.

17 Stop the engine and allow it to cool down completely, then remove the expansion tank filler cap carefully and top up the tank to the MAX level **(see illustrations)**. Refit the filler

cap and wash off any spilt coolant from the engine compartment and bodywork with plenty of clean water.

18 After refilling, check carefully all system components for signs of coolant leaks. A label should now be attached to the radiator or expansion tank stating the type and concentration of antifreeze used and the date installed. Any subsequent topping-up should be made with the same type and concentration of antifreeze.

19 If, after draining and refilling the system, symptoms of overheating are found which did not occur previously, then the fault is almost certainly due to trapped air at some point in the system causing an airlock and restricting the flow of coolant. Usually air is trapped because the system was refilled too quickly. In some cases, airlocks can be released by tapping or squeezing the appropriate coolant hose. If the problem persists, stop the engine and allow it to cool down completely before unscrewing the expansion tank filler cap, to allow the trapped air to escape.

27 Renew camshaft drivebelt

Renewal procedure is described in Chapter 2B.

28 Renew injection pump drivebelt

Renewal procedure is described in Chapter 2B.

Every 108 000 miles (175 000 km) or 9 years

29 Manual transmission oil renewal

Refer to *Manual transmission oil – draining and refilling* in Chapter 7.

Every 15 years, regardless of mileage

30 SRS system components renewal

1 The Supplementary Restraint System (SRS), which includes the airbag(s), and seat belt pretensioners, has components which contain pyrotechnic materials. Because these materials degrade with age, MG Rover specify that the following components must be renewed every 15 years:

Driver airbag module.
Passenger airbag module.
Seat belt pretensioners.
Rotary coupler.

2 Remove and refit information is given in Chapter 12. However, because of the safety critical nature of these components, and the need for special equipment to test their operation, we strongly recommend that renewal is done by an MG Rover dealer.

Chapter 2 Part A:
Petrol engine in-car repair procedures

Contents

Degrees of difficulty

Easy, suitable for novice with little experience | **Fairly easy,** suitable for beginner with some experience | **Fairly difficult,** suitable for competent DIY mechanic 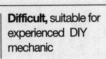 | **Difficult,** suitable for experienced DIY mechanic | **Very difficult,** suitable for expert DIY or professional

Specifications

General

Engine type	Four-cylinder in-line, four-stroke, liquid-cooled
Designation	K16 – 16 valves, four per cylinder
Bore:	
1.1 and 1.4 litre engines	75.00 mm
1.6 and 1.8 litre engines	80.00 mm
Stroke:	
1.1 litre engine	62.3 mm
1.4 and 1.6 litre engines	79.00 mm
1.8 litre engine	89.30 mm
Capacity:	
1.1 litre engine	1120 cc
1.4 litre engine	1396 cc
1.6 litre engine	1589 cc
1.8 litre engine	1796 cc
Firing order	1-3-4-2 (No 1 cylinder at timing belt end)
Direction of crankshaft rotation	Clockwise (seen from right-hand side of vehicle)
Compression ratio:	
1.1 litre engine	9.4:1
1.4 litre engine	10.4:1
1.6 and 1.8 litre engines	10.5:1
Minimum compression pressure (typical value)	10.0 bar
Maximum compression pressure difference between cylinders	
(typical value)	1.5 bar

Camshaft

Drive	Toothed belt from crankshaft
Belt tensioner	Automatic
Number of bearings	6 per camshaft
Bearing journal running clearance:	
Standard	0.060 to 0.094 mm
Service limit	0.150 mm
Camshaft endfloat:	
Standard	0.060 to 0.190 mm
Service limit	0.300 mm
Hydraulic tappet outside diameter	32.959 to 32.975 mm

Lubrication system

System pressure . . . . 1.7 to 3.5 bar @ idle speed
Pressure relief valve opening pressure . . . . 4.1 bar
Low oil pressure warning light comes on . . . . 0.3 to 0.5 bar
Oil pump clearances:
    Rotor endfloat . . . . 0.02 to 0.06 mm
    Outer rotor-to-body clearance . . . . 0.28 to 0.36 mm
    Rotor lobe clearance . . . . 0.05 to 0.13 mm

Torque wrench settings

	Nm	lbf ft
Alternator top mounting bracket nut/bolt	25	18
Big-end bolts:		
Stage 1	25	18
Stage 2	Angle-tighten through a further 45°	
Camshaft bearing carrier bolts	10	7
Camshaft cover bolts	10	7
Camshaft oil seal cover plate bolts	25	18
Camshaft sprocket bolt:		
M8 bolt	35	26
M10 bolt	65	48
Crankshaft pulley bolt	205	151
Cylinder head bolts:		
Stage 1	20	15
Stage 2	Angle-tighten through a further 180°	
Stage 3	Angle-tighten through a further 180°	
Engine oil drain plug:		
Steel sump	42	31
Alloy sump	25	18
Engine lifting bracket bolts	9	7
Engine lower steady-to-subframe bolt	80	59
Engine torsion bar bolts	25	18
Engine/transmission steady bar-to-transmission/sump bolt	45	33
Flywheel bolts*	85	63
Flywheel lower cover bolts	9	7
Hydramount/Restraint bar-to-RH body bracket bolts	45	33
LH mounting bracket-to-body bolts	55	41
LH mounting bracket-to-gearbox bracket bolts	100	74
LH mounting through-bolt	85	63
LH mounting-to-bracket nuts	45	33
Lower engine steady-to-sump bolt	45	33
Main bearing ladder-to-cylinder block bolts:		
Stage 1	5	4
Stage 2	15	11
Oil rail-to-main bearing ladder bolts	5	4
Oil pressure warning light switch	15	11
Oil pump-to-cylinder block bolts	9	7
RH mounting bracket-to-body bolts	25	18
RH mounting engine bracket-to-engine bolts	135	100
RH mounting engine bracket-to-Hydramount nut	85	63
Roadwheel nuts	See Chapter 10	
Spark plug cover screws	10	7
Spark plugs	25	18
Sump drain plug	28	21
Sump to bearing ladder:		
Short bolts	25	18
Long bolts	30	22
Timing belt lower cover bolts	9	6
Timing belt tensioner backplate clamp bolt	10	7
Timing belt tensioner pulley screw	45	33
Timing belt upper cover bolts	5	4

Use new bolts

1 General information and precautions

How to use this Chapter

This Part of the Chapter describes those repair procedures that can reasonably be carried out on the engine whilst it remains in the vehicle. If the engine has been removed from the vehicle and is being dismantled as described in Part C of this Chapter, any preliminary dismantling procedures can be ignored.

Note that whilst it may be possible physically to overhaul items such as the piston/connecting rod assemblies with the engine in the vehicle, such tasks are not usually carried out as separate operations and usually require the execution of several additional procedures (not to mention the cleaning of components and of oilways). For this reason, all such tasks are classed as major overhaul procedures and are described in Part C of this Chapter.

Engine description

The four cylinder in-line engine, with double overhead camshafts (DOHC) and sixteen valves, is mounted transversely at the front of the car.

The main structure of the engine consists of three major castings – the cylinder head, the cylinder block/crankcase, and the crankshaft main bearing ladder.

The three major castings are made from aluminium alloy, and are clamped together by ten long through-bolts which perform the dual role of cylinder head bolts and crankshaft main bearing bolts. An oil rail is fitted under the main bearing ladder, and to avoid disturbing the bottom end of the engine when removing the through-bolts, the oil rail is secured independently to the main bearing ladder (by two nuts), and the main bearing ladder is secured to the cylinder block/crankcase (by ten bolts).

The crankshaft runs in five main bearings. Thrustwashers are fitted to the centre main bearing (upper half) to control crankshaft endfloat.

The connecting rods rotate on horizontally-split bearing shells at their big-ends. The pistons are attached to the connecting rods by gudgeon pins which are an interference fit in the connecting rod small-end eyes. The aluminium alloy pistons are fitted with three piston rings, comprising two compression rings and an oil control ring.

The cylinder bores are formed by renewable wet liners which locate in the cylinder block/crankcase at their top ends. A bead of sealant around each liner prevents the escape of coolant into the sump.

The inlet and exhaust valves are each closed by coil springs and operate in guides pressed into the cylinder head. The valve seat inserts are pressed into the cylinder head and can be renewed separately if worn.

The camshafts are driven from the crankshaft by a toothed belt, with automatic tension control.

One camshaft operates two exhaust valves in each cylinder, and the other operates two inlet valves in each cylinder. The valves are opened via self-adjusting hydraulic tappets, which eliminate the need for routine checking and adjustment of valve clearances. The camshaft rotates in bearings, which are line bored directly into the cylinder head and the (bolted on) bearing carrier. This means that the cylinder head and bearing carrier are matched, and cannot be renewed separately. When fitted (to early engines only), the distributor is driven from the left-hand end of the inlet valve camshaft.

The electric fuel pump is submerged in the fuel tank.

The coolant pump is driven by the timing belt.

Lubrication is by means of an eccentric-rotor type pump driven directly from the timing belt end of the crankshaft. The pump draws oil through a strainer located in the sump, and then forces it through an externally-mounted full-flow cartridge-type oil filter into galleries in the oil rail and the cylinder block/crankcase, from where it is distributed to the crankshaft (main bearings) and camshaft. The big-end bearings are supplied with oil via internal drillings in the crankshaft, while the camshaft bearings and the hydraulic tappets receive a pressurised supply via drillings in the cylinder head. The camshaft lobes and valves are lubricated by oil splash, as are all other engine components.

Operations with engine in car

The following work can be carried out with the engine in the vehicle:
a) Compression pressure – testing.
b) Cylinder head cover – removal and refitting.
c) Crankshaft pulley – removal and refitting.
d) Timing belt covers – removal and refitting.
e) Timing belt – removal, refitting and adjustment.
f) Timing belt tensioner and sprockets – removal and refitting.
g) Camshaft oil seal(s) – renewal.
h) Camshafts and hydraulic tappets – removal, inspection and refitting.
i) Cylinder head – removal and refitting.
j) Cylinder head and pistons – decarbonising.
k) Sump – removal and refitting.
l) Oil pump – removal, overhaul and refitting.
m) Crankshaft oil seals – renewal.
n) Engine/transmission mountings – inspection and renewal.
o) Flywheel – removal, inspection and refitting.

Precautions

Note that a side-effect of the through-bolt engine design is that the crankshaft cannot be rotated once the through-bolts have been slackened. During any servicing or overhaul work the crankshaft must always be rotated to the desired position before the bolts are disturbed.

2 Compression test – description and interpretation

Note: *A suitable compression tester will be required for this test.*

1 When engine performance is down, or if misfiring occurs which cannot be attributed to the ignition or fuel systems, a compression test can provide diagnostic clues as to the engine's condition. If the test is performed regularly it can give warning of trouble before any other symptoms become apparent.

2 The engine must be fully warmed-up to normal operating temperature, the battery must be fully-charged and the spark plugs must be removed. The aid of an assistant will be required.

3 Disable the ignition system by disconnecting the ignition HT coil lead from the distributor cap and earthing it on the cylinder block. Use a jumper lead or similar wire to make a good connection.

4 Fit a compression tester to the No 1 cylinder spark plug hole. The type of tester which screws into the plug thread is preferred.

5 Have the assistant hold the throttle wide open and crank the engine on the starter motor. After one or two revolutions, the compression pressure should build-up to a maximum figure and then stabilise. Record the highest reading obtained.

6 Repeat the test on the remaining cylinders, recording the pressure in each.

7 All cylinders should produce very similar pressures. Any difference greater than that specified indicates the existence of a fault. Note that the compression should build-up quickly in a healthy engine. Low compression on the first stroke, followed by gradually increasing pressure on successive strokes, indicates worn piston rings. A low compression reading on the first stroke, which does not build-up during successive strokes, indicates leaking valves or a blown head gasket (a cracked head could also be the cause). Deposits on the undersides of the valve heads can also cause low compression.

8 If the pressure in any cylinder is reduced to the specified minimum or less (Rover do not specify figures, the values given in the Specifications are typical figures for a petrol engine), carry out the following test to isolate the cause. Introduce a teaspoonful of clean oil into that cylinder through its spark plug hole and repeat the test.

3.4 Camshaft sprocket timing marks (A) aligned with mark (B) on camshaft belt cover

3.5a Crankshaft pulley timing mark aligned with 90° BTDC mark on camshaft belt outer cover

3.5b Crankshaft sprocket dots (A) aligned each side of raised rib (B) on oil pump cover

9 If the addition of oil temporarily improves the compression pressure, this indicates that bore or piston wear is responsible for the pressure loss. No improvement suggests that leaking or burnt valves, or a blown head gasket, may be to blame.

10 A low reading from two adjacent cylinders is almost certainly due to the head gasket having blown between them and the presence of coolant in the engine oil will confirm this.

11 If one cylinder is about 20 percent lower than the others and the engine has a slightly rough idle, a worn camshaft lobe could be the cause.

12 If the compression reading is unusually high, the combustion chambers are probably coated with carbon deposits. If this is the case, the cylinder head should be removed and decarbonised.

13 On completion of the test, refit the spark plugs and reconnect the HT lead to the distributor cap.

3 Engine timing marks

1 The crankshaft pulley, crankshaft and camshaft sprockets each have timing marks which align only at 90° BTDC. At this position, all pistons are half-way up the bores, so there is less risk of engine damage whilst working on the engine. **Note:** *These marks do not indicate TDC.* Before starting any engine

overhaul procedures, align the timing marks at 90° BTDC as follows.

2 Apply the handbrake, chock the rear roadwheels, then jack up the front of the car and support it on axle stands (see *Jacking and Vehicle Support*). Remove the right hand front roadwheel.

3 Slacken lower bolt securing timing belt upper cover to engine. Remove the five bolts securing the upper cover to the rear cover, and remove the upper cover.

4 Using a spanner or socket on the crankshaft pulley nut, turn the crankshaft clockwise until the marks on the camshaft sprockets are aligned horizontally with the top face of the cylinder head – there is usually a mark on the rear cover which represents the top face of the head. The marks should be positioned to the right of the sprocket centres, and the EXHAUST arrows should point to the rear of the vehicle **(see illustration)**.

5 When these marks are aligned, the notch on the inner rim of the crankshaft pulley should be aligned with the vertical 90° BTDC mark on the on the timing belt lower cover. Similarly, if the crankshaft pulley is removed, two punched dots on the crankshaft sprocket should be aligned either side of the raised rib on the oil pump cover **(see illustrations)**.

6 Fit the roadwheel, and tighten the nuts to secure the wheel. Remove the stands and lower the vehicle to the ground. Use a torque wrench to tighten the roadwheel nuts to the specified torque.

7 Connect the battery earth lead.

4 Camshaft cover – removal and refitting

Later engine with no distributor

Removal

1 Disconnect the battery earth lead.

2 Release two clips and disconnect two breather hoses from the camshaft cover.

3 Remove three bolts securing coil/plug cover to camshaft cover, and remove the cover **(see illustration)**.

4 Note the position and clipping of the HT leads and cables running to the coils and camshaft position sensor. Release the HT leads, and pull the tubular connectors from the spark plugs next to the two coils **(see illustration)**.

5 Remove the two bolts attaching each coil to the camshaft cover, and pull the coils from the spark plugs **(see illustration)**.

6 Remove the bolt attaching the camshaft position sensor (CMP) to the camshaft cover. Release the sensor and position aside – note that an O-ring is fitted to the sensor **(see illustration)**.

7 Working in reverse order from the tightening sequence **(see illustration 4.10)**, progressively slacken and remove the bolts attaching the camshaft cover to the cylinder head.

8 Remove the cover and gasket – if the

4.3 Remove coil/plug cover

4.4 Pull connectors from spark plugs

4.5 Pull coils from spark plugs

gasket is in good condition, it need not be separated from the cover.

Refitting

9 Ensure that the gasket is in good condition, and that mating faces are clean. If a new gasket is being fitted, press it onto the cover dowels, with the embossed words towards the cover. 'Exhaust man side' must be towards the exhaust manifold **(see illustration)**.

10 Ensuring that the gasket remains in place, fit the cover. Fit the retaining bolts and tighten them all finger tight. Working in the illustrated sequence, use a torque wrench to tighten the bolts to the specified torque **(see illustration)**.

11 Ensure that the CMP sensor O-ring is in good condition, and lubricate it with engine oil. Fit the CMP sensor and bolt.

12 In the positions noted before removal – fit the coils' securing bolts. Fit the HT lead tubular connectors to the plugs next to the coils – position the HT leads and cables in the grooves and clips.

13 Fit the coil cover, and securing bolts. Connect the breather hoses to the cover, and reconnect the battery earth lead.

Early engine with distributor

Removal

14 Disconnect the battery earth lead.

15 Release two clips and disconnect two breather hoses from the camshaft cover. Remove the two bolts attaching the plug cover to the camshaft cover, and remove the cover. Disconnect the HT lead tubular connectors from the spark plugs, and withdraw the connectors from the cylinder head, with the clip plate and grommet from the left-hand end of the camshaft cover.

16 Working in reverse order from the tightening sequence **(see illustration 4.10)**, progressively slacken and remove the bolts attaching the camshaft cover to the cylinder head.

17 Remove the cover and gasket – if the gasket is in good condition, it need not be separated from the cover.

Refitting

18 Ensure that the gasket is in good condition, and that mating faces are clean. If a new gasket is being fitted, press it onto the cover dowels, with the embossed words towards the cover. 'Exhaust man side' must be towards the exhaust manifold.

19 Ensuring that the gasket remains in place, refit the cover. Fit the retaining bolts and tighten them all finger tight. Working in sequence, use a torque wrench to tighten the bolts to the specified torque **(see illustration 4.10)**.

20 Connect the HT lead tubular connectors the spark plugs, and locate the clip and grommet in the camshaft cover. Ensure that the HT leads are correctly routed, and then fit the plug cover and bolts.

21 Connect the breather hoses to the cover, and reconnect the battery earth lead.

4.6 Release CMP

4.9 Correctly positioned gasket

4.10 Bolt tightening sequence

5 Crankshaft pulley – removal and refitting

Removal

Note: *When slackening or tightening the pulley securing bolt, it is necessary to prevent the crankshaft from turning. This can be done by eg:*

1.1, 1.4 and 1.6 engines: A suitable device can be made using a short length of flat steel bar, and a nut and bolt.

1.8 engines: The starter motor must be removed, and the crankshaft locked by inserting a flat bar between two teeth on the starter ring gear.

1 Disconnect the battery earth lead.

2 Apply the handbrake, chock the rear roadwheels, then jack up the front of the car and support it on axle stands (see *Jacking and Vehicle Support*). Remove the right hand roadwheel.

3 Remove the alternator drivebelt (see

Chapter 5A), and the power steering pump drivebelt (see Chapter 10).

1.1, 1.4 and 1.6 engines

4 Remove the metal cover from the flywheel housing at the opposite side to the starter motor **(see illustration)**.

5 Fit the locking device – with the flat bar on the bolt, pass the bolt through the empty hole

5.4 Remove flywheel housing cover

**5.5 Crankshaft locking device –
1.4 and 1.6**

in the flywheel housing. Fit and tighten the nut, so that the bar is protruding in front of the teeth on the flywheel ring gear **(see illustration)**.

6 Have an assistant engage a suitable flat lever – such as a large screwdriver – between two teeth of the ring gear, and against the locking device bar, so that when anti-clockwise effort is applied to the pulley bolt, the crankshaft will be prevented from turning.

1.8 engines

7 Remove the starter motor – see Chapter 5A **(see illustration)**.

8 Have an assistant engage a suitable flat lever – such as a large screwdriver – between two teeth of the starter ring gear, so that when anti-clockwise effort is applied to the pulley bolt, the crankshaft will be prevented from turning.

All engines

9 Remove the pulley bolt and pull off the pulley.

Refitting

10 Ensuring that mating faces are clean, fit the pulley so that the pulley notch fits over the lug on the crankshaft sprocket **(see illustration)**. Fit the washer with the largest diameter against the pulley.

11 Lock the crankshaft, and use a torque wrench to tighten the pulley bolt to the specified torque.

1.1, 1.4 and 1.6 engines

12 Remove the locking device, and fit the metal cover to the flywheel housing.

6.3 Remove upper outer cover

**5.10 Align notch in pulley and lug on
sprocket**

1.8 engines

13 Fit the starter motor.

All engines

14 Fit the power steering pump and alternator drivebelts – adjust the alternator belt tension.

15 Fit the roadwheel, and tighten the nuts to secure the wheel. Remove the stands and lower the vehicle to the ground. Use a torque wrench to tighten the roadwheel nuts to the specified torque.

16 Connect the battery earth lead.

6 Timing belt covers

Upper outer cover

Removal

1 Disconnect the battery earth lead.
2 Slacken lower bolt securing timing belt upper cover to engine.
3 Remove five bolts securing upper cover to rear cover, and remove the upper cover. If it loose, remove the rubber seal **(see illustration)**.

Refitting

4 Before refitting, clean the cover.
5 Ensure that the rubber seal is correctly positioned. Fit the cover, slotting it over the lower bolt.
6 Fit the five top bolts. Use a torque wrench to tighten the bolts to the specified torque.

6.11 Remove lower outer cover

Lower outer cover

Removal

7 Slacken lower bolt securing the upper outer cover to engine.
8 Remove five bolts securing upper cover to rear cover. Lift the cover to clear the lower bolt, and remove the upper cover. If it loose, remove the rubber seal.
9 Remove the crankshaft pulley – see Section 5.
10 Remove the power steering pump belt tension roller assembly – see Chapter 10.
11 Remove three bolts securing the lower cover to the cylinder block, and remove the cover and, if attached, the rubber seal **(see illustration)**.

Refitting

13 Before refitting, clean the cover.
14 Ensure that the rubber seal is correctly positioned. Fit the cover and the bolts. Use a torque wrench to tighten the bolts to the specified torque.
15 Fit the power steering pump belt tension roller assembly.
16 Fit the crankshaft pulley. Locking crankshaft rotation as for removal, use a torque wrench to tighten the bolt to the specified torque.
17 Remove the locking device, and fit the metal cover to the flywheel housing.
18 Fit the upper outer cover.
19 Connect the battery earth lead.

Rear cover

Removal

19 Remove the outer timing belt covers as described previously in this Section.
20 Remove the camshaft sprocket(s) and the timing belt tensioner as described in Section 7.
21 Unscrew the securing bolts, and withdraw the timing belt rear cover **(see illustration)**.

Refitting

22 Refitting is a reversal of removal, but refit the timing belt tensioner and the camshaft sprocket(s) as described in Section 8, and tighten all fixings to the specified torque wrench settings.

6.21 Removing the rear timing belt cover

7.3a Timing belt, sprockets and covers – with automatic belt tensioner

1 Timing belt upper outer cover	6 Seal	13 Camshaft sprockets	18 Index wire
2 Bolt	7 Bolt	14 Bolt	19 Pointer
3 Seal	8 Bolt	15 Washer	20 Pillar bolt
4 Bolt	9 Crankshaft pulley	16 Timing belt tensioner bolt	21 Crankshaft sprocket
5 Timing belt lower outer cover	10 Washer	17 Timing belt tensioner	22 Bolt
	11 Crankshaft pulley bolt		23 Bolt
	12 Timing belt		24 Rear cover

7.3b Timing belt, sprockets and covers – with manual belt tensioner (early engines)

1 Timing belt upper outer cover	8 Bolt	15 Washer	20 Anchor bolt
2 Bolt	9 Crankshaft pulley	16 Timing belt tensioner pulley assembly	21 Tensioner backplate clamp bolt
3 Seal	10 Washer	17 Tensioner pulley Allen screw	22 Crankshaft sprocket
4 Bolt	11 Crankshaft pulley bolt	18 Tensioner pulley spring	23 Timing belt rear cover
5 Timing belt lower outer cover	12 Timing belt	19 Sleeve	24 Bolt
6 Seal	13 Camshaft sprockets		
7 Bolt	14 Bolt		

7 Timing belt and tensioner – removal

Caution: Store and handle belt with care. Do not use a belt that has been twisted or folded – reinforcing fibres may be damaged, and the belt may fail prematurely.

Note: *To preserve valve timing and prevent engine damage, the camshafts must not rotate when the timing belt has been removed. An inexpensive locking tool, which fits between the teeth of the camshaft sprockets, is available from most car parts and accessory outlets.*

1 Disconnect the battery earth lead.

2 Apply the handbrake, chock the rear roadwheels, then jack up the front of the car and support it on axle stands (see *Jacking and Vehicle Support*). Remove the right hand front roadwheel.

3 Release the coolant hose, which is routed past the timing belt upper cover, from three clips and move aside **(see illustrations)**.

4 Remove the timing belt upper outer cover – see Section 6.

5 Using a socket and extension bar on the crankshaft bolt, turn the crankshaft clockwise to align the camshaft sprocket timing marks at 90° BTDC – see Section 3.

6 Fit the camshaft locking tool **(see illustrations)**.

7 Remove the crankshaft pulley – see Section 5.

7.6a Camshaft sprocket locking tool

7.6b Sprocket locking tool in position

7.9 Remove power steering pipe clamp bolt

7.10 Tilt steady bar upward

7.11 Remove two bracket bolts

7.12 Remove restraint bar and mounting assembly

7.14 Tensioner and index wire

8 Timing belt and tensioner – refitting

Caution: Store and handle belt with care. Do not use a belt that has been twisted or folded – reinforcing fibres may be damaged, and the belt may fail prematurely.

1 Clean the sprockets and tensioner pulley.

Caution: If the sprockets are contaminated with oil, they must be soaked in a bath of solvent, and washed clean. The sprockets are made of a 'sintered' material which is porous. Any oil remaining in the material will seep out and contaminate the timing belt.

2 Ensure that the camshaft sprocket timing marks are aligned and locked.

3 Fit the timing belt tensioner, locating the index wire over the pillar bolt, and ensure that the tension lever is at 9 o'clock position. Fit a new Patchlok bolt, and tighten it so that it is just possible to move the tension lever **(see illustration)**.

4 If original belt is being refitted, ensure direction of rotation is correct. Using fingers only, fit the timing belt over the crankshaft sprocket, and then over the camshaft sprockets. **Note:** *Keep the belt taut between the crankshaft sprocket and the exhaust camshaft sprocket.* Locate the belt around the tension roller and coolant pump sprocket. Ensure that the belt is located centrally on all sprockets and roller **(see illustration)**.

5 Fit lower outer timing cover and bolts. Use a torque wrench to tighten bolts to specified torque.

Models with air conditioning

6 Have an assistant rotate the auxiliary drivebelt tension roller fully clockwise. Whilst the roller is held in this position, fit the locking pin into the hole in the backplate.

All models

7 Fit crankshaft pulley – see Section 5.

8 Using a 6 mm Allen key, rotate the tension lever anti-clockwise, and align the pointer notch with the index wire **(see illustrations)**. **Note:** *If original belt has been refitted, align the lower edge of the pointer notch with the index wire.*

8 Position a jack, with wooden block on top, under the engine sump, and adjust to support the weight of the engine and transmission.

9 Remove bolt and nut securing power steering pipe clamp to inside wheel arch, and move pipe aside **(see illustration)**.

10 Slacken the through-bolt securing engine upper steady bar to body. Remove through-bolt securing steady bar to right-hand engine mounting, and tilt bar upward, clear of the mounting **(see illustration)**.

11 Remove two bolts, which attach the two halves of the aluminium mounting bracket **(see illustration)**.

12 Remove two bolts securing rubber mounting backplate to body, and one nut securing restraint bar to body. Remove restraint bar and mounting assembly **(see illustration)**. **Note:** *If timing belt is to be re-used, mark direction of rotation with chalk.*

13 Remove and discard the timing belt tensioner bolt.

14 Disengage the index wire from behind the pillar bolt, and remove the tensioner **(see illustration)**.

Models with air conditioning

15 Hold the auxiliary drivebelt tensioner, and remove the locking pin. Allow tensioner to rotate fully anti-clockwise.

All models

16 Remove three bolts securing lower outer cover, and remove cover and rubber seal.

17 Using fingers only, ease the timing belt off the sprockets.

Caution: Do not rotate the crankshaft with the belt removed.

8.3 Tensioner in position with index wire over pillar bolt

8.4 Fitting belt over sprockets

8.8a Rotate tension lever clockwise

8.8b Align pointer notch with index wire

H44809

8.11 Rotate crankshaft and check camshaft alignment

Caution: Ensure that the pointer notch moves towards the index wire from above. If the notch passes the index wire, release all tension and repeat the procedure.

9 Whilst ensuring that the notch and index wire remain correctly aligned, use a torque wrench to tighten the tensioner bolt to the specified torque.

10 Remove the camshaft sprocket locking tool.

11 Using a suitable socket and bar on the crankshaft pulley, rotate the crankshaft two complete turns clockwise, and align the camshaft gear timing marks **(see illustration)**.

12 Check that the pointer is correctly aligned with the index wire. If it is not correctly aligned, slacken the tensioner bolt until it is just possible to move the tensioner lever.

13 Using a 6 mm Allen key, rotate the tensioner lever clockwise until the pointer is just above the index wire. Rotate the lever anti-clockwise until the pointer is correctly aligned with the index wire.

14 Whilst ensuring that the notch and index wire remain correctly aligned, use a torque wrench to tighten the tensioner bolt to the specified torque.

15 Rotate the crankshaft two turns clockwise, align the camshaft gear timing marks, and check that the pointer and index wire are correctly aligned.

16 Fit the engine mounting assembly and restraint bar and fit the bolts through the rubber mounting backplate, and restraint bar. Use a torque wrench to tighten the bolts to the specified torque.

17 Fit two bolts which attach the two halves

of the aluminium mounting bracket. Use a torque wrench to tighten the bolts to the specified torque.

18 Rotate the steady bar into position, and fit through-bolt, but do not tighten.

19 Lower and remove the jack and block from under the engine.

20 Use a torque wrench to tighten the steady bar through-bolts to the specified torque.

21 Fit the timing belt upper outer cover – see Section 6.

22 Position the coolant hose in the clips.

23 Fit the roadwheel, and tighten the nuts to secure the wheel. Remove the stands and lower the vehicle to the ground. Use a torque wrench to tighten the roadwheel nuts to the specified torque.

24 Connect the battery earth lead.

9 Camshaft oil seals –
removal and refitting

Note: *The following new parts are needed – camshaft oil seals. Right-hand (timing belt end) seals are black; left-hand (transmission end) seals are red.*

Right-hand seals

1 Remove the timing belt – see Section 7.

2 The camshaft sprockets are identical, but they should be marked so that they can be refitted in their original positions. With the camshaft sprocket locking tool in place between the sprockets – see Section 7 – slacken and remove the sprocket retaining

bolts and washers. Remove the locking tool **(see illustration).**

Caution: Do not rotate the camshafts or crankshaft.

3 Remove the sprockets from the camshafts. If the sprocket roll pins are loose, remove them and keep them with the sprockets.

4 To collect any spilled oil or debris, pack cloths around the area under the oil seals.

5 Punch or drill two small holes opposite each other in the oil seal. Screw a self-tapping screw into each hole, and pull on the screw with pliers to remove the seal.

6 Clean and dry the seal housing and sealing surface on the camshaft. Ensure that there are no burrs or raised edges.

Caution: The new oil seals must be fitted dry. Do not lubricate the seal recess, the seal lip, or the seal running surface on the shaft.

7 With the sealing lip facing inward, carefully locate the seal over the camshaft. Using a drift or socket, which contacts only the hard outer edge of the seal, tap the seal into place until it is seated correctly in the housing **(see illustration).**

8 Ensure that the roll pins are correctly located in the camshafts. Fit the camshaft sprockets, washers and bolts. Use a torque wrench to tighten the bolts to the specified torque.

9 Fit and tension the timing belt – see Section 8.

Exhaust camshaft left-hand seal

10 Disconnect the battery earth lead.

11 Remove the air cleaner assembly – see Chapter 4A.

9.2 Sprocket locking tool in position

9.7 Fit new inlet camshaft oil seal

9.12 Remove exhaust camshaft left-hand cover plate

A Cover plate   *B Securing bolts*

12 Remove the two bolts securing the cover plate, and remove the plate **(see illustration)**.
13 To collect any spilled oil or debris, pack cloths around the area under the oil seal.
14 Punch or drill two small holes opposite each other in the oil seal. Screw a self-tapping screw into each hole, and pull on the screw with pliers to remove the seal.
15 Clean and dry the seal housing and sealing surface on the camshaft. Ensure that there are no burrs or raised edges.
Caution: The new oil seal must be fitted dry. Do not lubricate the seal recess, the seal lip, or the seal running surface on the shaft.
16 With the sealing lip facing inward, carefully locate the seal over the camshaft. Using a drift or socket, which contacts only the hard outer edge of the seal, tap the seal into place until it is seated correctly in the housing.
17 Clean the cover mating faces, and fit the cover and bolts. Use a torque wrench to tighten the bolts to the specified torque.
18 Fit the air cleaner, and connect the battery earth lead.

Inlet camshaft left-hand seal

Later engines with no distributor

Note: *The procedure for renewing the inlet camshaft oil seal is the same as that for the exhaust camshaft oil seal, except:*

> *Before removing the cover plate, disconnect the camshaft sensor multi-plug.*

> *Connect the plug when the cover has been fitted.*

Early engines with distributor

Note: *The procedure for renewing the inlet camshaft oil seal, when a distributor is fitted, is the same as that when no distributor is fitted, except:*

> *When the air cleaner has been removed, remove the distributor assembly – see Chapter 5B.*

> *Before refitting the air cleaner, fit the distributor assembly.*

Note: *The following new parts are needed – MG Rover sealant GUG 705963GM, camshaft oil seals. Sixteen small plastic containers, numbered one to sixteen, will be needed to store the hydraulic tappets; fill each container with clean engine oil.*

Removal

1 Disconnect the battery earth lead.
2 Disconnect the multi-plug in the lead to the camshaft position sensor.
3 Remove the bolts securing the camshaft left-hand cover plates, and remove the plates.
4 Remove the timing belt – see Section 7.
5 Remove the camshaft cover – see Section 4.
6 Mark the camshaft sprockets so that they can be refitted in their original position. Fit the camshaft sprocket locking tool – see Section 7 – remove the bolts securing the sprockets, and remove the sprockets **(see illustration)**.
7 Remove five bolts securing the camshaft belt inner cover to the cylinder head, and remove the cover **(see illustration)**.
8 Working in the reverse of the tightening sequence, progressively slacken the twenty six bolts securing the camshaft carrier to the cylinder head **(see illustration 10.19)**. When all valve spring pressure is released, remove the bolts and the carrier. **Note:** *Mark the camshafts so that they can be fitted in their original position.*
9 Lift out the camshafts, and slide off the oil seals **(see illustration opposite)**.
10 Using a stick magnet, or rubber sucker, remove the hydraulic tappets.
Caution: Invert the tappets and place them in the numbered containers. Do not squeeze the tappet chambers together.

Inspection

11 Check the following components for signs of wear – eg, pitting/scoring:
> *Tappets, camshaft cams and bearing surfaces, camshaft carrier, tappet and bearing bores.*
12 If available, a micrometer can be used to check that the outer diameter of the tappets is within specified limits.
13 Renew any worn component.

Refitting

14 Note: *Do not use a metal scraper.* Clean and dry the mating faces of the cylinder head and camshaft carrier, ensuring that all traces of old sealant are removed. Clean camshaft carrier bolt holes and dowels, and blow out oilways.
15 Lubricate tappet bores and tappets with clean engine oil, and fit the tappets in their original bores. **Note:** *If new tappets are being fitted, they must be filled with clean engine oil before fitting.*

10.6 Sprocket locking tool in place

10.7 Remove the belt inner cover

10.9 Cylinder head components

1 Exhaust valve guide
2 Valve seat insert – exhaust
3 Exhaust valve
4 Inlet valve
5 Valve seat insert – inlet
6 Inlet valve guide
7 Gasket – cylinder head
8 Bolt – cylinder head
9 Cylinder head
10 Locating dowel
11 Valve stem oil seal
12 Valve spring
13 Valve spring cap
14 Collets
15 Hydraulic tappet
16 Camshaft seal
17 Inlet camshaft
18 Camshaft carrier
19 Bolt – camshaft carrier
20 Gasket – camshaft cover
21 Spark plug
22 HT lead and plug tube
23 Coil
24 Screws – coils to camshaft carrier
25 Coil and spark plug cover
26 Screw – coil and plug cover
27 Oil filler cap
28 Seal – oil filler cap
29 Bolt – CMP
30 Camshaft position sensor (CMP)
31 O-ring
32 Bolt – camshaft cover
33 Camshaft cover
34 Bracket – multi-plug
35 Bolt – multi-plug bracket
36 Blanking plate x 2
37 Bolt – blanking plate
38 Coolant temperature sensor
39 Gasket
40 Sealing washer
41 Bolt – coolant outlet elbow
42 Coolant outlet elbow
43 Gasket – coolant outlet elbow
44 Exhaust camshaft

H44828

10.17 **Correct position of camshaft roll-pins**

16 Lubricate the camshaft bearing journals and cams with clean engine oil.
17 Fit the camshafts and position the drive pin in the inlet camshaft at 4 o'clock, and the drive pin in the exhaust camshaft at 8 o'clock **(see illustration)**.
Caution: Ensure sealant is kept clear of oil feed holes and oil grooves. Assembly must be completed within 20 minutes of applying sealant.
18 Apply a continuous bead of sealant to the camshaft carrier, then spread to an even film using a roller **(see illustration)**.
19 Fit the camshaft carrier to the cylinder head, and fit the securing bolts. Use a torque wrench to tighten them progressively, and in the correct sequence, to the specified torque **(see illustration)**.
20 Clean the camshaft seal bores and running surfaces.
Caution: Oil seals must be fitted dry. Do not lubricate the seals or camshaft running surfaces.
21 With the sealing lip facing inward, carefully locate the seal over the camshaft. Using a drift or socket, which contacts only the hard outer edge of the seal, tap the seal into place until it is seated correctly in the housing **(see illustration 9.7)**.
22 Fit the camshaft cover – see Section 4.
23 Clean the camshaft cover plates. Fit the plates and bolts. Use a torque wrench to tighten the bolts to the specified torque.
24 Connect the multi-plug in the camshaft sensor lead.
25 Fit the camshaft belt inner cover and bolts. Use a torque wrench to tighten the bolts to the correct torque.
26 Fit the camshaft sprockets, and timing belt – see Section 8.
27 Connect the battery earth lead.

11 Cylinder head –
removed and refitting

Caution: Avoid rotating the crankshaft after the cylinder head bolts have been slackened. Long through-bolts clamp together the cylinder head, cylinder block and crankshaft bearing ladder. When these

10.18 **Apply a thin bead of sealant along the paths shown by the heavy black line**

10.19 **Camshaft carrier bolt tightening sequence**

are slackened, rotation of the crankshaft is difficult, or impossible.
Note: *Used with three cylinder head bolts, three large washers and tubular spacers are needed to clamp the cylinder liners after the cylinder head is removed.*
Note: *A turning/locking device for the camshaft sprockets is needed. A suitable device can be made using two pieces of flat bar – one piece approx. 14 in long, and the other approx. 7 in long – and three nuts and bolts. Align one end of each bar, and use one nut and bolt as a pivot for the two bars. Spread the ends of the bars to form a fork, and fit a bolt and nut through the fork end of each bar.*

11.6 **Remove exhaust front pipe nuts**

Note: *The following new parts are needed – camshaft timing belt and, possibly, cylinder head bolts.*

Removal

1 Disconnect the battery earth lead.

Early engines with distributor

2 Remove the distributor cover and HT leads – see Chapter 5B.

All engines

3 Drain cooling system – see Chapter 1A.
4 Remove and discard the timing belt – see Section 7.
5 Remove the exhaust manifold heat shield.
6 Remove two nuts securing exhaust front pipe to exhaust manifold. Release pipe and discard gasket **(see illustration)**.

Models with air conditioning

7 Remove exhaust manifold – see Chapter 4A.

All models

8 Remove the camshaft cover – see Section 6.
9 Disconnect the following wiring harness multi-plugs – for locations, see Chapter 4A:
a) *Oxygen sensor (release plug from bracket).*
b) *Engine coolant temperature sensor.*
c) *Throttle position sensor.*
d) *Fuel injector harness.*
e) *Intake air temperature sensor.*
f) *Idle air control valve.*

11.10 Disconnect radiator and heater hoses from outlet elbow

11.12 Disconnect intake and purge hoses from throttle housing

11.13 Release fuel hoses from pipes

10 Slacken clip, and disconnect radiator top hose from coolant outlet elbow **(see illustration)**.
11 Slacken clip, and disconnect the heater return hose from the coolant outlet elbow, and release clip from cylinder head.
12 Remove clips, and disconnect air intake hose, and purge hose from throttle housing **(see illustration)**.
13 To absorb any fuel spill, position cloths under fuel pipe connections. Depress plastic collars on hoses, and release hoses from pipes **(see illustration)**.
14 Release the throttle outer cable nut from the abutment bracket, and release the inner cable from the cam. Release the cable from the clip on the inlet manifold **(see illustration)**.
15 Depress plastic collar on quickrelease connector, and disconnect brake servo vacuum hose from inlet manifold **(see illustration)**.
16 Slacken clip, and disconnect coolant expansion tank hose from inlet manifold.
17 Working in the reverse of the tightening sequence, progressively slacken cylinder head bolts 1 to 6 **(see illustration 11.37a)**.
18 Remove the camshaft sprocket locking device.
Caution: Do not apply tools to the sprocket teeth.
19 Using the manufactured turning/locking device, engaged in two holes of the camshaft sprockets, turn the camshafts until bolts 7 and 8, under the camshaft reluctor segments, are accessible **(see illustration)**.
20 Working in the reverse of the tightening sequence, progressively slacken cylinder head bolts 7 to10 **(see illustration 11.37a)**. Carefully remove the bolts, and store them in their fitted order.
Caution: Bolts MUST be refitted in their original locations.
21 Avoid rotating the crankshaft after the cylinder head bolts have been removed. When these are removed, rotation of the crankshaft is difficult, or impossible. DO NOT attempt to rotate the crankshaft until the cylinder liners have been clamped in position.
22 Mark the camshaft sprockets so that they can be refitted on the correct camshaft. Using the manufactured turning/locking device to

11.14 Release throttle inner and outer cables

hold the sprockets, remove the sprocket securing bolts, and remove the sprockets.
23 Remove one bolt securing the dipstick support bracket. Remove five bolts securing the timing belt inner cover, and remove the cover.
Caution: Two dowels locate the cylinder head. DO NOT attempt to swivel the head, or tap it sideways. If the joint is difficult to break, use two cranked bars, fitted into

11.19 Slacken cylinder head bolts

11.15 Release vacuum servo hose

two cylinder head bolt holes, and rock the head gently.
24 Ensure that the oxygen sensor, in the exhaust manifold, is not damaged during head removal.
25 Using assistance, remove the cylinder head, and place it on wooden blocks **(see illustration)**. Discard the gasket.
26 Remove two location dowels from the cylinder block.
Caution: When using cylinder head bolts to clamp the liners, ensure that bolts are refitted in their original locations. Fit them carefully – DO NOT drop them into the holes.
27 Using the tubular spacers, and thick washers – which will sit over the top edge of two adjacent liners – fit three cylinder bolts through the spacers and washers, and tighten them sufficiently to prevent liner movement **(see illustration)**.

11.25 Using two cranked bars to break the cylinder head-to-cylinder block joint by rocking

11.27 Tubular spacers and washers used to clamp liners

11.29 Measure the length of cylinder head bolts

11.31a Fit a new gasket over the dowels

11.31b Ensure gasket marks are correctly positioned

11.37a Tighten bolts in correct sequence

11.37b Mark bolt heads for radial position

Refitting

28 Clean components:

Caution: Ensure that no debris is allowed to enter oil or coolant passages in the cylinder head or block. Seal them with tape or cloths.

Clean mating faces of exhaust pipe and exhaust manifold.

Clean the location dowels and fit them into the cylinder block.

Use a hard plastic or wooden scraper to clean the mating faces of the cylinder head and cylinder block. Check mating faces for damage.

Use a straight-edge and feeler gauge to check for cylinder head warp. If warp is more than 0.05 mm, the head must be skimmed or renewed.

To prevent carbon, from the piston crowns, getting down the bores, smear grease around the gap. Use a hard plastic or wooden scraper to clean the piston crowns. When cleaned, wipe away the grease and carbon.

Clean out the cylinder head bolt holes.

Wash and dry the cylinder head bolts.

Note: *If bolts have been used to clamp the liners, remove them one at time for washing and inspection, and then refit them.*

Checking cylinder head bolts

29 Check the bolts for any signs of wear or damage – renew any faulty bolt. Lightly oil the bolt threads, and carefully fit them into their original holes. Screw them in finger tight. Measure the distance from the cylinder block

surface to the underside of the bolt head. If the distance is less than 97 mm, the bolt may be re-used. If the distance is more than 97 mm, the bolt must be renewed. If several bolts are elongated, the full set should be renewed **(see illustration)**.

Caution: If the crankshaft has been turned, check that the dots on the crankshaft sprocket are aligned either side of the raised rib on the oil pump cover.

Caution: DO NOT rotate the crankshaft after the liner clamps have been removed.

30 Remove the cylinder liner clamps.

31 Ensuring that the word TOP is uppermost, and FRONT is towards the timing belt, locate a new, dry, cylinder head gasket over the dowels **(see illustrations)**.

32 Using assistance, locate the cylinder head on the cylinder block, ensuring that it fits over the dowels.

33 Clean and fit the timing belt inner cover. Use a torque wrench to tighten the bolts to the specified torque.

34 Align and secure the dipstick support bracket.

35 Ensure that camshaft sprocket drive pins are in position. Clean and fit the sprockets, washers and bolts. Using the locking device, hold the camshaft sprockets, and tighten the bolts to the specified torque.

36 Lightly oil the cylinder head bolt threads and underside of the heads. Being careful not to drop them, enter them into their correct holes, and tighten them finger tight.

37 Working in sequence, progressively tighten the bolts as follows **(see illustrations)**:

Note: *Rotate camshafts – as for removal – to gain access to bolts 3 and 4.*

Tighten all bolts to the Stage 1 torque wrench setting.

Mark each bolt to indicate a radial position reference.

Turn all bolts through 180°.

Turn all bolts through another 180°, and align radial marks.

Caution: If any bolt is over-tightened, back off 90° then realign radial marks.

38 Using the turning device, align the camshaft sprocket timing marks, and fit the sprocket locking device.

39 Completion of refitting is a reversal of the removal procedure, noting the following:

Ensure all electrical multi-plugs are correctly and securely connected.

Ensure all hoses and pipes are correctly and securely connected

Fill the cooling system with the correct mix of water and anti-freeze. – see Chapter 1A.

Check throttle cable adjustment

12 Sump –
removal and refitting

Note: *The following new parts are needed – MG Rover sealant GUG 705963GM. Two alignment pins are needed during refit; these can be made by cutting the heads off two M8 bolts.*

12.6 Remove steady bar through-bolt

Removal

1 Disconnect the battery earth lead.
2 Apply the handbrake, chock the rear roadwheels, then jack up the front of the car and support it on axle stands (see *Jacking and Vehicle Support*). Remove the right hand roadwheel.
3 Drain the engine oil – if necessary, see Chapter 1A. Clean and refit the drain plug, and tighten it to the specified torque. It is recommended that the oil filter is renewed.
4 Remove two nuts securing the exhaust front pipe to the exhaust manifold. Tie the pipe clear of the work area.
5 Slacken the through-bolt securing the engine lower steady bar to the rear subframe.
6 Remove the through-bolt securing the steady bar to the sump bracket, and release the bar from the bracket **(see illustration)**.
7 Remove three bolts securing the sump rear flange to the gearbox housing.
8 Working in the reverse of the tightening sequence, progressively slacken and remove fourteen sump bolts **(see illustration 12.17)**. Note that two longer bolts are fitted adjacent to the rear flange.
9 Using a mallet, tap the sump sideways to release the joint.

Refitting

10 Clean all traces of old sealant from the mating faces of the sump and bearing ladder, and clean inside the sump.
11 Screw the alignment pins into the bearing ladder **(see illustration)**.
Caution: After applying sealant, sump should be refitted immediately.
12 Apply a bead of sealant to the sump mating face, then spread to an even film using a roller.
13 Locate the sump over the alignment pins. Fit two bolts at positions 5 and 6, and tighten to 4 Nm.
14 Fit ten bolts in remaining holes, ensuring that the two long bolts are fitted adjacent to the rear flange. Lightly tighten all bolts.
15 Remove the alignment pins, and fit and lightly tighten the two remaining bolts.
16 Fit three bolts securing sump rear flange to gearbox housing. Lightly tighten, and then slacken the bolts – this aligns the sump flange and gearbox housing.

12.11 Fit two sump alignment pins

A Alignment pin locations
B Sump flange-to-cylinder block rear face alignment

17 Working in sequence, progressively tighten the bolts. Use a torque wrench to tighten the shorter and longer bolts to their specified torque **(see illustration)**.
18 Use a torque wrench to tighten the sump flange bolts to the specified torque.
19 Fit steady bar to sump bracket, and locate bolt and nut. Use a torque wrench to tighten steady bar front and rear bolts to the specified torque.
20 Clean exhaust front pipe and manifold mating faces. Using a new gasket, connect the pipe, and secure with two nuts. Use a torque wrench to tighten the nuts to the specified torque.
21 Fit the roadwheel, and tighten the nuts to secure the wheel. Remove the stands and lower the vehicle to the ground. Use a torque wrench to tighten the roadwheel nuts to the specified torque.
22 Fill the engine with new engine oil – see Chapter 1A.
23 Connect the battery earth lead.

13 Oil pump –
removal and refitting

Note: *The following new parts are needed – oil pump gasket, crankshaft right-hand oil seal, thread locking compound.*

Removal

1 Remove camshaft timing belt – see Section 7.
2 Remove the crankshaft sprocket.
3 Remove two bolts securing engine harness to oil pump.
4 Remove nine bolts securing oil pump to cylinder block – note the location of the M6x20 bolt **(see illustration)**.
5 To ease pump removal, remove lower bolt from timing belt inner cover.
6 Remove oil pump and discard gasket.

12.17 Tighten the bolts in the correct sequence

7 Remove and discard crankshaft front oil seal from oil pump housing.

Refitting

8 Ensuring that no debris enters the crankcase, clean the pump bolt holes in cylinder block. Clean the mating faces of the oil pump housing and cylinder block. Clean the crankshaft oil seal running surface. Clean off all traces of thread locking compound from the pump bolts.
9 Prime the pump by injecting clean engine oil into it, and turning the rotor by hand. Turn the pump rotor to align the inner gear drive with the flats on the crankshaft.
10 Fit a new gasket (dry) to the cylinder block.
11 Fit the oil seal sleeve protection sleeve – from the seal kit – over the end of the crankshaft.
12 Locate the oil pump on the cylinder block. Fit the bolts – ensure that the M6x20 bolt is fitted in the correct location, as noted during removal. Use a torque wrench to tighten the bolts to the specified torque.
13 With the protection sleeve still in place over the crankshaft, fit a new crankshaft oil seal over the sleeve, and tap into position using a suitable tube or socket. Remove the protection sleeve.

13.4 Remove pump securing bolts

A Wiring harness guide bolts
B Oil pump bolts
C M6 x 20 mm oil pump bolt

14.8 Oil pressure relief valve components

Caution: The new oil seal must be fitted dry. Do not lubricate the seal recess, the seal lip, or the seal running surface on the shaft.

14 Fit the lower bolt to the timing belt inner cover.

15 Fit the crankshaft sprocket to the crankshaft.

16 Fit the timing belt – see Section 8.

14 Oil pump pressure relief valve – removal and refitting

Note: *The following new parts are needed – relief valve Dowty sealing washer.*

Removal

1 Disconnect the battery earth lead.

15.5 Checking oil pump rotors for wear – see text for details

2 Apply the handbrake, chock the rear roadwheels, then jack up the front of the car and support it on axle stands (see *Jacking and Vehicle Support*). Remove the right hand front roadwheel.

3 Slacken three bolts securing the power steering pump pulley.

4 Remove the pump drivebelt – see Chapter 10.

5 Remove the pulley bolts and pulley.

6 Remove two nuts and bolts, and lower bolt securing the pump to the bracket. Remove the pump from the bracket, and tie clear of the work area.

7 Remove three bolts securing the pump bracket to the cylinder block, and remove the bracket. Note the position of the M10x90 bolt, and the spacers in the bracket.

8 Remove the sealing plug and washer, spring and valve – discard the washer **(see illustration)**.

9 Check that the valve and bore are not corroded or scored. **Note:** *Light corrosion may be removed using grade 600 emery cloth soaked in oil.* Check the valve slides freely in the bore.

10 Check the spring free length equals 38.9 mm.

11 If the valve is scored, or of the spring free length is less than specified, renew the complete valve assembly.

Refitting

12 Remove all traces of locking compound from the sealing plug threads.

13 Lubricate the valve with clean engine oil. Fit the valve and spring.

14 Fit a new Dowty washer to the plug, and coat the threads with locking compound. Fit and tighten the plug.

15 Fit the power steering pump bracket and three bolts – ensure that the M10x90 bolt is correctly located.

16 Locate the pump in the bracket – note that the position of the spacers may need to be adjusted to allow correct location of the pump. Fit two nuts and bolts, and lower bolt.

17 Clean the mating faces of the pump pulley. Fit the pulley, and lightly tighten the bolts.

18 Fit the pump drivebelt – see Chapter 10.

19 Use a torque wrench to tighten the pulley bolts to the specified torque.

15.9 Oil pump outer rotor identification mark (arrowed)

20 Fit the roadwheel, and tighten the nuts to secure the wheel. Remove the stands and lower the vehicle to the ground. Use a torque wrench to tighten the roadwheel nuts to the specified torque.

21 Connect the battery earth lead.

15 Oil pump – dismantling, inspection and reassembly

Note: *If oil pump wear is suspected, check the cost and availability of new parts (only available in the form of a repair kit) against the cost of a new pump. Examine the pump as described in this Section and then decide whether renewal or repair is the best course of action. A new pump cover sealing ring, and a new pressure relief valve plug sealing ring will be required on refitting.*

Dismantling

1 Remove the oil pump as described in Section 13.

2 Unscrew the Torx screws and remove the pump cover plate. Discard the sealing ring.

3 Note the identification marks on the outer rotor then remove both the rotors from the body.

Inspection

4 Inspect the rotors for obvious signs of wear or damage and renew if necessary. If the pump body or cover plate is scored or damaged, then the complete oil pump assembly must be renewed.

5 Using feeler blades of the appropriate thickness, measure the clearance between the outer rotor and the pump body, then between the tips of the inner and outer rotor lobes (a and b respectively) **(see illustration)**.

6 Using feeler blades and a straight-edge placed across the top of the pump body and the rotors, measure the rotor endfloat (c).

7 If any measurement is outside the specified limits, the complete pump assembly must be renewed.

8 Thoroughly clean the threads of the pump cover plate securing screws.

Reassembly

9 Lubricate the pump rotors with clean engine oil and refit them to the pump body, ensuring that the identification mark on the outer rotor faces outwards (ie, towards the pump cover) **(see illustration)**.

10 Lubricate a new sealing ring with clean engine oil, then fit the sealing ring to the pump body and refit the cover plate. Apply thread-locking compound to the threads of the cover plate screws and tighten them securely.

11 Check that the pump rotates freely, then prime it by injecting oil into its passages and rotating it. If a long time elapses before the pump is refitted to the engine, prime it again before installation.

16 Crankshaft oil seals – removal and refitting

Right-hand seal

Note: *The following new parts are needed – oil seal kit.*

Removal

1 Remove the camshaft timing belt – see Section 7.

2 Remove the crankshaft sprocket.

3 Punch, or drill, two small holes opposite each other in the seal. Screw self-tapping screws into the holes, and pull on the screws with pliers to remove the seal.

Refitting

4 Clean the seal recess.

Caution: The new oil seal must be fitted dry. Do not lubricate the seal recess, the seal lip, or the seal running surface on the shaft.

5 Fit the oil seal sleeve protection sleeve – from the seal kit – over the end of the crankshaft.

6 Fit a new crankshaft oil seal over the sleeve, and tap into position using a suitable tube or socket. Remove the protection sleeve.

7 Fit the crankshaft sprocket.

8 Fit the camshaft timing belt – see Section 8.

Left-hand seal

Note: *The following new parts are needed – oil seal, MG Rover sealant GAC 8000*

Removal

9 Remove the flywheel – see Section 17.

10 Using a smooth-ended flat-blade screwdriver, and taking care not to mark or damage the seal housing or crankshaft, ease the seal from the recess, and discard the seal.

Refitting

11 Clean the seal recess, and seal running surface.

12 The new oil seal must be fitted dry. Do not lubricate the seal recess, the seal lip, or the seal running surface on the shaft. The seal must be fitted immediately after applying sealant.

17.4 Fabricated locking tool in position

16.13 Apply sealant to oil seal

13 Apply a 1.5 mm bead of sealant to the new seal **(see illustration)**.

14 Using fingers only, ease the seal over the crankshaft, and push up to contact the cylinder block. Press the seal into the recess. If necessary, use a soft faced mallet to tap the seal into place. Before topping-up oil or rotating the crankshaft, allow the sealant to cure for at least 30 minutes.

Caution: When the seal is in position, leave it to settle for at least 1 minute.

15 Fit flywheel – see Section 17.

16 Top-up the engine oil.

17 Flywheel – removal and refitting

Removal

Note: *The following new parts are needed – 6 flywheel retaining bolts. When slackening or tightening the flywheel securing bolts, it is necessary to prevent the flywheel from turning. This can be done by, eg:*
Making and fitting a locking tool.
Fitting a long bolt into a gearbox mounting bolt hole

1 Remove the gearbox assembly – see Chapter 7.

2 Remove the clutch assembly – see Chapter 6.

3 Disconnect the crankshaft position sensor multi-plug. Remove the securing bolt, and remove the sensor.

4 Lock the flywheel **(see illustration)**:
Use a fabricated locking tool.
Fit a long bolt into one of the gearbox upper mounting bolt holes.

5 Have an assistant engage a suitable flat lever – such as a large screwdriver – between two teeth of the ring gear, and against the bolt, so that when anti-clockwise effort is applied to the flywheel bolts, the flywheel will be prevented from turning.

6 Remove and discard six flywheel securing bolts.

7 If necessary, get assistance to remove the heavy flywheel, which is located by dowels.

Refitting

8 Using a suitable thread tap, clean all old

thread locking compound from the flywheel bolt holes in the crankshaft.

9 Check the condition of the clutch contact surface. If it is scored or cracked, the flywheel must be renewed.

10 Check the ring gear for broken or missing teeth. If the ring gear is damaged, either the ring gear, or the flywheel assembly, must be renewed. **Note:** *The ring gear is a shrink fit on the flywheel, and requires controlled heating to expand it before fitting. Ring gear renewal should be carried out by an MG Rover dealer.*

11 Check the condition of the crankshaft sensor reluctor ring. If it is damaged, the flywheel must be renewed.

12 Clean the mating faces of the flywheel and crankshaft.

13 If necessary, get assistance to lift the heavy flywheel. Locate the flywheel over the dowels, and push onto the crankshaft, and fit six new bolts **(see illustration)**.

14 Lock the flywheel and, working in diagonal sequence, progressively tighten the bolts. Use a torque wrench to tighten the bolts to the specified torque.

15 Fit the crankshaft position sensor

16 Fit the clutch assembly – see Chapter 6.

17 Fit the gearbox assembly – see Chapter 7.

18 Engine/transmission mountings – Inspection, removal and refitting

Inspection

Note: *Normally, mountings will need renewing only if the rubber has hardened or cracked, or separated from the metal backing. Dependent upon the fault, such conditions may allow excess engine movement, leading to an impression of rough running, knocking or bumping. The mountings can be visually checked for rubber deterioration, and separation can be checked by levering with a pry bar between the rubber and metal backing. If any fault is found, the mounting must be renewed.*

Right-hand mounting (Hydramount)

Removal

1 Disconnect the battery earth lead.

17.13 Fit new flywheel bolts

18.3 Remove bolt from power steering pipe clamp

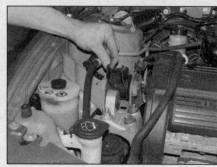

18.4 Tilt steady bar upwards

18.5 Remove mounting bracket bolts

18.6 Remove mounting and restraint bar

18.16 Remove outer part of steady bar and mounting attachment bolts

2 Position a jack, with wooden block on top, under the engine sump, and adjust to support the weight of the engine and transmission.

3 Remove bolt and nut securing power steering pipe clamp to inside wheel arch, and move pipe aside **(see illustration)**.

4 Slacken the through-bolt securing engine upper steady bar to body. Remove the through-bolt securing steady bar to right hand engine mounting, and tilt bar upwards, clear of the mounting **(see illustration)**.

5 Remove two bolts which attach the two parts of the aluminium mounting bracket – bottom half is attached to the front of the engine – top part is attached to the top of the rubber mounting assembly **(see illustration)**.

6 Remove the nut securing the top part of the bracket to the mounting assembly, and remove the bracket. Remove the nut securing rubber mounting backplate and restraint bar to body, and one nut securing restraint bar to body. Remove restraint bar and mounting assembly **(see illustration)**. **Note:** *Some*

models have an additional damper weight suspended from a bracket attached to the mounting securing nut.

Refitting

7 Fit the mounting assembly to the body, and fit and lightly tighten the rear nut.

8 Fit the top part of the mounting bracket over the mounting stud, and loosely fit the nut. Fit the two bolts which attach the top part of the mounting bracket to the engine mounted bottom part. Use a torque wrench to tighten the bolts to the specified torque.

9 Fit the restraint bar and nuts. Use a torque wrench to tighten the three nuts to the specified torque. Remove the jack and wooden block.

10 Use a torque wrench to tighten the nut on the mounting stud to the specified torque.

11 Fold down the steady bar over the mounting bush, and fit the through-bolt. Use a torque wrench to tighten both through-bolt nuts to the specified torque.

Left-hand mounting

Removal

12 Disconnect the battery earth lead.

13 Position a jack, with wooden block on top, under the engine sump, and adjust to support the weight of the engine and transmission.

14 Remove the battery – see Chapter 5A.

15 Remove the air cleaner – see Chapter 4A.

16 Remove two bolts securing left hand mounting steady bar, and remove the outer part of the bar **(see illustration)**.

17 Remove two bolts securing the mounting to gearbox bracket.

18 Remove the through-bolt securing the mounting to body bracket.

19 Lower engine/gearbox slightly, and remove mounting and loose rubbers.

Refitting

20 Fit loose rubbers to mounting bracket. Locate mounting in body bracket, and fit – but do not tighten – the through-bolt.

21 Adjust the height of the engine/transmission to align gearbox mounting bracket to mounting, and fit – but do not tighten – the bolts.

22 Fit – but do not tighten – the steady bar bolts.

23 Remove the jack and wooden block.

24 Use a torque wrench to tighten the following bolts to the specified torque:

Two mounting to gearbox bracket bolts.
Mounting through-bolt.
Two steady bar bolts.

25 Fit the battery – see Chapter 5A.

26 Fit the air cleaner – see Chapter 4A.

27 Connect the battery earth lead.

Chapter 2 Part B:
Diesel engine in-car repair procedures

Contents

Degrees of difficulty

Easy, suitable for novice with little experience	**Fairly easy,** suitable for beginner with some experience	**Fairly difficult,** suitable for competent DIY mechanic	**Difficult,** suitable for experienced DIY mechanic	**Very difficult,** suitable for expert DIY or professional 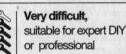

Specifications

General

Engine type	Four-cylinder in-line, four-stroke, liquid-cooled
Designation:	
Turbocharged and intercooled	20T2N
Bore	84.00 mm
Stroke	89.00 mm
Capacity	1994 cc
Firing order	1-3-4-2 (No 1 cylinder at timing belt end)
Direction of crankshaft rotation	Clockwise (seen from right-hand side of vehicle)
Compression ratio	19.5 : 1
Minimum compression pressure (typical figure)	18 to 20 bars
Maximum compression pressure difference between	
cylinders (typical figure)	3 bars
Maximum power (EEC)	100 bhp (74 kW) @ 4200 rpm
Maximum torque (EEC)	240 Nm (177 lbf ft) @ 2000 rpm

Camshaft

Drive	Toothed belt from crankshaft
Number of bearings	5
Bearing journal running clearance	0.043 to 0.094 mm
Camshaft endfloat (maximum)	0.510 mm
Hydraulic tappet outside diameter	34.959 to 34.975 mm

Lubrication system

System pressure	0.7 bar @ idle speed
Pressure relief valve opening pressure	4.5 bar
Low oil pressure warning light comes on	0.4 to 0.7 bar
Oil pump clearances:	
Rotor endfloat	0.03 to 0.08 mm
Outer rotor-to-body clearance	0.05 to 0.10 mm
Rotor lobe clearance	0.025 to 0.120 mm
Pressure relief valve spring free length	38.9 mm

Timing belt tensioner

Type	Semi-automatic
Spring free length	65.0 mm

Fuel injection pump belt tensioner

Type:
  Up to VIN No RF545050 .... Automatic
  From VIN No RF545051 .... Manual

Torque wrench settings

	Nm	lbf ft
Auxiliary drivebelt tensioner centre bolt	45	33
Big-end bolts (see text):		
Stage 1	20	15
Stage 2	Angle-tighten through a further 85°	
Big-end nuts (see text)	48	35
Camshaft bearing carrier bolts	11	8
Camshaft cover bolts	11	8
Camshaft sprocket bolt*:		
Stage 1	20	15
Stage 2	Angle-tighten through a further 90°	
Camshaft sprocket damper screws*	10	7
Crankshaft oil seal housing bolts	8	6
Crankshaft pulley bolt:		
Stage 1	63	46
Stage 2	Angle-tighten through a further 90°	
Cylinder head bolts:		
Stage 1	30	22
Stage 2	65	48
Stage 3	Angle-tighten through a further 90°	
Stage 4	Angle-tighten through a further 90°	
Cylinder head cover bolts	12	9
Engine lower steady bolts	85	63
Engine lower steady bracket-to-sump bolts	85	63
Engine oil drain plug	25	18
Flywheel bolts*:		
Stage 1	15	11
Stage 2	Angle-tighten through a further 90°	
Fuel injection pump drive (camshaft) sprocket*:		
Stage 1	20	15
Stage 2	Angle-tighten through a further 90°	
Fuel injection pump drive (camshaft) sprocket (adjuster) bolts	25	18
Fuel injection pump drivebelt backplate bolts	8	6
Fuel injection pump drivebelt tensioner pulley bolt	44	32
Hydramount/Restraint bar to RH mounting body bracket nuts	45	33
LH mounting bracket-to-body bolts	55	41
LH mounting bracket-to-gearbox bracket bolts	100	74
LH mounting through-bolt	85	63
Main bearing cap bolts	112	83
Oil cooler:		
M8 bolts	25	18
M10 bolts	45	33
Oil pressure warning light switch	16	12
Oil pump pick-up/strainer pipe bolts	8	6
Oil pump thermostatic valve plug	35	26
Oil pump-to-cylinder block bolts:		
M6 bolts	8	6
M10 bolt	45	33
Piston oil spray jet bolts	12	9
RH mounting body bracket-to-body bolts	25	18
RH mounting engine bracket-to-engine bolts	100	74
RH mounting engine bracket-to-Hydramount nut	85	63
Roadwheel nuts	See Chapter 10	
Sump bolts	25	18
Timing belt front cover bolts	5	4
Timing belt idler pulley nut	45	33
Timing belt idler pulley stud	12	9
Timing belt rear cover bolts	9	7
Timing belt tensioner pulley bolt	55	41
Transmission adapter plate-to-cylinder block bolts	45	33

*Use new bolts

1 General information and precautions

How to use this Chapter

This Part of the Chapter describes those repair procedures that can reasonably be carried out on the engine whilst it remains in the vehicle. If the engine has been removed from the vehicle and is being dismantled as described in Part D of this Chapter, any preliminary dismantling procedures can be ignored.

Note that whilst it may be possible physically to overhaul items such as the piston/connecting rod assemblies with the engine in the vehicle, such tasks are not usually carried out as separate operations and usually require the execution of several additional procedures (not to mention the cleaning of components and of oilways). For this reason, all such tasks are classed as major overhaul procedures and are described in Part D of this Chapter.

Engine description

The engine is of four-cylinder, in-line type, mounted transversely at the front of the vehicle with the clutch and transmission at its left-hand end. The engine is of eight-valve single overhead camshaft type.

The crankshaft runs in five main bearings. Thrustwashers are fitted to the centre main bearing (upper half) to control crankshaft endfloat. Individual main bearing caps are used, which are bolted directly to the cylinder block.

The connecting rods rotate on horizontally-split bearing shells at their big-ends. The pistons are attached to the connecting rods by fully floating gudgeon pins. The gudgeon pins are retained by circlips at each end. The aluminium alloy pistons are fitted with three piston rings, comprising two compression rings and an oil control ring.

The cylinders are bored directly into the cast iron cylinder block.

The inlet and exhaust valves are each closed by coil springs and operate in guides pressed into the cylinder head. The valve seat inserts are pressed into the cylinder head and can be renewed separately if worn.

The camshaft is driven by a toothed timing belt, and operates the valves via self-adjusting hydraulic tappets, thus eliminating the need for routine checking and adjustment of the valve clearances. The camshaft rotates in bearings which are line-bored directly into the cylinder head and the (bolted-on) bearing carrier. This means that the bearing carrier and cylinder head are matched, and cannot be renewed independently.

Unusually, the coolant pump is driven via a drive dog from the rear of the power steering pump, which is itself driven by the auxiliary drivebelt.

Lubrication is by means of an eccentric-rotor type pump driven directly from the timing belt end of the crankshaft. The pump draws oil through a strainer located in the sump, and then forces it through an externally-mounted full-flow cartridge-type oil filter into galleries in the oil rail and the cylinder block/crankcase, from where it is distributed to the crankshaft (main bearings) and camshaft. The big-end bearings are supplied with oil via internal drillings in the crankshaft, while the camshaft bearings and the hydraulic tappets receive a pressurised supply via drillings in the cylinder head. The camshaft lobes and valves are lubricated by oil splash, as are all other engine components.

Operations with engine in car

The following work can be carried out with the engine in the vehicle:
a) *Compression pressure – testing.*
b) *Cylinder head cover – removal and refitting.*
c) *Crankshaft pulley – removal and refitting.*
d) *Timing belt covers – removal and refitting.*
e) *Timing belt – removal, refitting and adjustment.*
f) *Timing belt tensioner and sprockets – removal and refitting.*
g) *Camshaft oil seals – renewal.*
h) *Camshaft and hydraulic tappets – removal, inspection and refitting.*
i) *Cylinder head – removal and refitting.*
j) *Cylinder head and pistons – decarbonising.*
k) *Sump – removal and refitting.*
l) *Oil pump – removal, overhaul and refitting.*
m) *Crankshaft oil seals – renewal.*
n) *Engine/transmission mountings – inspection and renewal.*
o) *Flywheel – removal, inspection and refitting.*

2 Compression and leakdown tests – description and interpretation

Compression test

Note: *A compression tester designed for diesel engines must be used for this test.*

1 When engine performance is down, or if misfiring occurs which cannot be attributed to the ignition or fuel systems, a compression test can provide diagnostic clues as to the engine's condition. If the test is performed regularly, it can give warning of trouble before any other symptoms become apparent.

2 A compression tester specifically intended for diesel engines must be used, because of the higher pressures involved. The tester is connected to an adapter which screws into the glow plug or injector hole. On these engines, an adapter suitable for use in the injector holes is preferable. It is unlikely to be worthwhile buying such a tester for occasional use, but it may be possible to borrow or hire one – if not, have the test performed by a garage.

3 Unless specific instructions to the contrary are supplied with the tester, observe the following points.
a) *The battery must be in a good state of charge, the air filter must be clean, and the engine should be at normal operating temperature.*
b) *All the injectors or glow plugs should be removed before starting the test.*
c) *The stop solenoid must be disconnected, to prevent the engine from running or fuel from being discharged.*

4 There is no need to hold the throttle pedal down during the test, because the diesel engine air inlet is not throttled.

5 Crank the engine on the starter motor. After one or two revolutions, the compression pressure should build up to a maximum figure, and then stabilise. Record the highest reading obtained.

6 Repeat the test on the remaining cylinders, recording the pressure in each.

7 The cause of poor compression is less easy to establish on a diesel engine than on a petrol one. The effect of introducing oil into the cylinders ('wet' testing) is not conclusive, because there is a risk that the oil will sit in the swirl chamber or in the recess in the piston crown instead of passing to the rings. However, the following can be used as a rough guide to diagnosis.

8 All cylinders should produce very similar pressures; a difference of more than 3.0 bars between any two cylinders usually indicates a fault. Rover do not specify compression pressure figures, so the figures given in the Specifications are typical figures for a diesel engine. Note that the compression should build-up quickly in a healthy engine; low compression on the first stroke, followed by gradually-increasing pressure on successive strokes, indicates worn piston rings. A low compression reading on the first stroke, which does not build-up during successive strokes, indicates leaking valves or a blown head gasket (a cracked head could also be the cause). Deposits on the undersides of the valve heads can also cause low compression.

9 A low reading from two adjacent cylinders is almost certainly due to the head gasket having blown between them; the presence of coolant in the engine oil will confirm this.

10 If the compression reading is unusually high, the combustion chambers are probably coated with carbon deposits. If this is the case, the cylinder head should be removed and decarbonised.

11 On completion of the test, refit the injectors or the glow plugs, and reconnect the stop solenoid.

Leakdown test

12 A leakdown test measures the rate at which compressed air fed into the cylinder is lost. It is an alternative to a compression test,

3.3 The timing mark (1) on the camshaft sprocket should be aligned with the raised rib on the rear timing belt cover (2)

and in many ways is better, since the escaping air provides easy identification of where a pressure loss is occurring (piston rings, valves or head gasket).

13 The equipment needed for leakdown testing is unlikely to be available to the home mechanic. If poor compression is suspected, have the test performed by a suitably-equipped garage.

3 Engine timing marks – general information

Note: *A suitable timing pin (which can be improvised using a 6.5 mm diameter twist drill) will be required for this operation.*

1 Locate the timing pin hole in the transmission mounting plate, at the rear left-hand corner of the engine. Access is difficult,

and it may be necessary to move surrounding hoses and wiring to one side for access.

2 Remove the upper outer timing belt cover as described in Section 6.

3 Using a suitable socket or spanner on the crankshaft pulley bolt, turn the crankshaft until the timing mark on the camshaft sprocket is aligned with the raised rib on the rear timing belt cover (see illustration).

4 It should now be possible to insert a 6.5 mm twist drill through the timing pin hole in the transmission mounting plate to engage with the timing hole in the flywheel (see illustration). The crankshaft is now locked in position with No 1 piston at TDC.

4 Camshaft cover – removal and refitting

Note: *The following new parts are needed – camshaft cover gasket, intake pipe-to-intake manifold gasket.*

Removal

1 Remove three screws securing the acoustic cover to the engine, and remove the cover (see illustrations).

2 Remove two bolts securing the EGR cooler outlet pipe to the air intake pipe (see illustration).

3 Remove the bolt securing the intake pipe to the camshaft cover bracket (see illustration).

4 Remove two bolts securing the intake pipe to the inlet manifold (see illustration).

5 Slacken the hose clip, and disconnect the

3.4 6.5 mm twist drill inserted through timing pin hole into flywheel

intercooler top hose from the intake pipe. Release the intake pipe and discard the gasket (see illustration).

6 Slacken the clip and disconnect the intercooler bottom hose from the turbocharger outlet pipe (see illustration).

7 Remove two bolts securing the turbocharger pipe to the engine.

8 Slacken the clip and remove the outlet pipe from the turbocharger outlet hose (see illustration).

9 Slacken the clip and disconnect the engine breather hose from the camshaft cover.

10 Remove the oil filler cap, and remove the bolt securing the brake servo pipe bracket to the top of the camshaft cover.

11 Remove twelve bolts securing the camshaft cover, and remove the cover.

12 Release the gasket from the camshaft cover and discard the gasket.

4.1a Remove the acoustic cover screws

4.1b Remove the acoustic cover

4.2 Remove the EGR cooler pipe bolts

4.3 Remove the bolt from the camshaft cover bracket

4.4 Remove the intake pipe bolts

4.5 Release the intake pipe

4.6 Disconnect intercooler hose from turbocharger pipe

4.8 Remove outlet pipe from turbocharger hose

4.13 Tighten camshaft cover bolts in sequence

Refitting

13 Refitting is a reversal of the removal procedure, noting:

Clean the mating faces of the camshaft cover and camshaft carrier.

Fit a new gasket to the camshaft cover, and to the intake manifold.

Use a torque wrench to tighten all bolts to the specified torque.

Tighten the camshaft cover bolts in sequence (see illustration).

5 Crankshaft pulley – removal and refitting

5.5a Remove pulley securing bolt

5.5b Remove pulley

Removal

1 Disconnect the battery earth lead.
2 Apply the handbrake, chock the rear roadwheels, then jack up the front of the car and support it on axle stands (see *Jacking and Vehicle Support*). Remove the right hand roadwheel.
3 Remove the auxiliary drivebelt – see Chapter 5A.
4 Insert a timing pin through the hole in the gearbox mounting plate – see Section 3. With a suitable socket or spanner on the crankshaft pulley nut, have an assistant to turn the crankshaft clockwise until the pin enters the hole in the flywheel and locks the crankshaft. Check that the timing marks on the camshaft sprocket damper, and on the timing belt rear cover, are aligned.
5 Remove the pulley securing bolt and pulley **(see illustrations)**.

Refitting

6 Clean the pulley and crankshaft. Fit the pulley and bolt.
7 Use a torque wrench to tighten the bolt to the specified torque.
8 Remove the timing pin.
9 Fit the auxiliary drivebelt – see Chapter 5A.
10 Fit the roadwheel, and tighten the nuts to secure the wheel. Remove the stands and lower the vehicle to the ground.
11 Use a torque wrench to tighten the roadwheel nuts to the specified torque.
12 Connect the battery earth lead.

6 Timing belt covers – removal and refitting

Upper outer cover

Removal

1 Unscrew the four bolts securing the upper outer timing cover to the rear cover, and withdraw the cover **(see illustrations)**.

Refitting

2 Refitting is a reversal of removal, but make sure that the sealing strips are correctly located in the cover.

Lower outer cover

Removal

3 Disconnect the battery negative lead.

4 Apply the handbrake, then jack up the front of the vehicle and support securely on axle stands (see *Jacking and Vehicle Support*). Remove the right-hand front roadwheel.
5 Remove the upper outer timing belt cover, as described previously in this Section.
6 Remove the crankshaft pulley as described in Section 5.
7 Unscrew the securing bolts, and withdraw the lower outer cover **(see illustrations)**.

Refitting

8 Refitting is a reversal of removal, bearing in mind the following points.
a) *Make sure that the sealing strips are correctly located in the timing belt covers.*
b) *Note that the three longer bolts fit at the bottom of the lower timing belt cover.*
c) *Refit the crankshaft pulley with reference to Section 5.*

6.1a Unscrew the securing bolts . . .

6.1b . . . and remove the upper outer timing belt cover

6.7a Unscrew the securing bolts . . .

6.7b . . . and remove the lower outer timing belt cover

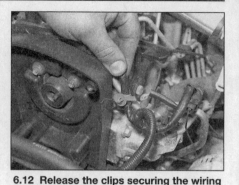

6.12 Release the clips securing the wiring harness to the timing belt cover

Upper rear cover

Removal

9 Remove the outer timing belt covers as described previously in this Section.

10 Remove the timing belt as described in Section 7.

11 Remove the camshaft sprocket as described in Section 8.

12 Where applicable, release the three clips securing the engine wiring harness to the rear timing belt cover **(see illustration)**.

13 Unscrew the five securing bolts, and remove the upper rear cover. Recover the sealing strip **(see illustrations)**.

Refitting

14 Examine the sealing strip, and renew if necessary.

15 Refit the upper rear cover, noting that the shorter securing bolts are used to secure the

top of the cover to the camshaft bearing carrier. Make sure that the sealing strip is correctly located.

16 Where applicable, clip the engine wiring harness into position on the rear timing belt cover.

17 Where necessary, refit the timing belt tensioner, and the camshaft sprocket as described in Section 8.

18 Refit the timing belt as described in Section 7.

19 Refit the outer timing belt covers, as described previously in this Section.

Lower rear cover

Removal

20 Remove the outer timing belt covers, as described previously in this Section.

21 Remove the timing belt as described in Section 7, and the timing belt tensioner

assembly as described in Section 8.

22 Unscrew the nut securing the timing belt idler pulley, and remove the pulley. Note that the mounting stud may be unscrewed with the nut.

23 Unscrew the two securing bolts, and remove the lower rear timing belt cover **(see illustrations)**. Recover the sealing strips.

Refitting

24 If the idler pulley stud was unscrewed with the nut, unscrew the nut from the stud (clamp the stud in a vice if necessary to allow the nut to be unscrewed).

25 Where applicable, clean the threads of the idler pulley stud, and the corresponding threads in the cylinder block, then apply thread-locking compound to the stud threads which screw into the cylinder block. Screw the stud into position, and tighten to the specified torque.

26 Examine the timing belt cover sealing strips, and renew if necessary.

27 Refit the lower rear timing belt cover, and tighten the securing bolts. Make sure that the sealing strips are correctly located.

28 Thoroughly clean the threads of the idler pulley nut, then coat the threads with thread-locking compound.

29 Refit the idler pulley to the stud, then refit the nut and tighten to the specified torque.

30 Refit the timing belt as described in Section 7.

31 Refit the outer timing belt covers as described previously in this Section.

6.13a Unscrew the upper rear timing belt cover securing bolts (arrowed) – viewed with the engine removed . . .

6.13b . . . then remove the upper rear timing belt cover

6.23a Unscrew the two securing bolts (arrowed) . . .

6.23b . . . and remove the lower rear timing belt cover

7 Timing belt – removal, inspection, refitting and adjustment

Note: *Rover tool No 18G 1719 or a suitable equivalent (see text) will be required to release the timing belt tensioner during this procedure.*

Removal

1 Disconnect the battery negative lead.

2 Lock the crankshaft at TDC (No1 cylinder) as described in Section 3. Remove the crankshaft pulley as described in Section 5.

3 Working on the right-hand side of the engine compartment, unscrew the bolt

7.3 Unscrew the bolt securing the power steering fluid pipe bracket to the body

securing the power steering fluid pipe bracket to the body, then move the pipes to one side, to improve access to the timing belt end of the engine **(see illustration)**.

4 Remove the right-hand engine mounting as described in Section 20.

5 Remove the outer timing belt covers, with reference to Section 6.

6 Unscrew the four securing nuts and two bolts, and remove the engine mounting cover plate **(see illustration)**.

7 If the original timing belt is to be re-used, mark the running direction on the belt, using chalk or tape.

8 Slacken the bolt securing the timing belt tensioner pulley **(see illustration)**.

9 Prise the timing belt tensioner access plug from the lower rear timing belt cover **(see illustration)**.

10 A suitable tool will now be required to release the timing belt tensioner. Rover technicians use service tool 18G 1719, but a suitable alternative can be improvised using a length of M6 threaded rod or a long bolt, and a nut **(see illustration)**.

11 Insert the tool through the hole in the lower rear timing belt cover, then screw the threaded rod or bolt into the tensioner plunger, and turn the nut on the tool to draw the plunger back, relieving the tension on the timing belt tensioner pulley **(see illustration)**.

12 Once the tensioner plunger has been released, tighten the tensioner pulley bolt.

13 Slide the timing belt from the sprockets

7.11 Screw the bolt (1) into the tensioner plunger, then tighten the nut (2) to draw the plunger back – engine removed for clarity

7.6 Removing the engine mounting cover plate

7.9 Prise the access plug from the rear timing belt cover – engine removed for clarity

and remove the belt **(see illustration)**. Do not rotate the crankshaft or the camshaft until the timing belt has been refitted.

Inspection

14 Check the timing belt carefully for any signs of uneven wear, splitting or oil contamination and renew it if there is the slightest doubt about its condition. If the engine is undergoing an overhaul and has covered more than 42 000 miles (65 000 km) since the original belt was fitted, it is advisable to renew the belt as a matter of course, regardless of its apparent condition. Note that MG Rover recommends that the belt be renewed as follows:

With manual tensioner for the fuel injection pump belt, every 48 000 miles (80 000 km) or 4 years, whichever comes first.

With automatic tensioner for the fuel injection pump belt, every 84 000 miles (140 000 km) or 7 years, whichever comes first.

15 If signs of oil contamination are found, trace the source of the oil leak and rectify it, then wash down the engine timing belt area and all related components to remove all traces of oil. If the timing belt sprockets have been subjected to prolonged oil contamination, they must be soaked in a suitable solvent bath, then thoroughly washed in clean solvent before refitting (the sprockets are manufactured from a porous material which will absorb oil – the oil will eventually be released and will contaminate the new belt if the sprockets are not cleaned).

7.8 Slackening the bolt securing the timing belt tensioner pulley – engine removed for clarity

7.10 Slacken the timing belt tensioner pulley bolt (1), then use Rover tool 18G 1719 (2) or alternative to release the tensioner

Refitting and adjustment

Note: *The manufacturer states that tensioning need only be carried out when a belt is (re)fitted. No retensioning is recommended once a belt has been fitted and therefore this operation is not included in the manufacturer's maintenance schedule. If the timing belt is thought to be incorrectly tensioned, then adjust the tension as described in the following paragraphs. If the timing belt has been disturbed, adjust its tension following the same procedure, omitting as appropriate the irrelevant preliminary dismantling/reassembly steps.*

7.13 Removing the timing belt

7.18 Refit the engine mounting cover plate – engine removed for clarity

16 Ensure that the timing marks on the camshaft sprocket and the rear timing belt cover are still aligned, and that the crankshaft is still locked in position using the timing pin inserted into the flywheel (see Section 3).

17 If a used belt is being refitted, ensure that the direction mark made on removal points in the normal direction of rotation. Fit the timing belt over the crankshaft and camshaft sprockets and around the idler pulley, ensuring that the belt front run is taut, ie, all slack is on the tensioner pulley side of the belt, then fit the belt around the tensioner pulley. Do not twist the belt sharply during refitting and ensure that the belt teeth are correctly seated centrally in the sprockets and that the timing marks remain in alignment (see Section 3).

18 Refit the engine mounting cover plate, and tighten the securing nuts and bolts securely **(see illustration)**.

19 Refit the lower outer timing belt cover and tighten the securing bolts to the specified torque **(see illustration)**.

20 Refit the right-hand engine mounting as described in Section 20.

21 Refit the crankshaft pulley, with reference to Section 5 (do not refit the roadwheel or lower the vehicle to the ground at this stage).

22 Refit and tension the auxiliary drivebelt as described in Chapter 5A

23 Slacken the timing belt tensioner pulley bolt.

24 Using the special tool, release the timing belt tensioner plunger, then remove the tool.

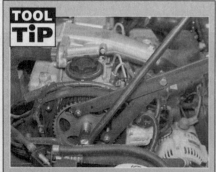

TOOL TIP

Using an improvised tool to prevent the camshaft from rotating whilst unscrewing the sprocket bolt.

7.19 Refitting the lower outer timing belt cover – engine removed for clarity

25 Lightly tighten the tensioner pulley bolt.

26 Remove the timing pin from the flywheel.

27 Using a spanner or a socket and extension bar on the crankshaft pulley bolt, rotate the crankshaft through two complete revolutions clockwise until the timing marks on the camshaft sprocket and the rear timing belt cover are aligned again.

28 Refit the timing pin, and engage it with the flywheel.

29 Slacken the timing belt tensioner pulley bolt, and allow the tensioner to push against the belt under the force of the plunger.

30 Tighten the timing belt tensioner pulley bolt to the specified torque.

Caution: Do not exceed the specified torque setting for the tensioner pulley bolt.

31 Remove the timing pin from the flywheel.

32 Refit the upper outer timing belt cover.

33 Refit the timing belt tensioner access plug to the lower rear timing belt cover.

34 Refit the power steering fluid pipe bracket securing bolt.

35 Refit the roadwheel and lower the vehicle to the ground, then reconnect the battery negative lead.

---

8 Timing belt tensioner and sprockets – removal, inspection and refitting

Camshaft sprocket

Note: *The following new parts are needed – camshaft sprocket securing bolt, three sprocket damper Torx head screws.*

8.5a Withdraw the camshaft sprocket . . .

Removal

1 Disconnect the battery negative lead.

2 Remove the timing belt as described in Section 7. Note that there is no need to remove the timing belt completely, provided that it is slipped from the camshaft sprocket. **Do not** rotate the crankshaft or the camshaft until the timing belt has been refitted.

3 Remove and discard three Torx head screws securing the sprocket damper, and remove the damper.

4 Slacken the camshaft sprocket retaining bolt and remove it, along with its washer. To prevent the camshaft from rotating, Rover technicians use service tool 18G 1521, but an acceptable substitute can be fabricated from two lengths of steel strip (one long, the other short) and three nuts and bolts. One nut and bolt should form the pivot of a forked tool with the remaining two nuts and bolts at the tips of the forks to engage with the sprocket spokes **(see Tool Tip)**. **Do not** allow the camshaft to rotate as the sprocket bolt is being loosened. Discard the sprocket bolt – a new one must be used on refitting.

5 Withdraw the sprocket from the camshaft, noting the locating roll-pin **(see illustrations)**. If the roll-pin is a loose fit in the end of the camshaft, remove it and store it with the sprocket for safe-keeping.

Inspection

6 Clean the sprocket thoroughly, and renew it if it shows signs of wear, damage or cracks.

Refitting

7 Where applicable, refit the roll-pin to the end of the camshaft, ensuring that its split is facing the centre of the camshaft, then refit the sprocket (ensure that it engages with the roll-pin), ensuring that the timing marks on the sprocket and rear timing belt cover are still aligned.

8 Prevent the sprocket from rotating by using the method employed on removal, then fit a **new** sprocket securing bolt, and tighten the bolt to the specified torque setting. **Do not** allow the camshaft to turn as the bolt is tightened.

9 Fit the sprocket damper, and fit three **new** Torx head screws. Use a torque wrench to tighten the screws to the specified torque.

8.5b . . . and recover the roll-pin (arrowed) if it is loose

8.12 Removing the crankshaft sprocket – engine removed for clarity

8.17 Removing the timing belt tensioner pulley assembly . . .

8.18 . . . and the spring and plunger – engine removed for clarity

10 Refit and tension the timing belt as described in Section 7, then reconnect the battery negative lead.

Crankshaft sprocket

Removal

11 Remove the timing belt as described in Section 7.
12 Remove the sprocket from the crankshaft (see illustration).

Inspection

13 Clean the sprocket thoroughly, and renew it if it shows signs of wear, damage or cracks.

Refitting

14 Refit the sprocket to the crankshaft, ensuring that it locates correctly on the crankshaft flattened section. Note that the sprocket flange must be innermost. Note that the notch in the sprocket flange should be pointing vertically upwards.
15 Refit and tension the timing belt as described in Section 7, then reconnect the battery negative lead.

Tensioner assembly

Removal

16 Remove the timing belt as described in Section 7.
17 Unscrew the tensioner pulley backplate securing bolt, and the tensioner pulley bolt, and remove the tensioner – take care, as the tensioner spring and plunger will be released from their housing as the tensioner is removed (see illustration).
18 Lift out the tensioner spring and plunger (see illustration).

Inspection

19 Clean the tensioner assembly but do not use any strong solvent which may enter the pulley bearing. Check that the pulley rotates freely on the backplate, with no sign of stiffness or of free play. Renew the assembly if there is any doubt about its condition or if there are any obvious signs of wear or damage. The same applies to the tensioner spring, which should be checked with great care as its condition is critical for the correct tensioning of the timing belt.
20 Check the tensioner spring for signs of

distortion, and check the spring free-length. If the free-length is not as specified, the spring must be renewed, as its condition is critical for the correct tensioning of the timing belt.
21 Check the tensioner plunger and the housing for signs of wear and corrosion. If there is any evidence of corrosion, the housing and the plunger must be renewed – **do not** attempt to remove corrosion using emery paper or by scraping.

Refitting

22 Thoroughly clean the tensioner components, paying particular attention to the plunger and the housing.
23 Smear the plunger with a little molybdenum disulphide-based grease, then locate the spring and plunger in the housing.
24 Position the tensioner on the engine, then refit the backplate securing bolt, and the tensioner pulley bolt. Tighten the backplate securing bolt securely, but do not tighten the pulley bolt at this stage.
25 Refit and tension the timing belt as described in Section 7.

9 Fuel injection pump drivebelt cover – removal and refitting

Removal

1 Unscrew the bolts securing the engine acoustic cover to the top of the cylinder head cover, then remove the acoustic cover from the engine.

10.6 A 9.5 mm diameter twist drill (arrowed) can be used to lock the fuel injection pump sprocket in position

2 Remove the air cleaner assembly as described in Chapter 4B.
3 Remove the five bolts securing the drivebelt cover to the backplate, and remove the cover.

Refitting

4 Refitting is a reversal of removal.

10 Fuel injection pump drivebelt 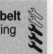 – removal, inspection, refitting and adjustment

Note: A reversible torque wrench will be required for this operation on models with a manual drivebelt tensioner.

Removal

1 Disconnect the battery negative lead.
2 Apply the handbrake, then jack up the front of the vehicle and support securely on axle stands (see Jacking and Vehicle Support). Remove the right-hand front roadwheel.
3 Remove the fuel injection pump drivebelt cover, as described in Section 9.
4 Rotate the crankshaft to bring No 1 piston to TDC, and insert the timing pin to lock the crankshaft in position, as described in Section 3.
5 A suitable locking pin must now be used to lock the fuel injection pump sprocket in position. Rover technicians use service tool 18G 1717, but an acceptable substitute can be improvised, using a 9.5 mm twist drill.
6 Push the locking tool through the hole in the fuel injection pump sprocket until it engages with the hole in the transmission mounting plate (see illustration).
7 If the original fuel injection pump drivebelt is to be re-used, mark the running direction on the belt, using chalk or tape.
8 A suitable tool will now be required to hold the camshaft stationary. Rover technicians use service tool 18G 1521, but alternatively, a 3/8 inch drive breaker bar can be used – engage the square drive end of the bar with the square cut-out in the sprocket. Hold the camshaft stationary, and slacken the four (adjuster) bolts securing the fuel injection pump drive sprocket to the camshaft (see illustrations). Do not allow the camshaft to rotate as the bolts are slackened.

10.8a Engage a breaker bar with the square cut-out (arrowed) in the fuel injection pump drive sprocket . . .

10.8b . . . to hold the sprocket stationary whilst slackening the sprocket adjuster bolts

10.9 Slacken the bolt securing the fuel injection pump drivebelt tensioner pulley

9 Slacken the Allen bolt securing the fuel injection pump drivebelt tensioner pulley, then move the tensioner away from the belt, and tighten the pulley bolt **(see illustration)**.
10 Slide the drivebelt from the sprockets **(see illustration)**. Do not rotate the camshaft or the fuel injection pump until the drivebelt has been refitted and tensioned.

Inspection

11 Check the fuel injection pump drivebelt carefully for any signs of uneven wear, splitting or oil contamination and renew it if there is the slightest doubt about its condition. If the engine is undergoing an over-haul and has covered more than 42 000 miles (65 000 km) since the original belt was fitted, renew the belt as a matter of course, regardless of its apparent condition.
12 If signs of oil contamination are found, trace the source of the oil leak and rectify it, then wash down the engine timing belt area and all related components to remove all traces of oil. If the timing belt sprockets have been subjected to prolonged oil contamination, they must be soaked in a suitable solvent bath, then thoroughly washed in clean solvent before refitting (the sprockets are manufactured from a porous material which will absorb oil – the oil will eventually be released and will contaminate the new belt if the sprockets are not cleaned).

Refitting and adjustment

Note: *The manufacturer states that tensioning*

need only be carried out when a belt is (re)fitted. No retensioning is recommended once a belt has been fitted and therefore this operation is not included in the manufacturer's maintenance schedule. If the belt is thought to be incorrectly tensioned, then adjust the tension as described in the following paragraphs. If the belt has been disturbed, adjust its tension following the same procedure, omitting as appropriate the irrelevant preliminary dismantling/reassembly steps.
13 Make sure that the four (adjuster) bolts securing the fuel injection pump drive sprocket to the camshaft are just slack enough to allow the sprocket to rotate within its elongated slots – the sprocket should not be able to tip on the end of the camshaft.
14 If a used belt is being refitted, ensure that the direction mark made on removal points in the normal direction of rotation. Fit the belt over the fuel injection pump sprocket, then rotate the sprocket on the camshaft fully clockwise within the elongated slots, then anti-clockwise, until the belt locates in the sprocket teeth – this procedure must be carried out to ensure correct belt tensioning **(see illustration)**. Ensure that the lower belt run is taut, ie, all slack is on the tensioner pulley side of the belt, then fit the belt around the tensioner pulley. Do not twist the belt sharply during refitting and ensure that the belt teeth are correctly seated centrally in the sprockets.
15 Slacken the tensioner pulley bolt.

Manual drivebelt tensioner

16 Engage a torque wrench, with a suitable square-drive extension, with the square hole in the tensioner backplate, and apply a torque of 6 Nm (4 lbf ft), whilst tightening the tensioner pulley bolt **(see illustration)**.
17 Hold the camshaft stationary, using the tool engaged with the camshaft (timing belt) sprocket, as during removal, then tighten the four fuel injection pump drive sprocket (adjuster) bolts to the specified torque.
18 Remove the locking pins from the flywheel and the fuel injection pump sprocket.
19 Rotate the crankshaft through two complete turns clockwise, then refit the locking pin to the flywheel.
20 Check that the camshaft timing mark is aligned with the mark on the rear timing belt cover (see Section 3).
21 Slacken the four (adjuster) bolts securing the fuel injection pump drive sprocket to the camshaft, then refit the locking pin to the fuel injection pump sprocket.
22 Slacken the tensioner pulley bolt, then re-engage the torque wrench with the square hole in the tensioner backplate, and again apply a torque of 6 Nm (4 lbf ft).
23 Tighten the tensioner pulley bolt to the specified torque.
24 It is now necessary to apply an **anti-clockwise** torque to the fuel injection pump drive sprocket to ensure that the lower run of the belt is taut as the sprocket adjuster bolts are tightened. If a second torque wrench is

10.10 Slide the fuel injection pump drivebelt from the sprockets

10.14 Rotate the sprocket fully clockwise, then anti-clockwise until the belt locates in the sprocket teeth

10.16 Engage a torque wrench with the square hole in the tensioner backplate and apply the specified torque whilst tightening the tensioner pulley bolt

available, apply an **anti-clockwise** torque of 25 Nm (18 lbf ft) to the sprocket centre bolt, whilst tightening the four sprocket adjuster bolts to the specified torque using a second torque wrench. If a second torque wrench is not available, apply a moderate anti-clockwise load to the sprocket centre bolt using a suitable spanner or socket, whilst tightening the sprocket adjuster bolts to the specified torque **(see illustration)**.

Automatic drivebelt tensioner

25 Rotate the tensioner **clockwise** until the index pointer passes the tension indicator.
26 Allow the tensioner to return **anti-clockwise** until the pointer is in line with the bottom edge of the tension indicator.
27 Hold the tensioner in that position and tighten it to the specified torque.

All models

28 Remove the locking pins from the flywheel and the fuel injection pump sprocket.
29 Refit the fuel injection pump drivebelt cover as described in Section 9.
30 Refit the roadwheel, then lower the vehicle to the ground and reconnect the battery negative lead.

11 Fuel injection pump drivebelt sprockets and tensioner – removal and refitting

Injection pump drive (camshaft) sprocket

Note: *A new sprocket securing bolt must be used on refitting.*

Removal

1 Remove the fuel injection pump drivebelt as described in Section 10.
2 A suitable tool will now be required to hold the camshaft stationary. Rover technicians use service tool 18G 1521, but an acceptable substitute can be fabricated from two lengths of steel strip (one long, the other short) and three nuts and bolts. One nut and bolt should form the pivot of a forked tool with the remaining two nuts and bolts at the tips of the forks to engage with the camshaft sprocket spokes **(see Tool Tip in Section 8)**. **Do not** allow the camshaft to rotate as the sprocket bolt is being loosened.
3 Hold the camshaft stationary, and slacken the centre bolt securing the fuel injection pump drive sprocket. Remove the bolt, and withdraw the sprocket from the end of the camshaft **(see illustration)**. Discard the sprocket bolt, a new bolt must be used on refitting.

Inspection

4 Clean the sprocket thoroughly, and renew it if it shows signs of wear, damage or cracks.

Refitting

5 Coat the threads of the new sprocket securing bolt with clean engine oil.

10.24 Applying an anti-clockwise load to the pump drive sprocket centre bolt whilst tightening the adjuster bolts to the specified torque

6 Locate the sprocket on the end of the camshaft, then prevent the camshaft from turning, as during removal, fit the sprocket securing bolt, and tighten the bolt to the specified torque in the two stages given (see *Specifications*).
7 Refit the fuel injection pump drivebelt as described in Section 10.

Injection pump sprocket

8 The procedure is described as part of the fuel injection pump removal procedure in Chapter 4B.

Tensioner

Removal

9 Remove the fuel injection pump drivebelt as described in Section 10.
10 Unscrew the tensioner pulley bolt and remove the tensioner.

Inspection

11 Clean the tensioner assembly but do not use any strong solvent which may enter the pulley bearing. Check that the pulley rotates freely on the backplate, with no sign of stiffness or of free play. Renew the assembly if there is any doubt about its condition or if there are any obvious signs of wear or damage.

Refitting

12 Refitting is a reversal of removal, but make sure that the peg on the engine engages

11.3 Removing the fuel injection pump drive (camshaft) sprocket

with the hole in the tensioner backplate **(see illustration)**. Refit the fuel injection pump drivebelt as described in Section 10.

12 Camshaft oil seals – renewal

Right-hand seal

1 Remove the camshaft sprocket as described in Section 8.
2 Punch or drill two small holes opposite each other in the oil seal. Screw a self-tapping screw into each hole, and pull on the screws with pliers to extract the seal.
3 Clean the seal housing and polish off any burrs or raised edges which may have caused the seal to fail.
4 Locate the seal against the recess, and draw the seal into position using a suitable socket and long M12 bolt, or threaded rod and bolt. Screw the bolt or threaded rod into the end of the camshaft, and turn the end of the bolt, or the nut to draw the seal into position **(see illustration 12.8)**. Alternatively, drive the seal into position using a suitable tubular drift, such as a socket, which bears only on the hard outer edge of the seal. Take care not to damage the seal lips during fitting and note that the seal lips should face inwards.
Caution: The new oil seal must be fitted dry. Do not lubricate the seal recess, the seal lip, or the seal running surface on the shaft.
5 Refit the camshaft sprocket as described in Section 8.

Left-hand seal

6 Remove the fuel injection pump drive sprocket from the end of the camshaft, and remove the fuel injection pump drivebelt tensioner, as described in Section 11.
7 Unscrew the three securing bolts, and remove the fuel injection pump drivebelt backplate.
8 Proceed as described in paragraphs 2 to 4. Ensure that the seal is fully seated In its recess **(see illustration)**.

11.12 Make sure that the peg (arrowed) on the engine engages with the hole in the tensioner backplate

12.8 Using a socket, a length of M12 threaded rod and a nut to draw the camshaft oil seal into position – cylinder head removed

9 Thoroughly clean the fuel injection pump drivebelt backplate, and camshaft bearing carrier and cylinder head mating faces, then refit the backplate, and tighten the securing bolts to the specified torque.
10 Refit the fuel injection pump drivebelt tensioner, then refit the pump drive sprocket, as described in Section 11.

13 Camshaft and hydraulic tappets – removal, inspection and refitting

HAYNES HINT *If faulty tappets are diagnosed and the engine's service history is unknown, it is always worth trying the effect of renewing the engine oil and filter (using only good quality engine oil of the recommended viscosity and specification) before going to the expense of renewing any of the tappets.*

Note: *The following new parts are needed – MG Rover sealant kit GUG 705963GM, camshaft oil seals.*

Removal

1 Remove the cylinder head cover, with reference to Section 4.
2 Remove the upper rear timing belt cover as described in Section 6.

3 Remove the fuel injection pump drive sprocket from the camshaft, and remove the fuel injection pump drivebelt tensioner, as described in Section 11.
4 Unscrew the three securing bolts, and remove the fuel injection pump drivebelt back-plate **(see illustrations)**. Note the location of the bracket secured by one of the bolts.
5 Working in the **reverse** order of the tightening sequence **(see illustration 13.26)**, progressively slacken the camshaft bearing carrier securing bolts by 2 to 3 turns – **do not** fully slacken the bolts at this stage.
6 Using a soft-faced mallet, gently tap the bearing carrier upwards to break the sealant bond between the bearing carrier and the cylinder head. Note that the bearing carrier is located on dowels.
7 Using the same reverse sequence **(see illustration 13.26)**, continue to progressively slacken the bearing carrier securing bolts until all the load on the bearing carrier is relieved (the load is due to the pressure of the valve springs pushing the camshaft upwards against the bearing carrier).
Caution: If the bolts are removed completely before the load on the bearing carrier is relieved, the carrier may be suddenly released, which may cause damage to the bearing surfaces and/or the camshaft.
8 Finally remove the bolts, and lift the bearing carrier from the camshaft and cylinder head **(see illustration)**.
9 Carefully lift out the camshaft, then remove and discard the camshaft oil seals **(see illustration opposite)**.
10 Obtain eight small, clean plastic containers and number them from 1 to 8.
11 Using a hydraulic sucker, or a small magnet, withdraw each hydraulic tappet in turn, invert it to prevent oil loss and place it in its respective container, which should then be filled with clean engine oil. **Do not** interchange the hydraulic tappets, and do not allow the hydraulic tappets to lose oil, as they will take a long time to refill with oil on restarting the engine, which could result in incorrect valve clearances.

Inspection

Note: *To measure the camshaft bearing running clearance, an American product known as Plastigauge can be used. This consists of a*

fine thread of perfectly round plastic which is compressed between the bearing surface and the camshaft journal. When the bearing carrier is removed, the plastic is deformed and can be measured with a special card gauge supplied with the kit. The running clearance is determined from this gauge. Plastigauge is sometimes difficult to obtain, but enquiries at one of the larger specialist motor factors should produce the name of a stockist in your area.
12 Check each hydraulic tappet for signs of obvious wear (scoring, pitting, etc) and for ovality. Renew if necessary. Using a micrometer, measure the outside diameter of the tappets – if the diameter of any tappet is outside the specified limits, it must be renewed.
13 If the engine's valve clearances have sounded noisy, particularly if the noise persists after initial start-up from cold, then there is reason to suspect a faulty hydraulic tappet. Only a good mechanic experienced in these engines can tell whether the noise level is typical, or if renewal is warranted of one or more of the tappets.
14 If the operation of any tappet is faulty, then it must be renewed.
15 Carefully remove all traces of old sealant from the mating surfaces of the camshaft bearing carrier and cylinder head, using a plastic scraper and suitable solvent if necessary. Examine the camshaft bearing journals and the cylinder head and bearing carrier bearing surfaces for signs of obvious wear or pitting. If any such signs are evident, renew the component(s) concerned.
16 To check the bearing journal running clearance, remove the hydraulic tappets (if not already done), carefully clean the bearing surfaces and refit the camshaft and bearing carrier with a strand of Plastigauge across each journal (see Note at the beginning of this sub-Section) **(see illustration)**. Tighten the bearing carrier bolts, in the specified order **(see illustration 13.26)**, to the specified torque wrench setting, whilst taking great care not to rotate the camshaft, then remove the bearing carrier and use the scale provided with the Plastigauge kit to measure the width of each compressed strand.
17 If the running clearance of any bearing is found to be beyond the specified service limit or beyond, fit a new camshaft and repeat the

13.4a Unscrew the securing bolts . . .

13.4b . . . and remove the fuel injection pump drivebelt backplate

13.8 Lifting off the camshaft bearing carrier

13.9 Cylinder head components

1 Oil filler cap
2 Camshaft cover
3 Gasket
4 Fuel injection pump backplate
5 Fuel injection pump camshaft sprocket
6 Fuel injection pump sprocket bolt
7 Manual fuel injection drivebelt tensioner
8 Tensioner pulley bolt
9 Tensioner pulley bolt
10 Automatic fuel injection drivebelt tensioner
11 Tappets
12 Collets
13 Spring retainers
14 Springs
15 Lower spring seat/stem oil seals
16 Valve guide
17 Valve guide
18 Valve seat
19 Valve seat
20 Valve
21 Valve
22 Cylinder head
23 Gasket
24 Thermostat housing
25 Roll-pin
26 Oil seal
27 Oil seal
28 Camshaft
29 Camshaft bearing carrier
30 Cylinder head bolt

H44878

check. If the clearance is still excessive, then the cylinder head (and matched bearing carrier) must be renewed.

18 To check camshaft endfloat, remove the hydraulic tappets (if not already done), carefully clean the bearing surfaces and refit the camshaft and bearing carrier. Tighten the bearing carrier bolts, in the specified order **(see illustration 13.26)**, to the specified torque wrench setting, then measure the endfloat using a Dial Test Indicator (DTI) or dial gauge mounted on the cylinder head, so that its tip bears on the front of the camshaft **(see illustration)**.

19 Tap the camshaft fully towards the gauge, zero the gauge, then tap the camshaft fully away from the gauge and note the gauge reading. If the endfloat measured is found to be greater than the maximum specified, fit a new camshaft and repeat the check. If the clearance is still excessive, then the cylinder head must be renewed.

20 The camshaft itself should show no signs of marks, pitting or scoring on the lobe surfaces. If such marks are evident, renew the camshaft.

21 If a camshaft is renewed, extract the roll-pins from the old one and fit the pins to the new camshaft, with the split in each roll-pin towards the camshaft centreline.

Refitting

22 Liberally oil the cylinder head hydraulic tappet bores and the tappets **(see illustration)**.

13.16 Position a strand of Plastigauge (arrowed) across each camshaft bearing journal

H29757

13.18 Checking camshaft endfloat using a dial gauge

13.22 Liberally oil the tappets

13.23 Position the camshaft so that the roll-pin (arrowed) at the timing belt end is in the 2 o'clock position

13.24a Apply a bead of sealant to the area indicated by the heavy black line

13.24b Squeeze out the sealant . . .

13.24c . . . then spread to an even film using a brush

13.26 Camshaft bearing carrier securing bolt tightening sequence

Note that if new tappets are being fitted, they must be charged with clean engine oil before installation. Carefully refit the tappets to the cylinder head, ensuring that each tappet is refitted to its original bore and is the correct way up. Some care will be required to enter the tappets squarely into their bores.

23 Liberally oil the camshaft bearings and lobes, then refit the camshaft. Position the camshaft so that the roll-pin in the front (timing belt sprocket end) of the camshaft is in the 2 o'clock position when viewed from the right-hand end of the engine **(see illustration)**.

24 Ensure that the locating dowels are pressed firmly into their recesses, check that the mating surfaces are completely clean, unmarked and free from oil, then apply a thin bead of the recommended sealant to the cylinder head mating surfaces of the camshaft bearing carrier. Carefully follow the

instructions supplied with the sealant kit. Spread the sealant to an even film using a brush or roller, taking care not to allow any sealant to enter the lubrication grooves **(see illustrations)**. Note that once the sealant has been applied, assembly must be completed within 20 minutes.

25 Refit the bearing carrier to the cylinder head, pushing it firmly into position. Fit the bearing carrier securing bolts, and tighten them finger-tight.

26 Working in sequence **(see illustration)**, progressively tighten the camshaft bearing carrier bolts by one turn at a time until the carrier touches the cylinder head evenly. Now go round again, working in the same sequence, tightening all bolts to the specified torque setting. Work only as described, to apply the pressure of the valve springs gradually and evenly on the carrier. Wipe off all surplus sealant so that none is left to find

its way into any oilways. Follow the sealant manufacturer's recommendations as to the time needed for curing – usually at least an hour must be allowed between application of the sealant and the starting of the engine.

27 Fit new camshaft oil seals, using a suitable tube or socket, with reference to Section 12.

28 Refit the fuel injection pump drivebelt backplate, then refit and tighten the securing bolts, making sure that the bracket is in place on the relevant bolt, as noted before removal.

29 Refit the fuel injection pump drivebelt tensioner and refit the pump drive sprocket to the camshaft, as described in Section 11.

30 Refit the upper rear timing belt cover as described in Section 6.

31 Refit the cylinder head cover, with reference to Section 4.

14 Cylinder head – removal and refitting

Note: *The following new parts are needed – cylinder head gasket, turbocharger oil return pipe gasket, turbocharger oil feed pipe sealing washers, camshaft sprocket bolt, fuel injection pump sprocket bolt, and possibly – cylinder head bolts.*

Note: *As they are disconnected, make a note or sketch of the position, route and clipping of all wires, harnesses, pipes and hoses.*

1 Disconnect the battery earth lead.

2 Remove three screws, and remove the engine acoustic cover.

3 Remove the air cleaner – see Chapter 4B.

4 Drain the cooling system – see Section 1B.

5 Apply the handbrake, chock the rear roadwheels, then jack up the front of the car and support it on axle stands (see *Jacking and Vehicle Support*).

6 Slacken the clip and disconnect the engine breather hose from the camshaft cover **(see illustration)**.

7 Disconnect the multi-plug from the MAF/IAT sensor on the air intake pipe between the air cleaner and the turbocharger **(see illustration)**.

8 Slacken the clip, and disconnect the air intake pipe from the turbocharger. Remove

14.6 Disconnect breather hose

14.7 Disconnect MAF/IAT multi-plug

14.8 Remove intake pipe

14.12 Disconnect EGR valve vacuum pipe

14.17 Remove EGR pipe bolts

the air intake pipe, MAF/IAT sensor and engine breather valve assembly. Cover or plug the turbocharger intake **(see illustration)**.

9 Remove three nuts, and disconnect the exhaust front pipe from the turbocharger.

10 Disconnect the boost pressure sensing pipe from the turbocharger (to the MAP sensor on the bulkhead).

11 Slacken two clips and disconnect two coolant pipes from the EGR cooler.

12 Disconnect the vacuum pipe from the EGR valve **(see illustration)**.

13 Slacken the clip, and disconnect the intercooler hose from the turbocharger outlet pipe.

14 Remove two bolts securing the turbocharger outlet pipe to the cylinder head.

15 Slacken the clip, and remove the outlet pipe from the turbocharger outlet hose. Cover or plug the outlet hose.

16 Slacken the clip, and disconnect the intercooler hose from the intake pipe.

17 Remove two bolts securing the EGR pipe to the intake pipe **(see illustration)**.

18 Remove the bolt securing the intake pipe bracket to the camshaft cover.

19 Remove two bolts and remove the intake pipe from the inlet manifold **(see illustration)**.

20 Remove the banjo bolt securing the oil feed pipe to the turbocharger, remove and discard the washers.

21 Remove two bolts securing the oil drain pipe to the turbocharger, and discard the gasket **(see illustration)**.

22 Remove two bolts securing the exhaust manifold to the support bracket.

23 Remove six bolts and six nuts securing the manifolds to the cylinder head, and remove the manifolds. Remove and discard the gasket.

24 Remove the fuel injection pump drivebelt – see Section 10.

25 Remove the fuel injection pump drivebelt sprocket and tensioner – see Section 11.

26 Remove three bolts securing the fuel injection pump belt backplate, and remove the plate.

27 Remove the camshaft drivebelt – see Section 7.

28 Remove the camshaft sprocket – see Section 8.

29 Release three clips securing the engine harness to the camshaft drivebelt rear cover.

30 Remove five bolts securing the rear cover to the cylinder head and cylinder block, and remove the cover **(see illustration)**.

31 Remove the bolt securing the brake servo vacuum pipe to the camshaft cover.

32 Release the clip, and disconnect the vacuum hose from the vacuum pump. Tie the pipe clear of the work area.

33 Remove three bolts securing the alternator upper mounting bracket, and remove the bracket.

34 Disconnect the multi-plug from the Engine Coolant Temperature (ECT) sensor **(see illustration)**.

35 Disconnect the wire from the coolant temperature gauge sensor **(see illustration)**.

36 Slacken the clip, and disconnect the radiator top hose from the coolant outlet elbow.

37 Remove the bolt attaching the dipstick tube to the outlet elbow.

38 Disconnect the multi-plug from the harness for the needle lift sensor in No 1 injector **(see illustration)**.

14.19 Remove intake pipe

14.21 Remove oil drain pipe bolts

14.30 Remove rear cover

14.34 Disconnect ECT multi-plug

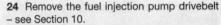

14.35 Disconnect temperature gauge sensor wire

14.38 Disconnect needle lift sensor multi-plug

14.40 Remove injector pipes

14.42 Remove glow plug supply wire

39 Pack absorbent cloths around the injectors.

Caution: To prevent damage to the injector pipes, use two spanners when slackening the connections.

40 Slacken the unions attaching the injector pipes to the injectors, and to the fuel injection pump. Carefully remove the pipes, and place them in a plastic bag. Plug the injector and fuel injection pump connections **(see illustration)**.

41 Disconnect the fuel spill return hose from No 3 injector. Plug the connections.

42 Remove the nut, and remove the glow plug supply wire from No 2 glow plug **(see illustration)**.

43 Remove twelve bolts, and remove the camshaft cover. Remove and discard the gasket **(see illustration)**.

44 Working in the reverse of the tightening sequence, progressively slacken and remove ten Torx head bolts securing the cylinder head

to the cylinder block **(see illustration)**.

Caution: Handle the cylinder head bolts carefully, and store them in fitted order. DO NOT remove the washers from the bolts.

45 Two dowels locate the cylinder head. The tips of the injectors and glow plugs protrude below the face of the head. DO NOT move the cylinder head sideways during removal. If necessary, carefully rock the cylinder head to release it from the cylinder block.

46 Using assistance lift off the cylinder head, and place on wooden blocks which are positioned away from the injectors and glow plugs **(see illustration)**.

47 Remove the gasket, and note the number of gasket thickness indicator holes 1, 2, or 3. The new gasket must have the same number of holes **(see illustration)**.

48 Plug or tape over the oil and water passage holes in the cylinder head and cylinder block. To prevent carbon entering the

gap between the piston and bore, smear a band of grease around the gap.

49 Use a hard wood or plastic scraper to remove all traces of gasket/carbon, etc, from the surfaces of the head and block. Scrape the carbon from the piston crowns. Wipe away the grease band, and wipe all surfaces.

50 Check surfaces for damage. Minor scratches are acceptable, but any more serious marking must be rectified by machining or component renewal. **Note:** *The cylinder head cannot be refaced.*

51 Check the cylinder head for distortion – see Chapter 2D.

52 Remove all tape/plugs from cylinder block and cylinder head.

53 Wash and dry the bolts. Check for signs of wear or damage. Check bolt length – if any bolt exceeds the maximum length of 243.41 mm, all bolts must be renewed **(see illustration)**.

54 Apply a light film of engine oil to the bolt threads, and the underside of the bolt heads.

Caution: DO NOT lubricate the underside of the washers.

55 Temporarily fit the crankshaft pulley bolt, and remove the crankshaft locking pin – see Section 3.

56 Using the pulley bolt, rotate the crankshaft anti-clockwise until No 1 and 4 pistons are approximately 25 mm below the face of the cylinder block.

57 Check that the camshaft drive pin is at 2 o'clock position. Remove the crankshaft pulley bolt.

58 Ensure that the two locating dowels are correctly located in the cylinder block **(see illustration)**.

14.44 Remove the cylinder head bolts

14.46 Lift off the cylinder head

14.47 Gasket thickness indicator holes

14.53 Measure the bolt length

14.58 Check locating dowels

14.59 Gasket TOP marking

14.61 Cylinder head bolt tightening
sequence

Caution: ensure that the new cylinder head gasket has the same number of thickness indicator holes as the original – ie, 1, 2 or 3 holes.

59 Fit the gasket – DRY – to the cylinder block, with TOP marking visible at the flywheel end **(see illustration)**.
60 Using assistance, lift the cylinder head onto the cylinder block, and locate on the dowels.
61 Carefully fit the cylinder head bolts. Use a torque wrench to tighten the bolts progressively in sequence and in the specified stages **(see illustration)**:
62 Further refitting is a reversal of the removal procedure, noting:
Ensure cables, pipes, hoses and harnesses are routed and clipped as noted during removal.
Use a torque wrench to tighten all fastenings to the specified torque.

Fill the cooling system – see Chapter 1B.
If necessary, bleed the fuel system – see Chapter 4B.
Start the engine and check for leaks.
Note: *If tappet noise is excessive run the engine at 2000 to 2500 rpm for 20 minutes. Do not exceed 3000 rpm until noise ceases.*

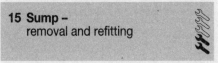

15 Sump –
removal and refitting

Note: *The following new parts are needed – MG Rover sealant kit GUG 705963GM, sump gasket, engine oil filter.*

Removal

1 Apply the handbrake, then jack up the front of the vehicle and support securely on axle stands (see *Jacking and Vehicle Support*).

2 Drain the engine oil (with reference to Chapter 1B if necessary), then clean and refit the engine oil drain plug, tightening it to the specified torque wrench setting. If the engine is nearing its service interval when the oil and filter are due for renewal, it is recommended that the filter is also removed and a new one fitted. After reassembly, the engine can then be refilled with fresh engine oil.
3 Remove the oil filter, with reference to Chapter 1B.
4 Remove the engine/transmission steady bar, as described in Section 20.
5 Unscrew the bolt securing the sump to the transmission support bracket **(see illustration)**.
6 Slacken the hose clip, and disconnect the brake vacuum pump oil drain pipe from the sump.
7 Unscrew the bolt securing the oil pipe bracket to the sump.
8 Working in the reverse order to the tightening sequence **(see illustration 15.16)**, progressively slacken the sump retaining bolts then remove them.
9 Break the joint by striking the sump with the palm of the hand, then lower the sump and withdraw it. Recover the gasket and discard it.
10 With the sump removed, take the opportunity to unbolt the oil pump pick-up/strainer pipe and clean it using a suitable solvent **(see illustrations)**. Recover the O-ring, and inspect the strainer mesh for signs of clogging or splitting – renew if necessary.

Refitting

11 Clean all traces of gasket from the mating surfaces of the cylinder block/crankcase and sump, then use a clean rag to wipe out the sump and the engine interior. Clean all traces of sealant from the crankshaft oil seal housing, main bearing caps, and cylinder block.
12 Refit the oil pump pick-up/strainer pipe, using a new O-ring, and tighten the securing bolts to the specified torque **(see illustration)**.
13 Using the specified sealant (see Note at the beginning of this Section), fill the grooves on each side of the right-hand main bearing cap, and the joints between the bearing cap and the cylinder block **(see illustration)**.
14 Apply a 1 mm thick bead of sealant to the

15.5 Unscrew the bolt (arrowed) securing the sump to the support bracket

15.10a Unscrew the securing bolts
(arrowed) . . .

15.10b . . . and remove the oil pump pick-up/strainer pipe

15.12 Refit the oil pump pick-up/strainer pipe using a new O-ring

15.13 Apply sealant as indicated in the text

15.14 Apply sealant to the joints between the left-hand oil seal housing, the left-hand main bearing cap and the cylinder block

joints between the crankshaft left-hand oil seal housing, the left-hand main bearing cap and the cylinder block **(see illustration)**. **Note:** *Do not apply the sealant until immediately prior to refitting the sump, and do not spread the bead of sealant.*

15 Fit a new gasket to the sump, ensuring that the lugs on the gasket engage with the corresponding holes in the sump, then offer up the sump to the cylinder block/crankcase then refit the sump retaining bolts, and tighten the bolts finger-tight only.

16 Working in sequence **(see illustration)**, tighten the sump bolts to the specified torque setting.

17 Further refitting is a reversal of removal, bearing in mind the following points.

a) *Tighten the bolt securing the sump to the transmission support bracket to the specified torque.*

16.4 Disconnect the oil cooler pipes (A) and the turbocharger oil feed pipe (B) from the oil pump housing

16.14a Apply a bead of sealant . . .

15.16 Sump bolt tightening sequence

b) *Refit the engine/transmission steady bar, as described in Section 20.*

c) *Fit a new oil filter and, on completion, refill the engine with oil as described in Chapter 1B.*

16 Oil pump – removal and refitting

Note: *The following new parts are needed – MG Rover sealant kit GUG 705963GM, oil pump gasket, crankshaft right-hand oil seal, oil cooler pipe O-ring, turbocharger oil feed pipe O-ring. The oil pressure relief valve can be dismantled without removing the oil pump from the vehicle – see Section 17 for details.*

16.11 Prise the crankshaft oil seal from the oil pump

16.14b . . . to the joints between the main bearing cap and the cylinder block – viewed with engine removed

Removal

1 Drain the engine oil (see Chapter 1B).

2 Remove the upper and lower rear timing belt covers as described in Section 6.

3 Remove the crankshaft sprocket from the front of the crankshaft.

4 Place a suitable container beneath the oil cooler pipe connections on the oil pump housing, then unscrew the unions and disconnect the oil cooler pipes **(see illustration)**. Recover the O-rings from the pipes and discard them.

5 Similarly, slacken the union, and disconnect the turbocharger oil feed pipe from the oil pump housing. Recover the O-ring and discard it.

6 Disconnect the wiring plug from the oil pressure switch.

7 Working in the reverse order to the tightening sequence **(see illustration 16.20)**, unscrew the oil pump securing bolts, noting the location of the single longer securing bolt at the bottom of the pump.

8 Withdraw the pump from the cylinder block, and recover the Woodruff key from the crankshaft if it is loose. Recover the gasket and discard it.

Refitting

9 Make sure that the oil pump bolt holes in the cylinder block are clean and dry.

10 Clean all traces of gasket from the cylinder block and oil pump mating faces, and remove all traces of sealant from the front main bearing cap.

11 If the original oil pump is to be refitted, prise the crankshaft oil seal from the pump, and discard it **(see illustration)**.

12 The new oil seal must be fitted dry. Do not lubricate the seal recess, the seal lip, or the seal running surface on the shaft.

13 Refit the Woodruff key to the crankshaft.

14 Using the specified sealant (see Note at the beginning of this Section), apply a 1 mm thick bead of sealant to the joints between the main bearing cap and the cylinder block **(see illustrations)**.

15 Fit a new oil pump gasket to the cylinder block **(see illustration)**.

16 If a new oil pump is being fitted, it will be supplied with a new crankshaft oil seal already fitted.

16.15 Fit a new gasket to the cylinder block – viewed with engine removed

16.20 Oil pump bolt tightening sequence

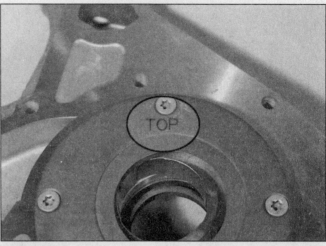

17.3a Some oil pumps have a TOP marking at the top of the cover plate

17 Turn the oil pump inner rotor as necessary to align the slot in the rotor with the Woodruff key in the crankshaft.

18 Slide the oil pump over the crankshaft, ensuring that the Woodruff key engages with the slot in the oil pump inner rotor.

19 Apply thread-locking compound to the oil pump securing bolts, then refit the securing bolts, ensuring that the single longer bolt is located at the bottom of pump in the position noted before removal.

20 Tighten the bolts to the specified torque, in sequence, noting the different torque setting for the longer bolt **(see illustration)**.

21 If the original oil pump has been refitted, fit a new crankshaft oil seal with reference to Section 18.

22 Further refitting is a reversal of removal, bearing in mind the following points.

a) *Use new O-rings when reconnecting the turbocharger oil feed pipe and the oil cooler pipes to the pump housing.*

b) *Refit the upper and lower rear timing belt covers as described in Section 6.*

c) *Refill the engine with oil as described in Chapter 1B.*

17 Oil pump –
dismantling, inspection and reassembly

Note: *Loctite 573 sealant, or a suitable equivalent will be required to seal the pump cover plate to the pump body on reassembly. A new pressure relief valve threaded plug, and a new thermostatic valve plug sealing washer will be required. Thread-locking compound will be required to coat the threads of the pump cover plate securing screws, and the thermostatic valve plug.*

1 The oil pump can be dismantled and checked as described in the following paragraphs, but no spare parts are available, and if wear or damage is found, the pump must be renewed as a complete unit.

17.3b Unscrew the securing screws . . .

Dismantling

2 Remove the oil pump as described in Section 16.

3 Make alignment marks between the pump cover plate and the pump body (note that some pumps have a TOP mark stamped at the top of the cover plate), then unscrew the Torx screws and remove the pump cover plate **(see illustrations)**.

4 Lift out the oil pump rotors, noting the punched identification marks on the front faces of the rotors, which face away from the cover plate **(see illustration)**.

5 The oil pressure relief valve can be

17.4 Lift out the oil pump rotors

17.3c . . . and remove the pump cover plate

dismantled, if required, without disturbing the pump. If this is to be done with the pump in position and the engine still installed in the vehicle, it will first be necessary to jack up the front of the vehicle and remove the right-hand roadwheel to gain access to the valve (see *Jacking and Vehicle Support*).

6 To dismantle the valve, unscrew the threaded plug and recover the valve spring and plunger **(see illustrations)**. Discard the threaded plug – a new one must be used on refitting.

7 Similarly, the thermostatic valve (which diverts the oil to the oil cooler) can be dismantled as follows **(see illustrations)**.

17.6a Unscrew the oil pressure relief valve threaded plug (using an oil plug drain key and a spanner) . . .

17.6b . . . then recover the valve spring . . .

17.6c . . . and the plunger

17.7a Unscrew the thermostatic valve plug . . .

17.7b . . . then withdraw the spring and valve assembly

17.9a Measure the clearance between the outer rotor and the pump body . . .

17.9b . . . and between the tips of the inner and outer rotors

a) Unscrew the thermostatic valve plug. Recover the sealing washer and discard it.
b) Withdraw the spring and valve assembly from the oil pump body. Do not attempt to separate the spring from the valve.

Inspection

8 Inspect the rotors for obvious signs of wear or damage and renew if necessary. If the pump body or cover plate is scored or damaged, then the complete oil pump assembly must be renewed.
9 Using feeler blades of the appropriate thickness, measure the clearance between the outer rotor and the pump body, then between the tips of the inner and outer rotor **(see illustrations)**.
10 Using feeler blades and a straight-edge placed across the top of the pump body and the rotors, measure the rotor endfloat **(see illustration)**.

11 If any measurement is outside the specified limits, the complete pump assembly must be renewed.
12 If the pressure relief valve plunger is scored, or if it does not slide freely in the pump body bore, then it must be renewed. Check the free length of the relief valve spring, which should be as specified **(see illustration)**.
13 Check the thermostatic valve spring for distortion and corrosion, and check that the valve slides freely in the pump body bore. If there are any signs of damage or wear to the spring or valve, the spring and valve assembly must be renewed. Thoroughly clean the threads of the valve plug, and the plug threads in the oil pump body.

Reassembly

14 Clean all traces of sealant from the mating faces of the oil pump body and the cover

plate. Thoroughly clean the threads of the cover plate securing bolts, and ensure that the cover plate bolt threads in the pump body are clean and dry – **do not** use a tap to clean the threads.
15 Lubricate the pump rotors with clean engine oil and refit them to the pump body, ensuring that the punched marks on the faces of the rotors face away from the pump cover plate **(see illustration)**.
16 Apply a 1 mm bead of the specified sealant (see Note at the beginning of this Section) to the edge of the pump cover plate, then refit the cover plate, ensuring that the marks made on the cover plate and pump body before removal are aligned (where applicable, the TOP marking should on the cover plate should be at the top of the pump).
17 Coat the threads of the cover plate securing screws with thread-locking compound, then refit and tighten the screws.

17.10 Measuring the rotor endfloat

17.12 Measure the free length of the oil pressure relief valve spring

17.15 The punched marks on the faces of the rotors must face away from the pump cover plate

18 Check that the pump rotates freely, then prime it by injecting oil into its passages and rotating it. If a long time elapses before the pump is refitted to the engine, prime it again before installation.

19 Lubricate the oil pressure relief valve bore, and the spring and plunger with clean engine oil. Refit the oil pressure relief valve plunger, ensuring that it is the correct way up, then install the spring. Fit a new threaded plug, and tighten the plug securely.

20 Lubricate the thermostatic valve, spring and the valve bore in the oil pump body with clean engine oil.

21 Clamp the oil pump body in a vice, with the thermostatic valve bore facing vertically upwards. The valve bore must be as near vertical as possible.

22 Insert the valve and spring assembly into the valve bore in the oil pump body, ensuring that the assembly is positioned centrally in the bore. The valve will not seat correctly in the valve plug if it is not positioned centrally.

23 Fit a new sealing washer to the valve plug, then coat the threads of the plug with thread-locking compound, and screw the plug into position by hand, making sure that the valve is not displaced as the plug is tightened.

24 When the plug has been fully screwed down, tighten it to the specified torque.

25 Refit the oil pump as described in Section 16.

18 Crankshaft oil seals – renewal

Right-hand seal

1 Remove the timing belt as described in Section 7.

2 Remove the crankshaft sprocket.

3 Punch or drill two small holes opposite each other in the seal. Screw a self-tapping screw into each and pull on the screws with pliers to extract the seal.

4 Clean the seal housing and polish off any burrs or raised edges which may have caused the original seal to fail.

5 Using a suitable tubular drift, such as a socket, which bears only on the hard outer edge of the seal, drive the seal into position. To protect the seal lip, wrap a thin layer of insulating tape around the crankshaft.

Caution: Do not lubricate the seal recess, the seal lip, or the seal running surface on the shaft.

6 Remove all traces of the insulating tape. Fit the crankshaft sprocket – see Section 7.

Left-hand seal

Note: *The seal is integral with the oil seal housing – a complete new housing/seal assembly must be fitted.*

Note: *The following new parts are needed – oil seal/housing assembly, MG Rover sealant kit GUG 705963GM (for sump joint).*

18.11 Slide the protector sleeve, oil seal and housing assembly over the end of the crankshaft – viewed with engine removed

7 Remove the flywheel as described in Section 19.

8 Remove the sump as described in Section 15.

9 Unscrew the securing bolts, and remove the crankshaft oil seal housing.

10 Thoroughly clean the oil seal running surface on the crankshaft, the oil seal housing mating faces on the cylinder block, and the bolt and dowel holes in the cylinder block.

⚠️ *Warning: Do not lubricate the oil seal or the seal running surfaces on the crankshaft. The new oil seal/housing assembly will be supplied fitted with a seal protector. Do not separate the protector sleeve from the oil seal, and do not touch the oil seal lip. If the seal is inadvertently touched, it must not be fitted, as the coating applied to the seal during manufacture will be destroyed, and this may result in oil leakage.*

11 Carefully slide the seal protector sleeve, oil seal and housing assembly over the end of the crankshaft, taking care not to touch the seal lip **(see illustration)**.

12 Locate the housing against the cylinder block, noting that the oil seal protector will be pushed out as the housing/seal assembly is pushed into position.

13 Refit the housing securing bolts, and tighten them to the specified torque in order **(see illustration)**.

14 Refit the sump as described in Section 15.

15 Refit the flywheel as described in Section 19.

19.3 Unscrewing a flywheel bolt – note tool (arrowed) to prevent flywheel from turning

18.13 Crankshaft rear oil seal housing bolt tightening sequence

19 Flywheel – removal, inspection and refitting

Note: *New flywheel retaining bolts must be used on refitting.*

Removal

1 Remove the clutch assembly as described in Chapter 6.

2 If not already done, turn the crankshaft until the locking pin can be inserted into the flywheel, as described in Section 3. Additionally, lock the flywheel by bolting a suitable tool to the transmission mounting plate, to engage with the flywheel ring gear teeth.

3 Slacken and remove the flywheel retaining bolts and discard them **(see illustration)**. The bolts must be renewed whenever they are disturbed.

4 Remove the flywheel **(see illustration)**. Do not drop it, as it is very heavy.

Inspection

5 If the flywheel clutch mating surface is deeply scored, cracked or otherwise damaged, then the flywheel must be renewed, unless it is possible to have it surface ground. Seek the advice of a Rover dealer or engine reconditioning specialist.

6 If the ring gear is badly worn or has missing teeth, then it must be renewed. This job is best left to a Rover dealer or engine reconditioning specialist. The temperature to

19.4 Lifting off the flywheel

19.8 Fit new flywheel securing bolts

19.9a Tighten the flywheel bolts to the specified torque . . .

19.9b . . . then through the specified angle

which the new ring gear must be heated for installation (350°C – shown by an even light blue colour) is critical and, if not done accurately, the hardness of the teeth will be destroyed.

Refitting

7 Clean the mating surfaces of the flywheel and crankshaft. Clean any remaining adhesive from the threads of the crankshaft threaded holes by carefully using a suitable tap.

8 Position the flywheel over the locating dowel in the end of the crankshaft, press it into place and fit six **new** bolts **(see illustration)**.

9 Lock the flywheel using the method employed on dismantling then, working in a diagonal sequence, progressively tighten the retaining bolts to the specified torque wrench setting in the two stages given **(see illustrations)**.

10 Refit the clutch assembly as described in Chapter 6.

---

20 Engine/transmission mountings – inspection, removal and refitting

Inspection

Note: *Normally, mountings will need renewing only if the rubber has hardened or cracked, or separated from the metal backing. Dependent upon the fault, such conditions may allow excess engine movement, leading to an impression of rough running, knocking or bumping.*

Note: *The mountings can be visually checked for rubber deterioration, and separation can be checked by levering with a pry bar between the rubber and metal backing. If any fault is found, the mounting must be renewed.*

Engine lower steady bar

Removal

1 Apply the handbrake, then jack up the front of the vehicle and support securely on axle stands (see *Jacking and Vehicle Support*).

2 Remove the engine undershield, with reference to Chapter 11 if necessary.

3 Working under the vehicle, unscrew the through-bolt securing the engine steady bar to the subframe **(see illustration)**.

4 Unscrew the through-bolt securing the steady bar to the bracket on the sump, then withdraw the steady bar **(see illustration)**.

Refitting

5 Refitting is a reversal of removal, but tighten the through-bolts to the specified torque.

Left-hand mounting

Removal

6 Disconnect the battery earth lead, and then the battery positive lead.

7 Remove the battery clamp, and lift out the battery.

8 Remove two bolts securing the engine control module (ECM) clamp to the battery tray. Tie the ECM/clamp clear of the work area

9 Remove the air cleaner – see Chapter 4B.

10 Remove three bolts securing the base of the battery tray, and slacken three bolts under the tray.

11 Where applicable, release the ABS fuse holder from the battery tray, and remove the tray **(see illustration)**.

12 Apply the handbrake, chock the rear roadwheels, then jack up the front of the car and support it on axle stands (see *Jacking and Vehicle Support*).

13 Remove the engine undertray – two nuts at rear and two bolts at front.

14 Position a trolley jack under the transmission, with a wooden block between the jack head and transmission housing. Raise the jack to just take the weight of the engine/transmission.

15 Remove nut cover and two nuts, and remove outer part of torsion link **(see illustration)**.

16 Remove the through-bolt securing the mounting to the body bracket.

17 Remove the two bolts securing the

20.3 Unscrew the through-bolt (arrowed) securing the engine steady bar to the subframe

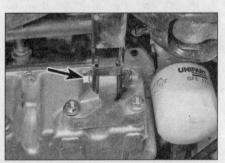

20.4 Unscrew the through-bolt (arrowed) securing the engine steady bar to the sump

20.11 Remove battery tray

20.15 Remove outer part of torsion link and mounting through-bolt

20.23 Remove steady to mounting bracket through-bolt

20.24a Remove the steady to body bracket through-bolt

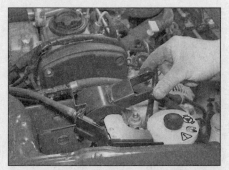

20.24b Remove the steady bar

20.25a Remove the restraint bar nuts

20.25b Remove the restraint bar

20.26 Remove the mounting bracket to mounting nut

mounting to the transmission housing, and remove the mounting.

Refitting

18 Refitting is a reversal of the removal procedure noting:

Use a torque wrench to tighten the bolts to the specified torque.

Right-hand mounting

Removal

19 Disconnect the battery earth lead.
20 Apply the handbrake, chock the rear roadwheels, then jack up the front of the car and support it on axle stands (see *Jacking and Vehicle Support*). Remove the right hand roadwheel.
21 Remove the engine undertray – two nuts at rear and two bolts at front.
22 Position a trolley jack under the sump,

with a wooden block between the jack head and sump. Raise the jack to just take the weight of the engine/transmission.
23 Remove the through-bolt securing the upper steady bar to the mounting bracket **(see illustration)**.
24 Remove the through-bolt securing the upper steady to the body bracket, and remove the steady bar **(see illustrations)**.
25 Remove the two nuts securing the restraint bar, and remove the bar **(see illustrations)**.
26 Remove the nut securing the mounting bracket to the mounting **(see illustration)**.
27 Remove the three bolts securing the mounting bracket to the engine, and remove the bracket **(see illustrations)**.
28 Remove the remaining bolt securing the mounting to the body, and remove the mounting.

Refitting

29 Refit is a reversal of the removal procedure, noting:

First fit the mounting to the body, and loosely tighten the nut.
Fit and align the mounting bracket, restraint bar and steady bar, and fit the bolts and nuts.
Use a torque wrench to tighten all bolts and nuts to the specified torque.

21 Engine oil cooler – removal and refitting

General

1 The engine coolant thermostat is located in the detachable lower housing of the cooler assembly **(see illustration)**.

20.27a Remove three bracket to engine bolts

20.27b Remove the mounting

21.1 Oil cooler attachment and connections

21.7 Oil cooler location

Removal

Note: *The following new parts are needed – oil pipe O-rings.*

2 Remove the radiator – see Chapter 3.

3 Slacken the clips and disconnect the following hoses:
Cooler bottom hose.
Cooler top hose.
Coolant pump hose.
Hoses from coolant rails.

4 Remove the bolt and oil pipe clamp.

5 Position a container under the cooler to collect spilled oil.

6 Slacken the union nuts and disconnect the cooler oil pipes. Discard the O-rings.

7 Remove three bolts, and remove the cooler assembly **(see illustration)**.

Refitting

8 Refitting is a reversal of the removal procedure, noting:
Fit new O-rings to the oil pipes.
Use a torque wrench to tighten the bolts and nuts to the specified torque.
Check/top-up the engine oil level.

22 Auxiliary drivebelt tensioner – removal and refitting

Removal

1 Remove the power steering drivebelt, as described in Chapter 10.

2 Remove the centre bolt securing the tensioner to the mounting bracket, and remove the tensioner.

Refitting

3 Locate the tensioner on the dowel then fit and tighten the centre bolt to the specified torque.

4 Refit the drivebelt.

Chapter 2 Part C:
Petrol engine removal and overhaul procedures

Contents

Degrees of difficulty

| Easy, suitable for novice with little experience | Fairly easy, suitable for beginner with some experience | Fairly difficult, suitable for competent DIY mechanic 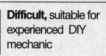 | Difficult, suitable for experienced DIY mechanic | Very difficult, suitable for expert DIY or professional |

Specifications

Cylinder block/crankcase

Material	Aluminium alloy
Cylinder liner bore diameter – 65 mm from top of bore:	
1.1 and 1.4 litre engines:	
Standard – grade A (Red)	74.970 to 74.985 mm
Standard – grade B (Blue)	74.986 to 75.000 mm
1.6 and 1.8 litre engines:	
Standard – grade A (Red)	80.000 to 80.015 mm
Standard – grade B (Blue)	80.016 to 80.030 mm

Crankshaft

Number of main bearings	5
Main bearing journal diameter	47.986 to 48.007 mm
Main bearing journal sizes:	
Grade 1	48.000 to 48.007 mm
Grade 2	47.993 to 48.000 mm
Grade 3	47.986 to 47.993 mm
Big-end journal diameter:	
1.1, 1.4 and 1.6 litre engines	42.986 to 43.007 mm
1.8 litre engine	47.986 to 48.007 mm
Big-end journal size grades:	
1.1, 1.4 and 1.6 litre engines:	
Grade A	43.000 to 43.007 mm
Grade B	42.993 to 43.000 mm
Grade C	42.986 to 42.993 mm
1.8 litre engine:	
Grade A	48.000 to 48.007 mm
Grade B	47.993 to 48.000 mm
Grade C	47.986 to 47.993 mm
Main bearing and big-end bearing journal maximum ovality	0.010 mm
Main bearing and big-end bearing running clearance	0.021 to 0.049 mm
Crankshaft endfloat:	
Standard	0.10 to 0.25 mm
Service limit	0.34 mm
Thrustwasher thickness	2.61 to 2.65 mm

Pistons and piston rings

Piston diameter:
  1.1 and 1.4 litre engines:
    Grade A . . . . 74.940 to 74.955 mm
    Grade B . . . . 74.956 to 74.970 mm
  1.6 and 1.8 litre engines:
    Grade A . . . . 79.975 to 79.990 mm
    Grade B . . . . 79.991 to 80.005 mm
Piston-to-bore clearance:
  1.1 and 1.4 litre engines . . . . 0.015 to 0.045 mm
  1.6 and 1.8 litre engines . . . . 0.010 to 0.040 mm
Piston ring end gaps (fitted 20 mm from top of bore):
  1.1 and 1.4 litre engines:
    Top compression ring . . . . 0.17 to 0.37 mm
    Second compression ring . . . . 0.37 to 0.57 mm
    Oil control ring . . . . 0.15 to 0.40 mm
  1.6 and 1.8 litre engines:
    Top compression ring . . . . 0.20 to 0.35 mm
    Second compression ring . . . . 0.28 to 0.48 mm
    Oil control ring . . . . 0.15 to 0.40 mm
Piston ring-to-groove clearance:
  1.1 and 1.4 litre engines:
    Top compression ring . . . . 0.040 to 0.080 mm
    Second compression ring . . . . 0.030 to 0.062 mm
    Oil control ring – all models . . . . 0.044 to 0.055 mm
  1.6 and 1.8 litre engines:
    Top compression ring . . . . 0.040 to 0.072 mm
    Second compression ring . . . . 0.030 to 0.062 mm
    Oil control ring . . . . 0.010 to 0.180 mm

Cylinder head

Material . . . . Aluminium alloy
Height . . . . 118.95 to 119.05 mm
Reface limit . . . . 0.20 mm
Maximum acceptable gasket face distortion . . . . 0.05 mm
Valve seat angle . . . . 45°
Valve seat width:
  Inlet . . . . 1.6 mm
  Exhaust . . . . 1.2 mm

Valves

Stem diameter:
  Inlet . . . . 5.952 to 5.967 mm
  Exhaust . . . . 5.947 to 5.962 mm
Guide inside diameter . . . . 6.000 to 6.025 mm
Stem-to-guide clearance:
  Inlet:
    Standard . . . . 0.033 to 0.063 mm
    Service limit . . . . 0.110 mm
  Exhaust:
    Standard . . . . 0.038 to 0.078 mm
    Service limit . . . . 0.110 mm
Valve spring free length . . . . 50.0 mm
Valve guide fitted height . . . . 6.0 mm
Valve stem installed height:
  New . . . . 38.93 to 39.84 mm
  Service limit . . . . 40.10 mm

Torque wrench settings

Refer to Part A of this Chapter

1 General information

Included in this part of the Chapter are details of removing the engine/transmission unit from the vehicle and general overhaul procedures for the cylinder head, cylinder block/crankcase and all other engine internal components.

The information given ranges from advice concerning preparation for an overhaul and the purchase of new parts to detailed step-by-step procedures covering removal, inspection, renovation and refitting of engine internal components.

After Section 6, all instructions are based on the assumption that the engine has been removed from the vehicle. For information concerning in-car engine repair, as well as the removal and refitting of those external components necessary for full overhaul, refer to Part A of this Chapter and to Section 6. Ignore any preliminary dismantling operations described in Part A that are no longer relevant once the engine has been removed from the vehicle.

2 Engine overhaul –
general information

It is not always easy to determine when, or if, an engine should be completely overhauled, as a number of factors must be considered.

High mileage is not necessarily an indication that an overhaul is needed, while low mileage does not preclude the need for an overhaul. Frequency of servicing is probably the most important consideration. An engine which has had regular and frequent oil and filter changes, as well as other required maintenance, should give many thousands of miles of reliable service. Conversely, a neglected engine may require an overhaul very early in its life. If a complete service does not remedy any problems, major mechanical work is the only solution.

Excessive oil consumption is an indication that piston rings, valve seals and/or valve guides are in need of attention. Make sure that oil leaks are not responsible before deciding that the rings and/or guides are worn. Perform a compression test to determine the likely cause of the problem (see Part A of this Chapter).

Check the oil pressure with a gauge fitted in place of the oil pressure switch and compare it with that specified (see Part A Specifications). If it is extremely low, the main and big-end bearings and/or the oil pump are probably worn out.

Loss of power, rough running, knocking or metallic engine noises, excessive valve gear noise and high fuel consumption may also point to the need for an overhaul, especially if they are all present at the same time.

An engine overhaul involves restoring all internal parts to the specification of a new engine. During an overhaul, the cylinder liners, the pistons and the piston rings are renewed. New main and big-end bearings are generally fitted and, if necessary, the crankshaft may be renewed to restore the journals. The valves are serviced as well, since they are usually in less than perfect condition at this point. While the engine is being overhauled, other components, such as the distributor (where fitted), starter and alternator, can be overhauled as well. The end result should be an as-new engine that will give many trouble-free miles.

Critical cooling system components such as the hoses, thermostat and coolant pump should be renewed when an engine is overhauled. The radiator should be checked carefully to ensure that it is not clogged or leaking. Also it is a good idea to renew the oil pump whenever the engine is overhauled.

Before beginning the engine overhaul, read through the entire procedure to familiarise yourself with the scope and requirements of the job. Overhauling an engine is not difficult if you follow carefully all of the instructions, have the necessary tools and equipment and pay close attention to all specifications. However, it can be time-consuming. Plan on the vehicle being off the road for a minimum of two weeks, especially if parts must be taken to an engineering works for repair or reconditioning. Check on the availability of parts and make sure that any necessary special tools and equipment are obtained in advance. Most work can be done with typical hand tools, although a number of precision measuring tools are required for inspecting parts to determine if they must be renewed. Often the engineering works will handle the inspection of parts and offer advice concerning reconditioning and renewal.

Always wait until the engine has been completely dismantled and all components, especially the cylinder block/crankcase, the cylinder liners and the crankshaft have been inspected before deciding what service and repair operations must be performed by an engineering works. Since the condition of these components will be the major factor to consider when determining whether to overhaul the original engine or buy a reconditioned unit, do not purchase parts or have overhaul work done on other components until they have been thoroughly inspected. As a general rule, time is the primary cost of an overhaul, so it does not pay to fit worn or substandard parts.

As a final note, to ensure maximum life and minimum trouble from a reconditioned engine, everything must be assembled with care in a spotlessly clean environment.

3 Engine/transmission removal –
methods and precautions

If you have decided that the engine must be removed for overhaul or major repair work, several preliminary steps should be taken.

Locating a suitable place to work is extremely important. Adequate work space, along with storage space for the vehicle, will be needed. If a shop or garage is not available, at the very least a flat, level, clean work surface is required.

Cleaning the engine compartment and engine/transmission before beginning the removal procedure will help keep things clean and organised.

An engine hoist or A-frame will also be necessary. Make sure the equipment is rated in excess of the combined weight of the engine and transmission. Safety is of primary importance, considering the potential hazards involved in lifting the engine/transmission unit out of the vehicle. The engine/transmission unit is removed by lifting it out from above the engine compartment.

If the engine/transmission unit is being removed by a novice, a helper should be available. Advice and aid from someone more experienced would also be helpful. There are many instances when one person cannot simultaneously perform all of the operations required when lifting the unit out of the vehicle.

Plan the operation ahead of time. Before starting work, arrange for the hire of or obtain all of the tools and equipment you will need. Some of the equipment necessary to perform engine/transmission removal and installation safely and with relative ease are (in addition to an engine hoist) a heavy duty trolley jack, complete sets of spanners and sockets as described at the rear of this Manual, wooden blocks and plenty of rags and cleaning solvent for mopping-up spilled oil, coolant and fuel. If the hoist must be hired, make sure that you arrange for it in advance and perform all of the operations possible without it beforehand. This will save you money and time.

Plan for the vehicle to be out of use for quite a while. An engineering works will be required to perform some of the work which the do-it-yourselfer cannot accomplish without special equipment. These places often have a busy schedule, so it would be a good idea to consult them before removing the engine in order to accurately estimate the amount of time required to rebuild or repair components that may need work.

Always be extremely careful when removing and refitting the engine/transmission unit. Serious injury can result from careless actions. Plan ahead, take your time and a job of this nature, although major, can be accomplished successfully.

4.3 Disconnect ECM multi-plug

4.5 Disconnect multi-plug from fusebox

4.11 Remove engine steady bar

4 Engine/transmission – removal

Caution: Read the notes in Section 3 – 'Engine/transmission removal – methods and precautions'.

Note: The following new parts are needed: power steering pump outlet hose O-ring and exhaust front pipe gasket. On 1.8 models only: gear selector rod roll-pin.

Note: Two lifting brackets, to bolt to the engine, are needed. These can be made from steel plate, and must be strong enough to carry the weight of the engine/transmission assembly. One bracket is to be bolted to the tapped hole adjacent to the dipstick tube, and the other is be bolted to the tapped holes for the exhaust camshaft rear cover plate.

Note: As they are disconnected, make a note or sketch of the position, route and clipping of all wires, harnesses, pipes and hoses.

1 Disconnect both battery leads – earth lead first. Remove the battery clamp, and lift out the battery.

2 Remove the air cleaner assembly – see Chapter 4A.

3 Remove two bolts securing the engine control module (ECM) to the battery tray. Disconnect the main engine harness multi-plug from the ECM. Seal the ECM and multi-plug in plastic bags, and tie clear of the work area **(see illustration)**.

4 Where applicable, release the ABS fuse holder from the battery tray. Remove three bolts from the base of the battery tray, and slacken three bolts under the tray. Lift out the tray.

5 Open the engine compartment fusebox. Remove the screw securing the positive lead to the fusebox, and disconnect the multi-plug in the fusebox **(see illustration)**.

6 Release two multi-plugs from the bracket adjacent to the charcoal canister on the bulkhead. Disconnect the engine harness multi-plugs from the main harness, and remove the engine harness from the bracket. Tie the engine harness across the top of the engine.

7 Apply the handbrake, chock the rear roadwheels, then jack up the front of the car and support it on axle stands (see Jacking and Vehicle Support). Remove the right hand front roadwheel.

8 Drain the engine oil and coolant – see Chapter 1A.

9 Drain the transmission oil – see Chapter 7.

10 Remove the bolt securing the negative lead to the starter motor.

11 Remove two bolts attaching the engine left hand steady bar to the engine bracket and engine mounting, and remove the steady bar **(see illustration)**.

12 Where fitted disconnect the cylindrical electrical connector adjacent to the left-hand engine mounting – the connector is in the lead going down to the roadwheel sensor at the right-hand front wheel **(see illustration)**.

13 Disconnect the clutch inner cable from the clutch release lever. Release the outer cable from the abutment bracket, and tie clear of the work area **(see illustration)**.

14 Slacken the clips and disconnect the following hoses:

*Radiator bottom hose from coolant rail.
Radiator top hose from outlet elbow.
Heater return hose from outlet elbow.
Expansion tank hose from inlet manifold.
Coolant hose from thermostat housing.
Heater hose from coolant rail.*

15 Release the heater hose from two clips on the coolant rail and engine harness.

16 Remove two nuts securing the exhaust pipe front section to the exhaust manifold, and discard the gasket.

17 Pack cloths around the fuel pipe connections. Depress the quick-release connectors, and disconnect the pipes **(see illustration)**.

Caution: Plug the pipe connections.

18 Release the throttle outer cable nut from the abutment bracket, and release the inner cable from the cam. Release the cable from the clip on the inlet manifold **(see illustration)**.

4.12 Disconnect cylindrical connector

4.13 Disconnect clutch cable

4.17 Disconnect fuel pipes

4.18 Release throttle cable

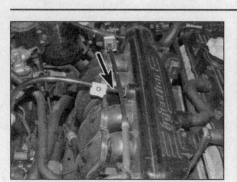

4.19 Disconnect brake servo pipe

4.26 Remove steady bar through-bolt

4.30 Release gear selector balljoints

19 Depress the collar on the quick-release connector, and disconnect the brake servo vacuum pipe from the inlet manifold (see illustration).

Air conditioned models

20 Remove the bolt securing the air conditioning pipe to the support bracket.
21 Fit a 13 mm spanner onto the hexagon on the belt tensioner, and rotate the spanner fully clockwise. To lock in this position, fit a suitable pin – not exceeding 3 mm diameter – into the tensioner backplate
22 Release the auxiliary drivebelt from the alternator and compressor.
23 Disconnect the air conditioning compressor multi-plug.
24 Remove three bolts securing the compressor, release the compressor, and tie clear of the work area.

All models

25 Disconnect both driveshafts from the transmission – see Chapter 8.
Caution: Tie-up the driveshafts to avoid strain on the outer joints, and to keep clear the area under the engine and transmission.
26 Slacken the through-bolt securing the engine/transmission lower steady bar to the subframe. Remove the through-bolt securing the steady bar to the sump bracket, and move the bar away from the engine (see illustration).
27 Position a container under the power steering pump.
28 Slacken the clip securing the inlet hose to the pump, and disconnect the hose.
29 Remove the bolt securing the outlet hose clamp to the bracket, and disconnect the outlet hose. Discard the O-ring
Caution: Plug the hose and pump connections.

1.1, 1.4 and 1.6 engines

30 Using a lever, or flat-blade screwdriver, release the balljoints from the gear selector lever, and the gearchange lever (see illustration).

1.8 engines

31 Remove the metal clip from the gear selector rod, and drive out the roll-pin (see illustration).
32 Remove the bolt securing the gearchange

steady bar to the gearbox, and release the steady bar and washers (see illustration).

All engines

33 Remove two bolts securing the exhaust camshaft rear cover plate to the cylinder head, and remove the plate. Use the two bolts to attach the manufactured lifting bracket. Tighten the bolt securely (see illustration).
34 Attach the other bracket to the side of the cylinder head, using the tapped hole adjacent to the dipstick tube. Tighten the bolt securely (see illustration).
35 Attach the lifting equipment to the lifting brackets, and connect to the hoist. Raise the hoist to just take the weight of the engine/transmission assembly.
36 Remove the engine right-hand and left-hand mountings – see part A of this Chapter.
37 Make a final check to ensure that all pipes, hoses, and cables, etc, have been

disconnected from the engine/transmission assembly, and tied clear of the work area.
38 With the aid of an assistant, raise the hoist slightly, and tilt the engine/transmission assembly to lower the gearbox. Taking care not to damage components in the engine bay, carefully raise the engine/transmission, and manoeuvre from the engine bay. Lower the assembly to the ground, and support on wooden blocks.

5 Engine/transmission – refitting

1 Fit the lifting equipment to the lifting brackets, and attach to the hoist.
2 With the aid of an assistant, raise the engine/transmission, and manoeuvre into the engine bay.

4.31 Drive out the roll-pin

4.32 Release gearchange steady bar

4.33 Remove exhaust camshaft cover plate – attach lifting bracket

4.34 Attach bracket to side of cylinder head

3 Further refitting is a reversal of the removal procedure, noting the following:

Fit both engine mountings and both steady bars – see part A of this Chapter.

Tighten all bolts sufficiently to secure the mountings and steady bars – but not to final tightness. Release the hoist and lifting equipment.

When the engine is settled on the mountings, use a torque wrench to tighten all mounting and steady bar bolts to the specified torque.

Use a torque wrench to tighten all nuts and bolts to the specified torque.

Fit a new O-ring the power steering outlet hose – lubricate the O-ring with PAS fluid before connecting the hose.

Fit a new gasket to the exhaust pipe front section.

Ensure that all cables and pipes are correctly connected, clipped and routed, as identified before removal.

Fill the engine with new oil, and fill the cooling system with a 50/50 mix of water and antifreeze. If drained, fill the gearbox with new oil – see Chapter 7.

Top-up and bleed the power steering system – see Chapter 10.

Check/adjust the throttle cable – see Chapter 4A.

6 Engine overhaul – dismantling sequence

Note: *When removing external components from the engine, pay close attention to details that may be helpful or important during refitting. Note the fitted position of gaskets, seals, spacers, pins, washers, bolts and other small items.*

1 It is much easier to work on the engine if it is mounted on a portable engine stand. These stands can often be hired from a tool hire shop. Before the engine is mounted on a stand, the flywheel should be removed so that the stand bolts can be tightened into the end of the cylinder block/crankcase (**not** the main bearing ladder).

2 If a stand is not available, it is possible to dismantle the engine with it blocked up on a sturdy workbench or on the floor. Be extra careful not to tip or drop the engine when working without a stand.

3 If you are going to obtain a reconditioned engine, all external components must be removed for transfer to the new engine (just as if you are doing a complete engine overhaul yourself). These components include the following:

a) Alternator mounting brackets.
b) Power steering pump and air conditioning compressor brackets (where fitted).
c) HT leads and spark plugs, and, on early engines, distributor components.
d) Thermostat and housing, coolant rail, coolant outlet elbow.
e) Dipstick tube.
f) Fuel injection system components.
g) All electrical switches and sensors.
h) Inlet and exhaust manifolds.
i) Oil filter.
j) Engine mountings.
k) Flywheel.

4 If you are obtaining a short motor (which consists of the engine cylinder block/crankcase and main bearing ladder, crankshaft, pistons and connecting rods all assembled), then the cylinder head, sump, oil pump, and timing belt will have to be removed also.

5 If you are planning a complete overhaul, the engine can be dismantled and the internal components removed in the following order:

a) Inlet and exhaust manifolds.
b) Timing belt, sprockets, tensioner and timing belt inner cover.
c) Cylinder head.
d) Flywheel.
e) Sump.
f) Oil pump.
g) Piston/connecting rod assemblies.
h) Crankshaft.

6 Before beginning the dismantling and overhaul procedures, make sure that you have all of the correct tools necessary.

7 Cylinder head – dismantling

Note: *New and reconditioned cylinder heads are available from the manufacturer and from engine overhaul specialists. Due to the fact that some specialist tools are required for dismantling and inspection, and new components may not be readily available, it may be more practical and economical for the home mechanic to purchase a reconditioned head rather than dismantle, inspect and recondition the original. A valve spring compressor tool will be required for this operation.*

1 With the cylinder head removed, if not already done, remove the inlet manifold as described in Chapter 4A.

2 Remove the camshaft(s) and hydraulic tappets, as described in Part A of this Chapter.

3 Using a valve spring compressor tool, compress each valve spring in turn until the split collets can be removed. Release the compressor and lift off the spring retainer and spring, then use a pair of pliers to extract the spring lower seat/stem seal (**see illustrations**).

4 Withdraw the valve through the combustion chamber.

5 It is essential that each valve is stored together with its collets, retainer and spring, and that all valves are kept in their correct sequence, unless they are so badly worn that they are to be renewed. If they are going to be kept and used again, place each valve assembly in a labelled polythene bag or similar small container (**see illustration**). Note that No 1 valve is nearest to the timing belt end of the engine. Label the valves No 1 inlet, No 1 exhaust, etc, to avoid confusion.

8 Cylinder head and valves – cleaning and inspection

Note: *If the engine has been severely overheated, it is best to assume that the cylinder head is warped and to check carefully for signs of this.*

Note: *Be sure to perform all the following inspection procedures before concluding that the services of a machine shop or engine overhaul specialist are required. Make a list of all items that require attention.*

1 Thorough cleaning of the cylinder head and valve components, followed by a detailed

7.3a Using a valve spring compressor to release the split collets

7.3b Extracting the spring lower seat/stem seal

7.5 Use a labelled plastic bag to keep together and identify the valve components

8.6a Checking a cylinder head gasket surface for distortion

8.6b Check the cylinder head gasket surface for distortion along the paths shown

8.7 Check valve seat wear by measuring valve stem installed height (A)

inspection, will enable you to decide how much valve service work must be carried out during the engine overhaul.

Cleaning

2 Scrape away all traces of old gasket material and sealing compound from the cylinder head.

3 Scrape away all carbon from the combustion chambers and ports, then wash the cylinder head thoroughly with paraffin or a suitable solvent.

4 Scrape off any heavy carbon deposits that may have formed on the valves, then use a power-operated wire brush to remove deposits from the valve heads and stems.

Inspection

Cylinder head

5 Inspect the head very carefully for cracks, evidence of coolant leakage and other damage. If cracks are found, a new cylinder head should be obtained.

6 Use a straight-edge and feeler blade to check that the cylinder head surface is not distorted (see illustrations). If it is, it may be possible to resurface it, provided that the specified reface limit is not exceeded in so doing, or that the cylinder head is not reduced to less than the specified height.

7 Examine the valve seats in each of the combustion chambers. If they are severely pitted, cracked or burned, then they will need to be renewed or recut by an engine overhaul specialist. If they are only slightly pitted, this can be removed by grinding-in the valve heads and seats with fine valve-grinding compound as described below. To check for excessive wear, refit each valve and measure the installed height of the stem tip above the cylinder head upper surface (see illustration). If the measurement is above the specified limit, repeat the test using a new valve. If the measurement is still excessive, renew the seat.

8 If the valve guides are worn, indicated by a side-to-side motion of the valve, new guides must be fitted. Measure the diameter of the existing valve stems (see below) and the bore of the guides, then calculate the clearance and compare the result with the specified value. If the clearance is excessive, renew the valves or guides as necessary.

9 Valve guides should be renewed by an engine overhaul specialist.

10 If the valve seats are to be recut, this must be done only after the guides have been renewed.

Valves

11 Examine the head of each valve for pitting, burning, cracks and general wear, then check the valve stem for scoring and wear ridges. Rotate the valve and check for any obvious indication that it is bent. Look for pits and excessive wear on the tip of each valve stem. Renew any valve that shows any such signs of wear or damage.

12 If the valve appears satisfactory at this stage, measure the valve stem diameter at several points by using a micrometer (see illustration). Any significant difference in the readings obtained indicates wear of the valve stem. Should any of these conditions be apparent, the valve(s) must be renewed.

13 If the valves are in satisfactory condition they should be ground (lapped) into their respective seats to ensure a smooth gas-tight seal. If the seat is only lightly pitted, or if it has been recut, fine grinding compound only should be used to produce the required finish. Coarse valve-grinding compound should not be used unless a seat is badly burned or deeply pitted. If this is the case, the cylinder head and valves should be inspected by an expert to decide whether seat recutting or even the renewal of the valve or seat insert is required.

14 Valve grinding is carried out as follows. Place the cylinder head upside down on a bench.

15 Smear a trace of (the appropriate grade of) valve-grinding compound on the seat face and press a suction grinding tool onto the valve head. With a semi-rotary action, grind the valve head to its seat, lifting the valve occasionally to redistribute the grinding compound. A light spring placed under the valve head will greatly ease this operation.

16 If coarse grinding compound is being used, work only until a dull, matt even surface is produced on both the valve seat and the valve, then wipe off the used compound and repeat the process with fine compound. When a smooth unbroken ring of light grey matt finish is produced on both the valve and seat, the grinding operation is complete. Do not grind in the valves any further than absolutely necessary, or the seat will be prematurely sunk into the cylinder head.

17 To check that the seat has not been over-ground, measure the valve stem installed height, as described in paragraph 7.

18 When all the valves have been ground-in, carefully wash off all traces of grinding compound using paraffin or a suitable solvent.

Valve components

19 Examine the valve springs for signs of damage and discoloration and also measure their free length using vernier calipers or by comparing each existing spring with a new component (see illustration).

8.12 Measuring valve stem diameter

8.19 Measuring valve spring free-length

9.2 Using a socket to fit a valve stem seal

10.5a Dipstick tube retaining bolts (arrowed)

20 Stand each spring on a flat surface and check it for squareness. If any of the springs are damaged, distorted or have lost their tension, then obtain a complete new set of springs.

9 Cylinder head – reassembly

Note: *A valve spring compressor tool will be required for this operation. New valve spring lower seat/stem oil seals will be required.*

1 Lubricate the valve stems with clean engine oil and insert each valve into its original location. If new valves are being fitted, insert them into the locations to which they have been ground.
2 Working on the first valve, dip the **new** spring lower seat/stem seal in clean engine oil then carefully locate it over the valve and onto the guide. Take care not to damage the seal as it is passed over the valve stem. Use a suitable socket or metal tube to press the seal firmly onto the guide **(see illustration)**.
3 Locate the spring on the seat, followed by the spring retainer.
4 Compress the valve spring and locate the split collets in the recess in the valve stem. Use a little grease to hold the collets in place. Release the compressor, then repeat the procedure on the remaining valves.
5 With all the valves installed, rest the cylinder head on wooden blocks or stands (**do not** rest the head flat on a bench) and, using a hammer and interposed block of wood, tap

10.7 Removing the oil rail

the end of each valve stem to settle the components.
6 Refit the hydraulic tappets and camshaft(s) as described in Part A of this Chapter.

10 Piston/connecting rod assembly – removal

Note: *Due to the design of the engine, it will become very difficult, almost impossible, to turn the crankshaft once the cylinder head bolts have been slackened. The manufacturer accordingly states that the crankshaft will be 'tight' and should not be rotated more than absolutely necessary once the head has been removed. If the crankshaft cannot be rotated, then it must be removed for overhaul work to proceed. With this in mind, during any servicing or overhaul work the crankshaft must always be rotated to the desired position **before** the bolts are disturbed. Whenever the piston/connecting rod assemblies are removed, the cylinder liners should be removed and resealed as a precaution against leakage after reassembly (see Section 13).*

Removal

Without removing crankshaft

1 Remove the timing belt, the camshaft sprocket(s) and timing belt tensioner, and the timing belt rear cover, as described in Part A of this Chapter.
2 Remove the camshaft(s) and hydraulic tappets, as described in Part A of this Chapter.

10.8 Mark the big-end bearing caps before removal – No 4 cylinder cap shown

3 If not already done, rotate the crankshaft (if necessary temporarily refit the crankshaft pulley bolt and use a spanner or socket to turn the crankshaft) through a quarter-turn clockwise, until Nos 1 and 4 cylinder pistons are at TDC (No 1 piston should have been positioned 90° BTDC to remove the timing belt).
4 Remove the cylinder head, as described in Part A of this Chapter. The crankshaft cannot now be rotated. Note that there is no need to fit cylinder liner clamps, as the cylinder liners should be removed and resealed whenever the piston/connecting rod assemblies are removed.
5 Slacken and remove the two dipstick tube retaining bolts and remove the tube from the cylinder block/crankcase **(see illustrations)**.
6 Remove the sump and unbolt the oil pump pick-up/strainer pipe from the oil rail, as described in Part A of this Chapter.
7 Unscrew the two retaining nuts and remove the oil rail **(see illustration)**.
8 Using a hammer and centre punch, paint or similar, mark each connecting rod big-end bearing cap with its respective cylinder number on the flat, machined surface provided. If the engine has been dismantled before, note carefully any identifying marks made previously **(see illustration)**. Note that No 1 cylinder is at the timing belt end of the engine.
9 Unscrew and remove the No 2 cylinder big-end bearing cap bolts and withdraw the cap, complete with bearing shell, from the connecting rod. If only the bearing shells are being attended to, push the connecting rod up and off the crankpin, ensuring that the connecting rod big-ends do not mark the cylinder bore walls, then remove the upper bearing shell. Keep the cap, bolts and (if they are to be refitted) the bearing shells together in their correct sequence. Repeat the procedure to disconnect No 3 cylinder big-end.
10 With Nos 2 and 3 cylinder big-ends disconnected, repeat the procedure (exercising great care to prevent damage to any of the components) to disconnect Nos 1 and 4 cylinder big-ends.
11 Remove the ridge of carbon from the top of each cylinder bore. Push each piston/connecting rod assembly up and remove it from the top of the bore, ensuring that the connecting rod big-ends do not mark the cylinder bore walls.
12 Note that the number previously stamped on each bearing cap should match the cylinder number stamped (by the manufacturers) on each connecting rod, which can be read once the connecting rod has been removed. If the mark stamped on any connecting rod does not match its correct cylinder, mark or label the connecting rod immediately to avoid confusion, so that each piston/connecting rod assembly can be refitted to its original bore.

10.5b Engine bottom end components

1 Oil pump	37 Crankshaft
2 Gasket	38 Dowel
3 Screw	39 Main bearing shells
4 Screw	40 Thrustwashers
5 Oil seal	41 Crankshaft oil seal
6 Engine oil level dipstick	42 Flywheel (with reluctor ring)
7 Dipstick tube	43 Flywheel bolt
8 Screw	44 Main bearing ladder
9 Screw	45 Bolt
10 Gasket	46 Bolt
11 Coolant pump	47 Dowel
12 O-ring	48 Oil rail
13 Pillar bolt	49 Stud
14 Bolt	50 Nut
15 Dowel pin	51 Oil filter adapter
16 Thermostat housing	52 Gasket
17 O-ring	53 Bolt
18 Gasket	54 Oil pressure switch
19 Thermostat	55 Sealing washer
20 Thermostat housing	56 Oil temperature switch (if fitted)
21 Screw	57 Washer
22 O-ring	58 Oil filter
23 Coolant rail	59 Sump
24 Screw	60 Gasket
25 Cooling system bleed screw	61 Bolt
26 Sealing washer	62 Engine oil drain plug
27 Cylinder block	63 Washer
28 Liner	64 Sump
29 Dowel	65 Bolt
30 Piston and connecting rod	66 Bolt
31 Big-end bearing cap	67 Engine oil drain plug
32 Connecting rod bolt	68 Washer
33 Big-end bearing shell	69 Oil pump pick-up/strainer pipe
34 Top compression ring	70 Screw
35 Second compression ring	71 O-ring
36 Oil control ring	72 Screw
	73 Blanking plate

H44874

Fit the bearing cap, shells and bolts to each removed piston/connecting rod assembly, so that they are all kept together as a matched set.

Alternative methods

13 If the engine is being completely dismantled and the cylinder head has been removed, either unbolt the main bearing ladder so that the crankshaft can be rotated with care, or remove the crankshaft completely and then remove the connecting rods and pistons.

Cylinder head bolts

Condition check

14 Check the condition of the cylinder head bolts, particularly their threads. (Note that if only the cylinder head has been removed, the bolts can be checked as described in Part A of this Chapter.) Keeping all bolts in their correct fitted order, wash them and wipe dry. Check each bolt for any sign of visible wear or damage, renewing as necessary. Note that if cylinder head bolts have been used to secure the cylinder liner clamps, each bolt and clamp

10.15 Measure the distance from the upper surface of the oil rail to the lower surface of the bolt head

should be removed one at a time for checking, and refitted immediately the bolt has been tested. Lightly oil the threads of each bolt, carefully enter it into its original hole in the oil rail (**do not** drop the bolt into the hole), and screw it in, by hand only, until finger-tight.

15 If the full length of the bolt thread is engaged with the hole in the oil rail, the bolt may be re-used. If the full length of the thread is not engaged, measure the distance from the upper surface of the oil rail to the lower surface of the bolt head (**see illustration**). If the distance measured is under 378 mm, the bolt may be re-used. If the distance measured is more than 378 mm, the bolt must be renewed. Considering the task these bolts perform and the pressures they must withstand, owners should consider renewing all the bolts as a

matched set if more than one of the original bolts fail inspection or are close to the limit.

16 Note that if any of the cylinder head bolt threads in the oil rail are found to be damaged, then the oil rail must be renewed. Thread inserts are not an acceptable repair in this instance.

11 Crankshaft – removal

Note: *The following procedure assumes that the crankshaft alone is being removed and therefore uses a slightly different sequence of operations to that given for the piston/connecting rod removal procedure in Section 10. Depending on the reason for dis-mantling, either sequence may be adapted as necessary. If the crankshaft endfloat is to be checked, this must be done when the crank-shaft is free to move. If a dial gauge is to be used, check after paragraph 1, but if feeler blades are to be used, check after paragraph 10.*

1 Remove the timing belt, sprockets, tensioner, and rear cover, as described in Part A of this Chapter.

2 Slacken and remove the two dipstick tube retaining bolts and remove the tube from the cylinder block/crankcase.

3 Remove the cylinder head, as described in Part A of this Chapter. The crankshaft cannot now be rotated.

4 Remove the oil pump, as described in Part A of this Chapter.

5 Remove the flywheel as described in Part A of this Chapter.

6 Remove the sump and unbolt the oil pump pick-up/strainer pipe from the oil rail, as described in Part A of this Chapter.

7 If cylinder liner clamps have been fitted, temporarily remove them (this is necessary because the cylinder head bolts used to secure the liner clamps screw into the oil rail), then unscrew the two retaining nuts and remove the oil rail.

8 Working in sequence, progressively unscrew the main bearing ladder retaining bolts by a turn at a time, then withdraw the ladder. Note the locations of the two locating dowels, and the main bearing shells, which should be removed from the ladder and stored in their correct fitted order (**see illustrations**).

9 If the cylinder liners are to be left in place in the cylinder block, refit the liner clamps, noting that suitable nuts and spacers will have to be screwed onto the lower ends of the cylinder head bolts to retain the clamps (the oil rail has now been removed).

10 Using a hammer and centre punch, paint or similar, mark each connecting rod big-end bearing cap with its respective cylinder number on the flat, machined surface provided. If the engine has been dismantled before, note carefully any identifying marks made previously. Note that No 1 cylinder is at the timing belt end of the engine.

11 Working on each cylinder in turn, unscrew and remove the big-end bearing cap bolts and withdraw the cap, complete with the lower bearing shell (**see illustration**). Push the connecting rods up and off their crankpins, then remove the upper bearing shells. Keep the cap, bolts and (if they are to be refitted) the bearing shells together in their correct sequence.

12 Carefully lift out the crankshaft (**see illustration**).

13 Withdraw the two thrustwashers from the No 3 main bearing location in the cylinder block.

14 Remove the upper main bearing shells from the cylinder block, noting their locations. The bearing shells must be kept in order, along with the lower bearing shells, so that they can be refitted (if applicable) in their original locations.

15 Check the condition of the cylinder head bolts as described in Section 10.

11.8a Crankshaft main bearing ladder bolt slackening sequence

A Bolts hidden in ladder flanges
B Location of single longer bolt

11.8b Removing the main bearing ladder – locating dowels arrowed

11.11 Removing No 1 cylinder big-end bearing cap and lower bearing shell

11.12 Lifting out the crankshaft

12 Cylinder block/crankcase – cleaning and inspection

Note: *During any cleaning operations, take care not to score the mating surfaces of the cylinder block/crankcase, bearing ladder and oil rail. It may be necessary to use a foam action gasket remover.*

Cleaning

1 For complete cleaning, remove the cylinder liners, all external components and all electrical switches/sensors.

2 Scrape all traces of gasket from the cylinder block/crankcase, bearing ladder and oil rail, taking care not to damage the gasket/sealing surfaces.

3 Remove all oil gallery plugs (where fitted). The plugs are usually very tight and may have to be drilled out and the holes retapped. Use new plugs when the engine is reassembled.

4 If any of the castings are extremely dirty, all should be steam-cleaned.

5 After the castings have been steam-cleaned, clean all oil holes and oil galleries one more time. Flush all internal passages with warm water until the water runs clear, then dry thoroughly and apply a light film of oil to all mating faces and to the liner surfaces to prevent rusting. If you have access to compressed air, use it to speed up the drying process and to blow out all the oil holes and galleries.

 Warning: Wear eye protection when using compressed air.

6 If the castings are not very dirty, you can do an adequate cleaning job with hot soapy water and a stiff brush. Take plenty of time and do a thorough job. Regardless of the cleaning method used, be sure to clean all oil holes and galleries very thoroughly and to dry all components well. Protect the liners as described previously to prevent rusting.

7 All threaded holes must be clean to ensure accurate torque readings during reassembly. To clean all threads, run the proper size tap into each of the holes to remove rust, corrosion, thread sealant or sludge, and to restore damaged threads. If possible, use compressed air to clear the holes of debris produced by this operation. A good alternative is to inject aerosol-applied water-dispersant lubricant into each hole, using the long spout usually supplied. Always wear eye protection when cleaning out holes in this way. After cleaning, ensure that all threaded holes in the cylinder block are dry. If not already done, now is a good time to check the condition of the cylinder head bolts, as described in Section 10.

8 Apply suitable sealant to the new oil gallery plugs, and insert them into the holes in the block. Tighten them securely.

9 If the engine is not going to be reassembled right away, cover it with a large plastic bag to keep it clean. Protect the cylinder liners as described previously to prevent rusting.

Inspection

10 Inspect all castings for cracks and corrosion. Look for stripped threads. If there has been any history of internal coolant leakage, it may be worthwhile having an engine overhaul specialist check the cylinder block/crankcase with special equipment. If defects are found, have them repaired, if possible, or renew the assembly.

11 Check the bore of each cylinder liner for scuffing and scoring. If the cylinder liner walls are badly scuffed or scored, obtain new cylinder liners.

12 Measure the diameter of each cylinder liner bore 65 mm from the top of the bore, both parallel to the crankshaft axis and at right angles to it. Compare the diameter with that specified. If any measurement exceeds the service limit, then the liner must be renewed.

13 To measure the piston-to-bore clearance, either measure the relevant cylinder liner bore (as described above) and piston skirt (as described in Section 14) and subtract the skirt diameter from the bore measurement, or insert each piston into the original cylinder liner bore, select a feeler blade and slip it into the bore along with the piston. The piston must be aligned exactly in its normal attitude and the feeler blade must be between the piston and bore on one of the thrust faces, 20 mm from the bottom of the bore.

14 If the piston-to-bore clearance is excessive, new cylinder liners and corresponding pistons will be required. If the piston binds at the lower end of the bore and is loose towards the top, then the bore is tapered. If tight spots are encountered as the piston/feeler blade is rotated in the bore, then the bore is out-of-round. In either case, new liners and pistons will be required.

15 Repeat the checking procedure for the remaining pistons and cylinder liners.

16 If the bores are in reasonably good condition and not worn to the specified limits, and if the piston-to-bore clearances can be maintained properly, then it may only be necessary to renew the piston rings. In this case, **do not** attempt to hone the cylinder liner bores to allow the new rings to bed-in.

H28706

13.8 Apply a 2 mm bead of sealant around the shoulder of the liner

13 Cylinder liners – removal and refitting

Note: *If desired, the cylinder liners can be removed with the main bearing ladder and crankshaft fitted. MG Rover sealant kit GGC 102 is needed to seal the liners.*

Removal

1 With the pistons removed, if not already done, remove the cylinder liner clamps.

2 If the original liners are to be refitted, make alignment marks between each liner and the cylinder block to ensure that each liner can be refitted in its exact original position. Use a felt-tipped pen or paint to make the marks – **do not** etch or stamp the liners.

3 Lay the cylinder block on its side, then use hand pressure to push the cylinder liners out from the top of the cylinder block. If the liners are to be re-used, mark each one using a piece of masking tape and writing the cylinder number on the tape.

Refitting

Note: *To enable cylinder liner retaining clamps to be fitted when the liners are fitted to the cylinder block, the crankshaft and main bearing ladder must be fitted to the cylinder block.*

4 If not already done, fit the crankshaft and main bearing ladder, as described in Section 19.

5 Support the cylinder block upright on blocks of wood.

6 If not already done, thoroughly clean the cylinder liner mating faces of the cylinder block, and clean away all traces of the cylinder liner sealant. If the original liners are to be refitted, also clean all sealant from the liners, and clean the liner mating faces, taking care not to remove the alignment and identification marks made during removal.

7 Ensure that the cylinder block and liners are dry.

8 Working on the first liner to be refitted, apply a continuous 2 mm bead of sealant, from kit GGC 102, around the shoulder of the liner **(see illustration)**.

9 If the original liners are being refitted, use the marks made on removal to ensure that each liner is refitted in its original bore, in its original location.

10 Insert each liner into its bore in the cylinder block/crankcase, ensuring that the liner is square to the bore. If the original liner is being refitted, make sure that the marks made on the liner and the cylinder block are aligned. Push the liner fully down until the shoulder on the liner seats against the cylinder block. **Do not** drop the liner into position.

11 Repeat the procedure to refit the three remaining cylinder liners.

12 Cylinder liner clamps should now be fitted to prevent the liners from being disturbed before the cylinder head is refitted. The

13.12a Rover cylinder liner clamps fitted to top face of cylinder block

13.12b Rover cylinder liner clamps are retained by screwing the cylinder head bolts into nylon blocks underneath the cylinder block

manufacturer's liner clamps are secured by the cylinder head bolts **(see illustrations)**. Equivalents can be improvised using large washers, tubular spacers and nuts.

14 Piston/connecting rod assembly – inspection

Cleaning

1 Before the inspection process can begin, the piston/connecting rod assemblies must be cleaned, and the original piston rings removed from the pistons.

2 Carefully expand the old rings over the top of the pistons. The use of two or three old feeler blades will be helpful in preventing the rings dropping into empty grooves **(see illustration)**. Be careful not to scratch the piston with the ends of the ring. The rings are brittle, and will snap if they are spread too far. They are also very sharp – protect your hands and fingers. Note that the third ring incorporates an expander. Always remove the rings from the top of the piston. Keep each set of rings with its piston if the old rings are to be re-used. Note which way up each ring is fitted to ensure correct refitting.

3 Scrape away all traces of carbon from the top of the piston. A hand-held wire brush (or a piece of fine emery cloth) can be used, once the majority of the deposits have been scraped away.

4 Remove the carbon from the ring grooves in the piston, using an old ring. Break the ring in half to do this (be careful not to cut your fingers – piston rings are sharp). Be careful to remove only the carbon deposits – do not remove any metal, and do not nick or scratch the sides of the ring grooves.

5 Once the deposits have been removed, clean the piston/connecting rod assembly with paraffin or a suitable solvent, and dry thoroughly.

Inspection

6 If the pistons and cylinder liner bores are not damaged or worn excessively, the original pistons can be refitted. Measure the piston diameters, and check that they are within limits for the corresponding bore diameters. Measure the diameter of each piston at right-angles to the gudgeon pin axis, 8 mm up from the bottom of the skirt.

7 If the piston-to-bore clearance is excessive (see Section 12), new cylinder liners and pistons will have to be fitted. Normal piston wear shows up as even vertical wear on the piston thrust surfaces, and slight looseness of the top ring in its groove. New piston rings should always be used when the engine is reassembled. Note that the piston and bore size grades are stamped on the piston crowns, and on the outer diameters of the cylinder liners.

8 Carefully inspect each piston for cracks around the skirt, around the gudgeon pin holes, and at the piston ring 'lands' (between the ring grooves).

9 Look for scoring and scuffing on the piston skirt, holes in the piston crown, and burned areas at the edge of the crown. If the skirt is scored or scuffed, the engine may have been suffering from overheating, and/or abnormal combustion which caused excessively high operating temperatures. The cooling and lubrication systems should be checked thoroughly. Scorch marks on the sides of the pistons show that blow-by has occurred. A hole in the piston crown, or burned areas at the edge of the piston crown, indicates that abnormal combustion (pre-ignition, knocking, or detonation) has been occurring. If any of the above problems exist, the causes must be investigated and corrected, or the damage will occur again. The causes may include incorrect ignition timing, inlet air leaks or incorrect air/fuel mixture.

10 Corrosion of the piston, in the form of pitting, indicates that coolant has been leaking into the combustion chamber and/or the cylinder liner. Again, the cause must be corrected, or the problem may persist in the rebuilt engine.

11 Check the piston-to-bore clearance by measuring the cylinder bore (see Section 12) and the piston diameter. Measure the piston 8 mm from the bottom of the skirt, at a 90° angle to the gudgeon pin **(see illustration)**. If the piston-to-bore clearance is excessive, new cylinder liners and corresponding pistons will be required.

12 Examine each connecting rod carefully for signs of damage, such as cracks around the big-end and small-end bearings. Check that the rod is not bent or distorted. Damage is highly unlikely, unless the engine has been seized or badly overheated. Detailed checking of the connecting rod assembly can only be carried out by a Rover dealer or engine repair specialist with the necessary equipment.

13 Note that the pistons and connecting rods are only available as an assembly. If a piston or connecting rod is to be renewed, it is therefore necessary to renew all four complete piston/connecting rod assemblies – it is not possible to fit a new piston to an existing connecting rod.

15 Crankshaft – inspection

Checking endfloat

1 If crankshaft endfloat is to be checked, this must be done when the crankshaft is still installed in the cylinder block/crankcase but is free to move.

2 Check endfloat by using a dial gauge in contact with the end of the crankshaft. Push the crankshaft fully one way and then zero the gauge. Push the crankshaft fully the other way and check the endfloat. The result can be compared with the specified amount and will give an indication as to whether new thrustwashers are required.

14.2 Using a feeler blade to aid removal of the piston rings

14.11 Measuring piston diameter

3 If a dial gauge is not available, feeler blades can be used. First push the crankshaft fully towards the flywheel end of the engine, then use feeler blades to measure the gap between the web of No 3 crankpin and the thrust-washer.

Inspection

4 Clean the crankshaft using paraffin or a suitable solvent, and dry it, preferably with compressed air if available. Be sure to clean the oil holes with a pipe cleaner or similar probe, to ensure that they are not obstructed.

 Warning: Wear eye protection when using compressed air.

5 Check the main and big-end bearing journals for uneven wear, scoring, pitting and cracking.

6 Big-end bearing wear is accompanied by distinct metallic knocking when the engine is running (particularly noticeable when the engine is pulling from low speed) and some loss of oil pressure.

7 Main bearing wear is accompanied by severe engine vibration and rumble – getting progressively worse as engine speed increases – and again by loss of oil pressure.

8 Check the bearing journal for roughness by running a finger lightly over the bearing surface. Any roughness (which will be accompanied by obvious bearing wear) indicates that the crankshaft requires regrinding (where possible) or renewal.

9 If the crankshaft has been reground, check for burrs around the crankshaft oil holes (the holes are usually chamfered, so burrs should not be a problem unless regrinding has been carried out carelessly). Remove any burrs with a fine file or scraper, and thoroughly clean the oil holes as described previously.

10 Using a micrometer, measure the diameter of the main and big-end (crankpin) bearing journals, and compare the results with the Specifications **(see illustration)**. By measuring the diameter at a number of points around each journal's circumference, you will be able to determine whether or not the journal is out-of-round. Take the measurement at each end of the journal, near the webs, to determine if the journal is tapered. The main bearing size grades are marked on the crankshaft front web, and the big-end bearing size grades are marked on the crankshaft rear web. In each case, the first letter or number relates to the No 1 bearing, the second to No 2, and so on.

11 Check the oil seal contact surfaces at each end of the crankshaft for wear and damage. If the seal has worn a deep groove in the surface of the crankshaft, consult an engine overhaul specialist; repair may be possible, but otherwise a new crankshaft will be required.

12 If the crankshaft journals are damaged, tapered, out-of-round or worn beyond the limits specified, the crankshaft must be renewed unless an engine overhaul specialist can be found who will regrind it and supply the necessary undersize bearing shells.

15.10 Measuring a crankshaft main bearing journal diameter

16 Main and big-end bearings – inspection

1 Even though the main and big-end bearings should be renewed during the engine overhaul, the old bearings should be retained for close examination, as they may reveal valuable information about the condition of the engine. The bearing shells are graded by thickness, the grade of each shell being indicated by the colour code marked on it.

2 Bearing failure can occur due to lack of lubrication, the presence of dirt or other foreign particles, overloading the engine, or corrosion **(see illustration)**. Regardless of the cause of bearing failure, the cause must be corrected (where applicable) before the engine is reassembled, to prevent it from happening again.

3 When examining the bearing shells, remove them from the cylinder block/crankcase, the main bearing ladder, the connecting rods and the connecting rod big-end bearing caps. Lay

16.2 Typical bearing shell failures

them out on a clean surface in the same general position as their location in the engine. This will enable you to match any bearing problems with the corresponding crankshaft journal.

Caution: Do not touch any shell's bearing surface with your fingers while checking it, or the delicate surface may be scratched.

4 Dirt and other foreign matter gets into the engine in a variety of ways. It may be left in the engine during assembly, or it may pass through filters or the crankcase ventilation system. It may get into the oil, and from there into the bearings. Metal chips from machining operations and normal engine wear are often present. Abrasives are sometimes left in engine components after reconditioning, especially when parts are not thoroughly cleaned using the proper cleaning methods. Whatever the source, these foreign objects often end up embedded in the soft bearing material, and are easily recognised. Large particles will not embed in the bearing, and will score or gouge the bearing and journal. The best prevention for this cause of bearing failure is to clean all parts thoroughly, and keep everything spotlessly-clean during engine assembly. Frequent and regular engine oil and filter changes are also recommended.

5 Lack of lubrication (or lubrication breakdown) has a number of interrelated causes. Excessive heat (which thins the oil), overloading (which squeezes the oil from the bearing face) and oil leakage (from excessive bearing clearances, worn oil pump or high engine speeds) all contribute to lubrication breakdown. Blocked oil passages, which usually are the result of misaligned oil holes in a bearing shell, will also oil-starve a bearing, and destroy it. When lack of lubrication is the cause of bearing failure, the bearing material is wiped or extruded from the steel backing of the bearing. Temperatures may increase to the point where the steel backing turns blue from overheating.

6 Driving habits can have a definite effect on bearing life. Full-throttle, low-speed operation (labouring the engine) puts very high loads on bearings, tending to squeeze out the oil film. These loads cause the bearings to flex, which produces fine cracks in the bearing face (fatigue failure). Eventually, the bearing material will loosen in pieces, and tear away from the steel backing.

7 Short-distance driving leads to corrosion of bearings, because insufficient engine heat is produced to drive off the condensed water and corrosive gases. These products collect in the engine oil, forming acid and sludge. As the oil is carried to the engine bearings, the acid attacks and corrodes the bearing material.

8 Incorrect bearing installation during engine assembly will lead to bearing failure as well. Tight-fitting bearings leave insufficient bearing running clearance, and will result in oil starvation. Dirt or foreign particles trapped

18.4 Measuring a piston ring end gap

18.9 Measuring piston ring-to-groove clearance

behind a bearing shell result in high spots on the bearing, which lead to failure.
Caution: Do not touch any shell's bearing surface with your fingers during reassembly; there is a risk of scratching the delicate surface, or of depositing particles of dirt on it.

9 As mentioned at the beginning of this Section, the bearing shells should be renewed as a matter of course during engine overhaul; to do otherwise is false economy. Refer to Sections 19 and 20 for details of bearing shell selection.

17 Engine overhaul – reassembly sequence

1 Before reassembly begins, ensure that all new parts have been obtained and that all necessary tools are available. Read through the entire procedure to familiarise yourself with the work involved and to ensure that all items necessary for reassembly of the engine are at hand. In addition to all normal tools and materials, it will be necessary to obtain suitable thread-locking compound, and various Rover sealants – refer to the relevant Sections in this Part of the Chapter and Part A for details. Carefully read the instructions supplied with the appropriate sealant kit.

2 In order to save time and avoid problems, engine reassembly can be carried out in the following order, referring to Part A of this Chapter when necessary. Where applicable,

use new gaskets and seals when refitting the various components.

a) Crankshaft.
b) Piston/connecting rod assemblies.
c) Oil pump.
d) Sump.
e) Flywheel.
f) Cylinder head.
g) Timing belt rear cover, tensioner and sprockets, and timing belt.
h) Engine external components.

3 At this stage, all engine components should be absolutely clean and dry, with all faults repaired, and should be laid out (or in individual containers) on a completely clean work surface.

18 Piston rings – refitting

1 Before fitting new piston rings, the ring end gaps must be checked as follows.

2 Lay out the piston/connecting rod assemblies and the new piston ring sets, so that the ring sets will be matched with the same piston and cylinder during the end gap measurement and subsequent engine reassembly.

3 Insert the top ring into the first cylinder liner bore, and push it down the bore using the top of the piston. This will ensure that the ring remains square with the cylinder walls. Position the ring 20 mm from the top of the bore. Note that the top and second

compression rings are different. The second ring is easily identified by the step on its lower surface.

4 Measure the end gap using feeler blades. Compare the measurements with the figures given in the Specifications **(see illustration)**.

5 If the gap is too small (unlikely if genuine Rover parts are used), it must be enlarged, or the ring ends may contact each other during engine operation, causing serious damage. Ideally, new piston rings providing the correct end gap should be fitted. As a last resort, the end gap can be increased by filing the ring ends very carefully with a fine file. Mount the file in a vice equipped with soft jaws, slip the ring over the file with the ends contacting the file face, and slowly move the ring to remove material from the ends. Take care, as piston rings are sharp, and are easily broken.

6 With new piston rings, it is unlikely that the end gap will be too large. If the gaps are too large, check that you have the correct rings for your engine and for the particular cylinder bore size.

7 Repeat the checking procedure for each ring in the first cylinder, and then for the rings in the remaining cylinders. Remember to keep rings, pistons and cylinders matched up.

8 Once the ring end gaps have been checked and if necessary corrected, the rings can be fitted to the pistons.

9 Check the ring-to-groove clearance by inserting the outside of each ring into the relevant groove, together with a feeler blade between the top surface of the ring and the piston land **(see illustration)**. If the grooves in the piston are excessively worn, new pistons may be required.

10 Fit the piston rings using the same technique as for removal. Fit the bottom (oil control) ring first, and work up. When fitting the oil control ring, first insert the wire expander, then fit the ring with its gap positioned 180° from the protruding wire ends of the expander. The oil control expander and ring gaps should be offset 30° either side of the gudgeon pin axis. Ensure that the rings are fitted the correct way up – the top surface of the rings is normally marked TOP **(see illustrations)**. Arrange the gaps of the top and second compression rings 120° from each other, away from the thrust side of the piston.

Note: *Always follow any instructions supplied with the new piston ring sets – different manufacturers may specify different procedures. Do not mix up the top and second compression rings, as they have different cross-sections.*

19 Crankshaft – refitting and main bearing clearance check

Selection of bearing shells

1 The main bearing running clearance is controlled in production by selecting one of

18.10a Piston ring fitting details and top surface markings

18.10b Piston ring end gap locations

A Top compression ring
B Second compression ring
C Oil control ring
D Oil control ring expander

three grades of bearing shell. The grades are indicated by a colour-coding marked on the edge of each shell which governs the shell's thickness, as follows:

 a) Green – Thin.
 b) Blue – Intermediate.
 c) Red – Thick.

2 If shells of differing grades are to be fitted to the same journal, the thicker shell must always be fitted to the main bearing ladder location. Bear this carefully in mind when ordering replacement shells for Nos 2, 3 and 4 bearings.

3 If the bearing shells are to be renewed, first check and record the main bearing code letters stamped on the right-hand front face of the main bearing ladder **(see illustration)**. The letters are read with the ladder inverted, No 1 bearing code letter at the top, then No 2 and so on (No 1 bearing is at the timing belt end of the engine).

4 Check and record the crankshaft journal grade code numbers stamped on the crankshaft front web, No 1 journal code first, then No 2, and so on. If the original crankshaft is to be re-used, the size grade can be checked by direct measurement, as described in Section 15.

5 Note that if the crankshaft is found to be excessively worn, then it must be renewed, and the code numbers of the new crankshaft must be used instead to select a new set of bearing shells.

6 Matching the codes noted to the following table, select a new set of bearing shells.

19.3 Crankshaft main bearing size code locations

Ladder code letter	Crankshaft code number	Shells
A	1	Blue, Blue
A	2	Red, Blue
A	3	Red, Red
B	1	Blue, Green
B	2	Blue, Blue
B	3	Red, Blue
C	1	Green, Green
C	2	Blue, Green
C	3	Blue, Blue

Main bearing clearance check

7 Clean the backs of the bearing shells and the bearing locations in both the cylinder block/crankcase and the main bearing ladder.

8 Press the bearing shells into their locations, ensuring that the tab on each shell engages in the notch in the cylinder block/crankcase or main bearing ladder location. Take care not to touch any shell bearing surface with your fingers.

9 Press the bearing shells with the oil grooves into the upper locations (in the cylinder block/crankcase). Note the following points:

 a) On all engines, grooved bearing shells are fitted to Nos 2, 3 and 4 upper bearing locations. Note the central locating tabs of the grooved shells.
 b) If bearing shells of differing grades are to be fitted to the same journal, the thicker shell must always be fitted to the main bearing ladder location.
 c) On all engines, if the original main bearing

shells are being re-used, these must be refitted to their original locations in the cylinder block/crankcase and main bearing ladder.

10 The main bearing running clearance should be checked if there is any doubt about the amount of crankshaft wear that has taken place, if the crankshaft has been reground and is to be refitted with non-Rover undersized bearing shells, or if non-genuine bearing shells are to be fitted. If the original crankshaft or a Rover part is to be installed, the shell selection procedure given above will produce the correct clearances, and a further check will not be necessary. If the clearance is to be checked, it can be done in either of two ways. Bear in mind that in order to check the bearing running clearance, the cylinder head must be refitted. Use the old cylinder head gasket when refitting the cylinder head (if a new one is used, it will effectively be destroyed when the cylinder head bolts are tightened, and cannot be used for final engine reassembly). If new cylinder head bolts are to be fitted during final reassembly, use the old bolts to secure the cylinder head for this check.

11 The first method (which will be difficult to achieve without a range of internal micrometers or internal/external expanding calipers) is to refit the main bearing ladder to the cylinder block/crankcase (where applicable remove the cylinder liner clamps), with bearing shells in place. With the ladder retaining bolts tightened to the specified torque setting in the two stages given and in the specified sequence **(see illustration 19.26)**, refit the oil rail and the cylinder head (see Part A of this Chapter), then measure the internal diameter of each assembled pair of bearing shells. If the diameter of each corresponding crankshaft journal is measured and then subtracted from

the bearing internal diameter, the result will be the main bearing running clearance.

12 The second (and more accurate) method is to use product known as Plastigauge. This consists of a fine thread of perfectly round plastic which is compressed between the bearing shell and the journal. When the shell is removed, the plastic is deformed and can be measured with a special card gauge supplied with the kit. The running clearance is determined from this gauge. Plastigauge is sometimes difficult to obtain, but enquiries at one of the larger specialist quality motor factors should produce the name of a stockist in your area. The procedure for using Plastigauge is as follows.

13 With the main bearing upper shells in place, carefully lay the crankshaft in position. **Do not** use any lubricant. The crankshaft journals and bearing shells must be perfectly clean and dry.

14 Cut several lengths of the appropriate size Plastigauge (they should be slightly shorter than the width of the main bearings) and place one length on each crankshaft journal axis **(see illustration)**.

19.14 Lay a length of Plastigauge on the journal to be measured, parallel to the crankshaft centre-line

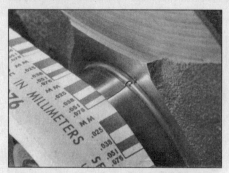

19.18 Using the scale on the Plastigauge envelope to check (at widest point) the width of crushed Plastigauge

19.24a If piston/connecting rod assemblies are refitted before main bearing ladder . . .

19.24b . . . care is required to hold crankshaft steady while connecting rod big-end cap bolts are tightened

15 With the main bearing lower shells in position, refit the main bearing ladder (where applicable, remove the cylinder liner clamps) and tighten the retaining bolts to the specified torque setting in the two stages given and in the specified sequence (**see illustration 19.26**). Take care not to disturb the Plastigauge.

16 Refit the oil rail and the cylinder head (see Part A of this Chapter). Use the old cylinder head gasket and, where applicable, the old cylinder head bolts – see paragraph 10). Do not rotate the crankshaft at any time during this operation.

17 Remove the cylinder head (slacken the bolts in the specified sequence – see Part A of this Chapter), the oil rail and the main bearing ladder. Do not disturb the Plastigauge or rotate the crankshaft.

18 Compare the width of the crushed Plastigauge on each journal to the scale printed on the Plastigauge envelope to obtain the main bearing running clearance (**see illustration**).

19 If the clearance is not as specified, the bearing shells may be the wrong grade (or excessively worn if the original shells are being re-used). Before deciding that different grade shells are needed, make sure that no dirt or oil was trapped between the bearing shells and the ladder or cylinder block/crankcase when the clearance was measured. If the Plastigauge was wider at one end than at the other, the journal may be tapered.

20 Carefully scrape away all traces of the Plastigauge material from the crankshaft and bearing shells using a fingernail or other object which is unlikely to score the shells.

Final crankshaft refitting

Note: *MG Rover sealant GUG 705963GM is needed to seal the cylinder block/crankcase.*

21 Carefully lift the crankshaft out of the cylinder block once more.

22 Using a little grease, stick the thrustwashers to each side of the No 3 main bearing upper location in the cylinder block/crankcase. Ensure that the oilway grooves on each thrustwasher face outwards.

23 Place the bearing shells in their correct locations, as described in paragraphs 7 to 9. If new shells are being fitted, ensure that all traces of the protective grease are cleaned off using paraffin. Wipe the shells dry with a lint-free cloth. Liberally lubricate each bearing shell in the cylinder block/crankcase, then lower the crankshaft into position so that Nos 2 and 3 cylinder crankpins are at TDC.

24 Refit the piston/connecting rod assemblies, with reference to Section 20 (**see illustrations**). Once all the piston/connecting rod assemblies have been refitted, leave Nos 1 and 4 pistons at the TDC position.

25 Thoroughly degrease the mating surfaces of the cylinder block/crankcase and the main bearing ladder. Apply the specified Rover sealant (see Note at the beginning of this sub-Section) to the mating surface of the cylinder

block/crankcase (**see illustration**), then spread the sealant to an even film using a brush or roller. Carefully follow the instructions supplied with the sealant kit. Assembly must be completed as soon as possible after the sealant has been applied (maximum of 20 minutes).

26 Lubricate the bearing shells in the main bearing ladder, then refit the bearing ladder, ensuring that the shells are not displaced and that the locating dowels engage correctly. Working progressively, by a turn at a time and in sequence (**see illustration**), tighten the ladder bolts to the specified torque wrench setting in the two stages given – ie, tighten all bolts in sequence to the Stage 1 setting, then tighten all bolts in sequence to the Stage 2 setting. The crankshaft cannot now be rotated.

27 Thoroughly degrease the mating surfaces of the oil rail and the main bearing ladder. Apply the Rover sealant to the oil rail mating surface (**see illustration**). Carefully follow the instructions supplied with the sealant kit.

28 Refit the oil rail, tightening the nuts to the specified torque wrench setting.

29 Refit the oil pump pick-up/strainer pipe and the sump, as described in Part A of this Chapter.

30 Fit a new crankshaft left-hand oil seal, then refit the flywheel, as described in Part A of this Chapter.

31 Refit the oil pump and fit a new crankshaft right-hand oil seal, as described in Part A of this Chapter.

19.25 Apply sealant to the cylinder block/crankcase mating surface along the paths shown by the heavy black lines – arrow indicates timing belt end of engine

19.26 Crankshaft main bearing ladder bolt tightening sequence

19.27 Apply sealant to the oil rail mating surfaces along the paths shown by the heavy black lines

32 Refit the cylinder head, as described in Part A of this Chapter. Rotate the crankshaft to position No 1 piston to the 90° BTDC position (see Section 3 in Part A of this Chapter).

33 Refit the dipstick tube to the cylinder block/crankcase, and tighten the securing bolts.

34 Refit the timing belt rear cover, the sprockets and timing belt tensioner, and the belt itself.

35 Using a torque wrench and socket applied to the crankshaft pulley bolt, check that the amount of force required to rotate the crankshaft does not exceed 31 Nm (23 lbf ft). If the effort required is greater than this, the engine must be dismantled again to trace and rectify the cause. This value takes into account the increased friction of a new engine and is much higher than the actual pressure required to rotate a run-in engine, so do not make allowances for tight components.

20 Piston/connecting rod assembly – refitting and big-end bearing clearance check

Selection of bearing shells

1 The big-end bearing running clearance is controlled in production by selecting one of three grades of bearing shell. The grades are indicated by a colour-coding marked on the edge of each shell which governs the shell's thickness, as follows:

  a) *Yellow – Thin.*
  b) *Blue – Intermediate.*
  c) *Red – Thick.*

2 If shells of differing grades are to be fitted to the same journal, the thicker shell must always be fitted to the big-end bearing cap location.

3 If the bearing shells are to be renewed, first check and record the codes stamped on the front face of each big-end bearing cap and connecting rod. The number stamped on the big-end bearing cap is the bearing size code, the number stamped on the connecting rod is the piston/rod assembly's cylinder number

20.4 Crankpin/big-end journal size code location

20.3 Big-end bearing size code number (A – on cap), cylinder number (B) and connecting rod weight code letter (C)

and the letter stamped on the connecting rod is the weight code **(see illustration)**.

4 Secondly, check and record the crankpin/big-end journal code letters stamped on the crankshaft rear web **(see illustration)**, No 1 journal code first, then No 2, and so on. If the original crankshaft is to be re-used, the code letter can be checked by direct measurement.

5 If the crankshaft is found to be excessively worn, then it must be renewed and the code letters of the new component must be used instead to select a new set of bearing shells.

6 Matching the codes noted to the following table, select a new set of bearing shells.

Cap code number	Crankshaft code letter	Shells
5	A	Blue, Blue
5	B	Red, Blue
5	C	Red, Red
6	A	Blue, Yellow
6	B	Blue, Blue
6	C	Red, Blue
7	A	Yellow, Yellow
7	B	Blue, Yellow
7	C	Blue, Blue

Big-end bearing clearance check

7 The big-end bearing running clearance should be checked if there is any doubt about the amount of crankshaft wear that has taken place, if the crankshaft has been reground and is to be refitted with non-Rover undersized bearing shells, or if non-genuine bearing shells are to be fitted. If the original crankshaft or a Rover part is to be installed, the shell selection procedure given previously will produce the correct clearances, and a further check will not be necessary. If the clearance is to be checked, it can be done in either of two ways.

8 The first method is to refit the big-end bearing cap to the connecting rod, with bearing shells in place. With the cap retaining bolts tightened to the specified torque, use an internal micrometer or vernier caliper to measure the internal diameter of each assembled pair of bearing shells. If the diameter of each corresponding crankshaft journal is measured and then subtracted from the bearing internal diameter, the result will be the big-end bearing running clearance.

9 The second method is to use Plastigauge (see Section 19). Place a strand of Plastigauge on each (cleaned) crankpin journal and refit the (clean) piston/connecting rod assemblies, shells and big-end bearing caps, tightening the bolts to the specified torque wrench setting. Take care not to damage the internal surfaces of the cylinder liner bores, and take care not to disturb the Plastigauge. **Do not** rotate the crankshaft during this procedure. Dismantle the assemblies without rotating the crankshaft, and compare the width of the crushed Plastigauge on each journal to the scale printed on the Plastigauge envelope to obtain the main bearing running clearance.

10 If the clearance is not as specified, the bearing shells may be the wrong grade (or excessively worn if the original shells are being re-used). Before deciding that different grade shells are needed, make sure that no dirt or oil was trapped between the bearing shells and the ladder or cylinder block/crankcase when the clearance was measured. If the Plastigauge was wider at one end than at the other, the journal may be tapered.

11 On completion of the measurement, carefully scrape off all traces of Plastigauge from the journals and shells using a fingernail or other object which will not score the components.

Piston/connecting rod refitting

Note: *MG Rover sealant GUG 705963GM is needed to seal the oil rail/main bearing ladder.*

12 Note that the following procedure assumes that the cylinder liners have been refitted to the cylinder block/crankcase (see Section 13), and that the crankshaft and main bearing ladder are in place. It is of course possible to refit the piston/connecting rod assemblies to the cylinder liner bores, to refit the crankshaft and to reassemble the piston/connecting rods on the crankshaft before refitting the main bearing ladder (see Section 19).

13 Clean the backs of the bearing shells and the bearing recesses in both the connecting rod and the big-end bearing cap. If new shells are being fitted, ensure that all traces of the protective grease are cleaned off using paraffin. Wipe the shells and connecting rods dry with a lint-free cloth.

14 Press the bearing shells into their locations, ensuring that the tab on each shell engages in the notch in the connecting rod or big-end bearing cap, and taking care not to touch any shell bearing surface with your fingers. Note the following points.

  a) *If bearing shells of differing grades are to be fitted to the same journal, the thicker shell must always be fitted to the big-end bearing cap location.*
  b) *On all engines, if the original big-end bearing shells are being re-used, these must be refitted to their original locations in the relevant connecting rod and big-end bearing cap.*

20.17a Arrow of FRONT marking on piston crown must point to timing belt end of engine

20.17b Using a piston ring compressor tool to clamp the piston rings

28 Refit the timing belt rear cover, sprocket(s), tensioner and the belt itself, as described in Part A of this Chapter.

29 Finally, using a torque wrench, check that the amount of force required to rotate the crankshaft does not exceed 31 Nm (23 lbf ft). If the effort required is greater than this, the engine must be dismantled again to trace and rectify the cause. This value takes into account the increased friction of a new engine and is much higher than the actual pressure required to rotate a run-in engine, so do not make allowances for tight components.

20.19a Tighten the connecting rod big-end cap bolts to the specified torque setting . . .

20.19b . . . then through the specified angle

21 Engine – initial start-up after overhaul

1 With the engine refitted to the vehicle, double-check the engine oil and coolant levels. Make a final check to ensure that everything has been reconnected and that there are no tools or rags left in the engine compartment.

2 To prevent the engine from starting during initial cranking, remove the fuel pump fuse from the engine bay fusebox – see *Wiring Diagrams*. Operate the starter motor and check that cranking is satisfactory, with no unusual noises. Ensure that the oil pressure warning light goes out during cranking.

3 Fit the fuel pump fuse. **Note:** *Because fuel system components will be empty, the engine may take longer than normal to start.*

4 Start the engine, and ensure that the oil pressure warning light goes off during cranking, or immediately the engine starts. Allow the engine to idle.

5 While the engine is idling, check for fuel, coolant and oil leaks. Do not be alarmed if there are some odd smells and smoke from parts getting hot and burning off oil deposits. If the hydraulic tappets have been disturbed, some valve gear noise may be heard at first; this should disappear as the oil circulates fully around the engine and normal pressure is restored in the tappets.

6 Keep the engine idling until hot coolant is felt circulating through the radiator top hose, check the ignition timing and idle speed and mixture (as appropriate), then stop the engine.

7 After a few minutes, recheck the oil and coolant levels and top up as necessary.

8 If new pistons, rings or crankshaft bearings have been fitted, the engine must be run-in for the first 500 miles (800 km). Do not operate the engine at full throttle or allow it to labour in any gear during this period. It is recommended that the oil and filter be changed at the end of this period.

15 Lubricate the cylinder bores, the pistons and piston rings, then lay out each piston/connecting rod assembly in its respective position.

16 Starting with assembly No 1, make sure that the piston rings are still correctly spaced (see Section 18), then clamp them in position with a piston ring compressor.

17 Insert the piston/connecting rod assembly into the top of liner No 1, ensuring that the arrow (or FRONT marking) on the piston crown faces the timing belt end of the engine. Note that the stamped marks on the connecting rod and big-end bearing cap should face the front (alternator bracket side) of the engine. Using a block of wood or a hammer handle against the piston crown, tap the assembly into the liner until the piston crown is flush with the top of the liner **(see illustrations)**.

18 Ensure that the bearing shell is still correctly installed in the connecting rod. Taking care not to mark the liner bores, liberally lubricate the crankpin and both bearing shells, then pull the piston/connecting rod assembly down the bore and onto the crankpin. Noting that the faces with the stamped marks must match (which means that the bearing shell locating tabs abut each other), refit the big-end bearing cap, tightening the bolts finger-tight at first.

19 Use a torque wrench to tighten the bolts evenly to the (Stage 1) torque wrench setting specified, then use an angular torque gauge to tighten the bolts evenly through the (Stage 2) angle specified **(see illustrations)**.

20 Repeat the procedure for the remaining three piston/connecting rod assemblies, but do not attempt to rotate the crankshaft.

21 Thoroughly degrease the mating surfaces of the oil rail and the main bearing ladder. Apply the specified Rover sealant to the oil rail mating surface **(see illustration 19.27)**. Carefully follow the instructions supplied with the sealant kit.

22 Refit the oil rail, tightening the nuts to the specified torque wrench setting.

23 Refit the oil pump pick-up/strainer pipe and the sump, as described in Part A of this Chapter.

24 Refit the cylinder head, as described in Part A of this Chapter.

25 Rotate the crankshaft to bring No 1 piston to the 90° BTDC position so that the crankshaft sprocket timing marks align (see Section 3 in Part A of this Chapter).

26 Refit the dipstick tube to the cylinder block/crankcase, and tighten the bolts securely.

27 Refit the hydraulic tappets and the camshaft(s), as described in Part A of this Chapter.

Chapter 2 Part D:
Diesel engine removal and general overhaul procedures

Contents

Degrees of difficulty

Easy, suitable for novice with little experience		Fairly easy, suitable for beginner with some experience		Fairly difficult, suitable for competent DIY mechanic	Difficult, suitable for experienced DIY mechanic	Very difficult, suitable for expert DIY or professional	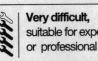

Specifications

Cylinder block/crankcase
Material .... Cast iron
Cylinder bore diameter .... 84.442 to 84.460 mm

Crankshaft
Number of main bearings 5
Main bearing journal diameter .... 60.703 to 60.719 mm
Big-end journal diameter .... 57.683 to 57.696 mm
Main bearing and big-end bearing running clearance .... 0.005 mm
Crankshaft endfloat .... 0.03 to 0.26 mm
Thrustwasher thickness .... 2.31 to 2.36 mm

Pistons and piston rings
Piston diameter .... 84.262 mm
Piston-to-bore clearance .... 0.18 to 0.20 mm
Piston ring end gaps (rings fitted 30 mm from top of bore):
    Top compression ring .... 0.25 to 0.27 mm
    Second compression ring .... 0.40 to 0.42 mm
    Oil control ring .... 0.30 to 0.32 mm
Piston ring end gaps (rings fitted to pistons):
    Top compression ring .... 0.30 to 0.50 mm
    Second compression ring .... 0.40 to 0.60 mm
    Oil control ring .... 0.25 to 0.50 mm
Piston ring-to-groove clearance:
    Top compression ring .... 0.115 to 0.135 mm
    Second compression ring .... 0.050 to 0.082 mm
    Oil control ring – all models .... 0.050 to 0.082 mm

Gudgeon pins
Diameter .... 29.995 to 30.000 mm

Cylinder head and camshaft carrier

Material .... Aluminium alloy
Maximum acceptable gasket face distortion .... 0.010 mm
Valve seat insert angle:
   Inlet .... 60°
   Exhaust .... 58° to 62°
Valve seat width .... 1.5 mm
Valve seat insert diameter:
   Inlet .... 35.697 mm
   Exhaust .... 31.05 to 31.55 mm
Cylinder head bolt length .... 243.41 mm

Valves

Stem diameter:
   Inlet .... 6.907 to 6.923 mm
   Exhaust .... 6.897 to 6.913 mm
Guide inside diameter .... 6.950 to 6.963 mm
Stem-to-guide clearance (measured at valve head, with valve head extended 10 mm from seat):
   Inlet .... 0.056 mm
   Exhaust .... 0.066 mm
Valve spring free length .... 37.0 mm
Valve guide fitted height .... 61.1 to 61.7 mm
Valve head recess below cylinder head face:
   Inlet .... 1.45 mm
   Exhaust .... 1.35 mm

Torque wrench settings

Refer to Part B of this Chapter

1 General information

Included in this part of the Chapter are details of removing the engine/transmission unit from the vehicle and general overhaul procedures for the cylinder head, cylinder block/crankcase and all other engine internal components.

The information given ranges from advice concerning preparation for an overhaul and the purchase of new parts to detailed step-by-step procedures covering removal, inspection, renovation and refitting of engine internal components.

After Section 5, all instructions are based on the assumption that the engine has been removed from the vehicle. For information concerning in-car engine repair, as well as the removal and refitting of those external components necessary for full overhaul, refer to Part B of this Chapter and to Section 5. Ignore any preliminary dismantling operations described in Part B that are no longer relevant once the engine has been removed from the vehicle.

2 Engine overhaul – general information

It is not always easy to determine when, or if, an engine should be completely overhauled, as a number of factors must be considered.

High mileage is not necessarily an indication that an overhaul is needed, while low mileage does not preclude the need for an overhaul. Frequency of servicing is probably the most important consideration. An engine which has had regular and frequent oil and filter changes, as well as other required maintenance, should give many thousands of miles of reliable service. Conversely, a neglected engine may require an overhaul very early in its life. If a complete service does not remedy any problems, major mechanical work is the only solution.

Excessive oil consumption is an indication that piston rings, valve seals and/or valve guides are in need of attention. Make sure that oil leaks are not responsible before deciding that the rings and/or guides are worn. Perform a compression or leakdown test to determine the likely cause of the problem (see Part B of this Chapter).

Check the oil pressure with a gauge fitted in place of the oil pressure switch and compare it with that specified. If it is extremely low, the main and big-end bearings and/or the oil pump are probably worn out.

Loss of power, rough running, knocking or metallic engine noises, excessive valve gear noise and high fuel consumption may also point to the need for an overhaul, especially if they are all present at the same time.

An engine overhaul involves restoring all internal parts to the specification of a new engine. During an overhaul, the pistons and the piston rings are renewed. New main and big-end bearings are generally fitted and, if necessary, the crankshaft may be renewed to restore the journals **(see illustration)**. The valves are serviced as well, since they are usually in less than perfect condition at this point. While the engine is being overhauled, other components, such as the distributor, starter and alternator, can be overhauled as well. The end result should be an as-new engine that will give many trouble-free miles.

Critical cooling system components such as the hoses, thermostat and coolant pump should be renewed when an engine is overhauled. The radiator should be checked carefully to ensure that it is not clogged or leaking. Also it is a good idea to renew the oil pump whenever the engine is overhauled.

Before beginning the engine overhaul, read through the entire procedure to familiarise yourself with the scope and requirements of the job. Overhauling an engine is not difficult if you follow carefully all of the instructions, have the necessary tools and equipment and pay close attention to all specifications. However, it can be time-consuming. Plan on the vehicle being off the road for a minimum of two weeks, especially if parts must be taken to an engineering works for repair or reconditioning. Check on the availability of parts and make sure that any necessary special tools and equipment are obtained in advance. Most work can be done with typical hand tools, although a number of precision measuring tools are required for inspecting parts to determine if they must be renewed. Often the engineering works will handle the inspection of parts and offer advice concerning reconditioning and renewal.

Always wait until the engine has been completely dismantled and all components,

2.6 Cylinder block components

1 Crankshaft pulley bolt
2 Crankshaft pulley
3 Camshaft belt drive gear
4 Crankshaft right-hand seal
5 Bolt – M10
6 Oil pump
7 Gasket – oil pump
8 Cylinder block
9 Gearbox adapter plate
10 Top compression ring
11 2nd compression ring

12 Oil control ring
13 Piston
14 Bolt – connecting rod – Type A engines
15 Nut – connecting rod – Type A engines
16 Big-end bearing shells
17 Big-end cap
18 Bolt – connecting rod – Type B and C engines
19 Connecting rod
20 Gudgeon pin circlips

21 Gudgeon pin
22 Crankshaft left-hand oil seal and housing
23 Dipstick
24 Dipstick tube
25 Crankshaft
26 Woodruff key
27 Main bearing upper shell
28 Main bearing lower shell
29 Thrustwasher
30 Main bearing caps

31 Main bearing cap bolt
32 O-ring
33 Oil strainer and pick-up tube
34 Bolt – sump
35 Sump
36 Gasket – sump
37 Banjo bolt
38 Oil squirt jet
39 Oil filter
40 Oil filter O-ring
41 Bolt – M10

especially the cylinder block/crankcase and the crankshaft have been inspected before deciding what service and repair operations must be performed by an engineering works. Since the condition of these components will be the major factor to consider when determining whether to overhaul the original engine or buy a reconditioned unit, do not purchase parts or have overhaul work done on other components until they have been thoroughly inspected. As a general rule, time is the primary cost of an overhaul, so it does not pay to fit worn or substandard parts.

As a final note, to ensure maximum life and minimum trouble from a reconditioned engine,

everything must be assembled with care in a spotlessly clean environment.

3 Engine/transmission removal – methods and precautions

If you have decided that the engine must be removed for overhaul or major repair work, several preliminary steps should be taken.

Locating a suitable place to work is extremely important. Adequate work space, along with storage space for the vehicle, will be needed. If a workshop or garage is not

available, at the very least a flat, level, clean work surface is required.

Cleaning the engine compartment and engine/transmission before beginning the removal procedure will help keep things clean and organised.

An engine hoist or A-frame will also be necessary. Make sure the equipment is rated in excess of the combined weight of the engine and transmission. Safety is of primary importance, considering the potential hazards involved in lifting the engine/transmission unit out of the vehicle. The engine/transmission unit is removed by lowering it out from under the front of the vehicle.

4.6 Remove two air cleaner attachment bolts

4.9 Remove battery tray

4.10a Engine bay fusebox

4.10b Disconnect cables at engine bay fusebox

If the engine/transmission unit is being removed by a novice, a helper should be available. Advice and aid from someone more experienced would also be helpful. There are many instances when one person cannot simultaneously perform all of the operations required when lowering the unit out of the vehicle.

Plan the operation ahead of time. Before starting work, arrange for the hire of or obtain all of the tools and equipment you will need. Some of the equipment necessary to perform engine/transmission removal and installation safely and with relative ease are (in addition to an engine hoist) a heavy duty trolley jack, complete sets of spanners and sockets as described at the back of this Manual, wooden blocks and plenty of rags and cleaning solvent for mopping-up spilled oil, coolant and fuel. If the hoist must be hired, make sure

that you arrange for it in advance and perform all of the operations possible without it beforehand. This will save you money and time.

Plan for the vehicle to be out of use for quite a while. An engineering works will be required to perform some of the work which the do-it-yourselfer cannot accomplish without special equipment. These places often have a busy schedule, so it would be a good idea to consult them before removing the engine in order to accurately estimate the amount of time required to rebuild or repair components that may need work.

Always be extremely careful when removing and refitting the engine/transmission unit. Serious injury can result from careless actions. Plan ahead, take your time and a job of this nature, although major, can be accomplished successfully.

4.11 Disconnect throttle sensor multi-plug

4.12 Remove acoustic cover

4 Engine/transmission – removal and refitting

Caution: Read the notes in Section 3 – 'Engine/transmission removal – methods and precautions'.
Note: *To allow the engine/transmission to be pulled out from under the vehicle, the front end must be raised to at least 770 mm – measured between the ground and lower edge of the front bumper. Ensure that safety stands, suitable for this height, are available.*
Note: *The following new parts are required – gear selector rod roll-pin, power steering pipe O-rings, front pipe to exhaust manifold gasket.*
Note: *As they are disconnected, make a note or sketch of the position, route and clipping of all wires, harnesses, pipes and hoses.*

Removal

1 Disconnect the battery earth lead, and then the battery positive lead.
2 Release the bonnet stay, and tieback the bonnet.
3 Drain coolant – see Chapter 1B.
4 Remove the battery clamp, and lift out the battery.
5 Disconnect the air outlet pipe from the end of the air cleaner, and the air inlet pipe from under the air cleaner
6 Remove two bolts attaching the air cleaner to the battery tray, and remove the air cleaner **(see illustration)**.
7 Remove three bolts securing the base of the battery tray, and slacken three bolts which attach the under part of the tray to the inner wing.
8 Disconnect the two engine harness multi-plugs from the Engine Control Module (ECM) on the battery tray.
9 Remove the battery tray and ECM **(see illustration)**.
10 Remove three screws attaching the engine bay fusebox to the inner wing **(see illustration)**. Disconnect the following electrical connections at the engine bay fusebox **(see illustration)**:
Alternator – red – cable from inside the box.
Engine harness multi-plug from inside the box.
Engine harness multi-plug under the box.
Close the fusebox, and tie clear of the work area.
11 Release the multi-plug from the throttle position sensor bracket, and disconnect the multi-plug **(see illustration)**.
12 Remove three screws securing the acoustic cover the engine, and remove the cover **(see illustration)**.
13 Disconnect the clutch cable – see Chapter 6 (PG1 gearbox).
14 Remove the terminal cover and nut, and disconnect the battery lead from the starter motor **(see illustration)**.
15 Release the clip securing the engine harness to the bulkhead. Release two engine

4.14 Disconnect battery lead from starter motor

4.15 Disconnect two multi-plugs

4.17 Disconnect MAF/IAT sensor multi-plug

harness multi-plugs from the bulkhead bracket, and disconnect from the main harness **(see illustration)**.

16 Remove the bolt attaching two earth leads to the gearbox housing.

17 Disconnect the multi-plug from the MAF/IAT sensor on the air intake pipe between the air cleaner and the turbocharger **(see illustration)**.

18 Slacken the clip, and disconnect the engine breather valve hose from the camshaft cover.

19 Slacken the clip, and disconnect the air intake pipe from the turbocharger **(see illustration)**.

Caution: Cover or plug the turbocharger outlet.

20 Release the clips, and disconnect the fuel supply and return hoses from the fuel rail.

Caution: Plug the ends of the pipes and connections.

21 Slacken the clip and disconnect the coolant hose from the coolant rail.

22 Slacken the clips, and disconnect two coolant hoses from the EGR cooler **(see illustration)**.

23 Disconnect the vacuum pipe from the EGR valve.

24 Disconnect the boost pressure sensing pipe from the turbocharger (to the MAP sensor on the bulkhead).

25 Disconnect the multi-plugs from the MAP sensor, and from the EGR control valve solenoid on the bulkhead **(see illustration)**.

26 Release the clip and disconnect the hose from the vacuum pump pipe above the camshaft cover.

27 Pack absorbent cloths under the hose/pipe connection of the power steering supply pipe to the steering rack. Use two spanners, and disconnect the hose and pipe **(see illustration)**.

Caution: Plug the ends of the pipes and connections.

28 Locate a container under the power steering reservoir. Release the reservoir from the inner wing bracket. Release the clip, and disconnect the supply hose from the reservoir **(see illustration)**.

Caution: Plug the ends of the pipes and connections.

29 Release the glow plug relay from the bracket on the inner wing under the power steering reservoir **(see illustration)**.

30 Slacken two clips, and remove the intercooler top hose. Slacken the upper clip of the intercooler bottom hose **(see illustration)**.

31 Slacken the clip, and disconnect the radiator top hose.

32 Slacken the clip, and disconnect the coolant bleed hose from the radiator. Tie the pipe clear of the work area.

4.19 Disconnect hose from turbocharger

4.22 Disconnect EGR cooler hoses

4.25 Disconnect MAP and EGR multi-plugs

4.27 Disconnect power steering hose from pipe

4.28 Disconnect power steering supply hose from reservoir

4.29 Release glow plug relay

4.30 Remove the intercooler top hose, and slacken bottom hose top clip

4.33 Disconnect fan multi-plug

4.44 Disconnect gearchange steady bar

33 Disconnect the multi-plug from the radiator cooling fan **(see illustration)**.
34 Remove the terminal cover, and disconnect the battery lead from the alternator.
35 Disconnect the multi-plug from the alternator.

Air conditioned models

36 Remove the bolt attaching the air conditioning pipe to the alternator upper mounting bracket.

All models

37 Apply the handbrake, chock the rear roadwheels, then jack up the front of the car and support it on axle stands (see the 'Note' at the beginning of this Section, and *Jacking and Vehicle Support*).
38 Remove the engine undertray – two nuts at rear and two bolts at front.
39 Drain the engine oil – see Chapter 1B. Fit a new drain plug washer, and refit the plug. Use a torque wrench to tighten the plug to the specified torque.
40 Drain the transmission oil – see Chapter 7.
41 Remove the front suspension front beam, and both tie rods – see Chapter 10.
42 Remove the exhaust front pipe – see Chapter 4B.
43 Slacken the clip, and remove the intercooler bottom hose. Slacken the clip, and disconnect the radiator bottom hose.
44 Remove the bolt, and disconnect the gearchange steady bar from the gearbox housing – retain two washers **(see illustration)**.
45 Remove the clip covering the selector rod

roll-pin. Using a suitable punch, drive out the roll-pin **(see illustration)**.
46 Release the gear selector rod from the selector shaft.
47 Slacken the through-bolt attaching the engine lower steady bar to the suspension rear beam. Remove the through-bolt attaching the bar to the sump bracket. Release the bar from the bracket, and fold away from the work area **(see illustration)**.
48 Disconnect both driveshafts from the transmission – see Chapter 8.
Caution: Tie-up the driveshafts to avoid strain on the outer joints, and to keep clear the area under the engine and transmission.

Air conditioned models

49 Fit a 15 mm ring spanner on the bolt in the centre of the auxiliary drivebelt tension roller. Rotate the pulley fully clockwise and hold in this position. Have an assistant release the drivebelt from the pulleys.
50 Disconnect the multi-plug from the air conditioning compressor.
51 Remove three bolts attaching the compressor to the mounting. Move the compressor away from the engine, and tie securely.

All models

52 Make a final check to ensure that all wires, pipes and hoses which connect to the engine or gearbox have been disconnected or released.
53 Attach lifting chains, with spreader bar, to the lifting eyes on the cylinder head. Attach the lifting tackle to a hoist, and raise the hoist

just enough to take the weight of the engine/transmission.
54 Remove the right-hand and left-hand engine steady bars and mountings – see Chapter 2B.
55 With assistance, lower the engine/transmission onto a suitable trolley, or wooden pallet on a trolley jack. Support the assembly, and withdraw from under the vehicle. Remove transmission assembly from engine (if necessary)
56 As they are disconnected, make a note or sketch of the position, route and clipping of any wires, or pipes which link to, or are attached, to the transmission. Disconnect wires and pipes.
57 Remove three lower bolts securing the transmission to the transmission mounting plate and the engine/transmission reinforcing bracket.
58 Remove the bolt at the rear of the engine, securing the transmission to the mounting plate.
59 Remove two nuts and bolts, and one bolt, securing the transmission to the mounting plate.
60 Ensuring that it is not allowed to hang on the input shaft, withdraw the transmission assembly from the rear of the engine.

Refitting

61 Refitting is a reversal of the removal procedure, noting:
Ensure cables, pipes and hoses are routed and clipped as noted during removal.
Use a torque wrench to tighten all fastenings to the specified torque.
After fitting the engine mountings and steady bars, fit and loosely tighten all the nuts and bolts. Allow the engine/transmission assembly to settle on the mountings before final tightening.
Fit a new roll-pin the gearchange rod, and secure with the clip.
Fit new O-rings to the power steering pipe connections.
Fill the transmission with oil – see Chapter 7.
Fill the engine with oil, and fill the cooling system – see Chapter 1B
Fill and bleed the power steering system – see Chapter10.
Check/adjust throttle operation.

4.45 Drive out roll-pin

4.47 Release steady bar from bracket

5 Engine overhaul – dismantling sequence

Note: *When removing external components from the engine, pay close attention to details that may be helpful or important during refitting. Note the fitted position of gaskets, seals, spacers, pins, washers, bolts and other small items.*

1 It is much easier to work on the engine if it is mounted on a portable engine stand. These stands can often be hired from a tool hire shop. Before the engine is mounted on a stand, the flywheel should be removed so that the stand bolts can be tightened into the end of the cylinder block/crankcase.

2 If a stand is not available, it is possible to dismantle the engine with it blocked up on a sturdy workbench or on the floor. Be extra careful not to tip or drop the engine when working without a stand.

3 If you are going to obtain a reconditioned engine, all external components must be removed for transfer to the new engine (just as if you are doing a complete engine overhaul yourself). These components include the following **(see illustrations)**:

a) *Alternator/brake vacuum pump assembly.*
b) *Air conditioning compressor (where applicable).*
c) *Power steering pump/coolant pump assembly.*
d) *Coolant outlet elbow.*
e) *Dipstick tube.*
f) *Fuel injection pump, drivebelt, fuel injectors, glow plugs, and associated fuel system components.*
g) *All electrical switches and sensors.*
h) *Inlet and exhaust manifolds.*
i) *Oil pipes, coolant pipes and brackets.*
j) *Oil cooler.*
k) *Oil filter.*
l) *Engine mounting brackets.*
m) *Flywheel.*
n) *Transmission mounting plate.*
o) *Ancillary mounting brackets.*

4 If you are obtaining a short motor (which consists of the engine cylinder block/crankcase, crankshaft, pistons and connecting rods all assembled), then the fuel

5.3a Unscrew the securing bolts . . .

5.3b . . . and remove the transmission mounting plate

injection pump drivebelt, timing belt, cylinder head, sump, oil pump, and oil cooler will have to be removed also.

5 If you are planning a complete overhaul, the engine can be dismantled and the internal components removed in the following order:

a) *Inlet and exhaust manifolds.*
b) *Timing and injection pump belts, sprockets, tensioner, and timing belt rear covers.*
c) *Cylinder head.*
d) *Flywheel.*
e) *Sump.*
f) *Oil pump.*
g) *Piston/connecting rod assemblies.*
h) *Crankshaft.*

6 Before beginning the dismantling and overhaul procedures, make sure that you have all of the correct tools necessary.

6 Cylinder head – dismantling

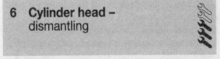

Note: *New and reconditioned cylinder heads are available from the manufacturer and from engine overhaul specialists. Due to the fact that some specialist tools are required for dismantling and inspection, and new components may not be readily available, it may be more practical and economical for the home mechanic to purchase a reconditioned head rather than dismantle, inspect and recondition the original. A valve spring compressor tool will be required for this operation.*

1 With the cylinder head removed, if not already done, remove the fuel injectors (see Chapter 4B) and the glow plugs (see Chapter 5C), then proceed as follows.

2 Remove the camshaft and hydraulic tappets, as described in Part B of this Chapter.

3 Using a valve spring compressor tool, compress each valve spring in turn until the split collets can be removed. Release the compressor and lift off the spring retainer and spring, then use a pair of pliers to extract the spring lower seat/stem seal **(see illustrations)**.

> **HAYNES HiNT**
>
> *If, when the valve spring compressor is screwed down, the spring retainer refuses to free and expose the split collets, gently tap the top of the tool directly over the retainer with a light hammer. This will free the retainer.*

4 Withdraw the valve through the combustion chamber.

5 It is essential that each valve is stored together with its collets, retainer and spring, and that all valves are kept in their correct sequence, unless they are so badly worn that they are to be renewed. If they are going to be kept and used again, place each valve assembly in a labelled polythene bag or similar small container **(see illustration)**. Note that No 1 valve is nearest to the timing belt end of the engine.

6.3a Using a valve spring compressor tool . . .

6.3b . . . compress the valve spring until the split collets can be removed

6.5 Place each valve assembly in a labelled polythene bag

7.6 Use a straight-edge and feeler blade to check the cylinder head for distortion

7.7 Checking the recess of a valve head below the surface of the cylinder head

7 Cylinder head and valves – cleaning and inspection

Note: *If the engine has been severely overheated, it is best to assume that the cylinder head is warped and to check carefully for signs of this.*

Note: *Be sure to perform all the following inspection procedures before concluding that the services of a machine shop or engine overhaul specialist are required. Make a list of all items that require attention.*

1 Thorough cleaning of the cylinder head and valve components, followed by a detailed inspection, will enable you to decide how much valve service work must be carried out during the engine overhaul.

Cleaning

2 Scrape away all traces of old gasket material and sealing compound from the cylinder head.

3 Scrape away all carbon from the combustion chambers and ports, then wash the cylinder head thoroughly with paraffin or a suitable solvent.

4 Scrape off any heavy carbon deposits that may have formed on the valves, then use a power-operated wire brush to remove deposits from the valve heads and stems.

Inspection

Cylinder head

5 Inspect the head very carefully for cracks, evidence of coolant leakage and other

7.11 Measuring a valve stem diameter

damage. If cracks are found, a new cylinder head should be obtained.

6 Use a straight-edge and feeler blade to check that the cylinder head surface is not distorted **(see illustration)**. Note that the cylinder head cannot be refaced, and must be renewed if the surface is distorted beyond the specified limit.

7 Examine the valve seats in each of the combustion chambers. If they are severely pitted, cracked or burned, then they will need to be renewed or recut by an engine overhaul specialist. If they are only slightly pitted, this can be removed by grinding-in the valve heads and seats with fine valve-grinding compound as described below. To check for excessive wear, refit each valve and measure the recess of the valve head below the surface of the cylinder head. This can be carried out with a dial gauge, or with a straight-edge and feeler blades **(see illustration)**. If the measurement is above the specified limit, the valve and the valve seat insert must be renewed.

8 If the valve guides are worn, indicated by a side-to-side motion of the valve, new guides and valves must be fitted. Measure the diameter of the existing valve stems (see below) and the bore of the guides, then calculate the clearance and compare the result with the specified value. If the clearance is excessive, renew the valves and guides as necessary. Note that the valve guides can only be renewed twice – if the guides need to be renewed for the third time, the cylinder head must be renewed. A mark on the camshaft side of the cylinder head, adjacent to the valve guide will be present if the valve

7.14 Grinding-in a valve using a suction grinding tool

guide has been renewed before: '+' indicates that the guide has been renewed once before, and '-' indicates that the guide has been renewed twice before.

9 Valve guide renewal is best carried out by an engine overhaul specialist, as the cylinder head must be evenly heated to remove and fit the guides, and the guides must be accurately reamed once fitted.

Valves

10 Examine the head of each valve for pitting, burning, cracks and general wear, then check the valve stem for scoring and wear ridges. Rotate the valve and check for any obvious indication that it is bent. Look for pits and excessive wear on the tip of each valve stem. Renew any valve that shows any such signs of wear or damage.

11 If the valve appears satisfactory at this stage, measure the valve stem diameter at several points by using a micrometer **(see illustration)**. Any significant difference in the readings obtained indicates wear of the valve stem. Should any of these conditions be apparent, the valve(s) must be renewed.

12 If the valves are in satisfactory condition they should be ground (lapped) into their respective seats to ensure a smooth gas-tight seal. If the seat is only lightly pitted, or if it has been recut, fine grinding compound only should be used to produce the required finish. Coarse valve-grinding compound should not be used unless a seat is badly burned or deeply pitted. If this is the case, the cylinder head and valves should be inspected by an expert to decide whether seat recutting or even the renewal of the valve or seat insert is required.

13 Valve grinding is carried out as follows. Place the cylinder head upside down on a bench.

14 Smear a trace of (the appropriate grade of) valve-grinding compound on the seat face and press a suction grinding tool onto the valve head. With a semi-rotary action, grind the valve head to its seat, lifting the valve occasionally to redistribute the grinding compound **(see illustration)**. A light spring placed under the valve head will greatly ease this operation.

15 If coarse grinding compound is being used, work only until a dull, matt even surface is produced on both the valve seat and the valve, then wipe off the used compound and repeat the process with fine compound. When a smooth unbroken ring of light grey matt finish is produced on both the valve and seat, the grinding operation is complete. Do not grind in the valves any further than absolutely necessary, or the seat will be prematurely sunk into the cylinder head.

16 To check that the seat has not been over-ground, measure the valve head recess, as described in paragraph 7.

17 When all the valves have been ground-in, carefully wash off all traces of grinding compound using paraffin or a suitable solvent.

Valve components

18 Examine the valve springs for signs of damage and discoloration and also measure their free length using vernier calipers or a rule, or by comparing each existing spring with a new component **(see illustration)**.

19 Stand each spring on a flat surface and check it for squareness. If any of the springs are damaged, distorted or have lost their tension, then obtain a complete new set of springs.

20 Check the hydraulic tappets as described in Part B of this Chapter.

8 Cylinder head – reassembly

Note: *A valve spring compressor tool will be required for this operation. New valve spring lower seat/stem oil seals will be required.*

1 Lubricate the valve stems with clean engine oil and insert each valve into its original location **(see illustration)**. If new valves are being fitted, insert them into the locations to which they have been ground.

2 Working on the first valve, dip the **new** spring lower seat/stem seal in clean engine oil then carefully locate it over the valve and onto the guide. Take care not to damage the seal as it is passed over the valve stem. Press the seal firmly onto the guide **(see illustration)**.

3 Locate the spring on the seat, followed by the spring retainer **(see illustrations)**.

4 Compress the valve spring and locate the

7.18 Measuring a valve spring free length

split collets in the recess in the valve stem. Use a little grease to hold the collets in place **(see illustration)**. Release the compressor, then repeat the procedure on the remaining valves.

5 With all the valves installed, rest the cylinder head on wooden blocks or stands (**do not** rest the head flat on a bench) and, using a hammer and interposed block of wood, tap the end of each valve stem to settle the components.

6 Refit the hydraulic tappets and camshaft as described in Part B of this Chapter.

9 Piston/connecting rod assembly – removal

Note: *The big-end bearing caps may be secured to the connecting rods by nuts, or*

bolts, depending on engine type. On engines where the big-end bearing caps are secured by bolts, 'fracture-split' connecting rod/bearing cap assemblies are fitted (big-end bearing caps secured by bolts) – each connecting rod/bearing cap is manufactured as a one-piece component, and then 'fractured' to give the connecting rod and bearing cap. On engines with fracture-split assemblies, each bearing cap is therefore perfectly matched to its respective connecting rod, and the big-end bolts are offset to prevent incorrect fitting of the bearing cap.

1 Remove the cylinder head as described in Chapter 2B.

2 Remove the sump and oil pick-up pipe, as described in Chapter 2B.

3 If the connecting rods and big-end caps are not marked to indicate their positions in the cylinder block (ie, marked with cylinder numbers), centre-punch them at adjacent points either side of the cap/rod joint. Note to which side of the engine the marks face **(see illustration)**.

4 Unscrew the big-end cap nuts or bolts (as applicable) from the first connecting rod, and remove the cap **(see illustration)**. Tape the cap and the shell together to enable subsequent examination. Similarly, the big-end cap nuts or bolts (as applicable) must be kept in their original locations, with their original connecting rod/bearing cap assemblies (refit the nuts/bolts once the relevant piston/connecting rod assembly has been removed).

5 Check the top of the cylinder bore for a

8.1 Lubricate the valve stems with clean engine oil

8.2 Fitting a valve spring lower seat/stem seal

8.3a Refit the spring . . .

8.3b . . . followed by the spring retainer

8.4 Use a little grease to hold the split collets in place

9.3 Connecting rod and big-end cap identification markings

9.4 Removing a big-end bearing cap

wear ridge. If evident, carefully scrape it away with a ridge reamer tool, otherwise the piston rings may jam against the ridge as the piston is pushed out of the block.

6 Place the wooden handle of a hammer

10.5 Checking crankshaft endfloat using a dial gauge

10.8 Removing a main bearing cap

11.1 Removing a piston oil spray jet

against the bottom of the connecting rod, and push the piston/rod assembly up and out of the cylinder bore. Take care to keep the connecting rods clear of the cylinder bore walls, and be careful not to damage the piston oil spray jets fitted to the cylinder block. Recover the bearing shell, and tape it to the connecting rod if it is to be re-used.

7 Remove the remaining three assemblies in a similar way. Rotate the crankshaft as necessary to bring the big-end nuts or bolts (as applicable) to the most accessible position.

10 Crankshaft – removal

Note: *A dial gauge will be required to check crankshaft endfloat.*

10.6 Main bearing cap identification markings

10.10 Extract the thrustwashers from the centre main bearing location

11.2 Removing a core plug using a slide hammer

1 Remove the flywheel, and the crankshaft left-hand oil seal, as described in Chapter 2B.
2 Remove the pistons and connecting rods, as described in Section 9.
3 Remove the oil pump as described in Chapter 2B.
4 Invert the cylinder block so that the crankshaft is uppermost.
5 Before removing the crankshaft, check the endfloat using a dial gauge in contact with the end of the crankshaft. Push the crankshaft fully one way, and then zero the gauge. Push the crankshaft fully the other way, and check the endfloat **(see illustration)**. The result should be compared with the specified limit, and will give an indication as to whether new thrust bearing shells are required.
6 The main bearing caps are normally numbered 1 to 5 from the timing belt end of the engine **(see illustration)**. If the bearing caps are not marked, centre-punch them to indicate their locations, and note to which side of the engine the marks face.
7 Starting with the centre bearing cap, and working progressively outwards, unscrew and remove the main bearing cap bolts. Keep all the bolts in their fitted order.
8 Using the fingers only, rock each main bearing cap until it is released from its locating dowels **(see illustration)**. **Do not** tap the bearing caps sideways to release them. Recover the bearing shells if they are loose, and tape them to their respective caps.
9 Lift the crankshaft from the crankcase. Take care, the crankshaft if heavy! Take care not to damage the piston oil spay jets fitted to the cylinder block.
10 Extract the upper bearing shells, and identify them for position. Similarly, extract the two thrustwashers from the centre bearing location **(see illustration)**.

11 Cylinder block/crankcase – cleaning and inspection

Cleaning

1 Before proceeding, unscrew the securing bolts, and remove the piston oil spray jets from the cylinder block **(see illustration)**. Note that each spray jet is located by a roll-pin.
2 For complete cleaning, ideally the core plugs should be removed, where fitted. Drill a small hole in the plugs, then insert a self-tapping screw, and pull out the plugs using a pair of grips or a slide hammer **(see illustration)**. Also remove all external components (senders, sensors, brackets, etc).
3 Scrape all traces of gasket from the cylinder block, taking particular care not to damage the cylinder head and sump mating faces.
4 Remove all oil gallery plugs, where fitted. The plugs are usually very tight – they may have to be drilled out and the holes retapped. Use new plugs when the engine is reassembled.

11.8 Clean out the threaded holes in the cylinder block using the correct-size tap

11.11 Apply thread-locking fluid to the oil spray jet securing bolts

11.15 Measuring a cylinder bore diameter using an internal micrometer

5 If the block is extremely dirty, it should be steam-cleaned.

6 If the block has been steam-cleaned, clean all oil holes and oil galleries one more time on completion. Flush all internal passages with warm water until the water runs clear. Dry the block thoroughly, and wipe all machined surfaces with a light oil. If you have access to compressed air, use it to speed the drying process, and to blow out all the oil holes and galleries.

 Warning: Wear eye protection when using compressed air.

7 If the block is relatively clean, an adequate cleaning job can be achieved with hot soapy water and a stiff brush. Take plenty of time, and do a thorough job. Regardless of the cleaning method used, be sure to clean all oil holes and galleries very thoroughly, dry the block completely, and coat all machined surfaces with light oil.

8 The threaded holes in the cylinder block must be clean, to ensure accurate torque readings when tightening fixings during reassembly. Run the correct-size tap (which can be determined from the size of the relevant bolt) into each of the holes to remove rust, corrosion, thread sealant or other contamination, and to restore damaged threads **(see illustration)**. If possible, use compressed air to clear the holes of debris produced by this operation. Do not forget to clean the threads of all bolts and nuts as well.

9 After coating the mating surfaces of the new core plugs with suitable sealant, fit them to the cylinder block. Make sure that they are driven in straight and seated correctly, or leakage could result. Special tools are available to fit the core plugs, but a large socket, with an outside diameter which will just fit into the core plug, will work just as well.

10 Where applicable, apply suitable sealant to the new oil gallery plugs, and insert them into the relevant holes in the cylinder block. Tighten the plugs securely.

11 Thoroughly clean the piston oil spray jets and their securing bolts. Examine the spray jets for damage or distortion, and renew if necessary. Ensure that the oil spray jets are clear, and that the locating roll-pins are in position in the cylinder block, then refit the

spray jets, ensuring that they locate with the roll-pins. Apply a little thread-locking fluid to the threads of each oil spray jet securing bolt, then refit the bolt and tighten to the specified torque **(see illustration)**.

Caution: Ensure that the thread-locking fluid does not enter the oil hole in the oil spray jet securing bolt.

12 If the engine is to be left dismantled for some time, refit the main bearing caps, tighten the bolts finger-tight, and cover the cylinder block with a large plastic bag to keep it clean and prevent corrosion.

Inspection

13 Visually check the block for cracks, rust and corrosion. Look for stripped threads in the threaded holes (it may be possible to recut stripped threads using a suitable tap). If there has been any history of internal coolant leakage, it may be worthwhile asking an engine overhaul specialist to check the block using special equipment. If defects are found, have the block repaired if possible, otherwise a new block may be the only option.

14 Examine the cylinder bores for taper, ovality, scoring and scratches. Start by carefully examining the top of the cylinder bores. If they are at all worn, a very slight ridge will be found on the thrust side. This marks the top of the piston ring travel.

15 Measure the bore diameter of each cylinder approximately 70 mm from the top of the bore, parallel to the crankshaft axis **(see illustration)**.

16 Next, measure the bore diameter at right-angles to the crankshaft axis. Compare the results with the figures given in the Specifications.

17 Repeat the procedure for the remaining cylinders.

18 If the cylinder wear exceeds the permitted tolerances, or if the cylinder walls are badly scored or scuffed, then the cylinder block and pistons **must** be renewed. Note that it is not possible to rebore the cylinder block, as only one size of piston is available for this engine. Similarly, **do not** attempt to hone or 'glaze-bust' the cylinder bores.

12 Piston/connecting rod assembly – inspection

1 Before the inspection process can begin, the piston/connecting rod assemblies must be cleaned, and the original piston rings removed from the pistons.

2 Carefully expand the old rings over the top of the pistons. The use of two or three old feeler blades will be helpful in preventing the rings dropping into empty grooves **(see illustration)**. Take care, however, as piston rings are sharp.

3 Scrape away all traces of carbon from the top of the piston. A hand-held wire brush, or a piece of fine emery cloth, can be used once the majority of the deposits have been scraped away.

4 Remove the carbon from the ring grooves in the piston, using an old ring. Break the ring in half to do this (be careful not to cut your fingers – piston rings are sharp). Be very careful to remove only the carbon deposits – do not remove any metal, and do not nick or scratch the sides of the ring grooves.

5 Once the deposits have been removed, clean the piston/connecting rod assembly with paraffin or a suitable solvent, and dry thoroughly. Make sure that the oil return holes in the ring grooves are clear.

6 If the pistons and cylinder bores are not damaged or worn excessively, the original pistons can be refitted. Normal piston wear shows up as even vertical wear on the piston

12.2 Removing a piston ring with the aid of a feeler blade

12.10a Measure the diameter of the pistons . . .

12.10b . . . across the bare metal surfaces (arrowed) of the piston skirt

thrust surfaces, and slight looseness of the top ring in its groove. New piston rings should always be used when the engine is reassembled.

7 Carefully inspect each piston for cracks around the skirt, at the gudgeon pin bosses, and at the piston ring lands (between the ring grooves).

8 Look for scoring and scuffing on the thrust faces of the piston skirt, holes in the piston crown, and burned areas at the edge of the crown. If the skirt is scored or scuffed, the engine may have been suffering from overheating, and/or abnormal combustion ('pinking') which caused excessively-high operating temperatures. The cooling and lubrication systems should be checked thoroughly. A hole in the piston crown, or burned areas at the edge of the piston crown indicates that abnormal combustion (pre-ignition, pinking, knocking, or detonation) has been occurring. If any of the above problems exist, the causes must be investigated and corrected, or the damage will occur again. The causes may include incorrect fuel injection pump timing, inlet air leaks, or a faulty fuel injector.

9 Corrosion of the piston, in the form of pitting, indicates that coolant has been leaking into the combustion chamber and/or the crankcase. Again, the cause must be corrected, or the problem may persist in the rebuilt engine.

10 Check the piston-to-bore clearance by measuring the cylinder bore (see Section 11) and the piston diameter. Measure the piston 44 mm from the bottom of the skirt, at a 90°

angle to the gudgeon pin. Note that the measurement should be made on the bare metal surfaces of the piston skirt, **not** on the graphite-coated areas **(see illustrations)**. Subtract the piston diameter from the bore diameter to obtain the clearance. If this is greater than the figures given in the Specifications, and the cylinder bore diameter is within limits, new pistons must be fitted. If the cylinder bore is worn beyond the specified limits, the block and pistons **must** be renewed. Note that it is not possible to rebore the cylinder block, as only one size of piston is available for this engine. Similarly, **do not** attempt to hone or glaze-bust the cylinder bores.

11 Alternatively, the piston-to-bore clearance can be measured as follows. Invert the piston, and slide it into the relevant cylinder bore, with the arrow on the piston crown pointing towards the flywheel end of the cylinder block. Position the piston with the bottom of the skirt 25 mm below the top of the cylinder bore. Using a feeler blade, measure the clearance between the piston skirt and the left-hand side of the cylinder bore (when viewed with the cylinder block inverted, from the timing belt end of the cylinder block).

12 Examine each connecting rod carefully for signs of damage, such as cracks around the big-end and small-end bearings. Check that the rod is not bent or distorted. Damage is highly unlikely, unless the engine has been seized or badly overheated. Detailed checking of the connecting rod assembly can only be carried out by a Rover dealer or engine repair specialist with the necessary equipment.

13 The gudgeon pins are of the floating type, secured in position by two circlips. The pistons and connecting rods can be separated as follows.

14 Using a small flat-bladed screwdriver, prise out the circlips, and push out the gudgeon pin **(see illustrations)**. Hand pressure should be sufficient to remove the pin. Identify the piston and rod to ensure correct reassembly. Discard the circlips – new ones **must** be used on refitting.

15 Examine the gudgeon pin and connecting rod small-end bearing for signs of wear or damage. It should be possible to push the gudgeon pin through the connecting rod bush by hand, without noticeable play. If the connecting rod bush is worn, the connecting rod must be renewed – it is not possible to renew the bushes.

16 Similarly, check the fit of the gudgeon pin in its relevant piston. The pin must be a tight sliding fit, with no perceptible side play.

17 Measure the diameter of the gudgeon pin **(see illustration)**. If the diameter is less than the specified limit, or if excessive side play in the piston is evident, the gudgeon pin and piston must be renewed as an assembly.

18 Repeat the checking procedure for the remaining pistons, connecting rods and gudgeon pins.

19 The connecting rods themselves should not be in need of renewal, unless seizure or some other major mechanical failure has occurred. Check the alignment of the connecting rods visually, and if the rods are not straight, take them to an engine overhaul specialist for a more detailed check.

20 Examine all components, and obtain any new parts from your Rover dealer. If new pistons are purchased, they will be supplied complete with gudgeon pins and circlips. Circlips can also be purchased individually. Note that on models with fracture split connecting rod/bearing cap assemblies (big-end bearing caps secured by bolts), if a connecting rod requires renewal, it can only be renewed as an assembly with the relevant bearing cap.

21 Position the piston in relation to the connecting rod, as follows **(see illustrations)**.

a) **On models where the big-end bearing caps are secured by nuts,** *the bearing*

12.14a Prise out the circlips . . .

12.14b . . . and push the gudgeon pin from the piston

12.17 Measuring the diameter of a gudgeon pin

shell tag recess in the connecting rod should be positioned to the left of the arrow on the piston crown, when the piston is viewed from the flywheel end.

b) **On models where the big-end bearing caps are secured by bolts,** *the cast boss on the connecting rod should be positioned on the same side of the assembly as the arrow on the piston crown.*

22 Apply a smear of clean engine oil to the gudgeon pin. Slide it into the piston and through the connecting rod small-end. Check that the piston pivots freely on the rod, then secure the gudgeon pin in position with two new circlips. Ensure that each circlip is correctly located in its groove in the piston.

23 On engines where the big-end bearing caps are secured by nuts, using the fingers only, check that each big-end bearing cap nut rotates freely on the threads of its respective bolt. If any nut is tight, then both bolts and nuts from the relevant connecting rod must be renewed.

24 On engines where the big-end bearing caps are secured by bolts, using the fingers only, check that each bolt turns freely in its connecting rod. If there is any sign of binding in the threads, the bolts must be renewed.

13 Crankshaft – inspection

1 Clean the crankshaft using paraffin or a suitable solvent, and dry it, preferably with compressed air if available. Be sure to clean the oil holes with a pipe cleaner or similar probe, to ensure that they are not obstructed.

 Warning: Wear eye protection when using compressed air.

2 Check the main and big-end bearing journals for uneven wear, scoring, pitting and cracking.

3 Big-end bearing wear is accompanied by distinct metallic knocking when the engine is running (particularly noticeable when the engine is pulling from low revs), and some loss of oil pressure.

4 Main bearing wear is accompanied by severe engine vibration and rumble – getting progressively worse as engine revs increase – and again by loss of oil pressure.

5 Check the bearing journal for roughness by running a finger lightly over the bearing surface. Any roughness (which will be accompanied by obvious bearing wear) indicates that the crankshaft requires renewing.

6 Using a micrometer, measure the diameter of the main and big-end bearing journals, and compare the results with the Specifications at the beginning of this Chapter **(see illustration)**. By measuring the diameter at a number of points around each journal's circumference, you will be able to determine whether or not the journal is out-of-round.

12.21a Piston and connecting rod identification

A *Assembly with big-end bearing cap secured by nuts*
B *Assembly with big-end bearing cap secured by bolts*

Take the measurement at each end of the journal, near the webs, to determine if the journal is tapered. If the crankshaft journals are damaged, tapered, out-of-round or excessively-worn, the crankshaft must be renewed. It is not possible to regrind the crankshaft.

7 Check the oil seal contact surfaces at each end of the crankshaft for wear and damage. If the seal has worn an excessive groove in the surface of the crankshaft, consult an engine overhaul specialist, who will be able to advise whether a repair is possible, or whether a new crankshaft is necessary.

14 Main and big-end bearings – inspection

1 Even though the main and big-end bearings **must** be renewed during the engine overhaul, the old bearings should be retained for close examination, as they may reveal valuable information about the condition of the engine.

2 Bearing failure can occur due to lack of

13.6 Measuring the diameter of a crankshaft big-end bearing journal

12.21b Where the bearing caps are secured by nuts, the bearing shell tag recess in the connecting rod . . .

12.21c . . . should be positioned to the left of the arrow on the piston crown when the piston is viewed from the flywheel end

lubrication, the presence of dirt or other foreign particles, overloading the engine, or corrosion **(see illustration)**. Regardless of the cause of bearing failure, the cause must be corrected (where applicable) before the engine is reassembled, to prevent it from happening again.

14.2 Typical bearing failures

3 When examining the bearing shells, remove them from the cylinder block/crankcase, the main bearing caps, the connecting rods and the connecting rod big-end bearing caps. Lay them out on a clean surface in the same general position as their location in the engine. This will enable you to match any bearing problems with the corresponding crankshaft journal.

4 Dirt and other foreign matter gets into the engine in a variety of ways. It may be left in the engine during assembly, or it may pass through filters or the crankcase ventilation system. It may get into the oil, and from there into the bearings. Metal chips from machining operations and normal engine wear are often present. Abrasives are sometimes left in engine components after reconditioning, especially when parts are not thoroughly cleaned using the proper cleaning methods. Whatever the source, these foreign objects often end up embedded in the soft bearing material, and are easily recognised. Large particles will not embed in the bearing, and will score or gouge the bearing and journal. The best prevention for this cause of bearing failure is to clean all parts thoroughly, and keep everything spotlessly-clean during engine assembly. Frequent and regular engine oil and filter changes are also recommended.

5 Lack of lubrication (or lubrication breakdown) has a number of interrelated causes. Excessive heat (which thins the oil), overloading (which squeezes the oil from the bearing face) and oil leakage (from excessive bearing clearances, worn oil pump or high engine speeds) all contribute to lubrication breakdown. Blocked oil passages, which usually are the result of misaligned oil holes in a bearing shell, will also oil-starve a bearing, and destroy it. When lack of lubrication is the cause of bearing failure, the bearing material is wiped or extruded from the steel backing of the bearing. Temperatures may increase to the point where the steel backing turns blue from overheating.

6 Driving habits can have a definite effect on bearing life. Full-throttle, low-speed operation (labouring the engine) puts very high loads on bearings, tending to squeeze out the oil film. These loads cause the bearings to flex, which produces fine cracks in the bearing face (fatigue failure). Eventually, the bearing material will loosen in pieces, and tear away from the steel backing.

7 Short-distance driving leads to corrosion of bearings, because insufficient engine heat is produced to evaporate off the condensed water and corrosive gases. These products collect in the engine oil, forming acid and sludge. As the oil is carried to the engine bearings, the acid attacks and corrodes the bearing material.

8 Incorrect bearing installation during engine assembly will lead to bearing failure as well. Tight-fitting bearings leave insufficient bearing running clearance, and will result in oil starvation. Dirt or foreign particles trapped

16.4 Measuring a piston ring end gap

behind a bearing shell result in high spots on the bearing, which lead to failure.

9 As mentioned at the beginning of this Section, the bearing shells must be renewed during engine overhaul, regardless of their condition.

15 Engine overhaul – reassembly sequence

1 Before reassembly begins, ensure that all new parts have been obtained and that all necessary tools are available. Read through the entire procedure to familiarise yourself with the work involved and to ensure that all items necessary for reassembly of the engine are at hand. In addition to all normal tools and materials, it will be necessary to obtain suitable thread-locking compound, and various Rover sealants – refer to the relevant Sections in this Part of the Chapter and Part B for details. Carefully read the instructions supplied with the appropriate sealant kit.

2 In order to save time and avoid problems, engine reassembly can be carried out in the following order, referring to Part B of this Chapter when necessary. Where applicable, use new gaskets and seals when refitting the various components.

a) *Crankshaft.*
b) *Piston/connecting rod assemblies.*
c) *Oil pump.*
d) *Sump.*
e) *Crankshaft left-hand oil seal and flywheel.*
f) *Cylinder head.*

16.9 Piston ring fitting details

g) *Timing belt rear cover, tensioner and sprockets, and timing belt.*
h) *Engine external components.*

3 At this stage, all engine components should be absolutely clean and dry, with all faults repaired, and should be laid out (or in individual containers) on a completely clean work surface.

16 Piston rings – refitting

1 Before fitting new piston rings, the ring end gaps must be checked as follows.

2 Lay out the piston/connecting rod assemblies and the new piston ring sets, so that the ring sets will be matched with the same piston and cylinder during the end gap measurement and subsequent engine reassembly.

3 Insert the top ring into the first cylinder bore, and push it down the bore using the top of the piston. This will ensure that the ring remains square with the cylinder walls. Position the ring 30 mm from the top of the bore. Note that the top and second compression rings are different. The second ring is easily identified by the step on its lower surface.

4 Measure the end gap using feeler blades **(see illustration)**. Compare the measurements with the figures given in the Specifications.

5 If the gap is too small (unlikely if genuine Rover parts are used), it must be enlarged, or the ring ends may contact each other during engine operation, causing serious damage. Ideally, new piston rings providing the correct end gap should be fitted. As a last resort, the end gap can be increased by filing the ring ends very carefully with a fine file. Mount the file in a vice equipped with soft jaws, slip the ring over the file with the ends contacting the file face, and slowly move the ring to remove material from the ends.

Caution: Take care, as the piston rings are sharp, and are easily broken.

6 With new piston rings, it is unlikely that the end gap will be too large. If the gaps are too large, check that you have the correct rings for your engine and for the particular cylinder bore size.

7 Repeat the checking procedure for each ring in the first cylinder, and then for the rings in the remaining cylinders. Remember to keep rings, pistons and cylinders matched up.

8 Once the ring end gaps have been checked and if necessary corrected, the rings can be fitted to the pistons.

9 Fit the piston rings using the same technique as for removal. Fit the bottom (oil control) ring first, and work up. Ensure that the rings are fitted the correct way up – the top surface of the rings is normally marked TOP **(see illustration)**. Arrange the gaps of the top and second compression rings 120° from

17.4a Ensure that the tab (arrowed) engages with the notch in the main bearing cap

17.4b Press the bearing shells into their locations in the cylinder block . . .

17.4c . . . making sure that they are located centrally

each other, away from the thrust side of the piston. **Note:** *Always follow any instructions supplied with the new piston ring sets – different manufacturers may specify different procedures. Do not mix up the top and second compression rings, as they have different cross-sections.*

17 Crankshaft – refitting

Note: *New main bearing shells must be fitted on reassembly.*

1 After inspecting the crankshaft, and renewing it if necessary, as described in Section 13, proceed as follows.

2 Check that the main bearing cap locating dowels are in position in the cylinder block, and that the main bearing cap bolt holes are clean and dry.

3 Clean the backs of the new bearing shells, and the bearing locations in both the cylinder block/crankcase and the main bearing caps. Ensure that all traces of the protective grease are cleaned off the new bearing shells using paraffin. Wipe the shells dry with a lint-free cloth.

4 Press the bearing shells into their locations in the cylinder block and bearing caps, noting that the bearing shells with the oil grooves fit into the upper locations (in the cylinder block/crankcase). Take care not to touch any shell bearing surface with your fingers. Ensure that the tab on each lower shell engages in the notch in the main bearing cap. The shells in the cylinder block/crankcase have no locating tabs, so make sure that they are located centrally and squarely in their respective positions **(see illustrations)**.

5 Using a little grease, stick the thrustwashers to each side of the centre main bearing upper location in the cylinder block/crankcase. Ensure that the oilway grooves on each thrustwasher face outwards **(see illustration)**.

6 Liberally lubricate each bearing shell in the cylinder block/crankcase, then lower the crankshaft into position **(see illustration)**.

7 Lubricate the bearing shells in the bearing caps, and the crankshaft journals, then fit the

bearing caps, ensuring that they engage with the locating dowels.

8 Ensure that the threads of the main bearing cap bolts are clean, then oil the threads of the bolts, and screw them into their original locations, finger-tight only at this stage **(see illustration)**.

9 Working from the centre main bearing cap outwards, progressively tighten the bearing cap bolts to the specified torque **(see illustration)**.

10 Now rotate the crankshaft, and check that it turns freely, with no signs of binding or tight spots.

11 Check the crankshaft endfloat with reference to Section 10. If the endfloat exceeds the specified limit, remove the crankshaft and fit new thrustwashers. If, with the new thrustwashers fitted, the endfloat is still excessive, the crankshaft must be renewed.

17.5 Ensure that the grooves (arrowed) on the thrustwashers face outwards

17.8 Oil the threads of the main bearing cap bolts

12 Refit the oil pump as described in Chapter 2B.

13 Refit the pistons and connecting rods as described in Section 18.

14 Refit the crankshaft left-hand oil seal and the flywheel as described in Chapter 2B.

18 Piston/connecting rod assembly – refitting

Caution: *Two different types of big-end bearing shells are available, one type for models with fracture-split connecting rod/big-end cap assemblies (big-end bearing caps secured by bolts), and one for models with conventional connecting rod/big-end cap assemblies (big-end bearing caps secured by nuts). The two bearing shell types are not*

17.6 Lubricate the bearing shells in the cylinder block/crankcase

17.9 Tighten the main bearing cap bolts to the specified torque

18.3a Where the big-end caps are secured by nuts, the locating tab (arrowed) on each shell must engage with the notch in the connecting rod

18.3b Where the big-end caps are secured by bolts, the bearing shells must be located centrally in the bearing caps

interchangeable, and it is vital that the correct bearing shells are fitted, depending on engine type – if in doubt, refer to a Rover dealer for advice.
Note: *New big-end bearing shells must be fitted on reassembly.*

1 After inspecting the crankshaft, and renewing it if necessary, as described in Section 13, proceed as follows.

2 Clean the backs of the new bearing shells, and the bearing locations in both the connecting rods and the big-end bearing caps. Ensure that all traces of the protective grease are cleaned off the new bearing shells using paraffin. Wipe the shells dry with a lint-free cloth.

3 Press the bearing shells into their locations. On models where the big-end caps are secured by nuts, ensure that the locating tab on each shell engages with the notch in the connecting rod or big-end cap. On models where the big-end caps are secured by bolts, the shells have no locating tabs, so make sure that they are located centrally and squarely in their respective positions in the connecting rods and bearing caps **(see illustrations)**. Take care not to touch any shell bearing surface with your fingers.

4 Liberally lubricate the big-end bearing journals on the crankshaft.

5 Lubricate No 1 piston and piston rings, and check that the ring gaps are correctly

positioned. The gaps of the top and second compression rings should be arranged 120° from each other, away from the thrust side of the piston.

6 Liberally lubricate the cylinder bore with clean engine oil.

7 Fit a ring compressor to No 1 piston, then insert the piston and connecting rod into the cylinder bore so that the base of the compressor stands on the block. With the crankshaft big-end bearing journal positioned at its lowest point, tap the piston carefully into the cylinder bore with the wooden handle of a hammer **(see illustration)**. Note that the arrow on the piston crown must point towards the timing belt end of the engine. Check that the cut-out in the piston skirt is positioned above the oil spray jet location. Take care not to allow the connecting rod (and the big-end bolts) to contact the cylinder bore.

8 Guide the connecting rod onto the big-end bearing journal, taking care not to displace the bearing shell, then refit the big-end bearing cap. On engines where the big-end bearing caps are secured by nuts, make sure that the tapered portion of the machined flat on the cap is facing towards the timing belt end of the engine. On engines where the big-end bearing caps are secured by bolts, make sure that the identification marks on the connecting rod and big-end cap are on the same side of the engine.

9 Lubricate the threads of the big-end studs or bolts (as applicable) with clean engine oil, then fit the nuts or bolts (as applicable), and tighten to the specified torque wrench setting **(see illustration)**. **Note:** *The torque wrench setting for engines where the big-end bearing caps are secured by nuts is different to that for engines where the bearing caps are secured by bolts.*

10 Repeat the procedure to refit the remaining three piston/connecting rod assemblies.

11 Refit the oil pick-up pipe and the sump, as described in Chapter 2B.

12 Refit the cylinder head as described in Chapter 2B.

19 Engine –
initial start-up after overhaul

1 With the engine refitted to the vehicle, double-check the engine oil and coolant levels. Make a final check to ensure that everything has been reconnected and that there are no tools or rags left in the engine compartment.

2 To prevent the engine from starting during initial cranking, remove the fuel pump fuse from the engine bay fusebox – see *Wiring Diagrams*. Operate the starter motor and check that cranking is satisfactory, with no unusual noises. Ensure that the oil pressure warning light goes out during cranking.

3 Prime the fuel system – see Chapter 4B.

4 Fit the fuel pump fuse. **Note:** *Because fuel system components will be empty, the engine may take longer than normal to start.*

5 When the preheating indicator lamp has gone out, start the engine, and ensure that the oil pressure warning light goes off during cranking, or immediately the engine starts. Allow the engine to idle.

6 While the engine is idling, check for fuel, coolant and oil leaks. Do not be alarmed if there are some odd smells and smoke from parts getting hot and burning off oil deposits. If the hydraulic tappets have been disturbed, some valve gear noise may be heard at first; this should disappear as the oil circulates fully around the engine and normal pressure is restored in the tappets.

7 Keep the engine idling until hot coolant is felt circulating through the radiator top hose, then stop the engine.

8 After a few minutes, recheck the oil and coolant levels and top up as necessary.

9 If new pistons, rings or crankshaft bearings have been fitted, the engine must be run-in for the first 500 miles (800 km). Do not operate the engine at full throttle or allow it to labour in any gear during this period. It is recommended that the oil and filter be changed at the end of this period.

18.7 Refitting a piston/connecting rod assembly using a piston ring compressor and a hammer handle

18.9 Tightening a big-end bearing cap nut to the specified torque

Chapter 3
Cooling, heating and ventilation systems

Contents

Degrees of difficulty

Easy, suitable for novice with little experience	**Fairly easy,** suitable for beginner with some experience	**Fairly difficult,** suitable for competent DIY mechanic	**Difficult,** suitable for experienced DIY mechanic	**Very difficult,** suitable for expert DIY or professional

Specifications

System

Type .... Pressurised, pump-assisted thermo-syphon with front mounted radiator and thermostatically-controlled electric cooling fan

Thermostat

Type .... Wax
Start of opening temperature:
  Petrol models .... 88 ± 2°C
  Diesel models .... n/a
Fully open temperature:
  Petrol models .... 100 ± 2°C
  Diesel models .... 82 ± 5°C

Expansion tank

Cap opening pressure .... 0.9 to 1.2 bar

Cooling fan

	On	Off
Operating temperature (petrol models):		
Models without air conditioning	104°C	98°C
Models with air conditioning:		
Low speed	104°C	98°C
High speed	112°C	106°C
Operating temperature (diesel models):		
Models without air conditioning	104°C	94°C
Models with air conditioning:		
Low speed	104°C	94°C
High speed	112°C	106°C

Torque wrench settings

Cooling system	Nm	lbf ft
Coolant pump bolts	10	7
Coolant rail-to-cylinder block bolts	25	18
Cooling fan housing bolts	9	7
Expansion tank bolts	5	4
Intercooler-to-radiator bolts	25	18
Radiator upper mounting bracket bolts (petrol models)	9	7
Radiator upper mounting bracket mounting bolts (diesel models)	25	18
Temperature gauge sender unit	15	11
Thermostat housing cover bolts	9	7

Torque wrench settings (continued)

	Nm	lbf ft
Heating system		
Heater blower motor mounting screw	10	7
Heater lower mounting nut	22	16
Air conditioning system		
Bonnet lock upright mounting bolts	9	7
Compressor refrigerant pipe union bolt	35	26
Compressor-to-mounting bracket bolts	25	18
Condenser mounting bolts	9	7
Condenser refrigerant pipe union screws	6	4
Receiver/drier clamp bracket screws	10	7
Receiver/drier refrigerant pipe union	5	4
Trinary switch	12	9

---

1 General information and precautions

General information

The cooling system is of the pressurised, pump-assisted thermo-syphon type. It consists of the front-mounted radiator, a translucent expansion tank mounted on the right-hand inner wing, a thermostatically-controlled electric cooling fan mounted on the rear of the radiator, a thermostat and a centrifugal coolant pump, as well as the connecting hoses **(see illustrations)**. The coolant pump is driven by the engine timing belt on petrol models. On diesel models, the coolant pump arrangement is unusual: the pump itself is mounted in a housing that is shared with the power steering pump. Drive is taken indirectly from the auxiliary drivebelt via a shaft that extends into the coolant pump housing from the rear of the power steering pump.

The cooling system is of the by-pass type, allowing coolant to circulate around the engine while the thermostat is closed. With the engine cold, the thermostat closes off the coolant feed from the bottom radiator hose. Coolant is then drawn into the engine via the heater matrix, inlet manifold and from the top of the cylinder block. This allows some heat transfer, by conduction, to the radiator through the top hose whilst retaining the majority of heat within the cylinder block.

The siting of the thermostat in the intake rather than the outlet side of the system ensures that the engine warms-up quickly by circulating a small amount of coolant around a shorter tract. This also prevents temperature build-up in the cylinder head prior to the thermostat opening.

When the coolant reaches a predetermined temperature, the thermostat opens and the coolant is allowed to flow freely through the top hose to the radiator. As the coolant circulates through the radiator, it is cooled by the in-rush of air when the vehicle is in forward motion. Airflow is supplemented by the action of the electric cooling fan when necessary. Upon reaching the bottom of the radiator, the coolant is now cooled and the cycle is repeated.

H44817

**1.1a Cooling system component layout –
1.4 and 1.6 litre petrol engine models without air conditioning**

1 Hose	6 Bleed screw	12 Hose
2 Heater control valve	7 Hose	13 Coolant pump
3 Expansion tank	8 Fan	14 Hose
4 Hose	9 Hose	15 Thermostat housing
5 Hose	10 Radiator	16 Hose
	11 Coolant outlet elbow	

**1.1b Cooling system component layout –
1.4 and 1.6 litre petrol engine models with
air conditioning, and 1.8 litre**

1   Hose
2   Heater control valve
3   Expansion tank
4   Hose
5   Hose
6   Bleed screw
7   Hose
8   Fan
9   Hose
10 Radiator
11 Coolant outlet elbow
12 Hose
13 Coolant pump
14 Hose
15 Thermostat housing
16 Hose

H44824

**1.1c Cooling system component layout –
diesel engine models**

1   Heater control valve
2   Hose
3   Hose
4   Hose
5   Expansion tank
6   Hose
6   Bleed screw
7   Hose
8   Hose
9   Radiator
10 Hose
11 Oil cooler
12 Hose
13 Thermostat housing
14 Fan
15 EGR cooler
16 Hose
17 Hose

H44825

With the engine at normal operating temperature, the coolant expands and some of it is displaced into the expansion tank. This coolant collects in the tank and is returned to the radiator when the system cools.

The electric cooling fan mounted behind the radiator is controlled by a thermostatic switch located in the radiator side tank. At a predetermined coolant temperature the switch contacts close, thus actuating the fan.

Precautions

Cooling system

When the engine is hot, the coolant in the cooling system is under high pressure. The increased pressure raises the boiling point of the coolant and this allows the coolant to circulate at temperatures close to 100°C without actually boiling. If the pressure is reduced suddenly, eg, by removing the expansion tank filler cap, the coolant will boil very rapidly, resulting in boiling water and steam being ejected through the expansion tank filler neck. This can happen very quickly and the risk of scalding is high.

For this reason, do not attempt to remove the expansion tank filler cap or to disturb any part of the cooling system whilst the engine is hot. Allow the engine to cool for several hours after switching off. When removing the expansion tank filler cap, as a precaution cover the cap with a thick layer of cloth, to avoid scalding, and slowly unscrew the filler cap until a hissing sound can be heard. When the hissing has stopped, showing that pressure is released, slowly unscrew the filler cap until it can be removed. If more hissing sounds are heard, wait until they have stopped before unscrewing the cap completely. At all times keep well away from the filler opening.

Do not allow antifreeze to come in contact with your skin or painted surfaces of the vehicle. Rinse off spills immediately with plenty of water. Never leave antifreeze lying around, it is fatal if ingested.

If the engine is hot, the electric cooling fan may start rotating even if the engine is not running, so be careful to keep hands, hair and loose clothing well clear when working in the engine compartment.

Air conditioning system

On models equipped with an air conditioning system, it is necessary to observe special precautions whenever dealing with any part of the system, its associated components and any items which necessitate disconnection of the system. If for any reason the system must be disconnected, entrust this task to your Rover dealer or a refrigeration engineer.

The air conditioning system pipes contains pressurised liquid refrigerant. The refrigerant is potentially dangerous, and should only be handled by qualified persons. If it is splashed onto the skin, it can cause severe frostbite. It is not itself poisonous, but in the presence of

3.13 Disconnect radiator top hose

a naked flame (including a cigarette), it forms a poisonous gas. Uncontrolled discharging of the refrigerant is dangerous and is also extremely damaging to the environment. For these reasons, disconnection of any part of the system without specialised knowledge and equipment is not recommended.

Electric cooling fan

If the engine is hot, the electric cooling fan may start rotating without warning even if the engine and ignition are switched off. Be careful to keep your hands, hair and any loose clothing well clear when working in the engine compartment.

2 Cooling system hoses – renewal

> **Warning: Never work on the cooling system when it is hot. Release any pressure from the system by loosening the expansion tank cap, having first covered it with a cloth to avoid any possibility of scalding.**

1 If inspection of the cooling system reveals a faulty hose, then it must be renewed as follows.

2 First drain the cooling system. If the coolant is not due for renewal, it may be re-used if collected in a clean container.

3 To disconnect any hose, use a screwdriver to slacken the clips then move them along the hose clear of the outlet. Carefully work the hose off its outlets. Do not attempt to

3.14 Disconnect radiator bottom hose

disconnect any part of the system when still hot.

4 Note that the radiator hose outlets are fragile. Do not use excessive force when attempting to remove the hoses. If a hose proves stubborn, try to release it by rotating it on its outlets before attempting to work it off. If all else fails, cut the hose with a sharp knife then slit it so that it can be peeled off in two pieces. Although expensive, this is preferable to buying a new radiator.

5 When fitting a hose, first slide the clips onto the hose then work the hose onto its outlets.

> **HAYNES HiNT** *If the hose is stiff, use soap as a lubricant or soften it by first soaking it in boiling water whilst taking care to prevent scalding.*

6 Work each hose end fully onto its outlet, check that the hose is settled correctly and is properly routed, then slide each clip along the hose until it is behind the outlet flared end before tightening it securely.

7 Refill the system with coolant.

8 Check carefully for leaks as soon as possible after disturbing any part of the cooling system.

3 Radiator and expansion tank – removal, inspect and refitting

Removal

Radiator – petrol engines

1 Disconnect the battery earth lead.

2 Drain the cooling system – see Chapter 1A.

3 Remove the radiator cooling fan – see Section 7.

4 Slacken the clip, and disconnect the top hose from the radiator.

5 Support the radiator,

6 Remove two bolts securing radiator top mounting brackets to the bonnet locking platform, and remove the brackets.

7 Disengage the radiator from the lower mountings.

8 Carefully lower and remove the radiator.

Radiator – diesel engines

9 Disconnect the battery earth lead.

10 Drain the cooling system – see Chapter 1B.

11 Remove the intercooler – see Chapter 4B.

12 Remove the radiator cooling fan – see Section 7.

13 Slacken the clip, and disconnect the top hose from the radiator **(see illustration)**.

14 Slacken the clip and disconnect the bottom hose from the radiator **(see illustration)**.

15 Slacken the clip, and disconnect the expansion tank hose from the radiator **(see illustration)**.

3.15 Disconnect expansion tank hose

3.16 Remove upper mounting

3.18 Lift out the radiator

16 Remove the bolt and upper mounting **(see illustration)**.
17 Disengage the radiator from the lower mounting.
18 Carefully lift and remove the radiator **(see illustration)**.

Expansion tank

19 Position a container to collect coolant from expansion tank.
20 Slacken clip and disconnect the coolant feed hose from the expansion tank.
21 Release clip and disconnect bleed hose from the expansion tank.
22 Remove two bolts securing tank to body, and remove tank.

Inspection

Radiator

23 If the radiator was removed because of clogging (causing overheating) then try reverse flushing or, in severe cases, use a radiator cleanser strictly in accordance with the manufacturer's instructions. Ensure that the cleanser is suitable for use in a copper/brass radiator. Refer to the relevant part of Chapter 1 for further information.
24 Use a soft brush and an air line or low pressure garden hose to clear the radiator matrix of leaves, insects etc.

Minor leaks from the radiator can be cured using a suitable sealant with the radiator in situ.

25 Major leaks or extensive damage should

be repaired by a specialist, or the radiator should be renewed or exchanged for a reconditioned unit.
26 Examine the mounting rubbers for signs of damage or deterioration and renew if necessary.

Expansion tank

27 Empty any remaining coolant from the tank and flush it with fresh water to clean it. If the tank is leaking it must be renewed but it is worth first attempting a repair using a proprietary sealant or suitable adhesive.
28 The expansion tank cap should be cleaned and checked whenever it is removed. Check that its sealing surfaces and threads are clean and undamaged and that they mate correctly with those of the expansion tank.
29 The cap's performance can only be checked by using a cap pressure-tester (cooling system tester) with a suitable adaptor. On applying pressure, the cap's pressure relief valve should hold until the specified pressure is reached, at which point the valve should open.
30 If there is any doubt about the cap's performance, then it must be renewed. Ensure that the new one is of the correct type and rating for your engine.

Refitting

31 Refitting is a reversal of the removal procedure, noting:
  Use a torque wrench to tighten bolts to correct torque.
  Top-up the cooling system with a 50/50 mix of water and antifreeze.

4 Thermostat –
removal, test and refitting

Removal

Petrol models

1 Note that access to the thermostat is very limited. Depending on the tools available, it may be easier to raise the front of the vehicle and to work from underneath, ensuring that the vehicle is securely supported on axle stands. In all cases, access is better if the air cleaner is removed.
2 Unbolt the coolant rail from the rear of the cylinder block/crankcase, then slacken the clips and disconnect the heater return hose and coolant rail hose from the thermostat housing **(see illustration)**.
3 Slacken and withdraw the bolt that secures the thermostat housing to the engine block. Note that on some models, the bolt also secure the dipstick tube support bracket in place **(see illustration)**.
4 Release the thermostat housing from the coolant pump and remove it from the vehicle **(see illustration)**.
5 Remove the O-ring seals from the housing stubs and discard them – new seals must be used on refitting.
6 Slacken and remove the three thermostat housing cover bolts, then lift off the housing cover. Remove the thermostat together with its rubber seal **(see illustration overleaf)**.

4.2 Disconnect the coolant rail and heater return hoses (arrowed) from the rear of the thermostat housing

4.3 Slacken and withdraw the bolt that secures the thermostat housing to the engine block

4.4 Release the thermostat housing from the pump and remove it from the vehicle (inlet manifold removed)

**4.6 Thermostat components –
petrol engines**

1 Bolt
2 O-ring seals
3 Thermostat
4 Rubber seal

Diesel engines

Note: *The thermostat is housed in the lower part of the engine oil cooler.*

7 Disconnect the battery earth lead.
8 Apply the handbrake, chock the rear roadwheels, then jack up the front of the car and support it on axle stands (see *Jacking and Vehicle Support*).
9 Remove the engine undertray – two nuts at rear, and two bolts at front.
10 Remove the front suspension front beam – see Chapter 10.
11 Drain the cooling system.
12 Position a container under the oil cooler **(see illustration)**
13 Slacken the clip and release the coolant hose from the thermostat housing at the lower end of the oil cooler.
14 Release the clip and remove the vacuum pump oil hose from the sump.
15 Remove three Torx head screws securing the thermostat housing to the oil cooler, and remove the housing.
16 Remove the O-ring from the oil cooler housing, and remove the thermostat **(see illustration)**.

Testing

17 If the thermostat remains in the open

4.12 Oil cooler location

position at room temperature, then it is faulty and must be renewed.
18 To test it fully, suspend the (closed) thermostat on a length of string in a container of cold water, with a thermometer beside it. Ensure that neither touches the side of the container **(see illustration)**.
19 Heat the water and check the temperature at which the thermostat begins to open. Compare this value with that specified. Continue to heat the water until the thermostat is fully open. The temperature at which this should happen is stamped in the unit's end **(see illustration)**. Remove the thermostat and measure the height of the fully opened valve, then allow the thermostat to cool down and check that it closes fully.
20 If the thermostat does not open and close as described, if it sticks in either position, or if it does not open at the specified temperature, then it must be renewed.

Refitting

Petrol engines

21 Refitting is a reversal of the removal procedure **(see illustration)**, noting:
  Clean the mating faces of the thermostat housing and cylinder block.
  Ensure that the thermostat is correctly seated on the shoulder machined into the housing mating surface.
  Fit a new rubber seal to the thermostat, and new O-rings to the housing stubs.
  Use a torque wrench to tighten the screws to the specified torque.

**4.16 Thermostat components –
diesel engines**

Fill the cooling system – see Chapter 1A.

Diesel engines

22 Refitting is a reversal of the removal procedure, noting:
  Clean the mating faces of the thermostat housing and oil cooler.
  Fit a new O-ring to the oil cooler.
  Use a torque wrench to tighten the screws to the specified torque.
  Fill the cooling system – see Chapter 1B.

5 Coolant pump –
removal and refitting

Removal

Petrol models

1 Coolant pump failure is usually indicated by coolant leaking from the gland behind the pump bearing, or by rough and noisy operation, usually accompanied by excessive pump spindle play. If the pump shows any of these symptoms then it must be renewed as follows.
2 Drain the cooling system, with reference to Chapter 1A.
3 Remove the timing belt, with reference to Chapter 2A.
4 Unscrew the five bolts securing the coolant pump to the cylinder block/crankcase. There are three flange bolts and two pillar bolts; note their relative positions to ensure correct refitting.

4.18 Testing the thermostat

4.19 The stamped marking (arrowed) indicates the temperature at which the thermostat starts to open

4.21 Correctly refitted thermostat and housing (petrol models)

5.6 Removing the coolant pump (petrol models)

5.11 Loosen the clip and disconnect the hose (arrowed) from the rear of the coolant pump (diesel models)

5.12 Removing coolant pump housing cover (diesel models)

5 Unscrew the single bolt securing the pump to the upper timing belt inner cover.

6 Withdraw the coolant pump and discard its sealing ring (which should be renewed whenever it is disturbed) **(see illustration)**.

7 Carefully clean the cylinder block/crankcase and coolant pump mating surfaces.

Diesel models without air conditioning

8 Drain the cooling system, with reference to Chapter 1B.

9 Raise the front of the vehicle and support it securely on axle stands (see *Jacking and Vehicle Support*).

10 Refer to Chapter 10 and remove the front suspension front beam.

11 Loosen the clip and disconnect the hose from the rear of the coolant pump **(see illustration)**.

12 Progressively slacken and withdraw the five securing bolts then remove the coolant pump housing cover. Collect the O-ring seal from the housing and discard it – a new seal must be used on refitting **(see illustration)**.

13 Withdraw the coolant pump from its housing. Collect the two O-ring seals and discard them – new seals must be used on refitting **(see illustration)**.

Diesel models with air conditioning

⚠ **Warning: This procedure involves discharging the refrigerant from the air conditioning system. This is a hazardous operation which MUST be carried out by a Rover dealer or air conditioning specialist. Note that the receiver/drier unit must be renewed whenever the air conditioning system is discharged.**

14 Refer to Chapter 5A and remove the alternator.

15 Drain the cooling system, with reference to Chapter 1B.

16 Slacken the hose clip, disconnect the intercooler air intake hose from the inlet manifold, and move it to one side.

17 Slacken the three hose clips, then disconnect and remove the coolant hose assembly from the radiator, coolant outlet elbow and the thermostat housing.

18 Loosen the clip, disconnect the hose from the front of the coolant pump and move the hose to one side.

19 Have the refrigerant discharged from the air conditioning system by a suitably-equipped expert – refer to the Warning given in Section 1 and the information given at the beginning of this sub-Section.

20 Slacken and withdraw the bolt that secures the refrigerant pipe union to the ports at the top of the air conditioning compressor. Remove the O-ring seals from the compressor ports and discard them – new seals must be used on refitting.

21 With reference to Chapter 9, unscrew the union and disconnect the vacuum pump oil supply from the cylinder block tapping.

22 Progressively slacken and withdraw the five securing bolts then remove the coolant pump housing cover. Collect the O-ring seal from the housing and discard it – a new seal must be used on refitting.

23 Withdraw the coolant pump from the

5.13 Withdrawing the coolant pump from its housing (diesel models)

5.26b ... and the pump housing cover

housing. Collect the two O-ring seals and discard them – new seals must be used on refitting.

Refitting

Petrol models

24 On refitting, install the pump using a new sealing ring and tighten all bolts to the specified torque wrench settings.

25 The remainder of the refitting procedure is the reverse of removal.

Diesel models without air conditioning

26 Refitting is a reversal of removal, noting the following points **(see illustrations)**:

a) *Use new O-ring seals and coat them with Loctite 405 sealing compound.*

b) *Ensure that the power steering pump drive lugs engage with those on the front of the coolant pump.*

5.26a Fit new O-ring seals (arrowed) to the coolant pump ...

5.26c Power steering pump drive lugs (A) must engage with those on the front of the coolant pump (B)

6.8 Remove idler pulley bracket

c) Tighten all bolts to the specified torque setting.

d) Refit the suspension front beam with reference to Chapter 10.

e) Refill the cooling system with reference to Chapter 1B.

Diesel models with air conditioning

27 Refitting is a reversal of removal, noting the following points:

a) Use new O-ring seals and coat them with Loctite 405 sealing compound.

b) Ensure that the power steering pump drive lugs engage with those on the front of the coolant pump.

c) Fit new O-ring seals to the air conditioning compressor and tighten the union securing bolt to the specified torque.

d) Tighten all bolts to the specified torque setting.

e) Refit the alternator with reference to Chapter 5A.

f) Fit a new receiver/drier unit with reference to Section 12.

g) Refill the cooling system with reference to Chapter 1B.

h) Have the air conditioning system recharged by a Rover dealer or air conditioning specialist.

6 Coolant pump housing (diesel engines) – removal and refitting

⚠️ **Warning: Before starting, the refrigerant must be recovered on models with air conditioning. When the work is completed, the system must be recharged. This procedure requires specialist knowledge and equipment, and can be done only by and MG Rover dealer, or air conditioning specialist.**

Removal

Note: The following new parts are needed – pump housing O-ring, Loctite 405.

Air conditioned models

1 Recover the air conditioning refrigerant – see Warning above.

6.14 Remove pump housing bolts

All models

2 Disconnect the battery earth lead.

3 Drain the cooling system – see Chapter 1B.

4 Apply the handbrake, chock the rear road wheels, then jack up the front of the car and support it on axle stands (see *Jacking and Vehicle Support*).

5 Remove the front suspension front beam – see Chapter 10.

6 Remove the alternator – see Chapter 5A.

7 Slacken the clip and disconnect the hose from the coolant pump.

Models without air conditioning

8 Remove three bolts securing the idler pulley bracket, and remove the bracket **(see illustration)**.

Models with air conditioning

9 Disconnect the multi-plug from the air conditioning compressor.

10 Remove three bolts securing the air conditioning compressor, and remove the compressor.

All models

11 Release the power steering reservoir from the bracket. Remove the cap and pour the fluid into a container.

7.3 Remove the nuts/bolts securing the housing assembly

6.15 Pump housing location

12 Position absorbent cloth under the reservoir.

13 Slacken the clip and disconnect the fluid outlet hose from the reservoir.

14 Remove six bolts securing the coolant pump housing to the cylinder block **(see illustration)**.

15 With assistance, remove the housing **(see illustration)**.

Refitting

16 Refitting is a reversal of the removal procedure, noting:

Lubricate the housing new O-ring with Loctite 405.

Use a torque wrench to tighten all fastenings to the correct torque.

Where applicable, have the air conditioning system recharged by an MG Rover dealer or specialist.

7 Electric cooling fan – removal and refitting

Petrol engines

Removal

1 Disconnect the battery earth lead.

2 Disconnect the fan harness multi-plug.

3 Remove two bolts securing the top of the fan assembly housing **(see illustration)**.

4 Release the assembly from the lower spigot.

5 Remove the fan assembly **(see illustration)**.

7.5 Remove the fan assembly

7.11 Release front grille

7.15 Remove the intercooler

7.16 Disconnect the multi-plug

Refitting

6 Refitting is a reversal of the removal procedure, noting:
Use a torque wrench to tighten the screws to the specified torque.

Diesel engines

Removal

7 Disconnect the battery earth lead, and then the positive lead.
8 Remove the battery clamp, and lift out the battery.
9 Remove the engine acoustic cover.
10 Remove the air cleaner – see Chapter 4B.
11 Remove two screws securing the front grille to the bonnet lock platform. Tilt the grille forwards and release the retaining pegs **(see illustration)**.
12 Slacken the clips and disconnect the top and bottom hoses from the intercooler.
13 Remove two Torx head bolts securing the intercooler to the radiator.
14 Remove the bolt and bracket securing the intercooler to the bonnet lock platform.
15 Release the intercooler from the lower mounting, and remove the intercooler **(see illustration)**.
16 Disconnect the fan harness multi-plug **(see illustration)**.
17 Remove two bolts securing the top of the fan assembly housing **(see illustration)**.
18 Release the assembly from the lower spigot, and remove the fan assembly **(see illustration)**.

8.2 Gauge and ECM sensor location

7.17 Remove fan housing bolts

Refitting

19 Refitting is a reversal of the removal procedure, noting:
Use a torque wrench to tighten the screws to the specified torque.

8 Cooling system sensors –
   removal and refitting

Note: *Both petrol and diesel engines have two coolant temperature sensors. One sensor feeds a signal to the ECM for engine fuelling and cooling fan operation. The other sensor feeds a signal to the temperature gauge.*
1 The gauge sensor is a thermistor, and has a resistance which decreases at a predetermined rate as temperature rises. When the coolant is cold, resistance is high, so current flow through the gauge is reduced and results in the needle pointing to 'cold'. The gauge is fed with a stabilised voltage from the instrument panel feed. The circuit is completed to earth via the sensor.

Petrol engines

Gauge sensor and ECM sensor

2 The temperature gauge sensor is screwed into the underside of the coolant outlet elbow, and is connected to the engine harness via a multi-plug. The ECM sensor is screwed into the side of the coolant outlet elbow, and is connected to the engine harness via a multi-plug **(see illustration)**.
3 Disconnect the battery earth lead.

7.18 Remove the fan assembly

4 Disconnect the multi-plug from the sensor.
5 Locate a container under the sensor to collect coolant.
6 Unscrew the sensor.
7 Refitting is a reversal of the removal procedure, noting:
Clean and degrease the sensor threads, and apply a smear of Loctite 577.
Use a torque wrench to tighten the sender to the specified torque.
Top-up the coolant level.

Diesel engines

Gauge sensor

8 The temperature gauge sensor is screwed into side of the cylinder head behind the alternator, and is connected to the engine harness via a Lucar connector at the end of a single integral wire.
9 Disconnect the battery earth lead.
10 Remove the engine acoustic cover.
11 Disconnect the Lucar connector from the engine harness adjacent to the dipstick, and pull the wire from behind the alternator.
12 Locate a container under the sensor to collect coolant.
13 Pass a cranked ring spanner over the sensor wire and onto the sensor. Unscrew the sensor.
14 Refitting is a reversal of the removal procedure, noting:
Clean and degrease the sensor threads, and apply a smear of Loctite 577.
Tighten the sensor to the specified torque.
Top-up the coolant level.

8.17 Disconnect sensor multi-plug

9.2a Heater coolant supply and return hoses (arrowed) on engine compartment bulkhead

9.2b Heater valve control cable (arrowed)

ECM sensor

15 The ECM sensor is screwed into the coolant outlet elbow attached to the side of the cylinder head, adjacent to the dipstick. It is connected to the engine harness via a multi-plug.

16 Disconnect the battery earth lead.

17 Disconnect the multi-plug from the sensor **(see illustration)**.

18 Locate a container under the sensor to collect coolant.

19 Unscrew the sensor.

20 Refitting is a reversal of the removal procedure, noting:

Clean and degrease the sensor threads, and apply a smear of Loctite 577.

Use a torque wrench to tighten the sender to the specified torque.

Top-up the coolant level.

9 Heater components – removal and refitting

Removal

Heater unit

1 Drain the cooling system.

2 Working in the engine compartment, slacken the hose clips and disconnect the heater supply and return hoses from the matrix outlets on the bulkhead. Disconnect the cable inner from the heater valve and free the cable outer from its retaining clip. Slacken and remove the heater lower mounting nut which is situated just to the left of the matrix outlets **(see illustrations)**.

3 Working inside the vehicle, remove the facia (see Chapter 11).

4 Release the vehicle wiring harness from the clip at the front of the heater unit **(see illustration)**.

5 Remove the securing screws and detach the heater duct from the heater outlet and blower motor **(see illustrations)**.

6 Unscrew the nuts that secure the heater unit to the mounting studs on the bulkhead **(see illustration)**.

7 Extract the stud fastener and separate the heater unit from centre console ducting **(see illustration)**.

8 Carefully lift the heater unit off its mounting studs and remove it from the vehicle **(see illustration)**. Keep the unit upright to prevent any coolant still inside the heater matrix from leaking out.

Heater matrix

9 Remove the heater unit (see the previous sub-Section).

9.2c Heater unit lower mounting nut (arrowed) on engine compartment bulkhead

9.4 Release the vehicle wiring harness from the clip (arrowed) at the front of the heater unit

9.5a Remove the securing screws (arrowed) . . .

9.5b . . . and detach the heater duct from the heater outlet and blower motor

9.6 Unscrew the nuts (arrowed) that secure the heater unit to the mounting studs on the bulkhead

9.7 Extract the stud fastener (arrowed) and separate the heater unit from centre console ducting

10 Undo the screw securing the matrix outlet pipe bracket to the heater unit and remove the bracket **(see illustrations)**.

11 Slacken and remove the two matrix cover retaining screws, then remove the cover and withdraw the matrix from the heater unit **(see illustrations)**.

12 If the matrix is leaking, it is best to obtain a new or reconditioned unit as home repairs are seldom successful. If it is blocked, it can sometimes be cleared by reverse flushing using a garden hose. Use a proprietary radiator cleaning product if absolutely necessary.

Heater blower motor

13 Disconnect the negative cable battery and position it away from the terminal.

14 Refer to Chapter 11 and remove the facia.

15 Release the radio antenna cable from the clip at the front of the heater unit.

16 Unplug the motor and resistor wiring harness connectors from the blower unit **(see illustrations)**.

17 Extra clearance may be gained by loosening the facia end support bracket bolts.

18 Slacken and withdraw the bolt that secures the blower unit to the end support bracket.

19 Undo and remove the two nuts securing the blower unit to its mounting studs **(see illustration)**.

20 Remove the securing screw, separate the blower unit from the heater unit duct then remove the blower unit from the vehicle **(see illustration)**.

9.8 Carefully lift the heater unit off its mounting studs and remove it from the vehicle

9.10b . . . and remove the bracket

21 To remove the blower motor, slacken the three securing screws and withdraw the motor from the blower unit. Disconnect the cooling hose from the motor body as it become accessible **(see illustrations)**.

9.10a Undo the screw securing the matrix outlet pipe bracket to the heater unit . . .

9.11a Slacken and remove the two matrix cover retaining screws . . .

Heater blower motor resistor

22 Refer to Chapter 11 and remove the glovebox from the facia.

23 Unplug the wiring connector, then undo the two retaining screws and remove the

9.11b . . . then remove the cover . . .

9.11c . . . and withdraw the matrix from the heater unit

9.16a Unplug the motor . . .

9.16b . . . and resistor wiring harness connectors from the blower unit

9.19 Blower unit mounting nuts and bolts (arrowed)

9.20 Removing the blower unit from the vehicle

9.21a Slacken and remove the three blower motor securing screws (arrowed) . . .

9.21b . . . and withdraw the blower motor assembly

9.21c Disconnect the cooling hose (arrowed) from the motor body as it become accessible

9.23a Undo the two retaining screws (arrowed) . . .

9.23b . . . and remove the resistor from the front of the heater assembly

9.27 Slacken the heater valve hose retaining clips (arrowed) then disconnect both hoses from the valve

resistor from the front of the heater assembly **(see illustrations)**.

Heater valve

24 Working in the engine compartment, disconnect the cable inner from the heater valve and free the cable outer from the retaining clip.
25 Slacken and remove the screws securing the heater valve to its mounting bracket at the engine compartment bulkhead.
26 Either drain the cooling system or clamp the coolant hoses on each side of the coolant valve to minimise the loss of coolant.
27 Slacken the hose retaining clips, then disconnect both hoses from the heater valve and remove the valve from the engine compartment **(see illustration)**. Mop up any spilt coolant immediately.

Refitting

Heater unit

28 Refitting is a reverse of the removal procedure, noting the following:
 a) *Ensure that the heater ducts are securely connected to the unit so that there are no air leaks or gaps.*
 b) *Check the operation of all heater cables before refitting the facia, ensuring that the relevant component moves smoothly from the fully-open to the fully-closed position. If necessary, adjustments can be made by releasing the relevant retaining clip and repositioning the cable outer.*
 c) *Ensure that the heater hoses are correctly reconnected and are securely held by the retaining clips.*

 d) *Tighten the heater lower mounting nut to the specified torque setting.*
 e) *Refill the cooling system as described in Chapter 1A or 1B as applicable.*

Heater matrix

29 Refitting is a reverse of the removal procedure.

Heater blower motor

30 Refitting is a reversal of the removal sequence, noting the following:
 a) *Ensure that the cooling hose is reconnected to the motor casing.*
 b) *Tighten the blower motor mounting screws to the specified torque setting.*
 c) *Ensure that the air recirculation cable and flap functions correctly before refitting the glovebox. If necessary, adjust by releasing the cable retaining clip and repositioning the cable outer.*

10.2 Removing the glovebox support bar

Heater blower motor resistor

31 Refitting is a reverse of the removal procedure.

Heater valve

32 Refitting is a reversal of the removal procedure. On completion, check the heater cable operates smoothly and replenish the cooling system (see Chapter 1A or 1B).

10 Heater/ventilation intake filter – renewal

1 Refer to Chapter 11 and remove the glovebox from the facia.
2 Slacken and remove the screws then lift off the glovebox support bar **(see illustration)**.
3 Release the clip and remove the cover from the side of the heater unit **(see illustration)**.

10.3 Release the clip and remove the cover from the side of the heater unit

11.1 Carefully pull the switch panel surround from the centre of the facia

11.3 Disconnect the air distribution control cable (A) from the heater unit lever and release the heater control cable (B) from the guide

11.4a Disconnect the purple fresh air ventilation flap control cable from the lever at the underside of the heater unit

4 Grasp the end of the filter element and withdraw it from the heater unit.

5 Refitting is a reversal of removal.

11 Heater controls – removal, refitting and adjustment

Removal

1 On pre-2004 models, refer to Chapter 11 and remove the centre console assembly and glovebox from the facia. On 2004 onward models, carefully pull the switch panel surround from the centre of the facia to release the seven retaining clips **(see illustration)**. Suitably identify the wiring connectors and disconnect them from the rear of the panel switches.

2 Release the stud fasteners by turning them through a quarter of a turn, then remove the fusebox cover from the underside of the facia.

3 Disconnect the brown air distribution control cable from the lever at the right-hand side of the heater unit. Release the green heater control cable from the guide on the side of the unit. Make a note of each cable fitted position to aid refitting **(see illustration)**.

4 Disconnect the purple and the (short) yellow fresh air ventilation flap control cables from the levers at the underside of the heater unit **(see illustrations)**.

5 Release the (long) yellow air recirculation control cable from the blower assembly **(see illustration)**.

6 Working in the engine compartment, disconnect the green heater control cable from the heater valve and release it from the bulkhead mounting clip (see Section 9 for details).

7 Slacken and remove the four securing screws and withdraw the heater control panel from the facia slightly **(see illustration)**.

8 Unplug the multi-way connectors from the rear of the heater control panel as they become accessible (2 connectors on models with a conventional heating system, 3 on models with air conditioning) **(see illustration)**.

9 Fully withdraw the control panel from the facia, feeding the control cables through the facia aperture **(see illustration)**.

10 If the control panel is to renewed, proceed as described from paragraphs 11 onwards.

11 Release the control cables from the heater control panel by slackening the clamp bracket screws and unhooking the cable end fittings from their respective control levers.

12 Carefully prise the rotary and slider knobs from the front of the control panel. Unclip the trim panel, the remove the two screws and remove the two-piece dial bezel.

13 Remove the two securing screws and withdraw the heater fan switch from the rear of the control panel.

11.4b Disconnect the (short) yellow fresh air ventilation flap control cable from the lever at the underside of the heater unit

11.5 Release the (long) yellow air recirculation control cable from the blower assembly

11.7 Remove the four securing screws (arrowed) and withdraw the heater control panel from the facia slightly

11.8 Unplug the multi-way connectors from the rear of the heater control panel as they become accessible

11.9 Fully withdraw the control panel, feeding the control cables through the facia aperture

14 Transfer the fan switch, bezel, trim panel, knobs and control cables to the new heater control panel.

Refitting and adjustment

15 Refitting is a reversal of removal, noting the following points:
 a) *Set the heater valve to the closed position before reconnecting the control cable.*
 b) *Set the heater control knob and the heater control lever on the heater unit to the cool positions before refitting the control cable.*
 c) *Set the air distribution control slider and the distribution control lever on the heater unit to the ventilation positions before refitting the control cable.*
 d) *Check the operation of all heater controls before refitting the centre console and glovebox.*

12 Air conditioning compressor drivebelt – inspection, adjustment and renewal

Inspection and adjustment

1 Refer to Chapter 1A or 1B as applicable.

Renewal

2 On petrol models, the air conditioning compressor is driven by the same drivebelt as the alternator; refer to the information given in Chapter 5A. On diesel models, all ancillaries are driven by a single auxiliary drivebelt; its renewal is described in Chapter 10 under *Power steering pump drivebelt – renewal.*

13 Air conditioning system components – removal and refitting

Compressor

⚠ **Warning: The air conditioning system must be professionally discharged before carrying out this procedure. Cap or plug the pipe lines as soon as they are disconnected to prevent the entry of moisture. Note that the receiver/drier unit must be renewed whenever the air conditioning system is discharged.**

Note: *The following new parts are needed – O-rings for air conditioning pipes, refrigerant oil to lubricate the O-rings.*

Petrol engines

1 Disconnect the battery earth lead.
2 Remove the front suspension beam – see Chapter 10.
3 Remove the alternator – see Chapter 5A.
4 Disconnect the multi-plug from the compressor clutch.
5 Remove the bolt securing the air conditioning pipe union to the compressor, and release the pipe union.

6 Remove and discard two O-rings from the compressor.
Caution: Plug or cap all pipes and connections.
7 Remove the top bolt attaching the compressor to the support housing.
8 Remove two lower bolts attaching the compressor to the support housing.
9 Remove the compressor from under the vehicle.
Caution: If a new compressor is being fitted, it will be filled with special oil. Before fitting, an exact amount of oil must be drained. This can only be done by an MG Rover dealer or air conditioning specialist.
10 Locate the compressor against the mounting bracket.
11 Fit the bolts attaching the compressor to the support housing. Use a torque wrench to tighten the bolts to the specified torque.
12 Clean the compressor and pipe connections.
13 Remove the plugs or caps. Lubricate two new O-rings with refrigerant oil, and fit them to the compressor.
14 Further refitting is a reversal of the removal procedure, noting:
 Have the air conditioning system recharged at an MG Rover dealer.

Diesel engines

15 Disconnect the battery earth lead.
16 Remove the front suspension beam – see Chapter 10.
17 Remove the auxiliary drivebelt – see Chapter 10.
18 Disconnect the multi-plug from the compressor clutch.
19 Remove the bolt attaching the air conditioning low-pressure pipe to the alternator upper mounting bracket.
20 Remove the bolt securing the air conditioning pipe union to the compressor, and release the pipe union.
21 Remove and discard two O-rings from the compressor.
Caution: Plug or cap all pipes and connections.
22 Remove the top bolt attaching the compressor to the support housing.
23 Remove two lower bolts attaching the compressor to the support housing.
24 Remove the compressor from under the vehicle.
Caution: If a new compressor is being fitted, it will be filled with special oil. Before fitting, an exact amount of oil must be drained. This can only be done by an MG Rover dealer or air conditioning specialist.
25 Locate the compressor against the mounting bracket.
26 Fit the bolts attaching the compressor to the support housing. Use a torque wrench to tighten the bolts to the specified torque.
27 Clean the compressor and pipe connections.
28 Remove the plugs or caps. Lubricate two

new O-rings with refrigerant oil, and fit them to the compressor.
29 Further refitting is a reversal of the removal procedure, noting:
 Have the system recharged at an MG Rover dealer.

Condenser

⚠ **Warning: The air conditioning system must be professionally discharged before carrying out this procedure. Cap or plug the pipe lines as soon as they are disconnected to prevent the entry of moisture. Note that the receiver/drier unit must be renewed whenever the air conditioning system is discharged.**

Note: *The following new parts are needed – O-rings for air conditioning pipes, refrigerant oil to lubricate the O-rings.*
30 Disconnect the battery earth lead.
31 Remove the condenser fan assembly – see the following sub-section.
32 Remove two bolts securing the air conditioning pipes to the condenser.
33 Disconnect the air conditioning pipes from the condenser.
34 Remove and discard two O-rings from the condenser
Caution: Plug or cap all pipes and connections.
35 Remove the condenser.
36 Refitting is a reversal of the removal procedure, noting:
 Have the air conditioning system recharged at an MG Rover dealer.

Condenser fan and motor

Removal

Note: *The following new parts are needed – O-ring for air conditioning pipes, and pressure sensor, refrigerant oil.*
37 Disconnect the battery earth lead.
38 Remove the front bumper – see Chapter 11.
39 Remove four bolts attaching the front bumper support beam, and remove the beam.
40 Remove three bolts securing the bonnet lock to the lock platform, and move the lock aside.
41 Remove three bolts securing the bonnet lock platform support bracket, and remove the bracket.
42 Disconnect the cooling fan multi-plug.
43 Remove two bolts securing the cooling fan assembly mounting brackets, and remove the brackets.
44 Ease the assembly forward, and remove two bolts securing the cooling fan assembly to the condenser. Release the fan assembly from the condenser, and remove the fan assembly.
45 Refitting is a reversal of the removal procedure, noting:
 Use a torque wrench to tighten all fastenings to the specified torque.

Receiver/drier unit

⚠️ **Warning: The air conditioning system must be professionally discharged before carrying out this procedure. Cap or plug the pipe lines as soon as they are disconnected to prevent the entry of moisture. Note that the receiver/drier unit must be renewed whenever the air conditioning system is discharged.**

46 Remove the front bumper – see Chapter 11.
47 Disconnect the multi-plug from the refrigerant pressure sensor.

48 Remove two bolts securing the receiver/drier unit mounting bracket to the body.
49 Remove two bolts securing the air conditioning pipe connections to the receiver/drier.
50 Disconnect the air conditioning pipe connections from the receiver/drier.
51 Remove and discard two O-rings from the condenser
Caution: Plug or cap all pipes and connections.
52 Remove the refrigerant pressure sensor, and remove and discard the O-ring from the sensor.

53 Slacken two screws securing the mounting bracket to the receiver/drier.
54 Remove the bracket and discard the receiver/drier.
55 Refitting is a reversal of the removal procedure, noting:

Fit the mounting bracket to a new receiver/drier unit, and remove blanking caps.
Lubricate new O-rings with refrigerant oil.
Use a torque wrench to tighten all fastenings to the specified torque.
Have the air conditioning system recharged at an MG Rover dealer.

Notes

Chapter 4 Part A:
Fuel and exhaust systems – petrol engines

Contents

Degrees of difficulty

Easy, suitable for novice with little experience		Fairly easy, suitable for beginner with some experience		Fairly difficult, suitable for competent DIY mechanic		Difficult, suitable for experienced DIY mechanic		Very difficult, suitable for expert DIY or professional	

Specifications

General

System type . . . . Rover modular engine management system (MEMS 3) indirect multi-point fuel injection system integrated with ignition system

Fuel pump

Type . . . . Electric roller vane pump in fuel tank
Maximum delivery pressure . . . . 4.1 bar
Regulated injection pressure . . . . 3.0 ± 0.2 bar

Idle settings (not adjustable – for reference only)

Idle speed . . . . 825 ± 50 rpm
Idle mixture (CO content) . . . . Less than 0.5 %

Torque wrench settings

	Nm	lbf ft
Crankshaft position sensor-to-flywheel housing bolt	6	4
Engine control module (ECM)-to-bracket nuts	4	3
Engine coolant temperature (ECT) sensor to housing	15	11
Exhaust joint nuts and bolts	50	37
Exhaust manifold securing nuts	45	33
Fuel feed pipe-to-fuel rail bolts	10	7
Fuel pump/gauge sender-to-fuel tank nuts	9	7
Fuel rail-to-manifold bolts	5	4
Heated oxygen sensor (HO₂S) to manifold/exhaust system	55	41
Idle air control valve (IACV)-to-manifold screws	6	4
Inlet manifold securing nuts and bolts	17	13
Intake air temperature (IAT) sensor to manifold	7	5
Throttle body-to-inlet manifold bolts	9	7
Throttle position sensor securing screws	1.5	1.1

1 General information and precautions

General information

The operation of the fuel injection system is described in more detail in Section 6.

Fuel is supplied from a tank mounted under the rear of the vehicle by an electric fuel pump mounted in the tank. The fuel pump also incorporates the fuel level gauge sender unit. The fuel passes through a filter, to the fuel injection system, which incorporates various sensors, actuators and an engine control module (ECM) **(see illustration)**.

The inducted air passes through an air cleaner, which incorporates a paper filter element to filter out potentially-harmful particles (serious internal engine damage can be caused if foreign particles enter through the air intake system).

The engine control module (ECM) controls both the fuel injection system and the ignition system, integrating the two into a complete engine management system. Refer to Chapter 5B for details of the ignition side of the system.

The exhaust system incorporates a catalytic converter to reduce exhaust gas emissions. Further details can be found in Chapter 4C, along with details of the other emission control systems and components.

Precautions

Before disconnecting any fuel lines, or working on any part of the fuel system, the system must be depressurised as described in Section 7.

Care must be taken when disconnecting the fuel lines. When disconnecting a fuel union or hose, loosen the union or clamp screw slowly, to avoid sudden uncontrolled fuel spillage. Take adequate fire precautions.

When working on fuel system components, scrupulous cleanliness must be observed, and care must be taken not to introduce any foreign matter into fuel lines or components.

After carrying out any work involving disconnection of fuel lines, it is advisable to check the connections for leaks; pressurise the system by switching the ignition on and off several times.

Electronic control units are very sensitive components, and certain precautions must be taken to avoid damage to these units as follows.

When carrying out welding operations on the vehicle using electric welding equipment, the battery and alternator should be disconnected.

Although the underbonnet-mounted modules will tolerate normal underbonnet conditions, they can be adversely affected by excess heat or moisture. If using welding equipment or pressure-washing equipment in the vicinity of an electronic module, take care not to direct heat, or jets of water or steam, at the module. If this cannot be avoided, remove the module from the vehicle, and protect its wiring plug with a plastic bag.

Before disconnecting any wiring, or removing components, always ensure that the ignition is switched off.

Do not attempt to improvise fault diagnosis procedures using a test lamp or multi-meter, as irreparable damage could be caused to the module.

After working on fuel injection/engine management system components, ensure that all wiring is correctly reconnected before reconnecting the battery or switching on the ignition.

Leaded fuel will damage the catalytic converter, so unleaded fuel must be used at all times. In addition, if unburnt fuel enters the catalytic converter, this may result in overheating and irreparable damage to the catalytic converter.

Damage to the catalytic converter may result if the following precautions are not observed:

a) Consult an approved dealer as soon as possible in the event of misfiring, irregular engine running after a cold start, a

H44644

1.2 Fuel delivery system

1 Injectors	3 Fuel return line	5 Fuel tank	7 Swirl pot
2 Fuel pressure regulator	4 Non-return valve	6 Fuel pump	8 Fuel filter

significant loss of engine power, or any other malfunction which may indicate a fault in the ignition system. If it is necessary to continue driving, do so for a short time at low engine speed, without labouring the engine.

b) *Avoid frequent cold starts one after another.*

c) *Avoid actuation of the starter for an unnecessarily long time during starting.*

d) *Do not allow the fuel tank to become empty.*

e) *Do not attempt to start the engine by push- or tow-starting – use jump leads (see 'Jump starting').*

⚠️ **Warning: Many of the procedures in this Chapter require the disconnection of fuel line connections, and the removal of components, which may result in some fuel spillage. Before carrying out any operation on the fuel system, refer to the precautions given in 'Safety first!' at the beginning of this manual, and follow them implicitly. Petrol is a highly-dangerous and volatile liquid, and the precautions necessary when handling it cannot be overstressed.**

2 Air cleaner assembly – removal and refitting

Removal

1 Remove the battery as described in Chapter 5A.

2 Release the hose clip, and disconnect the air intake trunking from the throttle body.

3 Unscrew the two bolts securing the air cleaner to the battery tray.

4 Release the air intake tube from the bottom of the air cleaner, then remove the air cleaner assembly from the engine compartment.

Refitting

5 Refitting is a reversal of removal.

3 Fuel tank and filler neck – removal, inspection and refitting

Fuel tank

Note: *During removal, note the locations and routing of all hoses to aid refitting.*

Removal

1 Disconnect the battery negative lead.

2 Chock the front wheels, then jack up the rear of the vehicle and support securely on axle stands (see *Jacking and Vehicle Support*).

3 Syphon the fuel from the tank into a clean metal container which can be sealed. Alternatively, working under the car, disconnect an accessible fuel line connection at the tank, and drain the fuel into a suitable container.

3.4 Unscrew the bolt (arrowed) securing the handbrake cable to the H-frame mounting

4 Unscrew the bolt securing the handbrake cable to the left-hand rear suspension H-frame mounting, and release the cable from the mounting (see illustration).

5 Remove the screw securing the fuel tank filler neck to the body. Note that the screw also secures the rear wheel arch liner.

6 Slacken the hose clip and disconnect the breather hose from the fuel filler neck (see illustration).

7 Slacken the hose clip and disconnect the filler hose from the fuel filler neck (see illustration 3.6).

8 Slacken the hose clips and disconnect the fuel feed and return hoses from the pipes under the rear of the vehicle (see illustration). Plug or cover the open ends of the hoses and pipes to prevent dirt entry.

9 Release the connector and disconnect the breather hose from the pipe.

10 Place a trolley jack under the fuel tank, with a block of wood between the jack and the tank.

11 Working at the rear of the fuel tank, unscrew the locknuts, then unscrew the two fuel tank strap securing nuts (see illustration).

12 Ensure that the jack is supporting the fuel tank, then release the fuel tank straps from the brackets on the body.

13 Lower the fuel tank until the fuel pump/gauge sender unit wiring connector can be reached, then separate the two halves of the connector, and withdraw the fuel tank from under the vehicle.

3.8 Disconnect the fuel feed and return hoses (arrowed) from the pipes

3.6 Disconnect the breather (1) and filler (2) hoses from the fuel filler neck

Inspection

14 If the tank contains sediment or water, it may be cleaned out using two or three rinses with paraffin. Shake vigorously using several changes of paraffin, but before doing so remove the fuel pump/gauge sender unit (see Section 8).

⚠️ **Warning: This procedure should be carried out in a well-ventilated area, and it is vital to take adequate fire precautions – refer to 'Safety first!' for further details.**

15 Any repairs to the fuel tank should be carried out by a professional. Do not under any circumstances attempt to weld or solder a fuel tank. Removal of residual fuel vapour requires several hours of specialist cleaning.

Refitting

16 Refitting is a reversal of removal, but ensure that all hoses are reconnected to their correct locations as noted before removal, and use new hose clips if necessary.

Fuel filler neck

Removal

17 Chock the front wheels, then jack up the rear of the vehicle and support securely on axle stands (see *Jacking and Vehicle Support*). Remove the left-hand rear roadwheel.

18 Remove the securing screws, and withdraw the rear left-hand wheel arch liner.

19 Remove the fuel filler cap, then reach up

3.11 Fuel tank strap locknut and securing nut (arrowed)

behind the filler neck and depress the three lugs securing the filler neck surround to the body and filler neck. Pull out the filler neck surround **(see illustration)**.

20 Working under the vehicle, slacken the hose clips, and disconnect the breather hose and the filler hose from the fuel filler neck.

⚠️ *Warning: Be prepared for fuel spillage, and have a suitable container ready to catch any fuel which may be released as the filler hose is disconnected.*

21 Withdraw the filler neck assembly from under the wheel arch.

Refitting

22 Refitting is a reversal of removal.

---

4 Throttle cable –
removal, refitting and adjustment

Removal

1 Slide the cable adjuster from the bracket on the throttle body/inlet manifold **(see illustration)**.
2 Slide the cable end fitting from the groove in the throttle lever, and disconnect the cable from the lever **(see illustration)**.
3 Release the cable from the clip on the inlet manifold.
4 Working at the engine compartment bulkhead, turn the collar on the throttle cable through 90°, and release the cable from the bulkhead.
5 Working in the driver's footwell, release the

3.19 Pulling out the fuel filler neck surround

two securing clips, and remove the lower facia trim panel.
6 Reach up under the facia, and pull the end of the cable forwards from the pedal, then squeeze the securing lugs and remove the plastic cable securing clip from the end of the pedal. Release the end of the cable from the pedal **(see illustration)**.
7 Pull the cable through the bulkhead into the engine compartment, and withdraw the cable from the vehicle.

Refitting

8 Refitting is a reversal of removal, but smear the bulkhead grommet with rubber grease and, on completion, check the cable adjustment as described in the following paragraphs.

Adjustment

Note: *Do not attempt to adjust the throttle stop screw during this procedure.*

9 Slide the cable adjuster from the bracket on the inlet manifold/throttle body, then position the cable adjuster against the rear of the bracket.
10 Hold the throttle lever on the throttle body in the fully closed position, ensuring that the cam on the throttle lever rests against the throttle stop screw.
11 Turn the cable adjuster as necessary until all freeplay is removed from the cable, without moving the throttle lever.
12 Slide the adjuster back into position in the bracket.
13 Have an assistant fully depress the throttle pedal, and check that the throttle lever moves to the fully open position, and returns to the fully closed position when the pedal is released.

---

5 Throttle pedal –
removal and refitting

Removal

1 Disconnect the end of the throttle cable from the pedal as described in Section 4.
2 Using a suitable pair of pliers, unhook the return spring from the pedal **(see illustration)**.
3 Working at the left-hand side of the pedal pivot shaft, prise off the securing clip, then slide the pedal assembly from the mounting bracket towards the right-hand side of the vehicle, until it can be removed **(see illustration)**.

Refitting

4 Refitting is a reversal of removal, but make sure that the securing clip is securely refitted.

---

6 Fuel injection system –
general information

The amount of fuel delivered, and the injection timing is controlled by the Modular Engine Management System (MEMS 3), which also controls the ignition system (see Chapter 5B).

Fuel is supplied from the rear-mounted fuel tank by an electric pump mounted in the tank, via a fuel filter, to the fuel rail. A fuel pressure

4.1 Slide the cable adjuster from the bracket . . .

4.2 . . . then slide the cable end fitting from the throttle lever

4.6 Depress the plastic clips (arrowed) and release the end of the throttle cable from the pedal

5.2 Unhook the return spring (arrowed) from the pedal

5.3 Prise off the throttle pedal securing clip (arrowed)

regulator mounted on the fuel rail maintains a constant fuel pressure to the fuel injectors. Excess fuel is returned from the regulator to the tank.

The fuel rail acts as a reservoir for the four fuel injectors, which inject fuel into the cylinder inlet tracts, upstream of the inlet valves. The injectors operate in pairs – the injectors for Nos 1 and 4 cylinders operate simultaneously, as do the injectors for Nos 2 and 3 cylinders.

The injectors are electronically controlled by the Engine Control Module (ECM). Each injector has a solenoid which, when energised by a pulse from the ECM, lifts the injector needle and fuel is sprayed into the cylinder.

The duration of the pulse determines the length of time the needle is lifted and, therefore, the amount of fuel injected. Pulse duration is calculated by the ECM, and is constantly varying to match engine operating and ambient conditions.

The fuelling, and ignition timing, calculation is based on information supplied to the ECM by the following sensors (see illustration):

a) *Throttle position sensor (TP) – mounted on the throttle body, the sensor provides a signal representing the amount and rate of throttle opening – ie, driver demand.*

b) *Crankshaft position sensor (CKP) – supplies a signal representing the speed and angular position of the crankshaft.*

c) *Camshaft position sensor (CMP) – attached to the camshaft cover, the sensor provides a signal representing the angular position of the camshaft, in relation to the angular position of the crankshaft.*

d) *Manifold absolute pressure (MAP) – located in the intake manifold, supplies a signal representing the amount of air entering the cylinders.*

e) *Engine coolant temperature (ECT) – located in the coolant outlet elbow from*

the cylinder head. The sensor provides a coolant temperature signal.

f) *Engine oil temperature – located on the filter housing, the sensor supplies an oil temperature signal.*

g) *Intake air temperature (IAT) – located on the intake manifold, the sensor provides a signal representing the temperature of the air entering the engine.*

h) *Heated oxygen sensors (HO_2S) – located in the exhaust manifold, upstream of the catalytic converter. (Some models have a second sensor located in the exhaust pipe, downstream of the converter.) The sensors provide signals representing the amount of oxygen in the exhaust gas, and allow the ECM to precisely control the air/fuel ratio around the ideal combustion ratio of 14.7:1.*

Idle speed is controlled by the ECM via an Idle Air Control Valve (IACV), which varies the amount of air bypassing the throttle valve.

6.6 Engine management system components

1 Fuel pressure regulator
2 Inertia switch
3 Malfunction indicator lamp
4 Idle Air Control valve – IAC
5 Fuel filter
6 Purge valve and canister
7 Fuel rail
8 Throttle housing
9-13 Relays (in fusebox)
    Main relay
    Air conditioning relay
    Cooling fan relay
14 Cooling fan relays – air conditioning only
15 Engine Control Module – ECM
16 Crankshaft position sensor – CKP
17 Air filter
18 Downstream oxygen sensor – HO_2S^*
19 Catalytic converter
20 Upstream oxygen sensor – HO_2S
21 Pre-catalyst
22 Throttle position sensor – TP
23 Engine Coolant Temperature sensor – ECT
24 Intake Air Temperature sensor – IAT
25 Camshaft Position sensor – CMP
26 Engine oil temperature sensor
27 Engine oil pressure switch
28 Ignition coils
29 Injectors x 4
30 Manifold Absolute Pressure sensor – MAP
* Certain models only

H44598

7.3 Slackening the fuel outlet pipe union to relieve the fuel pressure

Failure of certain sensors – either complete loss of signal, or sending an abnormal signal, will cause the ECM to default to preprogrammed values. In most cases this will be noticeable as poor or erratic engine performance.

Note that, if the crankshaft position (CKP) sensor signal is lost, the engine will not run.

Whenever a sensor fault occurs, a fault code is stored in a memory of the ECM. Using specialist diagnostic equipment, the codes can be extracted by Rover dealers.

All vehicle are fitted with a fuel inertia cut-off switch (see Section 11), which cuts off the fuel supply in the event of the vehicle being involved in an impact. The engine cannot be started if the switch is activated – the switch must be reset manually.

7 Fuel injection system – depressurising and priming

Depressurising

1 Disconnect the battery negative lead.

8.5 Fuel pump/sender unit mounting details

1 Securing nut	2 Fuel pump
	3 Seal

---

2 Position a wad of absorbent cloth around the outlet pipe union on the top of the fuel filter.

3 Counterhold the union on the fuel filter, and **slowly** slacken the fuel pipe union nut using a second spanner **(see illustration)**.

⚠ *Warning: Be prepared for the escape of some fuel. Take adequate fire precautions.*

4 Allow the fuel pressure to dissipate, then retighten the union nut.

Priming

5 The system is self-priming. Switch on the ignition, and wait for a few seconds before attempting to start the engine. There may be a short delay before the engine starts, as the fuel system components refill with fuel.

8 Fuel pump/fuel gauge sender unit – removal and refitting

Removal

1 The fuel pump/fuel gauge sender unit is mounted in the top of the fuel tank, and cannot be accessed with the tank in place.

2 Remove the fuel tank as described in Section 3.

3 Release the hose clamps, and disconnect the fuel feed and return hoses from the pipes at the top of the pump/sender unit. Plug or cover the open ends of the hoses and pipes to prevent dirt entry.

4 Unscrew the six nuts securing the pump/sender unit to the fuel tank.

5 Carefully slide the pump/sender unit from the fuel tank, taking care not to damage the sender unit float **(see illustration)**. Recover the seal.

Refitting

6 Examine the condition of the sealing ring, and renew if necessary, then thoroughly clean the mating faces of the tank and the pump/sender unit.

7 Refitting is a reversal of removal, tightening the pump/sender unit nuts to the specified torque setting. If necessary, renew the fuel hose clips and on completion, refit the fuel tank with reference to Section 3.

9 Fuel injection system – testing and adjustment

Testing

1 If a fault appears in the fuel injection system, first ensure that all the system wiring connectors are securely connected and free from corrosion. Ensure that the fault is not due to poor maintenance; ie, check that the air cleaner filter element is clean, that the spark plugs are in good condition and correctly

---

gapped (see Chapter 1A), that the cylinder compression pressures are correct (see Chapter 2A), and that the engine breather hoses are clear and undamaged (see Chapter 4C).

2 If the engine will not start, check that the fuel inertia cut-off switch has not operated (see Section 11). Push the switch button to reset if necessary.

3 If these checks fail to reveal the cause of the problem, the vehicle should be taken to a Rover dealer for testing. A wiring connector is provided on a bracket behind the centre console, into which a special electronic diagnostic tester can be plugged. The tester should locate the fault quickly and simply, avoiding the need to test all the system components individually, which is time-consuming, and also carries a risk of damaging the ECM.

Adjustment

4 Experienced home mechanics with access to a tachometer and an accurately calibrated exhaust gas analyser may be able to check the exhaust CO level and the idle speed. However, if either of these settings is found to be in need of adjustment, the vehicle must be taken to a Rover dealer for further testing.

5 No manual adjustment of the exhaust CO level or idle speed is possible.

10 Throttle body – removal and refitting

Note: *The following new parts are needed: throttle body O-ring, silicone grease.*
Note: *On completion, the engine may need to be retuned by an MG Rover dealer, using special electronic equipment.*

Removal

1 Disconnect the battery negative lead.

2 Slacken the hose clip securing the air intake trunking to the throttle body, and disconnect the trunking from the throttle body.

3 Disconnect the hose from the idle air control valve (IACV).

4 Disconnect the wiring plug from the throttle position sensor (TPS).

5 Release the hose clip(s), and disconnect the breather hose(s) from the throttle body.

6 Slide the cable adjuster from the bracket on the inlet manifold/throttle body.

7 Slide the cable end fitting from the groove in the throttle lever, and disconnect the cable from the lever.

8 Unscrew the four securing bolts, and withdraw the throttle body from the inlet manifold. Recover the O-ring and discard it.

Refitting

9 Clean the mating faces of the throttle body and inlet manifold.

10 Lubricate a new O-ring with silicone grease, and fit it to the throttle body.

11 Locate the throttle body on the inlet manifold, and fit and lightly tighten the four bolts.
Caution: Follow the bolt tightening procedure:
12 Working in sequence, use a torque wrench to tighten the bolts as follows **(see illustration):**
Tighten to 4 Nm.
Back off one flat.
Tighten to 9 Nm.
13 The remaining refitting is a reversal of the removal procedure.
14 If necessary, arrange engine tuning at an MG Rover dealer.

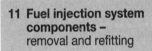

11 Fuel injection system components – removal and refitting

Fuel rail and injectors

Note: *The following new parts are needed – injector O-rings, silicone grease.*

Removal

1 Disconnect the battery earth lead. Remove the engine oil dipstick,
2 Depressurise the fuel system – see Section 7.
3 Release the clip and disconnect the vacuum pipe from the fuel pressure regulator,
4 Pack absorbent cloth under the fuel rail. Disconnect the fuel supply hose from the fuel rail. Plug the pipe connections **(see illustration).**
5 Remove two bolts securing the fuel rail to the inlet manifold.
6 Release the fuel rail and injectors from the inlet manifold, and remove the injector spacer.
7 Disconnect the multi-plugs from the injectors.
8 Remove the fuel rail complete with injectors.
9 Release the spring clips securing the injectors to the fuel rail, and remove the injectors.
10 Remove and discard two O-rings from

10.12 Bolt tightening sequence

each injector. Cover both ends of each injector with a protective cap.

Refitting

11 Refitting is a reversal of the removal procedure, noting:
Lubricate new O-rings with silicone grease and fit them to the injectors.
Use a torque wrench to tighten the fuel rail bolts to the specified torque.

Fuel pressure regulator

12 The fuel pressure regulator is integral with the fuel rail, and cannot be removed separately. If the fuel regulator is faulty, the complete fuel rail/regulator assembly must be renewed.

Idle air control valve

Note: *A new O-ring and suitable silicone grease will be required on refitting.*

Removal

13 The idle air control valve is located at the rear of the engine.
14 Disconnect the battery negative lead, then disconnect the wiring plug from the valve.
15 Remove the two screws securing the valve to the inlet manifold, then withdraw the

valve from the manifold **(see illustration).** Recover the O-ring and discard it.

Refitting

16 Refitting is a reversal of removal, tightening the valve securing screws to the specified torque setting. Use a new O-ring and lubricate the O-ring with a little silicone grease.

Intake air temperature sensor

Removal

17 The IAT sensor is located at the left-hand rear of the inlet manifold under the throttle cam assembly.
18 Disconnect the multi-plug from the sensor.
19 Unscrew the sensor from the inlet manifold.

Refitting

20 Clean the sensor threads and mating faces.
21 Fit the sensor to the inlet manifold and tighten the specified torque.
22 Connect the multi-plug, and battery earth lead.

Engine coolant temperature sensor

Note: *Loctite 577 is needed to seal the sensor.*

Removal

23 The IAT sensor is screwed into the side of the coolant outlet elbow, and is connected to the engine harness via a multi-plug. **Note:** *The temperature gauge sensor is screwed into the underside of the coolant outlet elbow (see illustration).*
24 Disconnect the battery earth lead.
25 Disconnect the multi-plug from the ECT sensor.
26 Locate a container under the sensor to collect coolant. Unscrew the sensor.

Refitting

27 Refitting is a reversal of the removal procedure, noting:
Clean and degrease the sensor threads, and apply a smear of Loctite 577.

11.4 Disconnect fuel supply hose

11.15 Idle air control valve (IACV) securing screws (arrowed)

11.23 Engine coolant temperature (ECT) sensor location (arrowed)

11.30 Throttle sensor location

11.33 Apply pressure to the shaded area only

11.41 MAP sensor location

Use a torque wrench to tighten the sender to the specified torque.
Top-up the coolant level.

Throttle position sensor

Note: *Whenever the sensor is removed or renewed, a 'throttle initialisation' procedure must be carried out. This can only be done by an MG Rover dealer, using special electronic equipment. Therefore, it is recommended that remove/refit, or renewal of the sensor should be done by an MG Rover dealer.*
Note: *The following new parts are needed – two Torx head screws and wave washers.*

Removal

28 Disconnect the battery earth lead.
Caution: The sensor can easily be damaged. Handle it with care. Do not twist, or apply leverage to the sensor.
29 Disconnect the multi-plug from the sensor.
30 Remove and discard two Torx head screws and wave washers securing the sensor to the throttle housing **(see illustration)**.
31 Remove the sensor specification plate, and pull the sensor from the throttle spindle.

Refitting

32 Clean the mating faces of the throttle housing and sensor.
33 Align the flat on the sensor with the flat on the throttle spindle, and push the sensor onto the spindle **(see illustration)**.
Caution: When pushing the sensor onto the throttle spindle, use fingers only, and apply pressure the shaded area only.

11.55 Remove CMP sensor

Caution: Do not rotate the sensor in clockwise direction. Rotate only anti-clockwise, and do not rotate beyond the sensor internal stops.
34 Rotate the sensor in an anti-clockwise direction to align the screw holes.
35 Fit the specification plate, wave washers and screws.
36 Tighten the screws to the specified torque – DO NOT exceed the specified torque.
37 Connect the multi-plug to the sensor.
38 Check that throttle operation is correct.
39 Connect the battery earth lead.
40 Arrange to have throttle initialisation carried out by an MG Rover dealer

Manifold Absolute Pressure sensor

Removal

41 The sensor is located on the forward face of the inlet manifold **(see illustration)**.
42 Disconnect the multi-plug from the sensor.
43 Remove two Torx head screws, and remove the sensor from the inlet manifold.

Refitting

44 Clean the sensor and manifold mating faces.
45 Fit the sensor to the manifold, and secure with two Torx head screws.
46 Connect the multi-plug to the sensor.

Heated oxygen sensor

Note: *The following new parts are needed – sensor sealing washer, exhaust manifold gasket.*

11.64 Remove ECM

Removal

47 Remove the exhaust manifold – see Section 12.
48 Unscrew the sensor from the exhaust manifold, and discard the sealing washer.

Refitting

49 Clean the sensor and manifold threads, and fit a new sealing washer to the sensor.
50 Fit the sensor to the manifold. Use a torque wrench to tighten the sensor to the specified torque.
51 Fit the exhaust manifold.

Camshaft position sensor

Removal

52 Disconnect the battery earth lead.
53 Remove three bolts securing the coil cover the camshaft cover, and remove the coil cover.
54 Release the sensor cable from the bracket, and disconnect the multi-plug.
55 Remove the bolt securing the sensor to the camshaft cover. Release the cable from the clip, and remove the sensor **(see illustration)**.

Refitting

56 Clean mating faces of sensor and camshaft cover.
57 Fit the sensor and bolt. Tighten the bolt securely.
58 Connect multi-plug, and secure in the bracket.
59 Fit the coil cover and bolts. Tighten the bolts securely.
60 Connect the battery earth lead.
61 Refitting is a reversal of the removal procedure.

Engine Control Module

Note: *If a new ECM is to be fitted it will need to be programmed with the code from the anti-theft security unit before the engine can be started. This can be done only by an MG Rover dealer using special equipment.*

Removal

62 Disconnect the battery negative lead.
63 Remove two bolts securing the ECM to the batter carrier.
64 Release the ECM and disconnect the multi-plugs. Remove the ECM **(see illustration)**.

Refitting

65 Refitting is a reversal of the removal procedure.

Fuel inertia cut-off switch

Removal

66 The switch is located at the right-hand side of the engine compartment bulkhead **(see illustration)**.
67 Disconnect the battery negative lead, then disconnect the wiring plug from the switch.
68 Remove the two securing screws and withdraw the switch from its mounting bracket.

Refitting

69 Refitting is a reversal of removal, but ensure that the switch is reset by pressing the button on the top of the switch.

Crankshaft position sensor

Removal

70 Disconnect the battery negative lead.
71 The sensor is mounted at the rear of the flywheel housing (at the left-hand end of the engine) **(see illustration)**. To improve access to the sensor, apply the handbrake, then jack up the front of the vehicle and support securely on axle stands (see *Jacking and Vehicle Support*).
72 Disconnect the wiring plug from the sensor.
73 Unscrew the bolt securing the sensor to the flywheel housing, then remove the sensor.

Refitting

74 Thoroughly clean the mating faces on the sensor and housing, then refit the sensor using a reversal of the removal procedure and tightening its bolt to the specified torque setting.

12 Manifolds – removal and refitting

Note: *Make a note of the routing and connections of all hoses, pipes and cables.*

Inlet manifold

Note: *The following new parts are needed – manifold gasket.*

Removal

1 Disconnect the battery earth lead.
2 Drain the cooling system – see Chapter 1A.
3 Position absorbent cloth around the fuel feed and return hose connections. Release the connectors, and disconnect fuel feed and return hoses.
Caution: Plug the connections.
4 Release/slacken the clips and disconnect the following hoses:
Air intake hose, and breather hose from throttle body.
Purge hose from inlet manifold.
IAC hose to throttle body.
Coolant hose from inlet manifold.

11.66 Fuel inertia cut-off switch location (arrowed)

5 Release cables and disconnect the following multi-plugs:
Throttle position sensor.
IAC valve.
MAP sensor.
6 Release throttle cable clips from the inlet manifold and fuel return pipe.
7 Release throttle cable adjustment nut from the abutment bracket, and release inner cable from the throttle cam.
8 Disconnect the breather hose from the inlet manifold
9 Depress the locking collar, and disconnect the brake servo hose from the inlet manifold.

11.71 Crankshaft position (CKP) sensor (1), securing bolt (2) and wiring plug (3)

10 Remove three screws, and remove the coil/plug cover.
11 Remove two bolts securing the right-hand ignition coil, and release the coil. Disconnect the coil multi-plugs, and release the coil harness from the retaining clips.
12 Release the injector multi-plug from the bracket, and disconnect the plug.
13 Working from the centre of the manifold outwards, progressively slacken and remove the four bolts and three nuts securing the manifold to the cylinder head **(see illustration)**.
14 Remove the manifold, and discard the gasket.

12.13 Manifold component layout

1 Inlet manifold
2 Nut x 7
3 Gasket – inlet manifold
4 Gasket – exhaust manifold
5 Exhaust manifold
6 Nut x 5
7 Nut
8 Heat shield – exhaust manifold
9 Bolt and washer x 2

12.16 Inlet manifold nut tightening sequence

Refitting

15 Clean the mating faces of the manifold and cylinder head, and ensure that metal inserts are fitted in the inlet manifold stud and bolt holes.

16 Using a new gasket, locate the manifold against the cylinder head, and fit the nuts and bolts. Use a torque wrench to tighten the nuts and bolts, in sequence, to the specified torque **(see illustration)**.

17 The remaining refitting is a reversal of the removal procedure, noting:

Refill the cooling system with a 50/50 mixture of water and antifreeze.
Check/adjust throttle cable operation.

Exhaust manifold

Note: *The following new parts are needed – manifold gasket.*

Removal

18 Disconnect the battery earth lead.
19 Remove the exhaust manifold heat shield.
20 Remove two nuts, and disconnect the exhaust front pipe from the exhaust manifold.
21 Release the oxygen sensor multi-plug from the bracket, and disconnect the plug.
22 Remove five nuts securing the manifold to the cylinder head, and remove the manifold, and discard the gasket **(see illustration 12.13)**.

Refitting

23 Clean the mating faces of the manifold and cylinder head, and fit a new gasket the studs in the cylinder head.
24 Locate the manifold against the cylinder head, and fit the nuts. Working from the centre nut outwards, use a torque wrench to tighten the nuts to the specified torque.
25 The remaining refitting is a reversal of the removal procedure.

Exhaust manifold heat shield

Removal

26 Disconnect the battery earth lead.
27 Remove the splash shield.
28 Remove the bolt securing the heat shield to the exhaust flange bracket.
29 Remove the nut and bolt securing the heat shield to the alternator and manifold brackets.

30 Fit a 13 mm spanner on the alternator belt tension pulley, and rotate the pulley fully clockwise to release belt tension. Lock in this position with a 3 mm pin pushed into the tensioner backplate.
31 Release the drivebelt from the alternator.
32 Remove the top bolt securing the alternator, and slacken the lower bolt.
33 Tilt the alternator forward to gain access the alternator bracket.
34 Remove the bolt securing the bracket. Turn the bracket clear of the alternator, and remove the bracket.
35 Remove the alternator bracket stud, and manoeuvre the heat shield from the engine.

Refitting

36 Refitting is a reversal of the removal procedure, noting:

Ensure that the drivebelt locates correctly in the grooves of all pulleys.
Relieve tension on the locking pin, and remove the pin from the tension pulley. Ensure that the pulley rotates to tension the belt correctly.
Use a torque wrench to tighten nuts and bolts to the specified torque.

---

13 Exhaust system – general information and component renewal

1 The exhaust system comprises three pipe sections – front, intermediate and tail. The pipe assemblies are connected to each other by flanges, secured by two nuts, and sealed with gaskets. The whole assembly is suspended on rubber mountings attached to the body **(see illustration opposite)**.

2 The front pipe, which connects to the exhaust manifold, includes a catalytic converter. To reduce engine vibration in the exhaust system, a corrugated pipe section, covered by metal braiding, is located between the manifold connecting flange and converter.

3 The intermediate and tail pipes each incorporate a silencer, which contain baffle plates and expansion chambers designed to reduce engine exhaust noise.

Note: *Renewing the complete system:*
Apply the handbrake, chock the rear road wheels, then jack up the front of the car as high as possible, and support it on axle stands (see 'Jacking and Vehicle Support').
Because of rust and corrosion, it may be quicker to separate pipe sections by cutting through them, instead of trying to slacken and remove the flange securing nuts.

Front pipe

Note: *the following new parts are needed – manifold flange gasket, front pipe-to-intermediate pipe gasket. Depending on their condition, new mounting rubbers may also be needed.*

13.5 Exhaust front pipe nuts

Removal

4 Apply the handbrake, chock the rear road wheels, then jack up the car and support it on axle stands (see *Jacking and Vehicle Support*).
5 Remove the two nuts securing the front pipe to the exhaust manifold **(see illustration)**.
6 Remove the two nuts attaching the front pipe to the intermediate pipe.
7 Release the mounting rubber from the support bracket, and remove the front pipe. Discard the gaskets.

Refitting

8 Clean the flange mating faces, fit new gaskets, and reconnect pipe flanges.
9 Fit the mounting rubbers to the body brackets.
10 Use a torque wrench to tighten the flange nuts to the specified torque.
11 Remove the stands, and lower the vehicle to the ground.

Intermediate pipe

Note: *the following new parts are needed – flange gaskets: front pipe-to-intermediate pipe, and intermediate pipe-to-tail pipe. Depending on their condition, new mounting rubbers may also be needed.*

Removal

12 Apply the handbrake, chock the rear roadwheels, then jack up the car and support it on axle stands (see *Jacking and Vehicle Support*).
13 Remove the two nuts securing the tail pipe to the intermediate pipe.
14 Remove the two nuts attaching the intermediate pipe to the front pipe.
15 Release two mounting rubbers from the support brackets, and remove the intermediate pipe. Discard the gaskets.

Refitting

16 Clean the flange mating faces, fit new gaskets, and reconnect pipe flanges.
17 Fit the mounting rubbers to the body brackets.
18 Use a torque wrench to tighten the flange nuts to the specified torque.
19 Remove the stands, and lower the vehicle to the ground.

13.1 Exhaust system component layout

1 Nut x 2
2 Gasket
3 Front pipe
4 Mounting rubber
5 Bolt and washer x 4
6 Heat shield – front pipe
7 Gasket
8 Heat shield – tail pipe
9 Mounting rubber
10 Tail pipe
11 Mounting rubber
12 Intermediate pipe
13 Nut x 2
14 Bolt and washer x 4
15 Heat shield –
      intermediate pipe
16 Nut x 2
17 Gasket
18 Bolt and washer x 4

H44597

Tail pipe

Note: *the following new parts are needed – flange gasket intermediate pipe-to-tail pipe. Depending on their condition, new mounting rubbers may also be needed.*

Removal

20 Apply the handbrake, chock the rear roadwheels, then jack up the car and support it on axle stands (see *Jacking and Vehicle Support*).

21 Remove the two nuts securing the tail pipe to the intermediate pipe.

22 Release three mounting rubbers from the support brackets, and remove the tail pipe. Discard the gasket.

Refitting

23 Clean the flange mating faces, fit new gaskets, and reconnect pipe flanges.

24 Fit the mounting rubbers to the body brackets.

25 Use a torque wrench to tighten the flange nuts to the specified torque.

26 Remove the stands, and lower the vehicle to the ground.

Chapter 4 Part B:
Fuel and exhaust systems – diesel engines

Contents

Degrees of difficulty

| **Easy,** suitable for novice with little experience | | **Fairly easy,** suitable for beginner with some experience | | **Fairly difficult,** suitable for competent DIY mechanic | | **Difficult,** suitable for experienced DIY mechanic | | **Very difficult,** suitable for expert DIY or professional | |

Specifications

General

System type . . . . Electronic diesel control (EDC) system direct diesel injection system

Idle speed (not adjustable – for reference only)

Models without intercooler . . . . 850 ± 50 rpm
Models with intercooler . . . . 805 ± 50 rpm

Torque wrench settings

	Nm	lbf ft
Catalytic converter-to-front pipe nuts	50	37
Crankshaft position (CKP) sensor bolt	8	6
Engine control module (ECM) bolts	4	3
Engine coolant temperature (ECT) sensor	15	11
Exhaust elbow-to-turbocharger bolts	25	18
Exhaust manifold support bracket bolt	25	18
Exhaust/inlet manifold-to-cylinder head bolts	33	24
Exhaust/inlet manifold-to-cylinder head nuts	25	18
Fuel injection pump fuel feed and return pipe unions	25	18
Fuel injection pump mounting bracket nuts and bolts	25	18
Fuel injection pump securing nuts	25	18
Fuel injection pump sprocket nut	60	44
Fuel injection pump vacuum pipe union	25	18
Fuel injector clamp bolt	25	18
Fuel injector feed pipe unions	20	15
Fuel shut-off solenoid	20	15
Intake air temperature (IAT) sensor	12	9
Intercooler-to-radiator bolts	25	18
Manifold absolute pressure (MAP) sensor bolt	9	7
Oil drain pipe-to-turbocharger nuts	10	7
Oil feed pipe-to-turbocharger nuts	20	15
Throttle position sensor nuts	4	3
Turbocharger pipe-to-cylinder head bolts:		
M6	10	7
M8	25	18
Turbocharger-to-exhaust manifold nuts	25	18

1 General information and precautions

General information

The operation of the fuel injection system is described in more detail in Section 6.

Fuel is supplied from a tank mounted under the rear of the vehicle, and then passes through a filter, to the fuel injection pump, which delivers the fuel to the injectors **(see illustration)**. The injection pump is controlled by an engine control module (ECM) on the basis of information provided by various sensors.

The inducted air passes through an air cleaner, which incorporates a paper filter element to filter out potentially-harmful particles (serious internal engine damage can be caused if foreign particles enter through the air intake system).

The engine control module (ECM) controls both the fuel injection pump and the preheating system, integrating the two into a complete engine management system. Refer to Chapter 5C for details of the preheating side of the system.

The exhaust system incorporates a catalytic converter to reduce exhaust gas emissions. Further details can be found in Chapter 4C, along with details of the other emission control systems and components.

Precautions

When working on fuel system components, scrupulous cleanliness must be observed, and care must be taken not to introduce any foreign matter into fuel lines or components.

After carrying out any work involving disconnection of fuel lines, it is advisable to check the connections for leaks; pressurise

H44645

1.2 Fuel delivery system

1 Fuel tank	4 Bleed screw	7 Fuel injector
2 Swirl pot	5 Fuel return line	8 Priming bulb
3 Fuel supply line	6 Fuel injection pump (FIP)	9 Fuel filter

2.4 Release the air cleaner clips

2.5 Remove two securing bolts

2.6 Remove the air cleaner

the system by cranking the engine several times.

Electronic control units are very sensitive components, and certain precautions must be taken to avoid damage to these units as follows.

When carrying out welding operations on the vehicle using electric welding equipment, the battery and alternator should be disconnected.

Although the underbonnet-mounted modules will tolerate normal underbonnet conditions, they can be adversely affected by excess heat or moisture. If using welding equipment or pressure-washing equipment in the vicinity of an electronic module, take care not to direct heat, or jets of water or steam, at the module. If this cannot be avoided, remove the module from the vehicle, and protect its wiring plug with a plastic bag.

Before disconnecting any wiring, or removing components, always ensure that the ignition is switched off.

Do not attempt to improvise fault diagnosis procedures using a test lamp or multi-meter, as irreparable damage could be caused to the module.

After working on fuel injection/engine management system components, ensure that all wiring is correctly reconnected before reconnecting the battery or switching on the ignition.

Damage to the catalytic converter may result if the following precautions are not observed:

a) Consult an approved dealer as soon as

possible in the event of misfiring, irregular engine running after a cold start, or a significant loss of engine power. If it is necessary to continue driving, do so for a short time at low engine speed, without labouring the engine.

b) Avoid frequent cold starts one after another.

c) Avoid actuation of the starter for an unnecessarily long time during starting.

d) Do not allow the fuel tank to become empty.

e) Do not attempt to start the engine by push- or tow-starting – use jump leads (see 'Jump starting').

2 Air cleaner assembly – removal and refitting

Note: *The following new parts are needed – air cleaner to IAT/MAF sensor housing O-ring.*

Removal

1 Disconnect the battery earth lead, and then the positive lead.
2 Remove the battery clamp and lift out the battery.
3 Release the coolant pipe from the clips on the air cleaner.
4 Release two clips securing the air cleaner upper housing to the IAT/MAF sensor housing on the air intake pipe **(see illustration)**.
5 Remove two bolts securing the air cleaner to the battery carrier **(see illustration)**.

6 From under the air cleaner, release the air intake pipe from the air cleaner lower housing.
7 Remove the air cleaner **(see illustration)**.

Refitting

8 Refitting is a reversal of the removal procedure, noting:
Fit a new O-ring to the IAT/MAF sensor housing.

3 Fuel tank and fuel filler neck – removal and refitting

Fuel tank

Removal

Note: *During removal, note the locations and routing of all hoses to aid refitting.*

1 Disconnect the battery negative lead.
2 Chock the front wheels, then jack up the rear of the vehicle and support securely on axle stands (see *Jacking and Vehicle Support*).
3 Syphon the fuel from the tank into a clean metal container which can be sealed. Alternatively, working under the car, disconnect an accessible fuel line connection at the tank, and drain the fuel into a suitable container.
4 Unscrew the bolt securing the handbrake cable to the left-hand rear suspension H-frame mounting, and release the cable from the mounting **(see illustration)**.
5 Remove the screw securing the fuel tank filler neck to the body, noting that the screw also secures the wheel arch liner.
6 Slacken the hose clip and disconnect the breather hose from the fuel filler neck **(see illustration)**.
7 Slacken the hose clip and disconnect the filler hose from the filler neck **(see illustration 3.6)**.
8 Slacken the hose clips and disconnect the fuel feed and return hoses from the pipes under the rear of the vehicle **(see illustration)**. Plug or cover the open ends of the hoses and pipes to prevent dirt entry.
9 Place a trolley jack under the fuel tank, with a block of wood between the jack and the tank.

3.4 Unscrew the bolt (arrowed) securing the handbrake cable to the H-frame mounting

3.6 Disconnect the breather (1) and filler (2) hoses from the fuel filler neck

3.8 Disconnect the fuel feed and return hoses (arrowed) from the pipes

3.10 Fuel tank strap locknut and securing nut (arrowed)

3.18 Pulling out the fuel filler neck surround

10 Working at the rear of the fuel tank, unscrew the locknuts, then unscrew the two fuel tank strap securing nuts **(see illustration)**.

11 Ensure that the jack is supporting the fuel tank, then release the fuel tank straps from the brackets on the body.

12 Lower the fuel tank until the fuel level gauge sender unit wiring connector can be reached, then separate the two halves of the connector, and withdraw the fuel tank from under the vehicle.

Inspection

13 If the tank contains sediment or water, it may be cleaned out using two or three rinses with paraffin. Shake vigorously using several changes of paraffin, but before doing so remove the fuel gauge sender unit (see Section 8).

14 Any repairs to the fuel tank should be carried out by a professional. Do not under any circumstances attempt to weld or solder a fuel tank.

Refitting

15 Refitting is a reversal of removal, bearing in mind the following points.

a) *Ensure that all hoses are reconnected to their correct locations as noted before removal, and use new hose clips if necessary.*

b) *On completion, prime the fuel system as described in Section 7.*

Fuel filler neck

Removal

16 Chock the front wheels, then jack up the rear of the vehicle and support securely on axle stands (see *Jacking and Vehicle Support*). Remove the left-hand rear roadwheel.

17 Remove the securing screws, and withdraw the rear left-hand wheel arch liner.

18 Remove the fuel filler cap, then reach up behind the filler neck and depress the three lugs securing the filler neck surround to the body and filler neck. Pull out the filler neck surround **(see illustration)**.

19 Working under the vehicle, slacken the hose clips, and disconnect the breather hose and the filler hose from the fuel filler neck. Be prepared for fuel spillage, and have a suitable container ready to catch any fuel which may be released as the filler hose is disconnected.

20 Withdraw the filler neck assembly from under the wheel arch.

Refitting

21 Refitting is a reversal of removal.

| 4 | Throttle cable – removal, refitting and adjust |

Removal

1 Disconnect the battery earth lead.

2 Release the outer cable adjustment nut from the sensor abutment bracket **(see illustration)**.

3 Release the inner cable from the sensor cam.

4 At the bulkhead, turn the outer cable collar through 90°, and release the cable.

5 Release three turnbuckles, and remove the panel from under the dashboard.

6 Depress the nylon clips, and release the inner cable from the throttle pedal, and remove the cable **(see illustration)**.

Refitting

7 Refitting is a reversal of the removal procedure, noting:

Feed the cable assembly through the bulkhead and connect the inner cable to the throttle pedal.

Smear rubber grease on both sides of the rubber seal, and secure the cable to the bulkhead.

Connect the inner cable to the cam, but do not fit the adjustment nut into the bracket.

Adjust

8 Hold the adjustment nut against the outer face of the bracket **(see illustration)**.

9 Hold the sensor cam in the fully closed position, and turn the adjustment nut until all slack is removed from the cable.

10 Fit the adjustment nut into the bracket,

11 Check that the cam moves the full throttle position when the pedal is pressed down.

12 Connect the battery earth lead.

4.2 Remove adjustment nut from bracket

4.6 Throttle cable collar and pedal connector

4.8 Hold adjustment nut against bracket

5 Throttle pedal – removal and refitting

Removal

1 Disconnect the end of the throttle cable from the pedal as described in Section 4.
2 Using a suitable pair of pliers, unhook the return spring from the pedal **(see illustration)**.
3 Working at the left-hand side of the pedal pivot shaft, prise off the securing clip, then slide the pedal assembly from the mounting bracket towards the right-hand side of the vehicle, until it can be removed **(see illustration)**.

Refitting

4 Refitting is a reversal of removal, but make sure that the securing clip is securely refitted.

6 Fuel injection control system – general information

The amount of fuel delivered, and the injection timing is controlled by the Electronic Diesel Control system (EDC) which also controls the preheat system, Exhaust Gas Recirculation system (EGR) and fuel cut-off solenoid for engine stop.

The fuelling, and injection timing, calculation is based on information supplied to the ECM by the following sensors **(see illustration)**:

a) *Crankshaft position sensor (CKP) sends signal representing the crankshaft speed and position.*
b) *Fuel injector needle lift sensor. Incorporated in number one injector, sends signal representing the start of No 1 cylinder injection sequence.*
c) *Engine coolant temperature (ECT).*
d) *Manifold absolute pressure (boost pressure) sensor (MAP), sends signal representing the pressure of the air entering the engine, The signal is used in conjunction with the intake air temperature sensor, to calculate the volume of oxygen in the air.*
e) *Road speed sensor, sends a signal representing the vehicle road speed, which operates the speedometer, and provides a signal to the ECM for idle stabilisation.*
f) *Throttle pedal position sensor (TP) The sensor is a potentiometer, which provides an electrical signal to the ECM representing the amount and rate of throttle opening – ie, driver demand.*
g) *Throttle control is 'drive by wire'. The sensor is connected to the pedal by a Bowden cable, and to the ECM by electrical cable.*
h) *Brake pedal switch, when closed by brake application, sends brake-applied signal.*

5.2 Unhook the return spring (arrowed) from the pedal

5.3 Prise off the throttle pedal securing clip (arrowed)

i) *Intake air temperature/Mass airflow sensor (IAT/MAF), supplies separate signals representing the mass air flow and intake air temperature.*

Signals from these sensors are constantly updated and processed by the ECM. The resultant calculations are compared with preprogrammed 'maps' which provide datum points for the amount of fuel required and injection timing, for many combinations of engine operating conditions.

Failure of certain sensors – either complete loss of signal, or sending an abnormal signal, will cause the ECM to default to

H44794

6.2 Electronic Diesel Control (EDC) components

1 Glow plug warning lamp
2 Engine malfunction lamp
3 Manifold Absolute Pressure sensor – MAP (Turbo boost pressure)
4 Road speed sensor
5 Crankshaft Position sensor – CKP
6 Intake air temperature/Mass Air Flow sensor – IAT/MAF
7 Main relay
8 Air conditioning compressor clutch relay
9 Cooling fan relay
10 Engine Control Module – ECM
11 Fuel Injection Pump – FIP
12 Standard fuel injector x 3
13 Glow plug x 4
14 Engine Coolant Temperature sensor – ECT
15 Glow plug relay
16 Throttle Position sensor – TP
17 No 1 fuel injector with needle lift sensor
18 Brake pedal switch

7.6 Slacken the bleed screw (1) and pump the rubber priming bulb (2)

preprogrammed values. In most cases this will be noticeable as poor or erratic engine performance.

Whenever a sensor fault occurs, the engine malfunction warning lamp, on the instrument panel, is lit, and a fault code is stored in a memory of the ECM. Using specialist diagnostic equipment, the codes can be extracted by MG Rover dealers.

7 Fuel system – priming and bleeding

1 After disconnecting any part of the fuel supply system or running out of fuel, it is necessary to prime the system and bleed off any air which may have entered the system components.
2 All models are fitted with a hand-operated priming pump, consisting of a rubber bulb located at the rear of the engine compartment in the fuel supply line to the fuel filter, and a bleed screw on top of the fuel filter.
3 To prime the system, proceed as follows.
4 If none of the fuel system components downstream of the fuel filter (including the fuel

8.5 Fuel gauge sender unit mounting details

1 Securing nuts	2 Sealing ring
	3 Sender unit

filter itself) have been disturbed, and the vehicle has not run out of fuel, it should be possible to proceed directly to paragraph 7.
5 Place a wad of absorbent cloth around the bleed screw on top of the fuel filter, then slacken the bleed screw.
6 Switch on the ignition so that the stop solenoid is energised, then pump the rubber priming bulb until fuel free from air bubbles emerges from the bleed screw **(see illustration)**. Tighten the bleed screw.
7 If not already done, switch on the ignition, then pump the priming bulb until resistance is felt, indicating that air has been expelled from the fuel injection pump. Switch off the ignition.
8 If air has reached the injectors, the high-pressure circuit must be bled as follows.
9 Place wads of clean, absorbent cloth around the fuel feed pipe unions at the injectors, then slacken the fuel pipe unions.
10 Crank the engine on the starter motor until fuel emerges from the unions, then stop cranking the engine and tighten the unions. Mop up any spilt fuel.
11 Start the engine with the accelerator fully depressed. Additional cranking may be necessary to finally bleed the system before the engine starts.

8 Fuel gauge sender unit – removal and refitting

Removal

1 The fuel gauge sender unit is mounted in the top of the fuel tank, and cannot be accessed with the tank in place.
2 Remove the fuel tank as described in Section 3.
3 Release the hose clamps, and disconnect the fuel feed and return hoses from the pipes at the top of the sender unit. Plug or cover the open ends of the hoses and pipes to prevent dirt entry.
4 Unscrew the six nuts securing the sender unit to the fuel tank.
5 Carefully slide the sender unit from the fuel tank, taking care not to damage the sender unit float. Recover the sealing ring **(see illustration)**.

10.3 Disconnect intercooler hose

Refitting

6 Examine the condition of the sealing ring, and renew if necessary, then thoroughly clean the mating faces of the tank and the sender unit.
7 Refitting is a reversal of removal, but if necessary, renew the fuel hose clips and, on completion, refit the fuel tank with reference to Section 3.

9 Fuel injection system – testing and adjustment

Testing

1 If a fault appears in the fuel injection system, first ensure that all the system wiring connectors are securely connected and free from corrosion. Ensure that the fault is not due to poor maintenance; ie, check that the air cleaner filter element is clean, that the cylinder compression pressures are correct (see Chapter 2B), and that the engine breather hoses are clear and undamaged (see Chapter 4C).
2 If the engine will not start, check the condition of the glow plugs (see Chapter 5C).
3 If these checks fail to reveal the cause of the problem, the vehicle should be taken to a Rover dealer for testing. A wiring connector is provided on a bracket under the facia, into which a special electronic diagnostic tester can be plugged. The tester should locate the fault quickly and simply, avoiding the need to test all the system components individually, which is time-consuming, and also carries a risk of damaging the ECM.

Adjustment

4 Idle speed, maximum speed and fuel injection pump timing are all controlled by the ECM, and no manual adjustment is possible.

10 Fuel injection pump – removal and refitting

Note: the following new parts are needed – fuel pipe sealing washers, intake manifold gasket.

Removal

1 Disconnect the battery earth lead.
2 Remove three screws securing the engine acoustic cover, and remove the cover.
3 Slacken the clip and disconnect the intercooler bottom hose from the air intake pipe **(see illustration)**.
4 Remove two bolts and release the EGR cooler pipe from the air intake pipe **(see illustration)**.
5 Remove the bolt securing the intake pipe to the cylinder head.
6 Remove two bolts securing the intake pipe to the inlet manifold and remove the intake pipe **(see illustration)**.

10.4 Release EGR cooler pipe

10.6 Remove the intake pipe

10.11 Flywheel/sprocket locking pin in position

7 Drain the cooling system – see Chapter 1B.
8 Slacken the clips at the radiator and coolant elbow, and disconnect the radiator top hose.
9 Slacken the clip and remove the radiator top hose from the oil cooler housing.
10 Remove the fuel injection pump drivebelt – see Chapter 2B.
11 Ensure that the sprocket locking pin is in position. Remove three Torx head bolts securing the flywheel/sprocket. Remove the locking pin, and remove the flywheel/sprocket **(see illustration)**.
12 Remove the nut and disconnect the harness feed lead from No 2 glow plug.
13 Release the injector needle lift sensor multi-plug from the fuel injection pump mounting bracket, and disconnect the plug from the engine harness **(see illustration)**.
14 Disconnect the fuel injection pump multi-plug.
15 Release the engine harness clips from the support brackets.
16 Remove the banjo bolt attaching the fuel feed pipe to the fuel injection pump, and discard the sealing washers.
Caution: Plug all pipes and connections as they are disconnected.
17 Disconnect the fuel return pipe from No 3 injector.
18 Remove the cap nut, and disconnect the fuel return pipe banjo from the fuel injection pump, and discard the sealing washers.
19 Pack absorbent cloth around the injector pipe connections.
20 Slacken No 1 and No 2 injector pipe unions at the injectors and fuel injection pump **(see illustration)**.
Caution: To prevent injector pipe damage, use two spanners when slackening the unions. Plug pipe connections after disconnection.
21 Disconnect the unions and remove the pipe assembly **(see illustration)**.
22 Slacken No 3 and No 4 injector pipe unions at the injectors and fuel injection pump.
23 Disconnect the unions and remove the pipe assembly.
24 Remove the bolt attaching the dipstick bracket the coolant elbow and move aside for access.

25 Remove four bolts securing the fuel injection pump support bracket to the cylinder block, and remove two nuts securing the bracket the fuel injection pump and move the bracket aside **(see illustration)**.
26 Remove two Torx head bolts and one nut securing the fuel injection pump to the gearbox adaptor plate, and remove the fuel injection pump and bracket.

Refitting

27 Refitting is a reversal of the removal procedure, noting:
Use a torque wrench to tighten all fastenings the specified torque.
Clean the mating faces of the fuel injection pump and gearbox adaptor plate.
Position fuel injection pump mounting bracket.
Fit the fuel injection pump to the gearbox adaptor plate and tighten the bolts and nut.

10.13 Disconnect the sensor multi-plug

10.21 Remove the pipe assembly

Fit the support bracket to the engine, and fit but do not tighten the bolts.
Fit and tighten the bolts securing the support bracket the fuel injection pump.
Tighten the bolts securing the support bracket the engine.
Fit No 3 and 4 injector pipes, followed by No 1 and 2 pipes.
Top-up the cooling system.

11 Fuel injectors – testing, removal and refitting

Removal

1 Disconnect the battery earth lead.
2 Remove three screws securing the engine acoustic cover, and remove the cover.

10.20 Slacken injector pipe unions

10.25 Remove support bracket bolts (1) and nuts (2)

11.3 Disconnect intercooler bottom hose

11.9 Remove the fuel return hose

11.12 Remove the clamp plates

11.13 Remove the injectors

3 Slacken the clip and disconnect the intercooler bottom hose from the turbocharger pipe **(see illustration)**.
4 Remove two bolts and release the EGR cooler pipe from the air intake pipe **(see illustration 10.4)**.
5 Remove the bolt securing the intake pipe to the cylinder head.
6 Remove two bolts securing the intake pipe to the inlet manifold and remove the intake pipe **(see illustration 10.6)**.
7 Pack absorbent cloth around the injector pipe connections.
8 Disconnect the needle lift sensor multi-plug from No 1 injector **(see illustration 10.13)**.
Note: *No 1 injector has an integral needle lift sensor.*
9 Remove the fuel return hose banjo bolts from the injectors, and discard the sealing washers **(see illustration)**.
10 Slacken the injector pipe unions at the

injectors and fuel injection pump **(see illustration 10.20)**.
Caution: To prevent injector pipe damage, use two spanners when slackening the unions. Plug pipe connections after disconnection.
11 Disconnect the pipes from the injectors and move aside.
Caution: Plug the pipe connections.
12 Remove the injector securing bolts and clamp plates **(see illustration)**.
13 Remove the injectors and discard the sealing washers **(see illustration)**.

Refitting

14 Refitting is a reversal of the removal procedure, noting:
  Clean the injectors and injector seats in the cylinder head.
  Fit new injector sealing washers with the

domed surface of the washer against the injector.
  Tighten the pipe connections to the specified torque.

12 Electronic Diesel Control (EDC) system components – removal and refitting

Crankshaft position sensor

Removal

1 Disconnect the battery negative lead.
2 The sensor is mounted at the rear of the flywheel housing (at the left-hand end of the engine) **(see illustration)**.
3 Disconnect the wiring plug from the sensor.
4 Unscrew the sensor securing bolt, then withdraw the sensor from its housing.

Refitting

5 Refitting is a reversal of removal.
6 Tightening the sensor securing bolt to the specified torque setting.

Engine coolant temperature sensor

Note: *Loctite 577 is needed to seal the sensor.*

Removal

7 The ECM sensor is screwed into the coolant outlet elbow attached to the side of the cylinder head, adjacent to the dipstick. It is connected the engine harness via a multi-plug.
8 Disconnect the battery earth lead.
9 Disconnect the multi-plug from the sensor **(see illustration)**.
10 Locate a container under the sensor to collect coolant. Unscrew the sensor.

Refitting

11 Refitting is a reversal of the removal procedure, noting:
  Clean and degrease the sensor threads, and apply a smear of Loctite 577.
  Use a torque wrench to tighten the sender to the specified torque.
  Top-up the coolant level.

Fuel temperature sensor

12 The sensor is integral with the fuel injection pump, and cannot be renewed separately.

Intake Air Temperature/ Mass Air Flow sensor

Removal

Note: *The following new parts are needed – sensor O-ring.*
13 Disconnect the battery earth lead.
14 Release the clip and disconnect the multi-plug from the sensor **(see illustration)**.
15 Slacken the clip securing the air intake hose to the sensor assembly
16 Release two clips securing the sensor assembly to the air cleaner.

12.2 Crankshaft position (CKP) sensor location (arrowed) – engine removed for clarity

12.9 Disconnect sensor multi-plug

17 Remove the sensor assembly and discard the O-ring.

Refitting

18 Refitting is a reversal of the removal procedure, noting:
Fit a new O-ring to the sensor assembly.

Fuel injector needle lift sensor

19 The sensor is an integral part of the No 1 cylinder fuel injector, and cannot be renewed separately. Fuel injector removal and refitting is covered in Section 11.

Vehicle speed sensor

20 The engine control module receives a vehicle speed signal from the same vehicle speed sensor used to provide a signal to the speedometer. Sensor removal and refitting details can be found in Chapter 7.

Fuel quantity servo position sensor

21 The sensor is integral with the fuel injection pump, and cannot be renewed separately.

Throttle position sensor

Removal

22 Disconnect the battery negative lead.
23 The sensor is located on the body panel at the right-hand side of the engine compartment.
24 Unscrew the two bolts securing the sensor mounting bracket to the body **(see illustration)**.
25 Slide the throttle cable adjuster from the cable bracket.
26 Slide the cable end fitting from the groove in the throttle position sensor lever.
27 Disconnect the wiring plug from the sensor, then unclip the wiring from the sensor bracket.
28 Unscrew the two nuts and bolts securing the sensor to the mounting bracket, and remove the sensor.

12.14 IAT/MAF sensor location

Refitting

29 Refitting is a reversal of removal, but reconnect and adjust the throttle cable as described in Section 4.

Manifold absolute pressure sensor

Removal

30 Disconnect the battery negative lead.
31 The sensor is located on the right-hand side of the engine compartment bulkhead.
32 Disconnect the wiring plug from the sensor, then release the hose clip and disconnect the vacuum hose from the sensor **(see illustration)**.
33 Unscrew the bolt securing the sensor to the mounting bracket, and remove the sensor.

Refitting

34 Refitting is a reversal of removal, tightening the sensor securing bolt to the specified torque setting.

Brake pedal switch

35 The engine control module receives a signal from the brake light switch which indicates when the brake are being applied. Brake light switch removal and refitting details can be found in Chapter 9, Section 25.

Engine Control Module

Note: *If a new ECM is to be fitted it will need to be programmed with the code from the anti-theft security unit before the engine can be started. This can be done only by an MG Rover dealer using special equipment.*

Removal

36 Disconnect the battery earth lead.
37 Remove two bolts and remove the ECM clamp from the battery carrier.
38 Release and disconnect two multi-plugs and remove the ECM.

Refitting

39 Refitting is a reversal of the removal procedure, noting:
If necessary, arrange programming of the module at an MG Rover dealer.

13 Turbocharger – description and precautions

Turbocharger assembly

By increasing the volume of air fed into the engine, the turbocharger allows a greater amount of fuel to be injected and burnt efficiently. The result is an increase in engine efficiency and power output, and a reduction in exhaust emissions.

The turbocharger has a single shaft in a specially-shaped housing. The housing is divided into two non-connecting chambers – one chamber housing a turbine wheel, and the other housing a compressor wheel. Both wheels are fixed to the single shaft.

Before passing into the exhaust outlet system, the engine exhaust gas passes through the turbine chamber, and spins the turbine wheel at high speed. Fixed to the other end of the common shaft, the compressor wheel also spins at high speed.

12.24 Throttle position sensor (TPS) mounting details

1 Throttle position sensor mounting bracket bolts *2 Throttle position sensor-to-mounting bracket bolts*

12.32 Manifold absolute pressure (MAP) sensor mounting details

1 Wiring plug *2 Vacuum hose* *3 Securing bolt*

13.4 Air intake system

| 1 Intercooler | 2 Air cleaner | 3 Turbocharger | 4 Intake manifold |

Before entering the intake manifold, the intake air enters the compressor housing and is compressed by the spinning compressor wheel. This increases the density of the air, and allows more to be forced into the engine. Consequently, more fuel can be burnt efficiently **(see illustration)**.

Intercooling

The air compression process raises the temperature of the air, so it expands and becomes less dense.

To counteract this drawback, after leaving the turbocharger, and before entering the engine, the air is passed through an intercooler.

The intercooler, mounted by the side of the cooling system radiator, is an air-to-air heat exchanger. Construction and operation of the intercooler is similar to that of the cooling system radiator. Engine intake air from the turbocharger, passing through the core tubes of the intercooler, is cooled by outside air passing across fins attached the core tubes.

As the volume of air entering the engine is

the same, it is effectively taking in a greater mass of air than before, meaning that more fuel can be burnt.

Boost pressure (the pressure in the inlet manifold) is limited by a wastegate, which diverts the exhaust gas away from the turbine wheel in response to a pressure-sensitive actuator.

The turbo shaft is pressure-lubricated by an oil feed pipe from the main oil gallery. The shaft 'floats' on a cushion of oil. A drain pipe returns the oil to the sump.

Precautions

The turbocharger operates at extremely high speeds and temperatures. Certain precautions must be observed to avoid premature failure of the turbo or injury to the operator.

Do not operate the turbo with any parts exposed. Foreign objects falling onto the rotating vanes could cause excessive damage and (if ejected) personal injury.

Do not race the engine immediately after start-up, especially if it is cold. Give the oil a few seconds to circulate.

Always allow the engine to return to idle speed before switching it off – do not blip the throttle and switch off, as this will leave the turbo spinning without lubrication.

Allow the engine to idle for several minutes before switching off after a high-speed run.

Observe the recommended intervals for oil and filter changing, and use a reputable oil of the specified quality. Neglect of oil changing, or use of inferior oil, can cause carbon formation on the turbo shaft and subsequent failure.

14 Turbocharger – removal and refitting

Note: *A new oil drain pipe gasket, a new exhaust front section-to-turbocharger elbow gasket, and new oil feed pipe sealing washers will be required on refitting.*

Removal

1 Disconnect the battery negative lead.
2 Apply the handbrake, then jack up the front of the vehicle and support securely on axle stands (see *Jacking and Vehicle Support*).
3 Unscrew the bolts securing the engine acoustic cover to the top of the cylinder head cover, then remove the acoustic cover from the engine.
4 Disconnect the exhaust front section from the turbocharger elbow, with reference to Section 18.
5 Loosen the hose clip, and disconnect the intercooler top hose from the intercooler **(see illustration)**.
6 Unscrew the two bolts securing the turbocharger pipe to the cylinder head and the engine lifting bracket **(see illustrations)**.
7 Loosen the hose clip securing the hose to the turbocharger, then remove the turbocharger pipe **(see illustration)**.
8 Slacken the hose clip, and disconnect the air intake hose from the turbocharger.
9 Unscrew the union bolt, and disconnect the oil feed pipe from the turbocharger **(see illustration)**. Recover and discard the two sealing washers.
10 Disconnect the manifold absolute pressure

14.5 Disconnecting the top hose from the intercooler

14.6a Unscrew the bolts (arrowed) securing the turbocharger pipe to the cylinder head . . .

14.6b . . . and the engine lifting bracket . . .

14.7 . . . then loosen the clip securing the hose to the turbocharger

14.9 Turbocharger oil feed pipe union bolt (arrowed)

14.10 Disconnecting the manifold absolute pressure (MAP) sensor pipe from the turbocharger

14.11 Unscrew the two bolts (arrowed) securing the oil drain pipe to the turbocharger

14.12 Unscrew the two bolts (arrowed) securing the exhaust elbow to the mounting bracket

14.13 Turbocharger securing nuts (arrowed)

(MAP) sensor pipe from the turbocharger (see illustration).

11 Unscrew the two bolts securing the oil drain pipe to the turbocharger (see illustration). Recover and discard the gasket.

12 Unscrew the two bolts securing the exhaust elbow to the mounting bracket (see illustration).

13 Support the turbocharger, then unscrew the three nuts securing the turbocharger to the exhaust manifold, and lift away the turbocharger, complete with the exhaust elbow (see illustration).

14 If desired, the exhaust elbow can be removed from the turbocharger after unscrewing the four securing nuts.

Refitting

15 If the exhaust elbow has been removed from the turbocharger, thoroughly clean the mating faces of the elbow and the turbocharger, then refit the elbow and tighten the securing nuts to the specified torque.

16 Further refitting is a reversal of removal, bearing in mind the following points:

a) Thoroughly clean the mating faces of the turbocharger and the manifold.

b) Tighten all fixings to the specified torque, where applicable.

c) Thoroughly clean the mating faces of the oil drain pipe and the turbocharger, and use a new gasket when reconnecting the pipe.

d) Reconnect the exhaust front section to

the turbocharger elbow, using a new gasket, with reference to Section 18.

e) Use new sealing washers when reconnecting the turbocharger oil feed pipe.

15 Turbocharger – examination and overhaul

1 With the turbocharger removed, inspect the housing for cracks or other visible damage.

2 Spin the turbine or the compressor wheel to verify that the shaft is intact and to feel for excessive shake or roughness. Some play is normal since in use the shaft is 'floating' on a film of oil. Check that the wheel vanes are undamaged.

16.4 Release front grille

3 The wastegate and actuator are integral with the turbocharger, and cannot be checked or renewed separately. Consult a Rover dealer or other specialist if it is thought that the wastegate may be faulty.

4 If the exhaust or induction passages are oil-contaminated, the turbo shaft oil seals have probably failed. (On the induction side, this will also have contaminated the intercooler, which if necessary should be flushed with a suitable solvent.)

5 No DIY repair of the turbo is possible. A new unit may be available on an exchange basis.

16 Intercooler – removal and refitting

Removal

1 Disconnect the battery earth lead.

2 Remove three screws and remove the engine acoustic cover.

3 Remove the air cleaner – see Section 2.

4 Remove two screws securing the front grille the bonnet lock platform. Tilt the grille forwards and release the retaining pegs (see illustration).

5 Slacken the clips and disconnect the top and bottom hoses from the intercooler.

6 Remove two Torx head bolts securing the intercooler the radiator.

7 Remove the bolt and bracket securing the intercooler to the bonnet lock platform.

8 Release the intercooler from the lower mounting, and remove the intercooler (see illustration).

Refitting

9 Refitting is a reversal of the removal procedure.

17 Manifolds – removal and refitting

1 The intake and exhaust manifolds share a common gasket (see illustration). To enable a new gasket to be fitted, both manifolds must be removed.

Removal

Note: *A new manifold gasket, a new oil drain pipe gasket, a new exhaust front section-to-turbocharger elbow gasket, new oil feed pipe sealing washers, and a new mass airflow sensor O-ring will be required on refitting.*

2 Disconnect the battery negative lead.

3 Unscrew the bolts securing the engine acoustic cover to the top of the cylinder head cover, then remove the acoustic cover from the engine.

16.8 Remove the intercooler

4 Slacken the hose clip, and disconnect the breather hose from the cylinder head cover.

5 Remove the mass airflow (MAF) sensor, as described in Section 12, then slacken the hose clip securing the air intake pipe to the turbocharger, and remove the intake pipe.

6 Slacken the clip securing the intercooler hose to the turbocharger pipe, then unscrew the two bolts securing the pipe to the cylinder head, disconnect the hose from the turbocharger, and remove the pipe/hose assembly.

7 Unscrew the union bolt, and disconnect the oil feed pipe from the turbocharger (see illustration). Recover and discard the two sealing washers.

8 Disconnect the manifold absolute pressure (MAP) sensor pipe from the turbocharger.

9 Disconnect the vacuum pipe from the exhaust gas recirculation (EGR) valve.

10 Unscrew the two bolts securing the EGR pipe to the inlet manifold.

11 Unscrew the two bolts securing the EGR valve to the exhaust manifold, and withdraw the valve. Recover and discard the gasket.

12 Disconnect the exhaust front section from the turbocharger elbow, with reference to Section 18.

13 Unscrew the two bolts securing the oil drain pipe to the turbocharger. Recover and discard the gasket.

14 Unscrew the two bolts securing the exhaust elbow to the mounting bracket (see illustration).

15 Slacken the six nuts and the four bolts securing the exhaust manifold to the cylinder head, then remove the nuts and bolts, noting the locations of the washers, where applicable (see illustration).

16 Carefully lift the exhaust manifold (complete with the turbocharger) from the cylinder head.

17 Disconnect the wiring plug from the inlet air temperature (IAT) sensor.

18 Slacken the hose clip, and disconnect the intercooler hose from the inlet manifold intake pipe.

19 Unscrew the bolt securing the inlet manifold to the bracket on the cylinder head cover.

17.7 Unscrew the union bolt and disconnect the oil feed pipe – engine removed for clarity

H44818

17.1 Manifold component layout

1	Air intake pipe	4	Inlet manifold	7	Bolt and washer x 4
2	Gasket – intake pipe to inlet manifold	5	Nut x 6	8	Bolt x 2
3	Bolt x 2	6	Exhaust manifold	9	Gasket – inlet and exhaust manifold

17.14 Unscrew the two bolts (arrowed) securing the exhaust elbow to the mounting bracket – engine removed for clarity

17.15 Unscrew the six bolts and four nuts (arrowed) securing the exhaust manifold to the cylinder head – engine removed for clarity

17.24 Manifold securing nut and bolt tightening sequence

20 Unscrew the two nuts securing the inlet manifold to the cylinder head, then withdraw the manifold. Recover and discard the gasket.

Refitting

21 Thoroughly clean the mating faces of the manifolds and the cylinder head, then position a new gasket on the cylinder head studs.
22 Manoeuvre the inlet manifold into position, then refit the securing nuts, but do not fully tighten them until after the exhaust manifold has been refitted.
23 Manoeuvre the exhaust manifold into position, then refit the nuts and bolts, ensuring that the washers are in place as noted before removal.
24 Tighten the inlet and exhaust manifold securing nuts and bolts to the specified torque (note that the torques for the nuts and bolts are different), in sequence **(see illustration)**.
25 Further refitting is a reversal of removal, bearing in mind the following points.
  a) *Tighten all fixings to the specified torque, where applicable.*
  b) *Thoroughly clean the mating faces of the oil drain pipe and the turbocharger, and use a new gasket when reconnecting the pipe.*

18.6 Unscrew the nuts (arrowed) and disconnect the exhaust front section from the catalytic converter

  c) *Use new sealing washers when reconnecting the turbocharger oil feed pipe.*
  d) *Reconnect the exhaust front section to the turbocharger elbow, using a new gasket, with reference to Section 18.*
  e) *Refit the mass airflow (MAF) sensor, using a new O-ring, with reference to Section 12.*

18 Exhaust system – general information and component renewal

1 The exhaust system comprises three pipe sections – front, intermediate and tail, and a catalytic converter **(see illustration overleaf)**. The pipe assemblies, and converter, are connected to each other by flanges, secured by studs and nuts, and sealed with gaskets. The whole assembly is suspended on rubber mountings attached to the body.
2 To reduce engine vibration in the exhaust system, a corrugated pipe section, covered by metal braiding, is located in the front pipe.
3 The tail pipe incorporates a silencer, which contains baffle plates and expansion chambers designed to reduce engine exhaust noise.
Note: *Renewing the complete system:*
  Raise the vehicle as high as possible, and support securely on axle stands (see 'Jacking and Vehicle Support').
  Because of rust and corrosion, it may be quicker to separate pipe sections by cutting through them, instead of trying to slacken and remove the flange securing nuts.

Front pipe

Note: *The following new parts are needed – manifold flange gasket, front pipe-to-catalytic converter pipe gasket. Depending on their condition, new mounting rubbers may also be needed*

Removal

4 Apply the handbrake, chock the rear roadwheels, then jack up the front of the car and support it on axle stands (see *Jacking and Vehicle Support*).
5 Remove the engine undertray.
6 Remove three nuts securing the front pipe to the catalytic converter **(see illustration)**.
7 Release the mounting rubber from the pipe bracket.
8 Remove the three nuts securing the front pipe to the turbocharger elbow **(see illustration)**.
9 Remove the front pipe, and discard the gaskets.

Refitting

10 Clean the flange mating faces.
11 Fit new gaskets the converter flange and manifold flange.
12 Attach the front pipe to the converter, and fit but do not tighten the nuts.
13 Raise the front pipe and engage the manifold flange, and fit the mounting rubber.
14 Tighten the nuts of both flanges securely.
15 Fit the undertray. Remove the stands, and lower the vehicle the ground.

Intermediate pipe

Note: *The following new parts are needed –*

18.8 Disconnect front pipe from turbocharger

flange gaskets: catalytic converter-to-intermediate pipe and intermediate pipe-to-tail pipe. Depending on their condition, new mounting rubbers may also be needed

Removal

16 Apply the handbrake, chock the rear roadwheels, then jack up the car and support it on axle stands (see *Jacking and Vehicle Support*).

17 Remove two nuts securing tail pipe to intermediate pipe. Release tail pipe and discard gasket.

18 Remove three nuts securing intermediate pipe to converter. Release and remove intermediate pipe, and discard gasket.

Refitting

19 Clean flange mating faces, and fit new gaskets.

20 Fit intermediate pipe to tail pipe, align and connect to converter flange.

21 Fit securing nuts to both flanges. Tighten the nuts securely.

22 Remove the stands, and lower the vehicle to the ground.

Tail pipe/silencer

Note: *The following new parts are needed – flange gasket intermediate pipe-to-tail pipe. Depending on their condition, new mounting rubbers may also be needed.*

Removal

23 Apply the handbrake, chock the rear roadwheels, then jack up the car and support it on axle stands (see *Jacking and Vehicle Support*).

24 Remove the two nuts securing the tail pipe/silencer to the intermediate pipe.

25 Release three mounting rubbers from the support brackets, and remove the tail pipe/silencer. Discard the gasket.

Refitting

26 Clean the flange mating faces, fit new gaskets, and reconnect pipe flanges.

27 Fit the mounting rubbers to the body brackets.

28 Tighten the flange nuts securely.

29 Remove the stands, and lower the vehicle to the ground.

Catalytic converter

Note: *The following new parts are needed – flange gasket: front pipe-to-converter and converter-to-intermediate pipe. Depending on their condition, new mounting rubbers may also be needed.*

Removal

30 Apply the handbrake, chock the rear roadwheels, then jack up the car and support it on axle stands (see *Jacking and Vehicle Support*).

31 Remove the three nuts securing the converter to the intermediate pipe, and three nuts securing the converter to the front pipe.

Caution: The converter can be easily damaged. Ensure that it is adequately supported during removal.

32 Release and lower the converter from both flanges. Discard the gaskets.

Refitting

33 Clean the flange mating faces, and f it new gaskets.

34 Carefully raise the converter into position, and reconnect pipe flanges.

35 Tighten the flange nuts securely.

36 Remove the stands, and lower the vehicle to the ground.

H44793

18.1 Exhaust system component layout

1 Front pipe	6 Catalytic converter	11 Nut x 2
2 Nut x 3	7 Gasket	12 Gasket
3 Rubber	8 Bolt and washer x 4	13 Tail pipe
mounting	9 Heat shield – tail	14 Rubber mounting
4 Nut x 3	pipe	15 Intermediate pipe
5 Gasket	10 Nut x 3	16 Rubber mounting

Chapter 4 Part C
Emission control systems

Contents

Degrees of difficulty

Easy, suitable for novice with little experience	**Fairly easy,** suitable for beginner with some experience	**Fairly difficult,** suitable for competent DIY mechanic	**Difficult,** suitable for experienced DIY mechanic	**Very difficult,** suitable for expert DIY or professional

Specifications

Torque wrench setting	**Nm**	**lbf ft**
Exhaust gas recirculation (EGR) valve bolts (diesel engines)	25	18

1 General information

Provided that the engine is correctly maintained, and is in good mechanical condition, the control systems will keep emissions within legal limits.

All models are fitted with the following control systems to reduce engine emissions released into the atmosphere **(see illustrations):**

Crankcase emission control

When the engine is running, a certain amount of combustion gas passes the pistons – 'blow-by' gases – and enters the crankcase. The amount of blow-by is dependent on the overall condition/wear of the engine.

When crankcase emission control is fitted, the blow-by gases from the crankcase are mixed with inlet air, and burned in the combustion chambers.

Exhaust emission control

To ensure optimum combustion efficiency, the engine management systems ensure extremely accurate metering of fuel, and ignition/injection timing.

To reduce harmful constituents from the exhaust gas, a catalytic converter is installed in the exhaust system. The converter contains a honeycomb of ceramic elements coated with special compounds – eg, palladium, rhodium and/or platinum. As the exhaust gases pass through the honeycomb, the coatings convert harmful emissions into inert by-products.

1.2a Emission control component layout – petrol engines

1	Crankcase breather hose to inlet manifold	3	Vent line to inlet manifold	6	Vent line from fuel tank
2	Crankcase breather hose to throttle body	4	EVAP canister	7	Two-way valve
		5	Vent line to atmosphere	8	Purge valve

Evaporative emission control (EVAP) – petrol engines only

The EVAP system reduces the level of hydrocarbons released into the atmosphere from fuel vapour.

Exhaust Gas Recirculation (EGR) – diesel engine only

Under certain running conditions, the vacuum-operated EGR valve on the exhaust manifold diverts exhaust gases into the inlet manifold, where they are used in the combustion process.

Petrol engines

Crankcase emission control

Ventilation is via the oil drain passages in the cylinder block and cylinder head, and two ports in the camshaft cover. The larger port is connected by plastic tube to the throttle body upstream of the throttle disc. The smaller port is connected by rubber hose to the inlet manifold. A restrictor and gauze oil separator prevent oil being drawn from the camshaft cover.

When the engine is running with the throttle disc closed, the depression downstream of the disc draws crankcase gases into the inlet manifold. From the upstream side of the disc, clean air is drawn into the crankcase to limit crankcase depression.

With the throttle disc wide open, both the upstream and downstream sides of the disc and the ports are subject to similar weak depression. Crankcases gases are drawn out of both ports, with most being drawn via the larger port into the throttle body.

Exhaust emission control

Petrol engine converters use platinum, rhodium and palladium.

Efficient operation of the converter is dependent upon careful control of the oxygen content of the exhaust gas. The oxygen sensor measures oxygen content in the exhaust system upstream of the catalytic converter. The sensor signal is used by the ECM to adjust fuelling.

The condition of the catalytic converter is monitored by the ECM, using a signal from a second sensor downstream of the converter.

EVAP

The main components are – EVAP canister, two-way valve, purge valve and connecting pipes.

Fuel vapour, created in the fuel tank as the fuel heats up, is held in the tank until pressure is sufficient to open the outward venting side of the two-way valve. When the valve opens excess vapour is released through a fuel cut-off valve and vapour separator into the EVAP canister. The vapour separator prevents condensing fuel from entering the vent pipes.

Charcoal in the canister absorbs and stores fuel from the vapour, and air with very little fuel vapour is vented to atmosphere.

The canister charcoal has a limited capacity, so fuel is purged via the purge valve into the inlet manifold, where it is burned during combustion. The valve, located in the top of the canister, is operated by the ECM. When the engine is above a certain temperature and speed, the valve is opened, and outside air is drawn through the charcoal and into the inlet manifold

When the fuel tank cools and pressure is reduced, the inward venting side of the two-way valve opens, and outside air is drawn through the EVAP canister, and into the tank.

Diesel engines

Crankcase emission control

Ventilation is via the oil drain passages in the cylinder block and cylinder head, and a port in the camshaft cover. A rubber hose connects the port to the crankcase pressure limiter valve on the turbocharger intake pipe. The limiter valve limits the depression produced in the crankcase.

A gauze oil separator prevents oil being drawn from the camshaft cover.

When the engine is running, the depression in the turbocharger intake pipe draws gases through the camshaft cover port and limiter valve.

As engine speed increases, the depression in the intake pipe increases and progressively closes the limiter valve, to maintain a fairly constant and safe pressure in the crankcase.

Exhaust emission control

Diesel engine catalytic converters use a platinum coating.

EGR

Under certain running conditions, the vacuum operated EGR valve on the exhaust manifold, diverts exhaust gases into the inlet manifold, where they are used in the combustion process.

The main result of this is to reduce combustion temperatures and, therefore, oxides of nitrogen emissions.

From the EGR valve, gases pass to the inlet manifold via a cooler, and a corrugated and insulated metal pipe. Engine coolant, passing through the EGR cooler, reduces the temperature of the exhaust gases, to further reduce emissions.

1.2b Emission control component layout – diesel engines

1 EGR solenoid
2 Vacuum line from EGR valve
3 Vacuum line from brake vacuum servo
4 EGR cooler to inlet manifold pipe
5 EGR cooler
6 EGR valve
7 Vacuum line to EGR solenoid
8 Crankcase breather hose
9 Crankcase pressure limiting valve

The valve is operated by a solenoid located on the engine bay bulkhead. The solenoid is controlled by the ECM.

2 Petrol engine emission control systems – testing and component renewal

Crankcase emission control

1 The components of this system require no attention other than to check that the hose(s) are clear and undamaged at regular intervals.

Evaporative emission control

Testing

2 If the system is thought to be faulty, disconnect the hoses from the charcoal canister and purge control valve and check that they are clear by blowing through them. Full testing of the system can only be carried out using specialist diagnostic equipment which is connected to the engine management system diagnostic wiring connector (see Chapter 4A). If the purge control valve or charcoal canister are thought to be faulty, they must be renewed.

Charcoal canister renewal

Note: *Note the locations of the hoses on the canister before removal to ensure correct refitting.*

3 The charcoal canister is located on the left-hand side of the engine compartment.
4 Disconnect the battery negative lead.
5 Trace the outlet hose back from the canister to the inlet manifold. Release the retaining clip and disconnect the hose from the manifold.
6 Trace the inlet hose back from the canister, then release the retaining clip and disconnect the hose from the fuel tank vent pipe.
7 Pull the canister breather hose from the hole in the front suspension rear beam **(see illustration)**.
8 Disconnect the wiring connector from the purge valve (mounted on the top of the canister) **(see illustration)**.
9 Unclip the canister from its mounting, and remove the canister/hose assembly from the engine compartment.
10 Refitting is a reverse of the removal procedure ensuring the hoses are correctly and securely reconnected, as noted before removal.

Purge valve renewal

11 The valve is integral with the charcoal canister, and cannot be renewed separately. If the valve is faulty, the complete charcoal canister assembly must be renewed.

Exhaust emission control

Testing

12 The performance of the catalytic converter can be checked only by measuring the exhaust gases using a good-quality,

2.7 Pull the charcoal canister breather hose (arrowed) from the hole in the front suspension rear beam – petrol engines

accurately-calibrated exhaust gas analyser, in accordance with the manufacturer's instructions.
13 If the exhaust gas CO level is too high, the vehicle should be taken to a Rover dealer so that the engine management system, particularly the heated oxygen sensor (HO_2S), can be thoroughly checked using the special diagnostic equipment. If no fault is found in the engine management system, the fault must be in the catalytic converter, which must be renewed.

Oxygen sensor renewal

14 Refer to Section 11 in Part A of this Chapter.

3 Diesel engine emission control systems – testing and component renewal

Crankcase emission control

Testing

1 The components of this system require no attention other than to check that the hose(s) are clear and undamaged at regular intervals. If the system is thought to be faulty, renew the crankcase pressure limiting valve.

Crankcase pressure limiting valve renewal

2 Slacken the retaining clip and disconnect the breather hose from the valve **(see illustration)**.

3.2 Crankcase pressure limiting valve location (arrowed) – diesel engines

2.8 Disconnect the wiring connector (arrowed) from the purge valve – petrol engines

3 Slacken the retaining clip, then ease the valve out from the intake pipe, and remove it from the engine compartment. Note the orientation of the valve to ensure correct refitting.
4 Refitting is the reverse of removal ensuring that the valve is orientated correctly, as noted before removal.

Exhaust emission control

Testing

5 The performance of the catalytic converter can be checked only by measuring the exhaust gases using a good-quality, accurately-calibrated exhaust gas analyser, in accordance with the manufacturer's instructions.
6 Before assuming that the catalytic converter is faulty, the vehicle should be taken to a Rover dealer so that the engine management system, and the fuel injectors, can be thoroughly checked using the special diagnostic equipment. If no fault is found in the engine management system or the fuel injectors, the fault must be in the catalytic converter, which must be renewed.

Catalytic converter renewal

7 Refer to Section 18 in Part B of this Chapter.

Exhaust Gas Recirculation

Testing

8 System testing can only be carried out by MG Rover dealers using special diagnostic equipment connected to the EDC system.

EGR valve renewal

Note: *The following new parts are needed – two EGR valve gaskets.*

9 Disconnect the battery earth lead.
10 Remove the engine acoustic cover.
11 Disconnect the vacuum pipe from the valve.
12 Remove two Allen screws securing the valve to the EGR cooler, and two Allen screws securing the valve to the exhaust manifold **(see illustration)**.
13 Remove the valve and discard the gaskets.

3.12 EGR valve location – diesel engines

3.18 EGR cooler location – diesel engines

3.23 EGR solenoid valve location (arrowed) – diesel engines

14 Refitting is a reversal of the removal procedure noting:
  Use new gaskets.
  Use a torque wrench to tighten the screws the specified torque.

EGR cooler renewal

Note: *The following new parts are needed – two EGR cooler gaskets.*
15 Disconnect the battery earth lead.
16 Remove the engine acoustic cover.
17 Drain the cooling system – see Chapter 1B.
18 Slacken the clips and disconnect two coolant hoses from the EGR cooler **(see illustration)**.
19 Remove two Allen screws securing the cooler the EGR valve.
20 Remove two Allen screws securing the cooler the EGR pipe.
21 Remove the cooler and discard the gaskets.
22 Refitting is a reversal of the removal procedure, noting:
  Use new gaskets.
  Tighten the screws securely.

EGR solenoid valve renewal

23 The valve is located at the right-hand side of the engine compartment bulkhead, next to the brake servo **(see illustration)**.
24 Disconnect the wiring plug from the valve, then disconnect the two hoses, noting their locations to ensure correct refitting.
25 Unscrew the two securing bolts, and withdraw the valve from its mounting bracket.
26 Refitting is a reversal of removal, but

make sure that the hoses are correctly reconnected as noted before removal.

---

4 Catalytic converter – precautions

1 The catalytic converter is a reliable and simple device which needs no maintenance in itself, but there are some facts of which an owner should be aware if the converter is to function properly for its full service life.

Petrol engine

a) *DO NOT use leaded petrol or LRP in a car equipped with a catalytic converter – the lead will coat the precious metals, reducing their converting efficiency and will eventually destroy the converter.*
b) *Always keep the ignition and fuel systems well-maintained in accordance with the manufacturer's schedule.*
c) *Consult an approved dealer as soon as possible in the event of misfiring, irregular engine running after a cold start, a significant loss of engine power, or any other malfunction which may indicate a fault in the ignition system. If it is necessary to continue driving, do so for a short time at low engine speed, without labouring the engine.*
d) *DO NOT switch off the ignition at high engine speeds.*
e) *DO NOT push- or tow-start the car – this will soak the catalytic converter in*

unburned fuel, causing it to overheat when the engine does start. Use jump leads (see 'Jump starting').
f) *Avoid frequent cold starts one after another.*
g) *DO NOT allow the fuel tank to become empty.*
h) *DO NOT use fuel or engine oil additives – these may contain substances harmful to the catalytic converter.*
i) *DO NOT continue to use the car if the engine burns oil to the extent of leaving a visible trail of blue smoke.*
j) *Remember that the catalytic converter operates at very high temperatures. DO NOT, therefore, park the car in dry undergrowth, over long grass or piles of dead leaves after a long run.*
k) *Remember that the catalytic converter is FRAGILE – do not strike it with tools during servicing work.*
l) *In some cases a sulphurous smell (like that of rotten eggs) may be noticed from the exhaust. This is common to many catalytic converter-equipped cars and once the car has covered a few thousand miles the problem should disappear.*
m) *The catalytic converter, used on a well-maintained and well-driven car, should last for between 50 000 and 100 000 miles – if the converter is no longer effective it must be renewed.*

Diesel engine

2 Refer to parts *e)* to *k)* of the petrol engine information given above.

Chapter 5 Part A:
Starting and charging systems

Contents

Degrees of difficulty

Easy, suitable for novice with little experience		Fairly easy, suitable for beginner with some experience		Fairly difficult, suitable for competent DIY mechanic		Difficult, suitable for experienced DIY mechanic		Very difficult, suitable for expert DIY or professional

Specifications

System type .... 12 volt, negative earth

Battery
Charge condition:
 Poor .... 12.5 volts
 Normal .... 12.6 volts
 Good .... 12.7 volts

Torque wrench settings	Nm	lbf ft
Petrol engines		
Alternator mounting bracket-to-engine bolt/nut	25	18
Alternator pulley nut	25	18
Alternator-to-mounting bracket nuts/bolts:		
With air conditioning	25	18
Without air conditioning	45	33
Battery cable-to-alternator nut	8	6
Drivebelt tensioner bolt	25	18
Starter motor bolts:		
1.1, 1.4 & 1.6 litre	25	18
1.8 litre	85	63
Starter motor support bracket nuts	25	18
Diesel engines		
Alternator lower fixing bolt/nut	45	33
Alternator lower upper fixing bolt	25	18
Alternator mounting bracket-to-coolant elbow bolts	25	18
Auxiliary drivebelt idler pulley bolts – no air conditioning	25	18
Auxiliary drivebelt tensioner bolt	45	33
Battery cable to-alternator stud	4	3
Drivebelt tensioner bolt	25	18
Starter motor bolts	80	59

1 General information and precautions

General information

The engine electrical system consists mainly of the charging and starting systems. Because of their engine-related functions, these components are covered separately from the body electrical devices such as the lights, instruments, etc (which are covered in Chapter 12). On petrol engine models refer to Part B for information on the ignition system, and on diesel models refer to Part C for information on the preheating system.

The electrical system is of the 12 volt negative earth type.

The battery is of the low maintenance or 'maintenance-free' (sealed for life) type and is charged by the alternator, which is belt-driven from the crankshaft pulley.

The starter motor is of the pre-engaged type incorporating an integral solenoid. On starting, the solenoid moves the drive pinion into engagement with the flywheel ring gear before the starter motor is energised. Once the engine has started, a one-way clutch prevents the motor armature being driven by the engine until the pinion disengages from the flywheel.

Further details of the various systems are given in the relevant Sections of this Chapter. While some repair procedures are given, the usual course of action is to renew the component concerned. The owner whose interest extends beyond mere component renewal should obtain a copy of the *Automotive Electrical & Electronic Systems Manual*, available from the publishers of this manual.

Precautions

It is necessary to take extra care when working on the electrical system to avoid damage to semi-conductor devices (diodes and transistors), and to avoid the risk of personal injury. In addition to the precautions given in *Safety first!* at the beginning of this manual, observe the following when working on the system:

• *Always remove rings, watches, etc, before working on the electrical system.* Even with the battery disconnected, capacitive discharge could occur if a component's live terminal is earthed through a metal object. This could cause a shock or nasty burn.

• *Do not reverse the battery connections.* Components such as the alternator, electronic control units, or any other components having semi-conductor circuitry could be irreparably damaged.

• If the engine is being started using jump leads and a slave battery, connect the batteries *positive-to-positive* and *negative-to-negative* (see *Jump starting*). This also applies when connecting a battery charger.

• Never disconnect the battery terminals, the alternator, any electrical wiring or any test instruments when the engine is running.

• Do not allow the engine to turn the alternator when the alternator is not connected.

• Never 'test' for alternator output by 'flashing' the output lead to earth.

• Never use an ohmmeter of the type incorporating a hand-cranked generator for circuit or continuity testing.

• Always ensure that the battery negative lead is disconnected when working on the electrical system.

• Before using electric-arc welding equipment on the car, disconnect the battery, alternator and components such as the fuel injection/ignition electronic control unit to protect them from the risk of damage.

The radio/cassette unit fitted as standard equipment by Rover is equipped with a built-in security code to deter thieves. If the power source to the unit is cut, the anti-theft system will activate. Even if the power source is immediately reconnected, the radio/cassette unit will not function until the correct security code has been entered. Therefore, if you do not know the correct security code for the radio/cassette unit **do not** disconnect the battery negative terminal of the battery or remove the radio/cassette unit from the vehicle. Refer to *Radio/cassette unit anti-theft system precaution* Section for further information.

2 Battery – testing and charging

Testing

Standard and low maintenance battery

1 If the vehicle covers a small annual mileage, it is worthwhile checking the specific gravity of the electrolyte every three months to determine the state of charge of the battery. Use a hydrometer to make the check and compare the results with the following table. Note that the specific gravity readings assume an electrolyte temperature of 15°C (60°F); for every 10°C (18°F) below 15°C (60°F) subtract 0.007. For every 10°C (18°F) above 15°C (60°F) add 0.007.

	Ambient temperature above 25°C (77°F)	Ambient temperature below 25°C (77°F)
Fully-charged	1.210 to 1.230	1.270 to 1.290
70% charged	1.170 to 1.190	1.230 to 1.250
Discharged	1.050 to 1.070	1.110 to 1.130

2 If the battery condition is suspect, first check the specific gravity of electrolyte in each cell. A variation of 0.040 or more between any cells indicates loss of electrolyte or deterioration of the internal plates.

3 If the specific gravity variation is 0.040 or more, the battery should be renewed. If the cell variation is satisfactory but the battery is discharged, it should be charged as described later in this Section.

Maintenance-free battery

4 In cases where a 'sealed for life' maintenance-free battery is fitted, topping-up and testing of the electrolyte in each cell is not possible. The condition of the battery can therefore only be tested using a battery condition indicator or a voltmeter.

5 If testing the battery using a voltmeter, connect the voltmeter across the battery and compare the result with those given in the Specifications under 'charge condition'. The test is only accurate if the battery has not been subjected to any kind of charge for the previous six hours. If this is not the case, switch on the headlights for 30 seconds, then wait four to five minutes before testing the battery after switching off the headlights. All other electrical circuits must be switched off, so check that the doors and tailgate are fully shut when making the test.

6 If the voltage reading is less than 12.2 volts, then the battery is discharged, whilst a reading of 12.2 to 12.4 volts indicates a partially-discharged condition.

7 If the battery is to be charged, remove it from the vehicle (Section 3) and charge it as described later in this Section.

Charging

Note: *The following is intended as a guide only. Always refer to the manufacturer's recommendations (often printed on a label attached to the battery) before charging a battery.*

Standard and low maintenance battery

8 Charge the battery at a rate of 3.5 to 4 amps and continue to charge the battery at this rate until no further rise in specific gravity is noted over a four hour period.

9 Alternatively, a 'trickle charger' charging at the rate of 1.5 amps can safely be used overnight.

10 Specially rapid 'boost' charges which are claimed to restore the power of the battery in 1 to 2 hours are not recommended, as they can cause serious damage to the battery plates through overheating.

11 While charging the battery, note that the temperature of the electrolyte should never exceed 37.8°C (100°F).

Maintenance-free battery

12 This battery type takes considerably longer to fully recharge than the standard type, the time taken being dependent on the extent of discharge, but it can take anything up to three days.

13 A constant voltage type charger is required, to be set, when connected, to 13.9 to 14.9 volts with a charger current below 25 amps. Using this method, the battery should be useable

within three hours, giving a voltage reading of 12.5 volts, but this is for a partially-discharged battery and, as mentioned, full charging can take considerably longer.

14 If the battery is to be charged from a fully-discharged state (condition reading less than 12.2 volts), have it recharged by your Rover dealer or local automotive electrician, as the charge rate is higher and constant supervision during charging is necessary.

3 Battery – removal and refitting

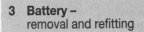

Note: *If a Rover radio/cassette unit is fitted, refer to 'Radio/cassette unit anti-theft system – precaution' in the Reference Section.*

Removal

1 The battery is located on the left-hand side of the engine compartment.

2 Slacken the clamp nut and disconnect the lead clamp from the battery negative (earth) terminal.

3 Lift the insulation cover and disconnect the positive terminal lead in the same way.

4 Unscrew the bolt and remove the battery retaining clamp, then lift the battery from the engine compartment **(see illustrations)**.

Refitting

5 Refitting is a reversal of removal, but smear petroleum jelly on the terminals after reconnecting the leads, and always reconnect the positive lead first, and the negative lead last.

4 Charging system – testing

Note: *Refer to the warnings given in 'Safety first!' and in Section 1 of this Chapter before starting work.*

1 If the ignition warning light fails to illuminate when the ignition is switched on, first check the alternator wiring connections for security. If satisfactory, check that the warning light bulb has not blown, and that the bulbholder is

3.4a Unscrew the bolt (arrowed) to remove the battery retaining clamp . . .

secure in its location in the instrument panel (see Chapter 12). If the light still fails to illuminate, check the continuity of the warning light feed wire from the alternator to the bulbholder. If all is satisfactory, the alternator is at fault and should be renewed or taken to an auto-electrician for testing and repair.

2 If the ignition warning light illuminates when the engine is running, stop the engine and check that the drivebelt is correctly tensioned (see Chapter 1A or 1B) and that the alternator connections are secure. If all is so far satisfactory, have the alternator checked by an auto-electrician.

3 If the alternator output is suspect even though the warning light functions correctly, the regulated voltage may be checked as follows.

4 Connect a voltmeter across the battery terminals and start the engine.

5 Increase the engine speed until the voltmeter reading remains steady; the reading should be approximately 12 to 13 volts, and no more than 14 volts.

6 Switch on as many electrical accessories (eg, the headlights, heated rear window and heater blower) as possible, and check that the alternator maintains the regulated voltage at around 13 to 14 volts.

7 If the regulated voltage is not as stated, the fault may be due to worn brushes, weak brush springs, a faulty voltage regulator, a faulty diode, a severed phase winding or worn or damaged slip-rings. The alternator should be renewed or taken to an auto-electrician for testing and repair.

3.4b . . . and lift the battery from the engine compartment

5 Alternator – removal and refitting

Petrol engine models

Without air conditioning

1 Disconnect the battery negative lead.

2 Remove one nut and two speed bolts securing the manifold heat shield to the exhaust manifold, and remove the heat shield **(see illustration)**.

3 Slacken the nut securing the cable to alternator, and release the cable.

4 Disconnect the multi-plug from the alternator.

5 Slacken the nut on the through-bolt attaching the alternator to the upper mounting bracket **(see illustration)**.

6 Remove the nut and bolt securing the alternator to the adjusting bracket **(see illustration)**.

7 Release drivebelt tension by turning the adjusting bolt anti-clockwise – the adjusting bolt screws into the end of the adjusting bracket **(see illustration)**.

Caution: Do not apply excessive torque to the bolt. If it seized, apply anti-seize compound.

8 Release the drivebelt from the alternator pulley.

9 Remove the upper through-bolt and nut, and lift out the alternator.

10 Clean the alternator and crankshaft pulleys.

5.2 Remove exhaust manifold heat shield

5.5 Slacken the through-bolt nut

5.6 Alternator adjusting bracket

5.7 Turn adjusting bolt anti-clockwise to release belt tension

11 Locate the alternator in the upper mounting bracket, and fit the through-bolt and nut. Loosely tighten the nut.

12 Fit the belt around the alternator pulley, ensuring that the belt locates correctly in the pulley grooves **(see illustration)**.

13 Fit the nut and bolt securing the alternator the adjusting bracket. Loosely tighten the nut.

14 Increase the drivebelt tension by turning the adjusting screw clockwise. Tension is correct when a force of 10 kg, applied at the centre of the belt upper run, deflects the belt by 6 to 8 mm.

15 Use a torque wrench to tighten the securing nuts to the specified torque.

16 Connect the multi-plug and cable, and tighten the cable nut,

17 Refit the exhaust manifold heat shield.

18 Connect the battery earth lead.

With air conditioning

19 Disconnect the battery earth lead.

20 Apply the handbrake, chock the rear roadwheels, then jack up the front of the car and support it on axle stands (see *Jacking and Vehicle Support*).

21 If fitted – remove the splash shield from under the engine.

22 Remove the bottom bolt securing the exhaust heat shield.

23 Fit a 13 mm spanner on the hexagon on the belt tension pulley, and rotate fully clockwise to release tension on the belt.

24 To hold the tension pulley in this position, fit a locking pin (max. 3 mm diameter) into the hole in the backplate, and against the stop on the tension pulley.

5.36 Remove the bracket stud

5.12 Alternator drive arrangement

Fixing points arrowed

25 Remove the alternator drivebelt from the alternator pulley.

26 Release the coolant hose clip from the front panel.

27 Remove the alternator upper mounting bolt.

28 Slacken the alternator lower nut.

29 Pivot the alternator away from the engine.

30 Remove the protective cap and disconnect the battery cable from the alternator.

31 Disconnect the alternator multi-plug.

32 Remove the bolt securing the heat shield to the cylinder block.

33 Remove the nut securing the heat shield to the alternator upper bracket.

34 Pull the heat shield bracket from the stud, and move the shield away from the engine **(see illustration)**.

35 Remove the bolt from the alternator bracket. Rotate the bracket to release and remove the bracket from the stud.

36 Using two nuts tightened together, remove the alternator bracket/heat shield stud from the cylinder block **(see illustration)**.

37 Remove the alternator lower through-bolt, and remove the alternator.

38 To ease fitting the alternator into the lower bracket, tap back the spacer in the through-bolt hole **(see illustration)**.

5.38 Alternator lower bracket and spacer

5.34 Pull the heat shield from the upper bracket stud

39 Fit the through-bolt into the rear hole of the lower bracket.

40 Locate the alternator in the lower bracket. Push the through-bolt through the bracket, and fit the nut – leave the nut loose.

41 Fit the upper bracket/heat shield stud.

42 Fit the upper bracket over the stud, and secure with the stud nut and front bolt.

43 Locate the heat shield over the stud. Fit the stud nut and heat shield top bolt – leave the nut and bolt loose.

44 Connect the battery cable and multi-plug.

45 Fit and tighten the heat shield bottom bolt, and fit the splash shield.

46 Remove the stands, and lower the vehicle the ground.

47 Tighten the heat shield upper nut and bolt.

48 Align the alternator in the upper bracket. Fit the upper through-bolt, and tighten the upper and lower through-bolts.

49 Fit the auxiliary drivebelt over the alternator pulley, and ensure that the belt is correctly located over the other pulleys.

50 Using the 13 mm spanner, pull the tension pulley clockwise, remove the locking pin and release the tension pulley **(see illustration)**.

51 Fit and tighten the coolant hose bracket bolt.

52 Connect the battery earth lead.

5.50 Alternator drive arrangement

Diesel engine models

53 The procedure is described as part of the brake vacuum pump removal and refitting procedure in Chapter 9.

6 Alternator – testing and overhaul

If the alternator is thought to be suspect, it should be removed from the vehicle and taken to an auto-electrician for testing. Most auto-electricians will be able to supply and fit brushes at a reasonable cost. However, check on the cost of repairs before proceeding as it may prove more economical to obtain a new or exchange alternator. Note that no spare brushes are available from Rover dealers.

7 Starting system – testing

Note: *Refer to the precautions given in 'Safety first!' and in Section 1 of this Chapter before starting work.*

1 If the starter motor fails to operate when the ignition key is turned to the appropriate position, the following possible causes may be to blame.
  a) *The battery is faulty.*
  b) *The electrical connections between the switch, solenoid, battery and starter motor are somewhere failing to pass the necessary current from the battery through the starter to earth.*
  c) *The solenoid is faulty.*
  d) *The starter motor is mechanically or electrically defective.*

2 To check the battery, switch on the headlights. If they dim after a few seconds, this indicates that the battery is discharged – recharge (see Section 2) or renew the battery. If the headlights glow brightly, turn the ignition switch to the start position, and observe the lights. If they dim, then this indicates that current is reaching the starter motor, therefore the fault must lie in the starter motor. If the lights continue to glow brightly (and no clicking sound can be heard from the starter motor solenoid), this indicates that there is a

8.11 Disconnect battery supply cable

8.3 Disconnect the battery supply lead

fault in the circuit or solenoid – see following paragraphs. If the starter motor turns slowly when operated, but the battery is in good condition, then this indicates that either the starter motor is faulty, or there is considerable resistance somewhere in the circuit.

3 If a fault in the circuit is suspected, disconnect the battery leads (including the earth connection to the body), the starter/solenoid wiring and the engine/transmission earth strap. Thoroughly clean the connections, and reconnect the leads and wiring, then use a voltmeter or test lamp to check that full battery voltage is available at the battery positive lead connection to the solenoid, and that the earth is sound. Smear petroleum jelly around the battery terminals to prevent corrosion – corroded connections are amongst the most frequent causes of electrical system faults.

4 If the battery and all connections are in good condition, check the circuit by disconnecting the wire from the solenoid blade terminal. Connect a voltmeter or test lamp between the wire end and a good earth (such as the battery negative terminal), and check that the wire is live when the ignition switch is turned to the 'start' position. If it is, then the circuit is sound – if not, the circuit wiring can be checked as described in Chapter 12.

5 The solenoid contacts can be checked by connecting a voltmeter or test lamp between the battery positive feed connection on the starter side of the solenoid, and earth. When the ignition switch is turned to the 'start' position, there should be a reading or lighted bulb, as applicable. If there is no reading or lighted bulb, the solenoid is faulty and should be renewed.

8.14 Remove the starter motor

8.5 Remove upper securing bolt

6 If the circuit and solenoid are proved sound, the fault must lie in the starter motor. In this event, it may be possible to have the starter motor overhauled by a specialist, but check on the cost of spares before proceeding, as it may prove more economical to obtain a new or exchange motor.

8 Starter motor – removal and refitting

Petrol engine models

Removal

1 Disconnect the battery earth lead.
2 Remove the air cleaner – see Chapter 4A.
3 Remove the nut securing the battery cable to the starter motor solenoid, and disconnect the cable **(see illustration)**.
4 Disconnect the Lucar connector from the starter solenoid.
5 Remove the starter motor upper securing bolt, and disconnect the earth lead **(see illustration)**.
6 Remove the two lower securing bolts, and remove the starter motor.

Refitting

7 Refitting is a reversal of the removal procedure, noting:
  Clean the mating faces of the starter motor and flywheel housing.
  Use a torque wrench to tighten all nuts and bolts to the specified torque.

Diesel engine models

Removal

8 Disconnect the battery earth lead.
9 Remove the air cleaner – see Chapter 4B.
10 Remove the engine undertray.
11 Remove the nut securing the battery supply cable to the starter motor solenoid, and disconnect the cable **(see illustration)**.
12 Disconnect the Lucar connector from the starter solenoid.
13 Remove the nut cover, slacken the inner nut, and remove the outer nut securing the torsion link.
14 Remove two bolts securing the starter motor, remove the torsion link assembly, and remove the starter motor **(see illustration)**.

11.1 Oil pressure switch (and oil temperature sensor) location – petrol engines

11.2 Oil pressure switch location – diesel engines

Refitting

15 Refitting is a reversal of the removal procedure, noting:

Clean the mating faces of the starter motor and flywheel housing.

Use a torque wrench to tighten all nuts and bolts to the specified torque.

9 Starter motor – testing and overhaul

If the starter motor is thought to be suspect, it should be removed from the vehicle and taken to an auto-electrician for testing. Most auto-electricians will be able to supply and fit brushes at a reasonable cost. However, check on the cost of repairs before proceeding as it may prove more economical to obtain a new or exchange motor.

10 Ignition switch – removal and refitting

The ignition switch is integral with the steering column lock. Removal and refitting of the ignition switch/steering column lock is described in Chapter 10.

11 Oil pressure warning light switch – removal and refitting

Location

Petrol engines

1 The oil pressure switch is screwed – at an angle – into the oil filter housing. Also screwed into the filter housing, adjacent to the pressure switch, is an oil temperature sensor which is used by the engine management system **(see illustration)**.

Diesel engines

2 The oil pressure switch is screwed into the top of the oil filter housing **(see illustration)**.

Removal

3 Disconnect the battery earth lead.

4 Jack up the front of the vehicle, and support securely on axle stands (see *Jacking and Vehicle Support*). Remove the right-hand front road wheel.

5 On diesel engine models, remove the engine undertray.

6 Disconnect the multi-plug from the switch.

7 Position a container under the switch to catch oil spill.

8 Unscrew the switch from the housing.

Refitting

9 Refitting is a reversal of the removal procedure, noting:

Clean and dry the switch threads.

Tighten the switch securely.

Check/top-up the engine oil level – see 'Weekly Checks'.

Chapter 5 Part B:
Ignition system – petrol engines

Contents

Degrees of difficulty

Easy, suitable for novice with little experience		Fairly easy, suitable for beginner with some experience		Fairly difficult, suitable for competent DIY mechanic		Difficult, suitable for experienced DIY mechanic		Very difficult, suitable for expert DIY or professional	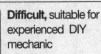

Specifications

General

System type	Rover modular engine management system (MEMS 3) ignition system integrated with indirect multi-point fuel injection system

Firing order	1-3-4-2 (No 1 cylinder at timing belt end)

Torque wrench settings	Nm	lbf ft
Engines with distributor:		
Ignition coil securing bolts:		
M6	9	7
M10	45	33
Rotor arm retaining screw	8	6
Engines with direct ignition:		
Plug top coils to camshaft cover	9	7
Spark plug/coil cover to camshaft cover	9	7
Spark plugs to cylinder head	25	18

1 General information and precautions

The ignition system produces the sparks to ignite the fuel/air mixture in each cylinder at precisely the right moment. The system is controlled by the Engine Control Module (ECM) which is the main component of the Modular Engine Management System (MEMS 3).

Early engines

Early engines have an ignition system with a single coil and distributor.

The coil is a transformer, which steps up the 12 volt battery supply to the many thousands of volts needed to jump the gap between the spark plug electrodes. The coil contains two sets of electrical windings. The low voltage – or 'primary' – winding is supplied from the battery, and the high voltage – or 'secondary' – winding supplies high voltage to the spark plugs.

The distributor is attached to the left-hand end of the cylinder head. The distributor shaft, which is an extension of the inlet valve camshaft, carries a rotor arm which distributes the high voltage to the spark plugs via four fixed contacts in the cap.

The low voltage supply is switched on and off by the Engine Control Module (ECM), which controls the Modular Engine Management System (MEMS) – see Chapter 4A.

When the ECM switches on the supply, a magnetic field is created in the primary winding. When the ECM switches off the supply, the magnetic field rapidly collapses and, by a process of 'electromagnetic induction', creates high voltage in the secondary winding. The duration of the on period, and the timing of the switch-off point, are controlled by the program in the ECM, and by signals fed to the ECM by various sensors which monitor engine operation – eg, engine speed, throttle position, crankshaft angular position, coolant temperature and intake air temperature.

Later engines

Later engines have two coils – one per two cylinders – but no distributor.

The system is, therefore, know as a 'distributorless' ignition system or, because the coils are connected directly to the spark plugs, as a 'direct ignition' system. The two coils are attached to the camshaft cover above the spark plugs for cylinders 1 and 3.

In this system, each cylinder is paired with the cylinder opposite in the firing order – 1 and 4, and 2 and 3. The ends of each coil secondary windings are attached to spark plugs for the paired opposites. These two plugs are in cylinders which are at Top Dead Centre (TDC) at the same time – one cylinder at TDC on the compression stroke, and the other at TDC on the exhaust stroke.

When the primary winding supply is switched off by the ECM, high voltage is supplied to both plugs simultaneously to

3.4 Ignition coil mounting details – viewed from underneath vehicle

1 Wiring connector   3 Coil securing
2 HT lead   bolts

complete the series circuit. The spark created by the plug in the cylinder on exhaust stroke is, of course not needed, so this method of firing is known as a 'wasted spark' system.

Because the polarity of the primary and secondary windings is fixed, one plug fires in a 'conventional' direction – ie, from centre electrode to side electrode, and the other plug fires in reverse – from side electrode to centre electrode.

Ignition timing

The precise point at which the spark is needed is constantly monitored and adjusted by the ECM. The ignition timing profile, for a wide range of engine operating conditions, is developed during engine testing, and programmed into the ECM. The ignition timing is not adjustable.

Precautions

Refer to the precautions to be observed given in Chapter 4A, Section 1.

⚠️ **Warning: The HT voltage generated by an electronic ignition system is extremely high and, in certain circumstances, could prove**

3.7 Disconnect breather hoses

fatal. Take care to avoid receiving electric shocks from the HT side of the ignition system. Do not handle HT leads, or touch the distributor or coil, when the engine is running. If tracing faults in the HT circuit, use well-insulated tools to manipulate live leads. Persons with surgically-implanted cardiac pacemaker devices should keep well clear of the ignition circuits, components and test equipment.

2 Ignition system – testing

⚠️ **Warning: DO NOT attempt to check for a spark by holding an HT cable a short distance from an earth point. The voltages are extremely high, and can easily cause injury or death. In addition, electronic components will be damaged.**
Caution: Electronic components are easily damaged by wrong connections, or attempted connection of unsuitable test equipment.
Note: If simple visual checks do not reveal the cause of any fault, the engine management system should have a full diagnostic check performed by and MG Rover dealer.

1 If an engine management system fault is suspected, carry out the following checks:
   Loose or dirty electrical connections/plugs.
   Chafing/frayed wiring.
   HT voltage tracking due to dampness.
   Air cleaner filter clean.

Engine breather hoses correctly fitted, and clear.
Coils and connections secure.
Early engines only – distributor components dry, and in good condition – see Section 4.
Spark plugs in good condition.
If the engine will not start, check that the fuel cut-off switch has not been triggered – see 'Roadside repairs'.

3 Ignition HT coil – removal and refitting

Early engines with distributor

Removal

1 The coil is mounted on the rear of the cylinder block.
2 Disconnect the battery negative lead, then apply the handbrake, jack up the front of the vehicle and support securely on axle stands (see Jacking and Vehicle Support).
3 Disconnect the wiring connector and HT lead from the coil.
4 Slacken and remove the three securing bolts, and remove the coil from the engine (see illustration).

Refitting

5 Refitting is the reverse of removal, but tighten the securing bolts to the specified torque.

Later engines with no distributor

Removal

6 Disconnect the battery earth lead.
7 Release two clips and disconnect two breather hoses from the camshaft cover (see illustration).
8 Remove three bolts securing coil/plug cover to camshaft cover, and remove the cover (see illustration).
9 Note the position and clipping of the HT leads and cables running to the coils. Release the HT leads, and pull the tubular connectors from the spark plugs next to the two coils (see illustration).
10 Remove the two bolts attaching each coil to the camshaft cover, and pull the coils from the spark plugs (see illustration).

3.8 Remove coil/plug cover

3.9 Pull off tubular connectors

3.10 Remove coil bolts

11 Disconnect the multi-plug from each coil, and remove the coils. Remove the HT lead from each coil **(see illustration)**.

Refitting

12 Refitting is a reversal of the removal procedure, noting:
Ensure that all cables are correctly connected, routed and clipped.
Use a torque wrench to tighten the coil securing bolts to the specified torque.

4 Distributor components –
   removal, inspection
   and refitting

Note: *A new rotor arm retaining screw will be required on refitting.*

Removal

1 Ensure the ignition is switched off.
2 Remove the air cleaner cover, with reference to Chapter 1A if necessary.
3 If the distributor cap is to be completely removed from the engine, check the HT leads for identification marks, and if none are present, label the leads to ensure correct refitting, then disconnect the HT leads from the distributor cap.
4 Unscrew the distributor cap securing screws, and remove the distributor cap **(see illustration)**.

3.11 Remove coil

5 If desired, the distributor shield can now be removed by passing it over the rotor arm.
6 If necessary, turn the crankshaft, using a suitable spanner or socket on the pulley bolt, until the rotor arm securing screw becomes accessible.
7 Unscrew the securing screw, and withdraw the rotor arm from the camshaft. Discard the screw, a new one must be used on refitting.

Inspection

8 Check the distributor cap for corrosion of the contact segments, and for signs of tracking, indicated by a thin black line between the segments. Make sure that the carbon brush in the centre of the cap moves

4.4 Unscrew the distributor cap securing screws and remove the distributor cap

freely, and stands proud of the surface of the cap. Renew the cap if necessary.
9 If the metal portion of the rotor arm is badly burnt or loose, renew the rotor arm. If slightly burnt or corroded, it may be cleaned with a fine file.

Refitting

10 Refitting is a reversal of removal, but use a new rotor arm retaining screw.

5 Ignition timing –
   checking and adjustment

The ignition timing profile is programmed into the ECM and cannot be adjusted.

Chapter 5 Part C:
Preheating system – diesel engines

Contents

Degrees of difficulty

Easy, suitable for novice with little experience	**Fairly easy,** suitable for beginner with some experience	**Fairly difficult,** suitable for competent DIY mechanic

Difficult, suitable for experienced DIY mechanic

Very difficult, suitable for expert DIY or professional

Specifications

Glow plugs
Type .... Bosch 0 250 202 025

Torque wrench settings

	Nm	lbf ft
Coolant outlet elbow bolts	25	18
Glow plugs	20	15

1 General description

To assist cold starting, diesel engines have a preheating system controlled by the Engine Control Module (ECM), which is the main component of the Electronic Diesel Control system (EDC).

A glow plug for each cylinder is installed in the cylinder head. Glow plugs are miniature electric heating elements with a heated probe at one end and an electrical connection at the other. The probe is positioned to preheat air and fuel spray entering the cylinder. Preheating improves fuel ignition and combustion, and so improves engine starting in cold weather.

The glow plugs are connected in parallel to a supply from a relay switched by the ECM, and the circuit is completed to earth via the plug bodies.

When the ignition switch is turned to position II, the relay is energised. Voltage is fed to the glow plugs, which heat up rapidly, and an indicator lamp on the instrument panel is lit. The length of time the relay is energised is determined by the coolant temperature signal fed to the ECM. At the end of the calculated time, the relay is de-energised, and the indicator lamp goes out. If the starter motor is operated before preheating is complete, the relay is de-energised and the lamp goes out.

2 Preheating system – testing

Caution: Electronic components are easily damaged by wrong connections, or attempted connection of unsuitable test equipment.
Note: *If the following checks do not reveal the cause of any fault, the engine management system should have a full diagnostic check performed by an MG Rover dealer.*

1 If the preheating system is thought to be faulty, carry out the following checks on the glow plugs.

2 Connect a voltmeter or 12 volt test lamp between the glow plug supply cable, and a good earth point on the engine.
Caution: Make sure that the live connection is kept well clear of the engine and bodywork.

3 Have an assistant activate the preheating system by turning the ignition key to the second position, and check that battery voltage is applied to the glow plug electrical connection. **Note:** *The supply voltage will be less than battery voltage initially, but will rise and settle as the glow plug heats up. It will then drop to zero when the preheating period ends and the safety cut-out operates.*

4 If no supply voltage can be detected at the glow plug, then the glow plug relay or the supply cable may be faulty.

5 To locate a faulty glow plug, first operate the preheating system to allow the glow plugs to reach working temperature, then disconnect the battery negative cable and position it away from the battery terminal.

6 Refer to Section 3, and remove the supply cable from the glow plug terminal. Measure the electrical resistance between the glow plug terminal and the engine earth. A reading of anything more than a few ohms indicates that the glow plug is defective.

7 As a final check, remove the glow plugs and inspect them visually, as described in Section 3.

8 If no problems are found, take the vehicle to a Rover dealer for testing using the appropriate diagnostic equipment.

3 Glow plugs – removal, inspection and refitting

Note: *The following new parts are needed – coolant outlet elbow seal, anti-seize compound. If plug No 4 is to be removed, the fuel injection pump must be removed.*

Removal

1 Disconnect the battery earth lead.

2 Remove the fuel injection pump – see Chapter 4B.

3 Remove the terminal nuts attaching the cables to the glow plugs, and disconnect the cables **(see illustration)**.

3.3 Disconnect cables

3.4 Remove glow plugs

4.1 Relay location

4 Unscrew the plugs from the cylinder head (see illustration).

Inspection

4 Inspect the plugs for any sign of damage. Burnt or eroded tips may be caused by incorrect injector spray pattern. Have the injectors tested if this sort of damage is found.
5 If the plugs are in good condition, operation of the plugs may be tested if a fused 12 volt DC supply is available – eg, a 12 volt battery, and suitable cables with fuse.
Caution: If the plugs are working, the tip will get red hot after a few seconds. Ensure that all connections are tight. Secure the plug so that it cannot touch any other component whilst voltage is applied, or whilst it is still hot. Allow the plug to cool before handling.

6 Connect the 12 volt positive supply cable to the plug terminal, and connect the negative cable to the plug body.
7 If the plug is working correctly, the tip should glow red after about 5 seconds. If the plug takes longer to glow red, or if it glows at a point other than the tip, it is faulty, and must be renewed.

Refitting

8 Refitting is a reversal of the removal procedure, noting:
   Clean the plugs and seating area in the cylinder head.
   Apply anti-seize compound to the plug threads.
   Use a torque wrench to tighten the plugs to the specified torque.
   Ensure that the feed cable is connected to plug No 2.

4 Glow plug relay –
   removal and refitting

Removal

1 The relay is attached to a bracket on the inner wing under the power steering fluid reservoir **(see illustration)**.
2 Disconnect the battery earth lead.
3 Release the relay from the mounting bracket, and disconnect the multi-plug.

Refitting

4 Refitting is a reversal of the removal procedure.

Chapter 6
Clutch

Contents

Degrees of difficulty

| Easy, suitable for novice with little experience | | Fairly easy, suitable for beginner with some experience | | Fairly difficult, suitable for competent DIY mechanic | | Difficult, suitable for experienced DIY mechanic | | Very difficult, suitable for expert DIY or professional | |

Specifications

Friction disc

Diameter:
   1.1, 1.4, and 1.6 litre petrol engine models . . . . 200 mm
   1.8 litre petrol engine models . . . . 215 mm
   Diesel engine models . . . . 228 mm
Minimum friction material thickness . . . . 1.5 mm
Minimum rivet head depth below surface of friction material . . . . 0.1 mm

Pressure plate

Maximum surface distortion . . . . 0.2 mm

Torque wrench settings	Nm	lbf ft
Clutch pressure plate-to-flywheel bolts:		
1.1, 1.4 and 1.6 litre petrol engine models	18	13
1.8 litre petrol engine models	26	19
Diesel engine models	26	19
Clutch release fork-to-shaft bolt (PG1-type transmission)	29	21

1.1a Clutch components – R65 gearbox

1 Flywheel
2 Flywheel bolts
3 Clutch friction disc
4 Clutch pressure plate
5 Pressure plate bolts
6 Release fork lower bush
7 Release fork and shaft
8 Release bearing
9 Release fork upper bush
10 Release lever

1.1b Clutch components – PG1 gearbox

1 Bolts – damper
2 Damper
3 Release lever
4 Oil seal – release shaft
5 Flywheel
6 Flywheel bolts
7 Clutch friction disc
8 Clutch pressure plate
9 Release bearing
10 Pressure plate bolts
11 Release fork

1 General information

The clutch is of single dry plate type, and consists of five main components: friction disc, pressure plate, diaphragm spring, cover and release bearing **(see illustrations)**.

The friction disc is free to slide along the splines of the transmission input shaft. The friction disc is held in position between the flywheel and the pressure plate by the pressure exerted on the pressure plate by the diaphragm spring. Friction lining material is riveted to both sides of the friction disc. Spring cushioning between the friction linings and the hub absorbs transmission shocks, and helps to ensure a smooth take-up of power as the clutch is engaged.

The diaphragm spring is mounted on pins, and is held in place in the cover by annular fulcrum rings.

The release bearing is located on a guide sleeve at the front of the transmission. The bearing is free to slide on the sleeve, under the action of the release arm that pivots inside the clutch bellhousing.

The release arm is operated by the clutch pedal, by means of a cable.

When the clutch pedal is depressed, the release arm is actuated by means of the cable. The release arm pushes the release bearing forwards, to bear against the centre of the diaphragm spring, thus pushing the centre of the diaphragm spring inwards. The diaphragm spring acts against the fulcrum rings in the cover. When the centre of the spring is pushed in, the outside of the spring is pushed out, so allowing the pressure plate to move backwards away from the friction disc.

When the clutch pedal is released, the diaphragm spring forces the pressure plate into contact with the friction linings on the friction disc. This simultaneously pushes the friction disc forwards on its splines, forcing it against the flywheel. The friction disc is now firmly sandwiched between the pressure plate and the flywheel, and drive is taken up.

2 Clutch cable – removal and refitting

R65-type transmission

Removal

1 Remove the air cleaner as described in Chapter 4A.

2 Working in the engine compartment, slide the clutch cable end fitting from the clutch release lever on the top of the transmission **(see illustration)**.

3 Release the cable sheath grommet from the bracket on the transmission **(see illustration 2.2)**.

2.2 Slide the end of the clutch cable from the release lever (1) and release the cable sheath grommet from the bracket (2) on the transmission

4 On right-hand-drive models, release the cable from the support bracket.

5 Working in the driver's footwell, release the three securing clips, and remove the fusebox cover.

6 Release the securing clips, and remove the driver's side lower facia trim panel.

7 Reach up behind the facia, and unhook the end of the clutch cable from the top of the pedal (**see illustration**).

8 Working in the engine compartment, pull the cable through the bulkhead into the engine compartment.

9 Note the cable routing, then release the cable from any remaining clips and brackets, and withdraw it from the vehicle.

Refitting

10 Commence refitting by lubricating the cable bulkhead bush with rubber grease.

11 Route the cable through the engine compartment, and through the bulkhead, as noted before removal.

12 Working in the driver's footwell, reconnect the cable to the top of the clutch pedal, then push the rubber bush on the cable fully into the bulkhead tube until the steel washer on the cable seats on the tube (**see illustration**).

13 Further refitting is a reversal of removal but, on completion, pull the clutch release lever on the transmission through its full range of movement, then release it to set the cable self-adjustment mechanism.

PG1-type transmission

Removal

14 Remove the air cleaner as described in the relevant Part of Chapter 4.

15 Apply the handbrake, then jack up the front of the vehicle and support securely on axle stands (see *Jacking and Vehicle Support*).

16 Working in the engine compartment, slide the clutch cable end fitting from the clutch release lever on the transmission (**see illustration**).

2.7 Unhook the end of the clutch cable (arrowed) from the pedal

2.16 Slide the clutch cable end fitting from the release lever on the transmission . . .

17 Release the cable sheath grommet from the bracket on the transmission (**see illustration**).

18 On right-hand-drive models, release the cable from the clip attached to the coolant hose.

19 Proceed as described in paragraphs 5 to 9.

Refitting

20 Proceed as described in paragraphs 10 to 13.

3 Clutch pedal – removal and refitting

Removal

1 Working in the driver's footwell, release the

3.4a Unscrew the clutch pedal retaining nut (arrowed) . . .

2.12 Push the bush on the cable fully into the bulkhead tube until the steel washer (arrowed) seats on the tube

2.17 . . . then release the cable sheath grommet from the bracket – PG1-type transmission

three securing clips, and remove the fusebox cover.

2 Release the securing clips, and remove the driver's side lower facia trim panel.

3 Unhook the end of the clutch cable from the top of the pedal.

4 Unscrew the pedal retaining nut from the left-hand end of the pedal pivot shaft, then slide the pedal from the pivot shaft, releasing the return spring from the pedal as it is removed – take care as a powerful return spring is fitted (**see illustrations**).

Refitting

5 Refitting is a reversal of removal, but ensure that the pedal return spring is securely reconnected to the pedal, and tighten the pedal retaining nut securely.

3.4b . . . then release the return spring (arrowed) from the pedal

4.4a Withdraw the pressure plate . . .

4.4b . . . and the friction disc

4 Clutch assembly –
removal, inspection
and refitting

⚠️ **Warning: Dust created by clutch wear and deposited on the clutch components may contain asbestos, which is a health hazard. DO NOT blow it out with compressed air, or inhale any of it. DO NOT use petrol (or petroleum-based solvents) to clean off the dust. Brake system cleaner or methylated spirit should be used to flush the dust into a suitable receptacle. After the clutch components are wiped clean with rags, dispose of the contaminated rags and cleaner in a sealed, marked container.**

Removal

1 Remove the transmission, as described in Chapter 7.

2 If the original clutch is to be refitted, make alignment marks between the clutch pressure plate and the flywheel, so that the clutch can be refitted in its original position.

3 Progressively unscrew the bolts securing the pressure plate to the flywheel.

4 Withdraw the pressure plate from the flywheel. Be prepared to catch the clutch friction disc, which may drop out of the cover as it is withdrawn, and note which way round the friction disc is fitted – the side of the disc facing the flywheel is normally marked 'Flywheel side' **(see illustrations)**.

4.7 Checking the surface of the pressure plate for flatness using a straight-edge and feeler blades

1 Feeler blades   *2 Straight-edge*

Inspection

5 With the clutch assembly removed, clean off all traces of dust using a dry cloth. Although most friction discs now have asbestos-free linings, some do not, and it is wise to take suitable precautions.

⚠️ **Warning: Asbestos dust is harmful, and must not be inhaled.**

6 Examine the linings of the friction disc for wear and loose rivets, and the disc for distortion, cracks, broken damping springs (where applicable) and worn splines. The surface of the friction linings may be highly glazed, but, as long as the friction material pattern can be clearly seen, this is satisfactory. If there is any sign of oil contamination, indicated by a continuous, or patchy, shiny black discolouration, the disc must be renewed. The source of the contamination must be traced and rectified before fitting new clutch components; typically, a leaking crankshaft oil seal or transmission input shaft oil seal – or both – will be to blame (renewal procedures are given in the relevant Part of Chapter 2, and Chapter 7 respectively). The disc must also be renewed if the lining thickness has worn down to, or just above, the level of the rivet heads.

7 Check the machined faces of the flywheel and pressure plate. If either is grooved, or heavily scored, renewal is necessary. The pressure plate must also be renewed if any cracks are apparent, or if the diaphragm spring is damaged or its pressure suspect. Check the surface of the pressure plate for flatness using

4.11 Check for markings (circled) on the friction disc which should face the flywheel

a straight-edge and feeler blades – renew the pressure plate if the distortion exceeds the specified limit **(see illustration)**.

8 With the clutch removed, it is advisable to check the condition of the release bearing, as described in Section 5.

Refitting

9 If new clutch components are to be fitted, where applicable, ensure that all anti-corrosion preservative is cleaned from the friction material on the disc, and the contact surfaces of the pressure plate.

10 It is important to ensure that no oil or grease gets onto the friction disc linings, or the pressure plate and flywheel faces. It is advisable to refit the clutch assembly with clean hands, and to wipe down the pressure plate and flywheel faces with a clean rag before assembly begins.

11 Apply a smear of molybdenum disulphide grease to the splines of the friction disc hub, then offer the disc to the flywheel, with the 'Flywheel side' marking facing the flywheel **(see illustration)**. Hold the friction disc against the flywheel while the pressure plate assembly is offered into position.

12 Fit the pressure plate assembly, where applicable aligning the marks on the flywheel. Ensure that the pressure plate locates over the dowels on the flywheel **(see illustration)**. Insert the securing bolts and washers, and tighten them finger-tight, so that the friction disc is gripped, but can still be moved.

13 The friction disc must now be centralised, so that when the engine and transmission are mated, the transmission input shaft splines will pass through the splines in the friction disc hub.

14 Centralisation can be carried out by inserting a round bar or a long screwdriver through the hole in the centre of the friction disc, so that the end of the bar rests in the spigot bearing in the centre of the crankshaft. Where possible, use a blunt instrument, but if a screwdriver is used, wrap tape around the blade to prevent damage to the bearing surface. Moving the bar sideways or up-and-down as necessary, move the friction disc in whichever direction is necessary to achieve centralisation. With the bar removed, view the friction disc hub in relation to the hole in the

4.12 Ensure that the pressure plate locates over the dowels (arrowed) on the flywheel

centre of the crankshaft and the circle created by the ends of the diaphragm spring fingers. When the hub appears exactly in the centre, all is correct. Alternatively, if a suitable clutch alignment tool can be obtained, this will eliminate all the guesswork, and obviate the need for visual alignment **(see illustration)**.

15 Tighten the pressure plate retaining bolts gradually in a diagonal sequence, to the specified torque. Remove the alignment tool.

16 Refit the transmission as described in Chapter 7.

5 Clutch release components – removal, inspection and refitting

Release bearing

1 Remove the transmission, as described in Chapter 7.

2 Disengage the bearing from the release fork, then pull the bearing forwards, and slide it from the guide sleeve in the transmission bellhousing **(see illustration)**.

3 Spin the release bearing, and check it for excessive roughness. Hold the outer race, and attempt to move it laterally against the inner race. If any excessive movement or roughness is evident, renew the bearing. If a new clutch has been fitted, it is wise to renew the release bearing as a matter of course.

4 Clean and then lightly grease the release bearing contact surfaces on the release fork. Similarly, lightly grease the guide sleeve.

5 Slide the bearing into position on the guide sleeve, then engage the bearing with the release lever.

6 Refit the transmission as described in Chapter 7.

Release fork and lever

R65-type transmission

Note: *A new release lever securing roll-pin will be required on refitting.*

7 Remove the release bearing, as described previously in this Section.

8 Using a suitable pin-punch, drive out the roll-pin securing the release lever to the release fork shaft, then slide the release lever from the shaft **(see illustration)**.

4.14 Using a clutch alignment tool to centralise the friction disc

9 Slide the release fork shaft upwards, and remove the shaft bushes from the transmission casing **(see illustration)**.

10 Withdraw the release fork shaft from the transmission.

11 Inspect the release bearing contact faces, and the pivot faces on the release fork and shaft for wear. Renew if excessive wear is evident.

12 Examine the pivot bushes, and renew if necessary.

13 Clean the components thoroughly, then smear the release fork shaft with a little molybdenum disulphide grease.

14 Slide the release fork shaft into position in the transmission, then fit the bushes, ensuring that the locating tags on the bushes engage with the slots in the transmission casing **(see illustration)**.

15 Slide the release fork shaft into position, then fit the release lever to the shaft, noting

that the lever faces away from the clutch housing, and secure with a new roll-pin.

16 Refit the release bearing as described previously in this Section.

PG1-type transmission

17 Remove the release bearing, as described previously in this Section.

18 Unscrew the bolt (and recover the washer) securing the release fork to the release lever shaft

19 Slide the release lever shaft from the transmission, and withdraw the release fork **(see illustration)**.

20 Inspect the release bearing contact faces, and the pivot faces on the release fork and shaft for wear. Renew if excessive wear is evident.

21 Examine the release lever shaft oil seal (located on top of the top pivot bush), and renew if necessary.

22 Examine the pivot bushes in the transmission casing for wear. If necessary the bushes can be renewed, as follows.

23 Carefully prise the lower bush from the transmission casing.

24 To remove the upper bush, carefully cut a longitudinal slot in the inner face of the bush, opposite the split in the bush, then prise the bush from the transmission casing.

25 Carefully drive the new bushes into position in the casing, using a suitable metal tube or socket (take care not to distort the bushes during fitting).

26 Clean the components thoroughly, then smear the release fork shaft with a little molybdenum disulphide grease.

5.2 Removing the clutch release bearing – R65-type transmission

5.8 Driving out the roll-pin securing the release lever – R65-type transmission

5.9 Removing a release fork shaft pivot bush – R65-type transmission

5.14 Align the pivot bush locating tags with the slots in the transmission casing (arrowed)

5.19 Removing the clutch release lever shaft – PG1-type transmission

5.27 **Refitting the clutch release fork –**
PG1-type transmission

5.29 **Refitting the clutch release bearing –**
PG1-type transmission

27 Position the release fork in the
transmission casing, noting that the securing
bolt fits from the front, then slide the release
lever shaft into position, passing it through the
fork **(see illustration)**. Note that the release
lever faces away from the clutch housing.
28 Align the holes in the release fork and
shaft, then refit the fork securing bolt,
ensuring that the washer is in place, and
tighten to the specified torque.
29 Refit the release bearing as described
previously in this Section **(see illustration)**.

Chapter 7
Manual transmission

Contents

Degrees of difficulty

Easy, suitable for novice with little experience	Fairly easy, suitable for beginner with some experience	Fairly difficult, suitable for competent DIY mechanic 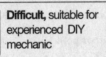	Difficult, suitable for experienced DIY mechanic 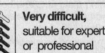	Very difficult, suitable for expert DIY or professional 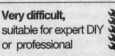

Specifications

General

Type	Manual, five forward speeds and reverse. Synchromesh on all forward speeds

Designation:
1.1, 1.4 and 1.6 litre petrol engine models	Rover R65
1.8 litre petrol engine models and diesel engine models	Rover PG1

Gear ratios:
R65-type transmission:
1st	3.417:1
2nd	1.947:1
3rd	1.333:1
4th	1.054:1
5th	0.854:1
Reverse	3.583:1

PG1-type transmission:
Petrol engine models:
1st	3.167:1
2nd	1.842:1
3rd	1.308:1
4th	1.033:1
5th	0.765:1
Reverse	3.000:1

Diesel engine models:
1st	3.250:1
2nd	1.895:1
3rd	1.222:1
4th	0.848:1
5th	0.648:1
Reverse	3.000:1

Final drive ratio:
1.1 litre petrol engines	3.765:1
1.4 litre petrol engines	3.765:1
1.6 litre petrol engines	3.556:1
1.8 litre petrol engines	4.200:1
Diesel engines	3.938:1

Lubrication

Recommended oil and capacity	See end of *Weekly checks* on page 0•17

Torque wrench settings

	Nm	lbf ft
R65-type transmission		
Drain plug	25	18
Engine steady bar-to-gearbox bolts	25	18
Filler/level plug	25	18
Flywheel front cover plate bolts	9	7
Flywheel rear cover plate bolt	9	7
Gear selector mounting-to-body bolts	22	16
Gearbox mounting bracket-to-engine mounting bolts	60	44
Gearbox mounting through-bolt	85	63
Gearbox-to-engine bolts	85	63
Gearbox-to-engine sump bolts	45	33
Gearchange linkage-to-rear beam bolts	24	18
LH engine mounting-to-body bolts	55	41
Reversing light switch	25	18
PG1-type transmission		
Drain plug	45	33
Earth lead-to-gearbox bolt	25	18
Engine-to-differential bolt	85	63
Filler/level plug	40	30
Front closing plate nuts and bolts	85	63
Gear selector mounting-to-body bolts	22	16
Gearbox lifting eye bolt	45	33
Gearbox mounting bracket-to-gearbox bolts	60	44
Gearbox-to-engine sump bolts	45	33
Gearbox-to-engine/mounting plate nuts and bolts*	85	63
Gearchange steady bar-to-gearbox	10	7
LH engine mounting-to-gearbox bolts	100	74
LH mounting-to-body bracket through-bolt	85	63
Reversing light switch	25	18

* Tighten in sequence

1 General information

The 5-speed transmission is contained in a casing bolted to the left-hand end of the engine.

Drive is transmitted from the crankshaft via the clutch to the input shaft, which has a splined extension to accept the clutch friction disc. The output shaft transmits the drive via the differential and driveshafts to the front wheels.

The input shaft runs in parallel with the output shaft. The input shaft and output shaft gears are in constant mesh, and selection of gears is by sliding synchromesh hubs, which lock the appropriate gears to the shafts.

Gear selection is via a floor-mounted lever and selector mechanism. The selector mechanism causes the appropriate selector fork to move its respective synchro-sleeve along the shaft, to lock the gear pinion to the synchro-hub. Since the synchro-hubs are splined to the gearshaft, this locks the pinion to the shaft, so that drive can be transmitted. To ensure that gearchanging can be made quickly and quietly, a synchromesh system is fitted to all forward gears, consisting of baulk rings and spring-loaded fingers, as well as the gear pinions and synchro-hubs. The synchromesh cones are formed on the mating faces of the baulk rings and gear pinions.

2 Manual transmission oil – draining and refilling

Note: *New filler/level plug and drain plug sealing washers must be used when refitting the plugs.*

1 This operation is much quicker and more efficient if the car is first taken on a journey of sufficient length to warm the engine/transmission up to normal operating temperature.

2 Park the car on level ground, and switch off the ignition. To improve access during draining, apply the handbrake, then jack up the front of the car and support it securely on axle stands (see *Jacking and Vehicle Support*). Note that the car must be lowered to the ground and level, to ensure accuracy, when refilling and checking the oil level.

3 Where applicable, remove the engine/transmission undershield to gain access to the filler/level and drain plugs.

4 Remove all traces of dirt from around the filler/level plug which is located on the left-hand side of the transmission, behind the driveshaft inboard joint. Unscrew the plug and recover the sealing washer **(see illustrations)**.

5 Position a suitable container under the drain plug which is also situated on the left-hand side of the transmission, below the driveshaft joint.

6 Unscrew the drain plug and allow the oil to drain into the container. If the oil is hot, take precautions against scalding. Clean both the filler/level plug and the drain plug, taking care

2.4a Transmission oil filler/level plug (1) and drain plug (2) locations – R65-type transmission

2.4b Transmission oil filler/level plug (1) and drain plug (2) locations – PG1-type transmission

to wipe any metallic particles off the magnetic inserts. Recover the sealing washers from the plugs, and discard them.

7 When the oil has finished draining, clean the drain plug threads in the transmission casing, fit a new sealing washer to the plug, and refit the drain plug. Tighten the plug to the specified torque. It the car was raised for the draining operation, now lower it to the ground.

8 Refilling the transmission is an awkward operation. Allow plenty of time for the oil level to settle properly before checking it. **Note:** *The car must be parked on flat level ground when checking the oil level.*

9 Using a tube inserted through the filler/level plug hole, slowly refill the transmission with the specified type of oil, until the level reaches the bottom of the filler/level plug hole. Allow plenty of time for the level to stabilise.

10 When the level is correct, refit the filler/level plug, using a new sealing washer, and tighten it to the specified torque.

3 Gearchange linkage – removal, refitting and adjustment

R65-type transmission

Removal

1 Apply the handbrake, then jack up the front of the vehicle and support securely on axle stands (see *Jacking and Vehicle Support*).

2 Although not strictly necessary, access to the gearchange linkage can be improved if the exhaust front pipe is first removed, as described in Chapter 4A.

3 Using a large flat-bladed screwdriver, carefully prise the gear linkage rod balljoints from the gear selector levers on the transmission, taking care not to damage the balljoints or their gaiters **(see illustration)**. Make a note of the location of each linkage rod (to ensure correct refitting), note which way round they are fitted, then detach both rod balljoints from the bellcrank assembly and remove the rods from the vehicle.

4 Prise the gear selector rod from the balljoints on the gearchange lever and bellcrank assembly, and manoeuvre the selector rod out from underneath the vehicle **(see illustration)**.

5 Working inside the vehicle, remove the centre console as described in Chapter 11.

6 With the console removed, carefully peel the rubber gaiter from the base of the gearchange lever, and slide the gaiter up the lever to gain access to the control rod pivot bolt and nut. Unscrew the nut, and remove the pivot bolt and thrustwashers.

7 Working underneath the vehicle, unscrew the nut securing the front of the control rod to the bellcrank pivot, then unscrew the two bolts and remove the retaining plate securing the rear of the control rod mounting to the body **(see illustration)**. Remove the mounting

3.3 Gearchange linkage assembly – R65-type transmission

Note: *On some models rods 27 and 29 are not adjustable*

1 Gearchange lever knob	11 Rubber seal	24 Bolt
2 Gearchange lever	12 Control rod	25 Spacer
4 Rubber cover	13 Pivot bolt	26 Bush
6 Mounting plate	14 Thrustwasher	27 Upper link rod
7 Seal	15 Spacer	28 Dust cover
8 Nut	16 Bush	29 Lower link rod
9 Selector rod	17 Nut	30 Bucket joint
10 Ball housing	22 Mounting plate	31 Bellcrank assembly
	23 Mounting rubber	32 Bolt

assembly, taking care not to lose its spacers, then manoeuvre the control rod out from underneath the vehicle.

8 If necessary, slacken and remove the three mounting bolts and remove the bellcrank from the subframe.

3.4 Prising the gear selector rod from the balljoint on the gearchange lever

3.7 Unscrew the two bolts (1) and remove the retaining plate (2) securing the control rod mounting to the body

3.14a Remove the metal clip . . .

3.14b . . . then drive out the roll-pin securing the selector rod to the selector shaft

9 If necessary, slacken and remove the gearchange lever housing retaining nuts and remove the seal, mounting plate and lever assembly from the vehicle.

10 Thoroughly clean all components and check them for wear or damage, renewing all worn or faulty items.

Refitting

11 Refitting is the reverse of the removal procedure, but check the linkage balljoints for wear and damage, and fit new components as

necessary, and apply a smear of grease to all the linkage pivot points and balljoints.

Adjustment

12 If a stiff, sloppy or imprecise gearchange leads you to suspect that a fault exists within the linkage, first dismantle it completely and check for wear or damage, then reassemble it, applying a smear of the approved grease to all bearing surfaces.

13 If this does not cure the fault, the vehicle should be examined by an expert, as the fault

must lie within the transmission itself. There is no adjustment as such in the linkage.

PG1-type transmission

Note: *A new gear selector rod-to-selector shaft roll-pin will be required on refitting.*

Removal

14 Remove the metal clip from the gear selector rod-to-selector shaft joint to expose the roll-pin, then drive out the roll-pin using a suitable pin punch, and release the selector rod from the selector shaft **(see illustrations)**.

15 Unscrew and remove the nut and pivot bolt securing the selector rod to the base of the gearchange lever, and remove the selector rod from the vehicle **(see illustration)**.

16 Working inside the vehicle, remove the centre console as described in Chapter 11, then release the gearchange lever rubber gaiter from the housing and slide it up the lever.

17 Working underneath the vehicle, unscrew and remove the bolts and retaining plate securing the gearchange steady rod rear mounting to the body. Remove the mounting rubber from the steady rod, taking care not to lose its spacers.

18 Unscrew and remove the bolt securing the gearchange steady rod to the transmission, and recover the washers **(see illustrations)**. Manoeuvre the steady rod and gearchange lever assembly out from underneath the vehicle – if necessary, the two can then be separated.

3.15 Gearchange linkage assembly – PG1-type transmission

1	Gearchange lever knob	3	Gear selector rod
2	Gearchange lever	4	Gearchange steady rod

H29822

3.18a Unscrew the bolt securing the gearchange steady rod to the transmission . . .

3.18b . . . and recover the washers

4.4 Levering out a driveshaft oil seal – R65-type transmission

4.6 Fitting a driveshaft oil seal using a socket – R65-type transmission

4.11 Remove guide sleeve bolts

19 If necessary, slacken and remove the retaining nuts and remove the gearchange lever plate assembly and seal.

20 Thoroughly clean all components and check them for wear and damage, renewing components if necessary.

Refitting

21 Refitting is a reversal of the removal, but use a new roll-pin to secure the gear selector rod to the selector shaft, and apply a smear of grease to all the linkage pivot points.

Adjustment

22 No adjustment of the gearchange linkage is possible.

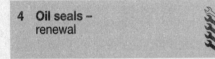

4 Oil seals – renewal

Driveshaft oil seals

Note: *Ensure that the correct type of new oil seal is obtained. Later transmissions use a modified seal, which cannot be fitted to earlier-type transmissions – refer to a Rover dealer for details.*

1 Apply the handbrake, then jack up the front of the car and support it securely on axle stands (see *Jacking and Vehicle Support*). Remove the appropriate front roadwheel.

2 Drain the transmission oil as described in Section 2, or be prepared for some oil loss as the driveshaft is removed.

3 Free the inboard end of the driveshaft from the transmission, as described in Chapter 8, and move it clear of the seal. Note that there is no need to disconnect the outboard end of the driveshaft from the hub. Support the driveshaft using wire or string, to avoid placing any strain on the driveshaft joints or gaiters.

4 Carefully prise the oil seal from the transmission using a large flat-bladed screwdriver **(see illustration)**.

5 Remove all traces of dirt from the area around the oil seal aperture, then apply a smear of grease to the outer lip of the new oil seal.

6 Ensure that the seal is correctly positioned, with its sealing lip facing inwards, and drive it

squarely into position, using a suitable tubular drift (such as a socket) which bears only on the hard outer edge of the seal **(see illustration)**. Ensure that the seal is seated correctly in the transmission recess.

7 Reconnect the inboard end of the driveshaft as described in Chapter 8.

8 Refill/top-up the transmission with the specified type of oil, and check the oil level as described in Section 2.

Input shaft oil seal

R65-type transmission

Note: *The following new parts are needed – release bearing guide sleeve (the seal is integral with the sleeve), three securing bolts for the release bearing guide sleeve.*

9 Remove the gearbox assembly – see Section 7.

10 Remove the clutch release bearing from the guide sleeve and release fork.

11 Remove and discard the three bolts securing the guide sleeve to the gearbox **(see illustration)**.

12 Remove and discard the guide sleeve.

13 Fit a new guide sleeve/seal over the input shaft, and align the bolt holes.

14 Fit three new bolts. Tighten the bolts securely.

15 Fit the release bearing over the guide sleeve and release fork.

16 Fit the gearbox assembly.

PG1-type transmission

17 To renew the input shaft oil seal, the transmission must be dismantled. This task should therefore be entrusted to a Rover dealer or transmission specialist.

Gear selector shaft oil seal

R65-type transmission

Note: *A new selector lever-to-shaft roll-pin will be required on refitting.*

18 Access to the selector shaft seal is greatly improved with the transmission removed. If the transmission is fitted to the vehicle, proceed as follows. If the transmission has been removed, proceed to paragraph 22.

19 Apply the handbrake, then jack up the front of the vehicle and support securely on axle stands (see *Jacking and Vehicle Support*). Remove the left-hand front roadwheel.

20 Remove the left-hand engine/transmission mounting as described in Chapter 2A.

21 Using a large flat-bladed screwdriver, carefully prise the gear linkage rod balljoint from the gear selector lever on the transmission, taking care not to damage the balljoint or its gaiter.

22 Using a suitable punch, and if necessary extension pieces, drive out the roll-pin securing the selector lever to the shaft **(see illustration)**. Access is extremely difficult. Discard the roll-pin.

4.22 Gearchange selector shaft oil seal fitting details – R65-type transmission

1 Link rod
2 Selector lever
3 Roll-pin
4 Oil seal

H29798

4.32 Gearchange selector shaft oil seal renewal – PG1-type transmission

1 Gearchange steady bar securing bolt
2 Metal clip
3 Roll-pin
4 Selector rod

H29799

4.34a Slide the gaiter from the selector shaft . . .

4.34b . . . and carefully prise out the oil seal

23 Lower the engine/transmission assembly slightly until the selector lever can be withdrawn from the shaft.

24 Carefully lever the seal from the transmission, taking great care not to damage the shaft or casing.

25 Before fitting a new seal, check the seal rubbing surface on the selector shaft for signs of burrs, scratches or other damage which may have caused the seal to fail in the first place. It may be possible to polish away minor faults of this sort using fine abrasive paper, however, more serious defects will require the renewal of the shaft.

26 Lubricate the new seal with a smear of clean transmission oil, then ease the seal into position. Press the seal squarely into position, using a socket which bears only on the hard

5.5 Disconnecting the reversing light switch – R65-type transmission

outer edge of the seal, ensuring that the seal lip faces inwards.

27 Refit the selector lever to the shaft, and secure it in position with a new roll-pin.

28 If the transmission is fitted to the vehicle, proceed as follows, otherwise refit the transmission.

a) Press the gear linkage rod balljoint into position on the selector lever.
b) Refit the left-hand engine/transmission mounting as described in Chapter 2A, then refit the roadwheel and lower the vehicle to the ground.

PG1-type transmission

29 Apply the handbrake, then jack up the front of the vehicle and support it securely on axle stands (see *Jacking and Vehicle Support*).

30 Drain the transmission oil as described in Section 2, or be prepared for fluid loss as the seal is removed.

31 Unscrew the bolt securing the gearchange steady bar to the transmission. Recover the two washers.

32 Remove the metal clip from the gear selector rod-to-selector shaft joint to expose the roll-pin **(see illustration)**.

33 Drive out the roll-pin using a suitable pin punch, then release the selector rod from the selector shaft, and move the rod and the gearchange steady bar to one side.

34 If the transmission oil has not been drained, have a container ready to catch

escaping oil, then slide the gaiter from the selector shaft, and carefully prise out the oil seal **(see illustrations)**.

35 Before fitting a new seal, check the seal rubbing surface on the selector shaft for signs of burrs, scratches or other damage which may have caused the seal to fail in the first place. It may be possible to polish away minor faults of this sort using fine abrasive paper, however, more serious defects will require the renewal of the selector shaft.

36 Lubricate the new seal with clean transmission oil, and ease it over the end of the selector shaft. Press the seal squarely into the transmission housing using a tube (such as a socket) which bears only on the hard outer edge of the seal.

37 Slide the gaiter onto the shaft, ensuring that the lip on the gaiter engages with the oil seal.

38 Slide the selector rod onto the shaft, and secure using a new roll-pin. Refit the metal clip over the selector shaft and roll-pin.

39 Refit the bolt securing the gearchange steady bar to the transmission, ensuring that the washers are in place, then tighten the bolt to the specified torque.

40 Lower the vehicle to the ground, then refill/top-up the transmission with the specified type of oil and check the oil level as described in Section 2.

5 Reversing light switch – testing, removal and refitting

Testing

1 The reversing light circuit is controlled by a plunger-type switch, located in the top of the transmission casing on R65-type transmissions, or in the side of the transmission casing on PG1-type transmissions. If a fault develops in the circuit, first ensure that the circuit fuse has not blown.

2 To test the switch, first disconnect the wiring connector. Use a multimeter (set to the resistance function), or a battery-and-bulb test circuit, to check that there is continuity between the switch terminals only when reverse gear is selected. If this is not the case, and there are no obvious breaks or other damage to the wires, the switch is faulty, and must be renewed.

R65-type transmission

Note: *A new sealing washer will be required on refitting.*

Removal

3 Disconnect the battery negative lead.

4 To improve access to the switch, remove the air cleaner assembly as described in Chapter 4A.

5 Disconnect the switch wiring connector, then unscrew the switch, and remove it from the top of the transmission **(see illustration)**. Recover the sealing washer and discard it.

Refitting

6 Refitting is a reversal of removal, but use a new sealing washer, and tighten the switch to the specified torque setting.

PG1-type transmission

Note: *A new sealing washer will be required on refitting.*

Removal

7 The switch is located in the front of the transmission casing **(see illustration)**. Disconnect the battery negative lead.

8 Apply the handbrake, then jack up the front of the vehicle and support it securely on axle stands (see *Jacking and Vehicle Support*). Where necessary, remove the engine/transmission undershield to gain access to the switch.

9 Trace the wiring back from the switch, freeing it from any relevant retaining clips, and separate the two halves of the wiring connector(s).

Caution: Be prepared for possible oil loss when the switch is removed, and have ready a suitable plug to plug the aperture in the transmission whilst the switch is removed.

10 Wipe clean the area around the switch then unscrew the switch. Recover and discard the sealing washer. If necessary, plug the switch aperture to minimise oil loss.

Refitting

11 Refitting is a reversal of removal, but use a new sealing washer, and tighten the switch to the specified torque setting. If oil was lost during the removal procedure, check the transmission oil level and top up if necessary.

---

6 Vehicle speed sensor – removal and refitting

Note: *A new speedometer drive O-ring will be required on refitting.*

Removal

1 All models are fitted with an electrically-operated speedometer, which uses a signal provided by the vehicle speed sensor, mounted on the top of the transmission housing, next to the inboard end of the right-hand driveshaft **(see illustration)**.

2 Disconnect the battery negative lead.

3 To gain access to the speedometer sensor, apply the handbrake then jack up the front of the vehicle and support it securely on axle stands (see *Jacking and Vehicle Support*).

4 Disconnect the wiring connector from the vehicle speed sensor then unscrew the sensor securing nut, and remove the sensor from the top of the speedometer drive assembly **(see illustration)**.

5 Slacken and remove the retaining bolt, and withdraw the speedometer drive assembly

5.7 Reversing light switch location – PG1-type transmission (transmission removed)

6.4 Removing the vehicle speed sensor – PG1-type transmission

from the transmission housing, along with its O-ring **(see illustration)**.

Refitting

6 Lubricate a new O-ring with a smear of clean transmission oil, then fit the O-ring to the speedometer drive housing.

7 Ease the speedometer drive assembly into position in the transmission, ensuring that the drive and driven pinions are correctly engaged. Refit and tighten the retaining bolt.

8 Fit the speed sensor to the top of the drive assembly, ensuring that the sensor drive pin is correctly engaged with the pinion, and securely tighten the sensor securing nut.

9 Reconnect the wiring connector to the speed sensor then lower the vehicle to the ground, and reconnect the battery negative lead.

7.5 Remove battery tray

6.1 Vehicle speed sensor location (arrowed) – R65-type transmission

6.5 Removing the speedometer drive assembly – PG1-type transmission

---

7 Manual transmission – removal and refitting

1.1, 1.4 and 1.6 litre petrol engine models

Removal

1 Disconnect both battery leads – earth lead first.

2 Remove the battery clamp, and lift out the battery.

3 Remove the air cleaner assembly – see Chapter 4A.

4 Disconnect two multi-plugs from the engine control module (ECM).

5 Where applicable, release the ABS fuseholder from the battery tray. Remove three bolts from the base of the battery tray, and slacken three bolts under the tray. Lift out the tray with ECM **(see illustration)**.

6 Apply the handbrake, chock the rear roadwheels, then jack up the front of the car and support it on axle stands (see *Jacking and Vehicle Support*).

7 Remove the front roadwheels.

8 Remove the starter motor – see Chapter 5A.

9 Disconnect the multi-plugs from the vehicle speed sensor, and the reversing light switch.

10 Release the battery positive lead from the clip on the gearbox.

11 Disconnect the clutch inner cable from the release lever, and release the outer cable from the abutment bracket, and tie clear of the work area **(see illustration)**.

7.11 Disconnect clutch cable

7.12 Remove gear linkage balljoints

7.13 Remove engine steady bar

7.15 Remove rear cover plate

12 Using a large flat-blade screwdriver, carefully remove the gear linkage rod balljoints from the gearchange levers, and tie clear of the work area **(see illustration)**.
13 Remove the two bolts attaching the engine left-hand steady bar to the engine bracket and engine mounting, and remove the steady bar **(see illustration)**.
14 Remove the two bolts securing the clutch cable support bracket to the flywheel housing, and remove the bracket.
15 Remove the bolt securing the flywheel rear cover plate to the flywheel housing, and remove the plate **(see illustration)**.
16 Disconnect the inboard ends of both driveshafts – see Chapter 8. Support, or tie up, the shafts to prevent strain on the joints.
17 Drain the transmission oil – see section 2.
18 Remove the left-hand front suspension tie-rod – see Chapter 10.
19 Release two clips attaching the starter

motor cable the flywheel front cover plate.
20 Remove three bolts securing the front cover plate to the flywheel housing, and remove the plate **(see illustration)**.
21 Fit a suitable lifting eye to the hole at the top of the transmission housing. Attach a hoist and lifting tackle to the lifting eye. Take the weight of the transmission with the lifting equipment **(see illustration)**.
22 Position a jack, with a wooden block on top, under the engine, and raise the jack to support the weight of the engine.
23 Remove the left-hand engine mounting – see Chapter 2A.

7.20 Remove front cover plate

7.21 Fit lifting eye and attach lifting tackle

24 Remove two upper transmission-to-engine securing bolts.
25 Remove five lower transmission-to-engine securing bolts.
Caution: Do not allow the transmission to hang on the clutch shaft.
26 With assistance, release the transmission from the engine – it is located on two dowels.
27 Carefully lower the transmission to the ground. Disconnect the lifting tackle, and withdraw the transmission from under the vehicle.

Refit
28 Clean the mating faces of the engine and flywheel housing.
29 Check that the clutch friction disc is centralised – see Chapter 6.
30 Apply a little high-melting point grease to the splines of the input shaft.
31 With assistance, position the transmission under the vehicle, and connect the lifting tackle.
32 Raise the transmission behind the engine, and manoeuvre into position. Locate on two dowels. Fit five lower transmission-to-engine securing bolts.
33 Clean and degrease two upper transmission-to-engine securing bolts. Apply Loctite 243 to the bolt threads, and fit the bolts. Use a torque wrench to tighten all bolts to the specified torque.
34 The remaining refitting is a reversal of the removal procedure, noting:
  Use a torque wrench to tighten all bolts and nuts to the specified torque.
  Refill the transmission with oil – see Section 2.

1.8 litre petrol engine models
Note: *A new gear selector rod-to-selector shaft roll-pin will be required on refitting.*

Removal
35 Disconnect the battery negative lead. Apply the handbrake, then jack up the front of the vehicle and support it securely on axle stands (see *Jacking and Vehicle Support*).
36 Proceed as described in paragraphs 4 to 8.
37 Where applicable, release the ABS fuseholder from the battery tray, then unscrew the four upper bolts and the three lower bolts securing the battery tray, and remove the battery tray.
38 Disconnect the clutch cable from the clutch release lever, with reference to Chapter 6 if necessary, then release the cable from the transmission bracket, and move the cable to one side.
39 Unscrew the bolts securing the earth lead to the transmission.
40 Trace the wiring back from the reversing light switch, locate the wiring connector(s), and separate the two halves of the wiring connector(s).
41 Disconnect the exhaust front pipe from the manifold as described in Chapter 4A.
42 Unscrew the bolt securing the gearchange steady bar to the transmission. Recover the two washers.

43 Remove the metal clip from the gear selector rod-to-selector shaft joint to expose the roll-pin **(see illustration 4.32)**.

44 Drive out the roll-pin using a suitable pin punch, then release the selector rod from the selector shaft, and suspend the rod and the gearchange steady bar clear of the working area.

45 Disconnect the inboard ends of the driveshafts from the transmission, as described in Chapter 8. Note that there is no need to disconnect the outboard ends of the driveshafts from the hubs. Support the driveshafts using wire or string, to avoid placing any strain on the driveshaft joints or gaiters.

46 Remove the left-hand front suspension tie-rod, as described in Chapter 10.

47 Disconnect the wiring plug from the vehicle speed sensor.

48 On models with air conditioning, unscrew the bolt securing the air conditioning refrigerant pipe to the bracket on the transmission.

49 If not already done, position a hydraulic jack under the engine sump, with a block of wood between the jack head and sump to spread the load.

50 Remove the left-hand engine/transmission mounting as described in Chapter 2A or 2B, as applicable.

51 Lower the engine/transmission assembly slightly, then unscrew the two bolts securing the left-hand engine/transmission mounting bracket to the transmission.

52 Unscrew the centre upper transmission casing-to-differential housing bolt, then bolt a suitable lifting bracket to the transmission, by refitting and tightening the bolt **(see illustration)**.

53 Connect a hoist and lifting tackle to the lifting eye, and raise the hoist to just take the weight of the engine/transmission assembly.

54 Make sure that the engine and transmission are adequately supported, then unscrew the two upper engine-to-transmission bolts, and remove the mounting bracket.

55 Unscrew the two lower engine-to-transmission bolts.

56 Unscrew the bolt at the rear of the engine, securing the engine to the transmission **(see illustration)**.

57 Unscrew the two nuts and bolts securing the flywheel front cover plate, then remove the cover plate and unscrew the remaining engine-to-transmission nut and bolt **(see illustration)**.

58 With the aid of an assistant, carefully pull the transmission from the engine (the transmission locates on dowels in the mounting plate), ensuring that the weight of the transmission is not allowed to hang on the input shaft while it is engaged with the clutch friction disc. It may be necessary to rock the transmission gently to release it from the engine. Take care not to damage any of the surrounding components in the engine compartment.

7.52 Bolt a lifting bracket to the transmission using the centre upper transmission casing-to-differential housing bolt (arrowed)

59 Carefully lower the transmission to the ground, then disconnect the lifting tackle, and withdraw the transmission from under the front of the vehicle.

Refitting

60 Commence refitting by checking that the clutch friction disc is centralised as described in Chapter 6.

61 Apply a little high melting-point grease to the splines of the transmission input shaft. Do not apply too much, as this may contaminate the clutch.

62 Position the transmission under the front of the vehicle, then reconnect the lifting tackle, and lift the transmission into position in the engine compartment.

63 Ensure that the locating dowels are in place in the mounting plate, then carefully offer the transmission to the engine, until the locating dowels are engaged, ensuring that the weight of the transmission is not allowed to hang on the input shaft as it is engaged with the clutch friction disc.

64 Refit the transmission-to-engine nut and bolt, and tighten to the specified torque.

65 Refit the bolt at the rear of the engine, securing the engine to the transmission, and tighten to the specified torque.

66 Fit the two lower engine-to-transmission bolts, and tighten them to the specified torque.

67 Refit the flywheel front cover plate, then refit and tighten the securing nuts and bolts.

68 Refit the upper engine-to-transmission bolts, and tighten to the specified torque.

69 Further refitting is a reversal of removal, bearing in mind the following points:

a) Tighten all fixings to the specified torque, where applicable.

b) Refit the left-hand engine/transmission mounting as described in Chapter 2A or 2B, as applicable.

c) Refit the left-hand front suspension tie-rod as described in Chapter 10.

d) Reconnect the driveshafts to the transmission as described in Chapter 8.

7.56 Unscrew the rear engine-to-transmission bolt (arrowed) – 1.8 litre petrol models

e) Use a new roll-pin when reconnecting the gear selector rod to the selector shaft.

f) Reconnect the exhaust front section to the manifold with reference to Chapter 4A.

g) Refit the starter motor as described in Chapter 5A.

h) On completion, refill the transmission with oil as described in Section 2.

Diesel engine models

Note: A new gear selector rod-to-selector shaft roll-pin will be required on refitting.

Removal

70 Disconnect the battery negative lead.

71 Apply the handbrake, then jack up the front of the vehicle and support it securely on axle stands (see Jacking and Vehicle Support).

72 Remove the starter motor as described in Chapter 5A.

73 Remove the engine control module (ECM) and the engine management relay module, as described in Chapter 4B.

74 Remove the battery, with reference to Chapter 5A if necessary.

7.57 Unscrew the nuts and bolts (1) securing the flywheel front cover plate and the remaining transmission-to-engine nut and bolt (2)

7.76 Removing the battery tray – diesel engine model

7.77 Disconnecting the clutch cable – diesel engine model

7.78 Unscrew the bolt (arrowed) securing the earth lead to the transmission

75 Unscrew the two bolts securing the engine compartment fusebox to the body, and move the fusebox to one side.
76 Unscrew the four upper bolts and the three lower bolts securing the battery tray, then remove the battery tray (see illustration).
77 Disconnect the clutch cable from the clutch release lever, with reference to Chapter 6 if necessary, then release the cable from the transmission brackets, and move the cable to one side (see illustration).
78 Unscrew the bolt securing the earth lead to the transmission (see illustration).
79 Trace the wiring back from the reversing light switch, locate the wiring connector(s), and separate the two halves of the wiring connector(s).
80 Remove the mass airflow (MAF) sensor, with reference to Chapter 4B.
81 Unscrew the nut securing the coolant pipe to the transmission mounting plate (see illustration).
82 Proceed as described in paragraphs 42 to 53.
83 Unscrew the three lower bolts securing the transmission to the transmission mounting plate and the engine/transmission reinforcing bracket (see illustration).
84 Unscrew the bolt at the rear of the engine, securing the transmission to the mounting plate.
85 Unscrew the two nuts and bolts securing the transmission to the mounting plate, then unscrew the remaining bolt securing the transmission to the mounting plate.
86 Carefully withdraw the transmission from

the engine (the transmission locates on dowels in the mounting plate), ensuring that the weight of the transmission is not allowed to hang on the input shaft while it is engaged with the clutch friction disc.

Refitting

87 Proceed as described in paragraphs 60 to 63.
88 Further refitting is a reversal of removal, bearing in mind the following points:
a) Tighten all fixings to the specified torque, where applicable.
b) Refit the left-hand engine/transmission mounting as described in Chapter 2B.
c) Refit the left-hand front suspension tie-rod as described in Chapter 10.

7.83 Engine-to-transmission fixings – diesel engine models

1 Lower transmission-to-mounting plate bolts
2 Rear transmission-to-mounting plate bolt
3 Transmission-to-mounting plate nuts and bolts

7.81 Unscrew the coolant pipe securing nut (arrowed) – diesel engine models

d) Reconnect the driveshafts to the transmission as described in Chapter 8.
e) Use a new roll-pin when reconnecting the gear selector rod to the selector shaft.
f) Refit the starter motor as described in Chapter 5A.
g) On completion, refill the transmission with oil as described in Section 2.

8 Manual transmission overhaul – general information

Overhauling a manual transmission unit is a difficult and involved job for the DIY home mechanic. In addition to dismantling and reassembling many small parts, clearances must be precisely measured and, if necessary, changed by selecting shims and spacers. Internal transmission components are also often difficult to obtain, and in many instances, extremely expensive. Because of this, if the transmission develops a fault or becomes noisy, the best course of action is to have the unit overhauled by a specialist repairer, or to obtain an exchange reconditioned unit.

Nevertheless, it is not impossible for the more experienced mechanic to overhaul the transmission, provided that the necessary special tools are available, and the job is done in a deliberate step-by-step manner, so that nothing is overlooked.

The tools necessary for an overhaul include internal and external circlip pliers, bearing pullers, a slide hammer, a set of pin punches, a dial test indicator, and possibly a hydraulic press. In addition, a large, sturdy workbench and a vice will be required.

During dismantling of the transmission, make careful notes of how each component is fitted, to make reassembly easier and more accurate.

Before dismantling the transmission, it will help if you have some idea of what area is malfunctioning. Certain problems can be closely related to specific areas in the transmission, which can make component examination and replacement easier. Refer to the Fault finding Section of this manual for more information.

Chapter 8
Driveshafts

Contents

Degrees of difficulty

Easy, suitable for novice with little experience	Fairly easy, suitable for beginner with some experience	Fairly difficult, suitable for competent DIY mechanic	Difficult, suitable for experienced DIY mechanic	Very difficult, suitable for expert DIY or professional

Specifications

Driveshafts

Type . . . . Unequal-length solid steel shafts, splined to inner and outer constant velocity joints, dynamic damper on both shafts

Torque wrench settings

	Nm	lbf ft
Driveshaft retaining nut	180	133
Roadwheel nuts	See Chapter 10	

1 General information and precautions

General information

Drive is transmitted from the differential to the front wheels by means of two unequal length, solid steel driveshafts.

Both driveshafts are splined at their outer ends to accept the wheel hubs and are threaded so that each hub can be fastened by a large nut. The inner end of each driveshaft is splined to accept the differential sun gear and has a groove to accept the circlip which secures the driveshaft to the sun gear **(see illustration)**.

Constant velocity (CV) joints are fitted to both ends of each driveshaft to ensure the smooth and efficient transmission of drive at all possible angles as the roadwheels move up-and-down with the suspension and as they turn from side-to-side under steering. Both inner and outer CV joints are of the ball-and-cage type.

A dynamic damper is fitted to each driveshaft to reduce harmonic vibrations and resonance.

Precautions

The driveshaft retaining nuts are extremely tight; ensure the car is securely supported when slackening and tightening them.

The only new parts listed are the inner CV

1.2 Driveshaft assembly

1	Circlip	5	Small gaiter retaining clip	10	Large gaiter retaining clip
2	Inner joint and shaft assembly	6	Damper clip	11	Stopper ring
3	Large gaiter retaining clip	7	Dynamic damper	12	Circlip
4	Gaiter	8	Small gaiter retaining clip	13	Outer joint assembly
		9	Gaiter	14	Seal
				15	Driveshaft nut

H29769

3.3 Using a hammer and punch to release driveshaft nut staking

3.6 Using a universal balljoint separator to separate balljoint shanks

3.7 Pull swivel hub outwards and disengage driveshaft outer CV joint

joint/driveshaft assemblies, the outer CV joint assemblies and the rubber gaiters. The gaiters are supplied in a kit with the necessary sachets of grease and clips.

If any CV joint is worn or damaged, it cannot be reconditioned and must be renewed. In the case of the inner joints, this means that the complete joint/shaft assembly must be renewed.

2 Driveshaft rubber gaiters and constant velocity joints – inspection

1 Refer to the relevant Part of Chapter 1 and if the checks carried out indicate wear, proceed as follows.

2 Remove the roadwheel trim. If the staking is still effective, the driveshaft nut should be correctly tightened. If in doubt, use a torque wrench to check that the nut is securely fastened and restake it. Refit the wheel trim. Repeat this check on the remaining driveshaft nut.

3 Road test the vehicle and listen for a metallic clicking from the front as the vehicle is driven slowly in a circle on full lock. If a clicking noise is heard, this indicates wear in the outer CV joint. This means that the joint must be renewed as reconditioning is not possible.

4 If vibration, consistent with road speed, is felt through the vehicle when accelerating, there is a possibility of wear in the inner CV joints.

3 Driveshafts – removal and refitting

Removal

1 Chock the rear wheels, firmly apply the handbrake then jack up the front of the vehicle and support it on axle stands (see *Jacking and Vehicle Support*). Remove the appropriate front roadwheel.

2 Drain the gearbox oil (see Chapter 7).

3 Using a hammer and suitable punch, tap up the staking securing the driveshaft retaining nut to the groove in the CV joint (see illustration). Note that a new driveshaft retaining nut must be obtained for reassembly.

4 Have an assistant firmly depress the brake pedal to prevent the front hub from rotating then, using a socket and extension bar, slacken and remove the driveshaft retaining nut. Discard the nut.

5 Slacken and remove the bolt and washer securing the anti-roll bar drop link to the lower suspension arm, then the two bolts securing the tie bar to the lower suspension arm.

6 Extract the split pins and undo the nuts securing the steering gear track rod end balljoint and the lower suspension arm balljoint to the swivel hub. Remove the nuts and release the balljoint tapered shanks using a universal balljoint separator (see illustration).

7 Carefully pull the swivel hub assembly

outwards and withdraw the driveshaft outer CV joint from the hub assembly (see illustration). If necessary, the shaft can be tapped out of the hub using a soft-faced mallet.

Caution: Take care to avoid damaging the driveshaft threads.

8 To release the inner CV joint, insert a suitable flat bar between the joint and gearbox housing, then carefully lever the joint out of position, whilst taking great care not to damage the driveshaft oil seal (see illustration).

9 Support the inner CV joint whilst withdrawing it from the gearbox, to ensure the oil seal is not damaged, then remove the driveshaft from the vehicle.

Refitting

10 Before fitting the driveshaft, examine the gearbox housing driveshaft oil seal for signs of damage or deterioration and, if necessary, renew it. Similarly, inspect the oil seal which is fitted to the outer CV joint for damage or deterioration and renew if necessary. Regardless of its apparent condition, renew the circlip which is fitted to the groove in the inner CV joint splines as a matter of course (see illustrations).

11 Thoroughly clean the driveshaft splines and the apertures in the gearbox and hub assembly. Apply a thin film of grease to the oil seal lips and to the driveshaft splines and shoulders. Check that all gaiter clips are securely fastened.

12 Ensure that the circlip fitted to the inner

3.8 Carefully lever driveshaft inner CV joint out of housing

3.10a Inspect outer CV joint oil seal (arrowed)

3.10b Inner CV joint circlip (arrowed) must be renewed

3.12 Refit driveshaft inner CV joint, taking care not to damage driveshaft oil seal . . .

3.13 . . . and engage outer CV joint with swivel hub

3.16a Fit the new driveshaft nut . . .

CV joint is located securely in its groove, then locate the joint splines with those of the differential sun gear, taking great care not to damage the oil seal. Push the joint fully into the gearbox **(see illustration)**. Check that the joint is securely retained by the circlip by pulling the shaft outwards.

13 Locate the outer CV joint splines with those of the swivel hub and slide the joint back into position in the hub **(see illustration)**.

14 Insert the lower suspension arm and track rod balljoints into their respective locations in the swivel hub and tighten the retaining nuts to the specified torque (see Chapter 10). Secure both nuts in position using new split pins.

15 Refit the bolts securing the trailing arm and anti-roll bar drop link to the lower suspension arm and tighten them to the specified torque (see Chapter 10).

16 Fit the new driveshaft retaining nut and tighten it to the specified torque setting whilst an assistant firmly depresses the brake pedal. Release the brake, check that the hub rotates freely, then stake the nut firmly into the groove on the CV joint using a suitable punch **(see illustrations)**.

17 Refit the roadwheel then lower the vehicle to the ground. Tighten the wheel nuts to the specified torque.

18 Refill the gearbox with the correct type and quantity of oil, then check that the level is correct as described in Chapter 7.

3.16b . . . and tighten it to the specified torque

3.16c Stake driveshaft nut firmly into CV joint groove

4 Using a soft-faced mallet, sharply strike the inner member of the joint to drive it off the end of the shaft **(see illustration)**. The outer joint is retained on the driveshaft by a circular section circlip and striking the joint in this manner forces the circlip into its groove, so allowing the joint to slide off.

5 Once the joint assembly has been removed, remove the circlip from the groove in the driveshaft splines and discard it. A new circlip must be fitted on reassembly.

6 Withdraw the rubber gaiter from the driveshaft.

7 With the CV joint removed from the driveshaft, thoroughly clean the joint using paraffin or a suitable solvent and dry it thoroughly. Inspect the joint as follows.

8 Move the inner splined driving member from side-to-side to expose each ball in turn at the top of its track. Examine the balls for cracks, flat spots or signs of surface pitting.

9 Inspect the ball tracks on the inner and outer members. If the tracks have widened, the balls will no longer be a tight fit. At the same time check the ball cage windows for wear or cracking between the windows.

10 If, on inspection any of the CV joint, components are found to be worn or damaged, it will be necessary to renew the complete joint assembly, since no components are available separately. If the joint is in satisfactory condition, obtain a repair kit consisting of a new gaiter, retaining clips and the correct type and quantity of grease.

Fitting

11 Tape over the splines on the end of the driveshaft, then fit the small retaining clip onto the gaiter and carefully slide the gaiter onto the shaft.

4	Driveshaft rubber gaiters – renewal

Outer joint

Removal

1 Remove the driveshaft from the vehicle.

2 Secure the driveshaft in a vice equipped with soft jaws and release the two rubber gaiter retaining clips by raising the locking tangs with a screwdriver and then raising the end of the clip with pliers. If necessary, the gaiter retaining clips can be cut to release them **(see illustration)**.

3 Slide the rubber gaiter down the shaft to expose the outer CV joint.

4.2 Cutting gaiter clips to release them

4.4 Driving outer CV joint off driveshaft end

4.12 Ensure stopper ring and new circlip are correctly located before fitting outer CV joint

4.17 Using correct tool to tighten gaiter clip – side-cutters can be used if care is exercised

4.22 Cutting inner CV joint clip to release it

12 Remove the tape then, ensuring that the stopper ring is securely located in its groove, fit a new circlip to the groove in the driveshaft splines **(see illustration)**. Engage the help of an assistant for the following operations.

13 Position the CV joint over the splines on the driveshaft until it abuts the circlip.

14 Using two small screwdrivers placed one either side of the circlip, compress the clip and at the same time have your assistant firmly strike the end of the joint with a soft-faced mallet. This should not require an undue amount of force. If the joint does not spring into place, remove it, reposition the circlip and try again. Do not force the joint, otherwise the circlip will be damaged.

15 Check that the circlip holds the joint securely on the driveshaft end then pack the joint with the grease supplied. Work the grease well into the ball tracks whilst twisting the joint and fill the rubber gaiter with any excess.

16 Ease the gaiter over the joint and place the large retaining clip in position. Ensure that the gaiter is correctly located in the grooves on both the driveshaft and CV joint.

17 Using pliers, pull the large retaining clip and fold it over until the end locates between the two raised tangs. Hold the clip in this position and bend the tangs over to lock the clip in position. Remove any slack in the gaiter retaining clip by carefully compressing the raised section of the clip. In the absence of

the special tool, a pair of side-cutters may be used **(see illustration)**. Secure the small retaining clip using the same procedure.

18 Check that the CV joint moves freely in all directions, then refit the driveshaft.

Inner joint

Removal

19 Remove the outer CV joint and gaiter as described in paragraphs 1 to 5.

20 Tape over the splines on the driveshaft and carefully remove the outer CV joint rubber gaiter.

21 Release the dynamic damper retaining clip and slide the damper off the end of the driveshaft.

 HAYNES HiNT *Use liquid soap as a lubricant if necessary to aid damper removal and clean off any rust deposits or similar using emery cloth.*

22 Release the inner joint gaiter retaining clips and slide the gaiter off the shaft **(see illustration)**.

23 Thoroughly clean the joint using paraffin, or a suitable solvent, and dry it thoroughly. Inspect the joint as described in paragraphs 8 and 9.

24 If, on inspection the CV joint components are found to be worn or damaged, it will be

necessary to renew the complete joint and shaft assembly, since the joint is not available separately. If the joint is in satisfactory condition, obtain a repair kit consisting of a new gaiter, retaining clips and the correct type and quantity of grease. Although not strictly necessary, it is also recommended that the outer CV joint gaiter is renewed, regardless of its apparent condition.

Fitting

25 Pack the joint with the grease supplied in the gaiter kit. Work the grease well into the ball tracks whilst twisting the joint **(see illustration)**.

26 Clean the shaft, using emery cloth to remove any rust or sharp edges which may damage the gaiter, then slide the inner joint gaiter along the driveshaft.

27 Locate the gaiter in the grooves on the joint and shaft and fit both the large and small retaining clips. Secure the clips in position as described in paragraph 17 and check that the joint moves freely in all directions.

28 Lubricate the shaft and position a new retaining clip on the dynamic damper flange. Slide the dynamic damper onto the shaft so that its clip flange is innermost (faces the inner CV joint). Position the damper **(see illustration)**, then secure it in position with the retaining clip.

29 Remove any surplus lubricant from the shaft and refit the outer CV joint.

4.25 Pack inner CV joint with grease supplied in gaiter kit

4.28 Position dynamic damper specified distance from outer end of driveshaft

Right-hand driveshaft – 405 to 411 mm
Left-hand driveshaft – 148 to 154 mm

Chapter 9
Braking system

Contents

Degrees of difficulty

Easy, suitable for novice with little experience	Fairly easy, suitable for beginner with some experience	Fairly difficult, suitable for competent DIY mechanic	Difficult, suitable for experienced DIY mechanic	Very difficult, suitable for expert DIY or professional

Specifications

Brake system

Type .... Dual hydraulic circuit, split diagonally. Disc front brakes. Disc or drum rear brakes, depending on model. Vacuum servo-assistance on all models. Cable-operated handbrake, acting on rear brakes.

Front brakes

Type .... Disc, with single piston sliding caliper
Disc diameter .... 262 mm
Disc wear limit:
  Solid .... 11.00 mm
  Ventilated .... 19.00 mm
Maximum disc run-out .... 0.04 mm
Brake pad friction material minimum thickness .... 3.0 mm

Rear brakes

Models with drum brakes

Type .... Single drum with leading and trailing shoes
Drum diameter:
  New .... 203.2 mm
  Maximum diameter after machining .... 204 mm
Maximum drum ovality .... 0.012 mm
Brake shoe friction material minimum thickness .... 2.0 mm
ABS rear wheel sensor-to-reluctor ring .... 0.5 mm
Handbrake lever travel .... 8 to 12 clicks

Models with disc brakes

Type .... Disc, with single piston sliding caliper
Disc diameter .... 239 mm
Disc wear limit .... 8.0 mm
Maximum disc run-out .... 0.06 mm
Brake pad friction material minimum thickness .... 3.0 mm
Handbrake lever travel .... 10 to 14 clicks

Torque wrench settings

	Nm	lbf ft
ABS front wheel sensor retaining screw	6	4
ABS modulator union nuts	14	10
ABS rear wheel sensor retaining bolts (drum)	45	33
ABS rear wheel sensor retaining screws (disc)	6	4
ABS wheel sensor wiring bracket bolts	10	7
Caliper bleed screw	10	7
Caliper bracket-to-hub/trailing arm bolts	108	80
Caliper guide pin bolt	27	20
Caliper hose union bolt	34	25
Disc retaining screws	5	4
Drum retaining screws	7	5
Handbrake cable-to-underbody retaining bolts	22	16
Handbrake lever-to-floorpan bolts	22	16
Handbrake warning light switch screw	5	4
Master cylinder brake pipe union nuts	19	14
Master cylinder-to-servo unit nuts	15	11
Proportioning valve mounting bolts	10	7
Proportioning valve union nuts	19	14
Roadwheel nuts	See Chapter 10	
Servo-to-bulkhead nuts	13	10
Servo vacuum hose-to-inlet manifold union bolt	50	37
Vacuum pump-to-alternator bolts	8	6
Wheel cylinder bleed screw	7	5
Wheel cylinder brake pipe union	19	14
Wheel cylinder-to-backplate bolts	8	6

1.1a Non-ABS braking system component layout

1 Primary hydraulic circuit
2 Secondary hydraulic circuit
3 Brake pipe – pressure regulating valve to right-hand front hose
4 Brake pipe – pressure regulating valve to left-hand front hose
5 Brake pipe – pressure regulating valve to right-hand rear hose
6 Brake pipe – pressure regulating valve to left-hand rear hose
7 Brake pipe – hose to rear wheel cylinder
8 Brake flexible hose – brake pipe to front brake caliper
9 Brake flexible hose – rear wheel
10 Handbrake cable
11 Proportioning valve

1.1b ABS braking system component layout

1 Primary hydraulic circuit
2 Secondary hydraulic circuit
3 Brake pipe – modulator to pressure regulating valve
4 Brake pipe – modulator to pressure regulating valve
5 Brake pipe – modulator to right-hand front hose
6 Brake pipe – modulator to left-hand front hose
7 Brake pipe – modulator to right-hand rear hose
8 Brake pipe – modulator to left-hand rear hose
9 Proportioning valve*
10 Handbrake cable
11 Brake flexible hose – brake pipe to front brake caliper
12 Brake flexible hose – brake pipe to rear brake caliper
* Not operational when ABS/EBD is fitted

1 General information and precautions

General information

The brakes are operated by hydraulic pressure. For safety, the hydraulic system is split diagonally into two circuits – LH front and RH rear, and RH front and LH rear. Failure in any one circuit does not affect the other (**see illustrations opposite**).

Pressure on the footbrake operates the two independent sections of a tandem master cylinder.

Fluid pressure from the master cylinder is supplemented by vacuum assistance.

On petrol engine vehicles, vacuum is provided by inlet manifold depression. On diesel engine vehicles, vacuum is provided by a vacuum pump attached to the alternator.

To reduce the possibility of rear wheel lock-up during severe braking, a brake pressure proportioning valve limits the pressure applied to the rear brakes (not with EBD – see below). Pressure to the front brakes also passes through the proportioning valve, but this is for distribution only.

All models are fitted with front disc brakes, actuated by single piston, sliding-type calipers which ensure that equal pressure is applied to each disc pad. The brake discs may be solid or ventilated, depending on variant.

Rear drum or disc brakes may be fitted, depending on model. The drum brakes incorporate leading and trailing shoes which are actuated by twin piston wheel cylinders. A self-adjusting mechanism is incorporated, to automatically compensate for brake shoe wear. As the brake shoe linings wear, the footbrake operation automatically operates the adjuster mechanism quadrant, which effectively lengthens the shoe strut and repositions the brake shoes to remove the lining-to-drum clearance.

The rear disc brakes are actuated by a single piston sliding caliper, which incorporates a mechanical handbrake mechanism.

On all models, the handbrake is operated by a floor-mounted lever and employs twin cables to provide an independent mechanical means of rear brake application.

Anti-lock Braking System

Electronically-controlled ABS is standard on certain models, and is an option on all others.

ABS reduces the possibility of skidding, by preventing wheel lock-up on loose/slippery surfaces.

The system comprises a modulator block which contains an ABS Electronic Control Unit (ECU), hydraulic solenoid valves and accumulators, and an electrically-driven return pump. One sensor is fitted to each roadwheel. The purpose of the system is to prevent wheel locking during heavy braking. This is achieved by automatic release of the brake on the relevant (locking) wheel, followed by reapplication of the brake.

The solenoid valves are controlled by the ECU which receives signals from the four roadwheel sensors, which in turn monitor the speed of rotation of each wheel. By comparing these speed signals from the four wheels, the ECU can determine the speed at which the vehicle is travelling. It can then use this speed to determine when a wheel is decelerating at an abnormal rate compared to the speed of the vehicle and therefore predict when a wheel is about to lock. During normal operation, the system functions in the same way as a non-ABS braking system.

If the ECU senses that a wheel is about to lock, the ABS system enters the 'pressure maintain' phase. The ECU operates the relevant solenoid valve in the modulator block which then isolates the brake caliper on the wheel which is about to lock from the master cylinder, effectively sealing in the hydraulic pressure.

If the speed of rotation of the wheel continues to decrease at an abnormal rate, the ABS system then enters the 'pressure decrease' phase, where the electrically-driven return pump operates and pumps the hydraulic fluid back into the master cylinder, releasing pressure on the brake caliper/wheel cylinder so that the brake is released. Once the speed of rotation of the wheel returns to an acceptable rate, the pump stops and the solenoid valve opens thereby allowing the hydraulic master cylinder pressure to return to the caliper/wheel cylinder which then reapplies the brake. This cycle can be carried out at up to 10 times a second.

The action of the solenoid valves and return pump creates pulses in the hydraulic circuit. When the ABS system is functioning, these pulses can be felt through the brake pedal.

The solenoid valves connected to the front calipers operate independently, but the valve connected to the rear calipers, together with the proportioning valve, operates both calipers (or wheel cylinders in the case of models with rear drum brakes) simultaneously.

Operation of the ABS system is entirely dependent on electrical signals. To prevent the system responding to any inaccurate signals, a built-in safety circuit monitors all signals received by the ECU. If a spurious signal or low battery voltage is detected, the ABS system is automatically shut down and the warning lamp on the instrument panel is illuminated to inform the driver that the ABS system is not operational. Under these circumstances, the braking system operates as a conventional, non-ABS braking system.

If a fault does develop in the ABS system the vehicle must be taken to a Rover dealer for fault diagnosis and repair.

Electronic Brake force Distribution (EDB)

On later vehicles with ABS, Electronic Brake force Distribution is incorporated into the ABS system.

To prevent wheel lock-up, EDB regulates the braking pressure applied to each wheel independently.

When EBD is incorporated in the system, a brake proportioning valve is not fitted.

Precautions

Hydraulic fluid is poisonous. Wash off immediately and thoroughly in the case of skin contact and seek immediate medical advice if any fluid is swallowed or gets into the eyes. Certain types of hydraulic fluid are inflammable and may ignite if brought into contact with hot components.

When servicing any hydraulic system, it is safest to assume that the fluid is flammable and to take precautions against the risk of fire, as though it were petrol being handled. Hydraulic fluid is also an effective paint stripper and will attack plastics. If any is spilt, it should be washed off immediately using copious quantities of fresh water.

Hydraulic fluid is hygroscopic, that is, it absorbs moisture from the air. Brake fluid that has become contaminated with water may boil under heavy braking, causing brake fade and so must be considered unfit for further use. When topping-up or renewing fluid, always use the recommended type and ensure that it comes from a newly-opened container.

When working on brake components, take care not to disperse brake dust into the air, or to inhale it, since it may contain asbestos which is a health hazard.

When servicing any part of the system, work carefully and methodically. Also observe scrupulous cleanliness when overhauling any part of the hydraulic system. Always renew components (in axle sets, where applicable) if in doubt about their condition and use only genuine Rover replacement parts, or at least those of known good quality.

2 Brake pedal – removal and refitting

Removal

1 Working inside the vehicle, undo the three screws and remove the right-hand lower facia panel. Release the stud clips and lower the felt panel to expose the pedal mountings.

2 Extract the R-clip and clevis pin securing the servo unit pushrod to the brake pedal (**see illustration**).

3 Using pliers, carefully unhook the brake pedal return spring from the pedal to release all the spring tension.

4 Slacken and remove the nut and washers (as applicable) from the brake pedal pivot bolt then withdraw the pivot bolt and remove the brake pedal and return spring.

5 Examine all brake pedal components for signs of wear, paying particular attention to the pedal bushes, pivot bolt and return spring, renewing as necessary.

2.2 Extract the R-clip (arrowed) and clevis pin securing the servo unit pushrod to the brake pedal (facia removed)

Refitting

6 Refitting is a reverse of the removal procedure. Lubricate the bushes, pivot bolt and clevis pin with multi-purpose grease.
7 On completion, check the operation of the pedal and ensure that it returns smoothly to its at rest position under the pressure of the return spring.

3 Vacuum servo unit – testing, removal and refitting

Testing

1 To test the operation of the servo unit, depress the footbrake several times to exhaust the vacuum, then start the engine whilst keeping the pedal firmly depressed. As the engine starts, there should be a noticeable 'give' in the brake pedal as the vacuum builds up. Allow the engine to run for at least two minutes then switch it off. If the brake pedal is now depressed it should feel normal, but further applications should result in the pedal feeling firmer, with the pedal stroke decreasing with each application.
2 If the servo does not operate as described, inspect the servo unit check valve, see Section 4.

3.9 Remove four flange nuts

1 Servo unit
   mounting nuts
2 Pushrod clevis pin
3 R-clip

3 If the servo unit still fails to operate satisfactorily, the fault lies within the unit itself.
4 Repairs to the unit are possible but special tools are required and the work should be entrusted to a suitably-equipped Rover dealer.

Removal

Note: *The following new parts are needed – clevis pin securing clip, servo unit gasket.*
Caution: The domed nut on the pushrod must not be adjusted. The servo gasket acts as a spacer – the correct gasket must be fitted.
5 At the right-hand, under the dashboard, release three turnbuckles, and remove the fusebox cover.
6 Remove the brake master cylinder – see Section 9.
7 Taking care not to damage or displace the sealing grommet, disconnect the vacuum hose from the servo unit.
8 Remove and discard the spring clip from the clevis pin which connects the servo unit pushrod to the brake pedal. Remove the clevis pin.
9 Remove four flange nuts securing the servo unit to the engine bay bulkhead. Remove the servo unit and gasket **(see illustration)**.

Refitting

10 Check the vacuum hose sealing grommet for damage or deterioration – renew the grommet if damaged.
11 Fit a new gasket to the servo unit. **Note:** *The gasket must be the correct MG Rover part.*
12 Locate the servo unit over the four studs, and fit the nuts – check that the push-rod fork locates correctly over the brake pedal.
13 Use a torque wrench to tighten the nuts to the specified torque.
14 Grease and fit the clevis pin. Secure the pin with a new spring clip.
15 Fit the fusebox cover, and secure with the turnbuckles.
16 Carefully connect the vacuum hose, ensuring that the grommet is not displaced.
17 Fit the master cylinder – see Section 9.
18 Start the engine and check for leaks at the vacuum connection, and check operation of the brakes.

4 Vacuum servo unit check valve – removal, testing and refitting

Note: *The vacuum servo unit check valve is only available as part of the vacuum hose assembly. Do not try to remove the valve, the servo unit connection, or the inlet manifold union from the hose or air leaks may ensue, necessitating renewal of the hose assembly.*

Removal

1 Carefully unplug the hose connection from the vacuum servo unit taking care not to damage the sealing grommet.

2 On petrol models, unscrew the union bolt securing the vacuum hose assembly to the inlet manifold and withdraw the hose assembly from the engine compartment. Remove the union bolt from the hose end and discard the sealing washers.
3 On diesel models, release the hose clips and disconnect the vacuum hose from the vacuum pump pipe.

Testing

4 Examine the hose for damage, splits, cracks or general deterioration. Make sure that the check valve inside the hose is working correctly by blowing through the hose from the servo unit connection end. Air should flow in this direction but not when blown through from the inlet manifold union. Renew the hose and check valve assembly if at all suspect.
5 Examine the servo unit sealing grommet for signs of damage or deterioration and renew if necessary.

Refitting

6 Position a new sealing washer on each side of the hose union and refit the hose-to-inlet manifold union bolt (petrol models). Ensure that the hose union locating pin is correctly situated between the lugs on the manifold then tighten the union bolt to the specified torque setting. On diesel models, reconnect the hose to the vacuum pump pipe and secure it in position with the clip.
7 Carefully ease the hose connection into the servo unit sealing grommet, taking care not to displace or damage the grommet.
8 On completion, start the engine and check the vacuum hose-to-servo unit connection for signs of air leaks.

5 Hydraulic fluid – level check and renewal

Refer to *Weekly Checks* and Chapter 1A or 1B.

6 Hydraulic system – bleeding

⚠ *Warning: Refer to the 'Precautions' given at the end of Section 1, before handling brake fluid.*

Caution: Hydraulic fluid is an effective paint stripper and will attack plastics. If any is spilt onto painted components or bodywork, it should be washed off immediately with clean, warm water.

General

1 The correct operation of any hydraulic system is only possible after removal of all air from the components and circuit. This is achieved by bleeding the system.

2 During the bleeding procedure, add only clean, unused hydraulic fluid of the recommended type. Never re-use fluid that has already been bled from the system. Ensure that sufficient fluid is available before starting work.

3 If there is any possibility of incorrect fluid being already in the system, the brake components and circuit must be flushed completely with uncontaminated, correct fluid and new seals should be fitted to the various components.

4 If hydraulic fluid has been lost from the system, or air has entered because of a leak, then ensure that the fault is cured before proceeding further.

5 Park the vehicle on level ground, chock the roadwheels to prevent movement and then release the handbrake. Start the engine and allow it to idle.

6 Check that all pipes and hoses are secure, unions tight and bleed screws closed. Clean any dirt from around the bleed screws.

7 Unscrew the master cylinder reservoir cap and top the master cylinder reservoir up to the MAX level line. Refit the cap loosely and remember to maintain the fluid level at least above the MIN level line throughout the procedure or there is a risk of air being drawn into the system during the bleeding procedure.

8 There is a number of one-man, do-it-yourself brake bleeding kits currently available from motor accessory shops. It is recommended that one of these kits is used whenever possible as they greatly simplify the bleeding operation and also reduce the risk of expelled air and fluid being drawn back into the system. If such a kit is not available, then the basic (two-man) method must be used which is described in detail below.

9 If a kit is to be used, prepare the vehicle as described previously and follow the kit manufacturer's instructions as the procedure may vary slightly according to the type being used. Generally, they are as outlined below in the relevant sub-section.

10 Whichever method is used, the same sequence must be followed (paragraphs 11 and 12) to ensure the removal of all air from the system.

Bleeding sequence

11 If the system has been only partially disconnected and suitable precautions were taken to minimise fluid loss, it should be necessary only to bleed that part of the system (ie: the primary or secondary circuit).

12 If the complete system is to be bled, then it should be done working in the following sequence:

1) *Left-hand front brake.*
2) *Right-hand rear brake.*
3) *Right-hand front brake.*
4) *Left-hand rear brake.*

Bleeding

Basic (two-man) method

13 Collect a clean glass jar, a suitable length of plastic or rubber tubing which is a tight fit over the bleed screw and a ring spanner to fit the screw. The help of an assistant will also be required.

14 Remove the dust cap from the first screw in the sequence. Fit the spanner and tube to the screw, place the other end of the tube in the jar and pour in sufficient fluid to cover the end of the tube.

15 Ensure that the master cylinder reservoir fluid level is maintained at least above the MIN level line throughout the procedure.

16 Have the assistant fully depress the brake pedal several times to build-up pressure, then maintain it on the final stroke.

17 While pedal pressure is maintained, unscrew the bleed screw (approximately one turn) and allow the fluid and air to flow into the jar. The assistant should maintain pedal pressure, following it down to the floor if necessary and should not release it until instructed to do so. When the flow stops, tighten the bleed screw again, release the pedal slowly and recheck the reservoir fluid level.

18 Repeat the steps given in paragraphs 16 and 17 until the fluid emerging from the bleed screw is free from air bubbles. If the master cylinder has been drained and refilled and air is being bled from the first screw in the sequence, allow approximately five seconds between cycles for the master cylinder passages to refill.

19 When a flow of clean air-free fluid is passing into the container and, whilst the pedal is held down, tighten the bleed screw securely – do not overtighten the screw. Remove the tube and fit the dust cap

20 Repeat the procedure on the remaining screws in the sequence until all air is removed from the system and the brake pedal feels firm again.

Using a one-way valve kit

21 As their name implies, these kits consist of a length of tubing with a one-way valve fitted to prevent expelled air and fluid being drawn back into the system. Some kits include a translucent container which can be positioned so that the air bubbles can be more easily seen flowing from the end of the tube **(see illustration)**.

22 The kit is connected to the bleed screw,

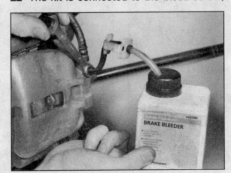

6.21 Using a one-way valve kit to bleed the braking system

which is then opened. The user returns to the driver's seat and depresses the brake pedal with a smooth, steady stroke and slowly releases it. This sequence is repeated until the expelled fluid is clear of air bubbles.

23 Note that these kits simplify work so much that it is easy to forget the master cylinder reservoir fluid level. Ensure that this is maintained at least above the MIN level line at all times.

Using a pressure bleeding kit

24 These kits are usually operated by the reservoir of pressurised air contained in the spare tyre, although note that it will probably be necessary to reduce the pressure to a lower limit than normal. Refer to the instructions supplied with the kit.

25 By connecting a pressurised, fluid-filled container to the master cylinder reservoir, bleeding can be carried out simply by opening each screw in turn (in the specified sequence) and allowing the fluid to flow out until no more air bubbles can be seen in the expelled fluid.

26 This method has the advantage that the large reservoir of fluid provides an additional safeguard against air being drawn into the system during bleeding.

27 Pressure bleeding is particularly effective when bleeding 'difficult' systems or when bleeding the complete system at the time of routine fluid renewal.

All methods

28 When bleeding is complete and firm pedal feel is restored, wash off any spilt fluid, tighten the bleed screws securely and refit their dust caps.

29 Check the hydraulic fluid level and top-up if necessary (see *Weekly checks*).

30 Discard any hydraulic fluid that has been bled from the system as it will not be fit for re-use.

31 Check the feel of the brake pedal. If it feels at all spongy, air must still be present in the system and further bleeding is required. Failure to bleed satisfactorily after a reasonable repetition of the bleeding procedure may be due to worn master cylinder seals.

7	**Hydraulic pipes and hoses –** inspection

Refer to Chapter 1A or 1B.

8	**Hydraulic pipes and hoses –** renewal

1 If any pipe or hose is to be renewed, minimise fluid loss by removing the master cylinder reservoir cap and then tightening it down onto a piece of polythene (taking care not to damage the sender unit) to obtain an airtight seal. Alternatively, flexible hoses can

8.1 Using a brake hose clamp to minimise fluid loss

be sealed by using a proprietary brake hose clamp, while metal brake pipe unions can be plugged (if care is taken not to allow dirt into the system) or capped immediately they are disconnected **(see illustration)**. Place a wad of rag under any union that is to be disconnected to catch any spilt fluid.

2 If a flexible hose is to be disconnected, unscrew the brake pipe union nut before removing the spring clip which secures the hose to its mounting bracket.

3 To unscrew the union nuts it is preferable to obtain a proprietary brake pipe spanner of the correct size. These spanners are available from most large motor accessory shops **(see illustration)**. Failing this, a close-fitting open-ended spanner will be required, though if the nuts are tight or corroded, their flats may be rounded-off if the spanner slips. In such a case, a self-locking wrench is often the only way to unscrew a stubborn union but it follows that the pipe and the damaged nuts must be renewed on reassembly. Always clean a union and surrounding area before disconnecting it. If disconnecting a component with more than one union, make a careful note of the connections before disturbing any of them.

4 If a brake pipe is to be renewed, then it can be obtained from a Rover dealer, already cut to length and with the union nuts and end

flares in place. All that is then necessary is to bend it to shape, following the line of the original, before fitting it to the vehicle. Alternatively, most motor accessory shops can make up brake pipes from kits but this requires very careful measurement of the original to ensure that the replacement is of the correct length. The safest answer is usually to take the original to the shop as a pattern.

5 On refitting, do not overtighten the union nuts. The specified torque wrench settings, where given, are not high and it is not necessary to exercise brute force to obtain a sound joint; brake union threads are very fine and can easily be accidentally stripped. When refitting flexible hoses, always renew any sealing washers used.

6 Ensure that the pipes and hoses are correctly routed with no kinks and that they are secured in the clips or brackets provided. After fitting, remove the polythene from the reservoir and bleed the hydraulic system. Wash off any spilt fluid and check carefully for fluid leaks.

9 Master cylinder – removal, overhaul and refitting

> ⚠️ **Warning: Do not syphon brake fluid by mouth as it is poisonous.**

Note: *Before attempting to overhaul the master cylinder, check the price and availability of individual components and compare this with the price of a new or reconditioned unit, as overhaul may not be viable on economic grounds alone.*

Removal

1 Remove the master cylinder reservoir cap, having disconnected the sender unit wiring connector, and syphon all hydraulic fluid from the reservoir. Do not syphon the fluid by mouth

8.3 Using a brake pipe spanner to unscrew a union nut

as it is poisonous but use a syringe or an old poultry baster. Alternatively, open any convenient bleed screw in the system and gently pump the brake pedal to expel the fluid through a plastic tube connected to the screw.

2 Wipe clean the area around the brake pipe unions on the side of the master cylinder and place absorbent rags beneath the pipe unions to catch any surplus fluid. Unscrew the two union nuts and carefully withdraw the pipes **(see illustration)**. Plug or tape over the pipe ends and master cylinder orifices to minimise loss of brake fluid and to prevent the entry of dirt into the system. Wash off any spilt fluid immediately with clean water.

3 Slacken and remove the two nuts and spring washers securing the master cylinder to the vacuum servo unit then withdraw the unit from the engine compartment **(see illustration)**. Remove the O-ring (where fitted) from the rear of the master cylinder and discard it.

Overhaul

4 Remove the master cylinder from the vehicle as described above and clean it thoroughly.

5 Carefully prise the reservoir from the master cylinder body and remove the two mounting seals **(see illustrations)**.

9.2 Master cylinder brake pipe unions (arrowed) – non-ABS model

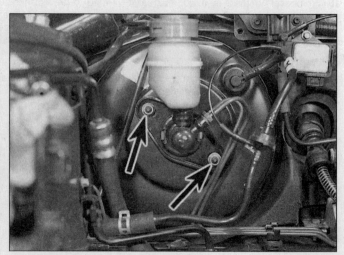

9.3 Master cylinder-to-vacuum servo unit nuts (arrowed) – non-ABS model

6 Prepare a clean working surface and proceed as follows.

Non-ABS system

7 Using a wooden dowel, press the primary piston in as far as possible and extract the secondary piston stop-pin from the reservoir inlet port, then remove the retaining circlip.

8 Noting the order of removal and the direction of fitting of each component, withdraw the piston assemblies with their springs and seals, tapping the body onto a clean wooden surface to dislodge them. If necessary, clamp the master cylinder body in a vice (fitted with soft jaw covers) and use compressed air of low pressure (applied through the secondary circuit fluid port) to assist the removal of the secondary piston assembly.

9 Thoroughly clean all components using only methylated spirit, isopropyl alcohol or clean hydraulic fluid as a cleaning medium. Never use mineral-based solvents such as petrol or paraffin which will attack the hydraulic system's rubber components. Dry the components immediately using compressed air or a clean, lint-free cloth.

10 Check all components and renew any that are worn or damaged. Check particularly the cylinder bores and pistons. The complete assembly should be renewed if these are scratched, worn or corroded. If there is any doubt about the condition of the assembly or of any of its components, renew it. Check that the body's inlet and bypass ports are clear.

11 If the assembly is fit for further use, obtain a repair kit. Renew all seals and O-rings disturbed on dismantling, never re-use them. Renew also any other items included in the repair kit.

12 On reassembly, soak the pistons and new seals in clean hydraulic fluid. Smear clean fluid into the cylinder bore.

13 Fit the new seals to their pistons, using only the fingers to manipulate them into the grooves.

14 Insert the pistons into the bore by using a twisting motion to avoid trapping the seal lips. Ensure that all components are refitted in the correct order and the right way round.

15 Press the secondary piston assembly fully up into the bore using a clean wooden dowel, then refit the stop-pin.

16 Refit the primary piston assembly, then secure it in position with a new circlip.

17 Press the new mounting seals into the master cylinder body and carefully refit the reservoir ensuring that it is pressed fully into position.

ABS system

18 Carefully prise out the dust cap from the rear of the master cylinder body and remove the flat washer.

19 Using a wooden dowel, press the primary piston in as far as possible and extract the circlip and washer. Withdraw the primary piston assembly and spring.

20 Undo the grub screw from the underside of the master cylinder body then use the wooden

9.5a Non-ABS master cylinder components

1 Master cylinder reservoir	6 Seal	10 O-ring
2 Seals	7 Secondary piston	11 Vacuum seal backing
3 Cylinder body	8 Seal	ring
4 Spring	9 Primary piston	12 Vacuum seal
5 Seal support	assembly	13 Transfer housing

9.5b ABS master cylinder components

1 Master cylinder reservoir	5 Secondary piston assembly	9 Primary piston assembly
2 Seals	6 Secondary piston stop-pin	10 Washer
3 Cylinder body	7 Stop-pin screw	11 Circlip
4 Spring	8 Spring	12 Flat washer
		13 Transfer housing

11.2a Remove caliper lower guide pin bolt . . .

11.2b . . . and pivot caliper away from disc

11.3 Removing circular shim from caliper piston

dowel to press the secondary piston into the body and withdraw the secondary piston retaining pin. Extract the secondary piston assembly and spring. If necessary, the piston can be dislodged by tapping the master cylinder body on a wooden block.

21 Examine and overhaul the master cylinder components as described above in paragraphs 9 to 14.

22 Fit the spring to the secondary piston assembly and use a clean wooden dowel to press the assembly fully into the master cylinder bore. Align the slot in the piston with the retaining pin hole then insert the secondary piston retaining pin. Refit the grub screw and tighten it securely.

23 Fit the spring to the primary piston assembly and press the assembly into position using the wooden dowel. Refit the washer and secure the piston assembly in position with the circlip, ensuring that it is correctly located in its groove in the master cylinder bore.

24 Fit the flat washer and refit the dust cap to the rear of the master cylinder body.

25 Align the lugs on the new mounting seals with the slots in the master cylinder body and press them into position. Carefully refit the reservoir, ensuring that it is pressed fully into the master cylinder body.

Refitting

26 Remove all traces of dirt from the master cylinder and servo unit mating surfaces, then fit a new O-ring to the groove on the master cylinder body.

27 Fit the master cylinder to the servo unit,

ensuring that the servo unit pushrod enters the master cylinder bore centrally. Refit the master cylinder washers and mounting nuts and tighten them to the specified torque.

28 Wipe clean the brake pipe unions then refit them to the master cylinder ports and tighten them to the specified torque setting.

29 Refill the master cylinder reservoir with new fluid and bleed the hydraulic system, as described in Section 6.

10 Front brake pads – inspection

Refer to the information given in Chapter 1A or 1B.

11 Front brake pads – renewal

⚠️ *Warning: Renew both sets of front brake pads at the same time. Never renew the pads on only one wheel as uneven braking may result. The dust created by pad wear may contain asbestos, which is a health hazard. Never blow it with compressed air or inhale it. An approved filtering mask should be worn when working on the brakes. DO NOT use petroleum-based solvents to clean brake parts the rubber sealing components may be damaged; use brake cleaner or methylated spirit only.*

Removal

1 Chock the rear wheels, firmly apply the handbrake then jack up the front of the vehicle and support it on axle stands (see *Jacking and Vehicle Support*). Remove both front roadwheels.

2 Remove the caliper lower guide pin bolt whilst, if necessary, using a slim open-ended spanner to prevent the guide pin itself from rotating. Pivot the caliper away from the disc to gain access to the brake pads and tie it to the suspension strut using a piece of wire **(see illustrations)**.

3 Remove the circular shim which is fitted to the caliper piston **(see illustration)**.

4 Remove the brake pads from the caliper mounting bracket whilst noting the correct position of the pad retainer springs and pad shims **(see illustration)**.

5 Measure the thickness of friction material remaining on each brake pad **(see illustration)**. If either pad is worn at any point to the specified minimum thickness or less, all four pads must be renewed. Also, the pads should be renewed if any are fouled with oil or grease as there is no satisfactory way of degreasing friction material once contaminated. If any of the brake pads are worn unevenly or fouled with oil or grease, trace and rectify the cause before reassembly. New brake pad kits are available from Rover dealers and include new shims and pad retainer springs.

6 If the brake pads are still serviceable, carefully clean them using a clean, fine wire brush or similar, paying particular attention to the sides and back of the metal backing. Clean out the grooves in the friction material (where applicable) and pick out any large embedded particles of dirt or debris. Carefully clean the pad retainer springs and the pad locations in the caliper body and mounting bracket.

Fitting

7 Prior to fitting the pads, check that the guide pins are free to slide easily in the caliper bracket and check that the rubber guide pin gaiters are undamaged **(see illustration)**. Brush the dust and dirt from the caliper and piston but **do not** inhale it as it is injurious to health. Inspect the dust seal around the piston

11.4 Removing pads with springs and shims

11.5 Measuring thickness of brake pad friction material

11.7 Check condition of guide pins and galters before refitting pads

11.8 Fit pad retainer springs to caliper bracket . . .

11.9 . . . and fit shims on pads

for damage and the piston for evidence of fluid leaks, corrosion or damage. Renew as necessary.

8 On refitting, first fit the pad retainer springs to the caliper mounting bracket **(see illustration).**

9 Apply a thin smear of high-temperature brake grease (silicone- or PBC/Poly Butyl Cuprysil-based) or anti-seize compound to the sides and back of each pad's metal backing and to those surfaces of the caliper body and mounting bracket which bear on the pads. Fit the shims to the back of both pads and apply a thin smear of lubricant to the back of each shim. Do not allow the lubricant to foul the friction material **(see illustration).**

10 Install the brake pads in the caliper mounting bracket, ensuring that the friction material is against the disc.

11 If new brake pads have been fitted, the caliper piston must be pushed back into the cylinder to make room for them. Either use a G-clamp or similar tool, or use suitable pieces of wood as levers. Provided that the master cylinder reservoir has not been overfilled with hydraulic fluid there should be no spillage but keep a careful watch on the fluid level while retracting the piston. If the fluid level rises above the MAX level line at any time, the surplus should be syphoned off or ejected via a plastic tube connected to the bleed screw.

12 Apply a thin smear of the recommended lubricant (see above) to the circular shim and fit the shim to the caliper piston. Pivot the caliper body down over the brake pads then refit the bottom guide pin bolt and tighten it to the specified torque wrench setting.

13 Check that the caliper body slides smoothly in the mounting bracket, then depress the brake pedal repeatedly until the pads are pressed into firm contact with the brake disc and normal (non-assisted) pedal pressure is restored.

14 Repeat the above procedure on the remaining front brake caliper.

15 Refit the roadwheels, then lower the vehicle to the ground and tighten the roadwheel nuts to the specified torque setting.

16 On completion, check the hydraulic fluid level (see *Weekly checks*).

12 Front brake caliper – removal, overhaul and refitting

⚠ *Warning: Brake hydraulic fluid may be under considerable pressure in a pipeline, take care not to allow hydraulic fluid to spray into the face or eyes when loosening a connection.*

Removal

1 Chock the rear wheels, firmly apply the handbrake, jack up the front of the vehicle and support on axle stands (see *Jacking and Vehicle Support*). Remove the appropriate front roadwheel.

2 Minimise fluid loss either by removing the master cylinder reservoir cap and then tightening it down onto a piece of polythene to obtain an airtight seal (taking care not to damage the sender unit), or by using a brake hose clamp, a G-clamp or a similar tool to clamp the flexible hose.

3 Clean the area around the union, then undo the brake hose union bolt and disconnect the hose from the caliper. Plug the end of the hose and the caliper orifice to prevent dirt entering the hydraulic system. Discard the sealing washers as they must be renewed whenever disturbed.

4 Unscrew the two caliper guide pin bolts whilst, if necessary, using a slim open-ended spanner to prevent the guide pins themselves from rotating **(see illustration).**

12.4 Front brake caliper components

1 Bleed screw	6 Pad retainer spring	10 Outer pad shim
2 Caliper body	7 Caliper mounting	11 Piston seal
3 Guide pin bolt	bracket	12 Piston
4 Guide pin	8 Inner pad shim	13 Dust seal
5 Gaiter	9 Brake pads	14 Circular shim

5 Carefully lift the caliper assembly off the brake pads and remove the circular shim from the caliper piston. Note that the brake pads need not be disturbed and can be left in position in the caliper mounting bracket.

Overhaul

6 With the caliper on the bench, wipe away all traces of dust and dirt.

 Warning: Avoid inhaling the dust as it is injurious to health.

7 Withdraw the piston from the caliper body and remove the dust seal. The piston can be withdrawn by hand or if necessary, pushed out by applying compressed air to the union bolt hole. Only low pressure should be required such as is generated by a foot pump; place a block of wood at the end of the piston, to prevent it striking the caliper as it is ejected from the bore.

8 Using a small screwdriver, extract the piston hydraulic seal whilst taking great care not to damage the caliper bore.

9 Withdraw the guide pins from the caliper mounting bracket and remove the guide pin gaiters.

10 Thoroughly clean all components using only methylated spirit, isopropyl alcohol or clean hydraulic fluid as a cleaning medium.

 Warning: Never use mineral-based solvents such as petrol or paraffin which will attack the hydraulic system's rubber components.

 HAYNES HINT *Dry the components immediately using compressed air or a clean, lint-free cloth. Use compressed air to blow clear the fluid passages.*

11 Check all components and renew any that are worn or damaged. Check particularly the cylinder bore and piston. These should be renewed (note that this means the renewal of the complete body assembly) if they are scratched, worn or corroded in any way. Similarly, check the condition of the guide pins and their bores in the mounting bracket. Both guide pins should be undamaged and (when cleaned) a reasonably tight sliding fit in the mounting bracket bores. If there is any doubt about the condition of any component, renew it.

12 If the assembly is fit for further use, obtain the appropriate repair kit. Components are available from Rover dealers in various combinations.

13 Renew all rubber seals, dust covers and caps. Also the sealing washers disturbed on dismantling.

14 On reassembly, ensure that all components are absolutely clean and dry.

15 Soak the piston and the new piston (fluid) seal in clean hydraulic fluid. Smear clean fluid on the cylinder bore surface.

16 Fit the new piston (fluid) seal using only the fingers to manipulate it into the cylinder

13.3 Using a micrometer to measure brake disc thickness

bore groove. Fit the new dust seal to the piston and refit it to the cylinder bore using a twisting motion, ensuring that the piston enters squarely into the bore. Press the piston fully into the bore, then secure the dust seal to the caliper body.

17 Apply the grease supplied in the repair kit, or a good quality high-temperature brake grease (silicone- or PBC/Poly Butyl Cuprysil-based) or anti-seize compound, to the guide pins and fit the new gaiters. Fit the guide pins to the caliper mounting bracket, ensuring that the gaiters are correctly located in the grooves on both the guide pin and mounting bracket.

Refitting

18 Refit the circular shim to the piston and carefully slide the caliper into position over the brake pads. Refit the caliper guide pin bolts and tighten them to the specified torque setting.

19 Position a new sealing washer on each side of the hose union and refit the brake hose union bolt. Ensure that the brake hose union is correctly positioned between the lugs on the caliper then tighten the union bolt to the specified torque setting.

20 Remove the brake hose clamp, where fitted, and bleed the hydraulic system. Providing the precautions described were taken to minimise brake fluid loss, it should only be necessary to bleed the relevant front brake.

21 Refit the roadwheel then lower the vehicle to the ground and tighten the roadwheel nuts to the specified torque.

13.4 Using a dial gauge to check brake disc run-out

13 Front brake disc – inspection, removal and refitting

Note: *If either brake disc requires renewal, both should be renewed at the same time to ensure even and consistent braking.*

Inspection

1 Chock the rear wheels, firmly apply the handbrake, jack up the front of the vehicle and support on axle stands (see *Jacking and Vehicle Support*). Remove the appropriate front roadwheel.

2 Slowly rotate the brake disc so that the full area of both sides can be checked. Remove the brake pads if better access is required to the inboard surface. Light scoring is normal in the area swept by the brake pads but if heavy scoring is found, then the disc must be renewed. The only alternative to this is to have the disc surface-ground until it is flat again, but this must not reduce the disc to less than the minimum thickness specified.

3 It is normal to find a lip of rust and brake dust around the disc's perimeter. This can be scraped off if required. If, however, a lip has formed due to excessive wear of the brake pad swept area, particularly on the outer edge of the disc, then the disc's thickness must be measured by using a micrometer **(see illustration)**. Take measurements at several places around the disc at the inside and outside of the pad swept area. If the disc has worn at any point to the specified minimum thickness or less, then it must be renewed. Note that a large variation in the thickness of the disc around its circumference may be caused by poor disc seating and can cause brake judder.

4 If the disc is thought to be warped, it can be checked for run-out (at a point 6.0 mm in from the disc's outer edge) by either using a dial gauge mounted on any convenient fixed point, while the disc is slowly rotated, or by using feeler blades to measure (at several points all around the disc) the clearance between the disc and a fixed point, such as the caliper mounting bracket **(see illustration)**. If the measurements obtained are at the specified maximum or beyond, the disc is excessively warped and must be renewed. However, it is worth checking first that the hub bearing is in good condition. Also, try the effect of removing the disc, cleaning the hub and disc mating surfaces and turning the disc through 180° to reposition it on the hub. If run-out is still excessive, the disc must be renewed.

5 Check the disc for cracks, especially around the stud holes, and any other wear or damage. Renew it if any of these are found.

Removal

6 Unscrew the two bolts securing the caliper mounting bracket to the swivel hub and slide the caliper assembly off the disc **(see**

13.6 Removing caliper assembly

13.7a Removing disc retaining screws (jacking holes arrowed)

13.7b Drawing off a disc using two 8 mm bolts

illustration). Using a piece of wire or string, tie the caliper to the front suspension coil spring to avoid placing any strain on the hydraulic brake hose.

7 Use chalk or paint to mark the relationship of the disc to the hub, then remove the two screws securing the brake disc to the hub and remove the disc. If the disc is a tight fit on the hub it can be drawn off by screwing two bolts into the jacking holes provided **(see illustrations)**.

Refitting

8 Thoroughly clean the mating surfaces of the hub and brake disc, using a wire brush or fine grade emery paper. Remove all traces of brake dust and corrosion to ensure that the disc seats correctly.

9 The remainder of the refitting procedure is the reverse of the removal procedure, noting the following:

  a) *Where applicable, observe the disc alignment markings made during removal.*

  b) *If a new disc is being fitted, use a suitable solvent to wipe any preservative coating from the disc before fitting it.*

  c) *Fit and tighten the brake disc screws to their specified torque, then fit the brake caliper and mounting bracket using only the upper mounting bolt. Check the disc run-out, as described earlier in this Section, before proceeding.*

  d) *Tighten the caliper mounting bracket bolts and roadwheel nuts to their specified torque wrench settings.*

14 Brake proportioning valve – testing, removal and refitting

Testing

1 The valve is mounted on the engine compartment bulkhead.

2 Specialist equipment is required to check valve performance. If the valve is thought to be faulty, the vehicle should be taken to a suitably-equipped Rover dealer for testing. However, in the event of an internal failure, brake fluid will seep from the plug on the front face of the valve which is situated directly

below the upper two hose unions **(see illustration)**. Repairs are not possible; if the valve is thought to be faulty, it must be renewed.

Removal

3 Disconnect the sender unit wiring connector and unscrew the master cylinder reservoir filler cap. Place a piece of polythene over the filler neck and securely refit the cap (taking care not to damage the sender unit). This will minimise brake fluid loss during subsequent operations. As an added precaution, place absorbent rags beneath the proportioning valve brake pipe unions.

4 Wipe clean the area around the brake pipe unions on the proportioning valve, then make a note of how the pipes are arranged for reference on refitting. Unscrew the union nuts and carefully withdraw the pipes. Plug or tape over the pipe ends and valve orifices to minimise the loss of brake fluid and to prevent the entry of dirt into the system. Wash off any spilt fluid immediately with cold water.

5 Slacken the two bolts which secure the valve to the bulkhead and remove it from the engine compartment.

Refitting

6 Refit the proportioning valve to the bulkhead and tighten its mounting bolts to the specified torque.

7 Wipe the brake pipe unions clean and refit them to the valve, using the notes made on dismantling to ensure they are correctly positioned. Tighten the union nuts to the specified torque.

14.2 Brake proportioning valve plug (arrowed) – diesel-engined, non-ABS model

8 Remove the polythene from the master cylinder reservoir filler neck and bleed the complete hydraulic system.

15 Rear brake shoes – inspection

  Refer to the information given in Chapter 1A or 1B as applicable.

16 Rear brake shoes – renewal

> ⚠ **Warning: Brake shoes must be renewed on both rear wheels at the same time. Never renew the shoes on only one wheel as uneven braking may result.**

Removal

1 Remove the brake drum (see Section 17).

2 Working carefully and noting all precautions, remove all traces of brake dust from the brake drum, backplate and shoes.

3 Measure the thickness of friction material remaining on each brake shoe at several points. If either shoe is worn at any point to the specified minimum thickness or less, all four shoes must be renewed as a set. Also, the shoes should be renewed if any are fouled with oil or grease as there is no satisfactory way of degreasing friction material once it is contaminated.

4 If any of the brake shoes are worn unevenly or fouled with oil or grease, trace and rectify the cause before reassembly.

5 To remove the brake shoes, first remove the shoe retainer springs and pins, using a pair of pliers to press in each retainer clip until it can be rotated through 90° and released. Ease the shoes out one at a time from the lower pivot point to release the tension of the return spring, then disconnect the lower return spring from the leading shoe. Ease the upper end of both shoes out from their wheel cylinder locations, and disconnect the handbrake cable from the trailing shoe. The brake shoe and adjuster strut assembly can

16.5a Rear drum brake assembly

1 Dust cap
2 Bleed screw
3 Backplate
4 Plug for brake shoe release access hole
5 Seal
6 Wheel cylinder
7 Brake shoes
8 Upper shoe return spring
9 Adjuster strut assembly
10 Strut return spring
11 Brake drum
12 Drum securing screw
13 Lower shoe return spring
14 Strut quadrant spring
15 Shoe retaining pin spring clip
16 Backplate securing screw
17 Shoe lining inspection hole
18 Shoe retaining pin
19 Wheel cylinder securing screw

now be manoeuvred out of position and away from the backplate (see illustrations). Do not depress the brake pedal until the brakes are reassembled. Wrap a strong elastic band around the wheel cylinder pistons to retain them.

Caution: Take great care to avoid damaging the wheel cylinder seals when removing the brake shoes.

6 With the brake shoe assembly on the worksurface, make a note of the fitted positions of the adjuster strut and springs to use as guide on reassembly (see illustration). Carefully ease the adjuster strut from its slot in the trailing shoe and remove the short spring which secures the two components together. Detach the upper return spring and separate the shoes and strut.

7 Examine the adjuster strut assembly for signs of wear or damage, paying particular attention to the adjuster quadrant and knurled wheel. If damaged, the strut assembly must be renewed. Renew all the brake shoe return springs regardless of their apparent condition.

8 Peel back the rubber protective caps and check the wheel cylinder for fluid leaks or other damage. Check that both cylinder pistons are free to move easily.

Fitting

Caution: Do not allow lubricant to come into contact with the brake linings or dust covers.

9 Clean the backplate, and apply a thin smear of Molykote 111, or anti-seize compound, to all the surfaces which contact the shoes, including the adjuster and wheel cylinder pistons.

10 Ensure the handbrake lever stop on the trailing shoe is correctly engaged with the lever and is pressed tight against the brake shoe (see illustration).

11 Fully extend the adjuster strut quadrant and fit the leading brake shoe into the adjuster strut slot, ensuring that the strut spring and knurled wheel are situated on the underside of the strut assembly. Using a screwdriver, move the quadrant away from the knurled wheel and set it in the minimum adjustment position.

12 Fit the upper return spring to its respective location on the leading shoe. Fit the trailing shoe to the upper return spring

16.5b Remove brake shoe retainer springs . . .

16.5c . . . unhook lower return spring . . .

16.5d . . . and manoeuvre shoe and adjuster strut assembly away from backplate

16.6 Correct fitted positions of adjuster strut and springs

16.10 Ensure handbrake stop lever is correctly located

and carefully ease the shoe into position in the adjuster strut slot. Once in position, fit the small spring which secures the trailing shoe to the strut assembly.

13 Remove the elastic band fitted to the wheel cylinder and manoeuvre the shoe and strut assembly into position on the backplate. Locate the upper end of both shoes with the wheel cylinder pistons and fit the handbrake cable to the trailing shoe operating lever. Fit the lower return spring to both shoes and ease the shoes into position on the lower pivot point.

14 Tap the shoes to centralise them with the backplate, then refit the shoe retainer pins and springs and secure them in position with the retainer clips. Check that the adjuster quadrant is still in the minimum adjuster position and if necessary, reset as follows. Place a block of wood between the trailing shoe and hub, to prevent the shoe moving forwards, then lever the leading shoe away from the hub to release the brake shoe return spring pressure on the adjuster quadrant. With the shoe held in this position, reset the quadrant to the minimum adjustment setting **(see illustration)**. Once the adjuster strut is correctly set, ease the leading shoe back into position then remove the block of wood and check that the shoes are still central.

15 Refit the brake drum and repeat the above operation on the remaining rear brake assembly.

16 On completion, apply the footbrake repeatedly to set the shoe-to-drum clearance, until normal (non-assisted) brake pedal operation returns.

17.3 Removing brake drum retaining screws (jacking holes arrowed)

17.4a Location of shoe release access hole and plug (arrowed)

16.14 Reset adjuster strut prior to refitting drum

17 Check handbrake cable operation and, if necessary, adjust as described in Chapter 1A or 1B.

18 Refit the roadwheels then lower the vehicle to the ground and tighten the roadwheel nuts to the specified torque.

19 Check and if necessary top up the hydraulic fluid level (see *Weekly checks*).

---

17 Rear brake drum –
removal, inspection
and refitting

Note: *If either brake drum requires renewal, both should be renewed at the same time to ensure even and consistent braking.*

Removal

1 Chock the front wheels then jack up the rear of the vehicle and support it on axle stands (see *Jacking and Vehicle Support*). Remove the appropriate rear wheel.

2 Use chalk or paint to mark the relationship of the drum to the hub.

3 With the handbrake firmly applied to prevent drum rotation, unscrew the drum retaining screws **(see illustration)**. Fully release the handbrake cable and withdraw the drum.

17.4b Releasing handbrake mechanism stop lever

Remove rubber grommet (A) and use small screwdriver to depress handbrake lever stop (B)

4 If the drum will not pull away, first check that the handbrake is fully released. If the drum will still not come away, remove the grommet from the rear of the backplate and, using a small screwdriver, disengage the handbrake lever stop from behind the lever to increase the shoe-to-drum clearance. If removal is still difficult, slacken the handbrake cable adjusting nut (see Section 24). If the drum is still held firm, it can be drawn off the shoes by screwing two bolts into the jacking holes provided **(see illustrations)**.

Inspection

5 Working carefully, remove all traces of brake dust from the drum.

⚠️ *Warning: Avoid inhaling the dust as it is injurious to health.*

6 Scrub clean the outside of the drum and check it for obvious signs of wear or damage such as cracks around the roadwheel stud holes. Renew the drum if necessary.

7 Examine carefully the inside of the drum. Light scoring of the friction surface is normal but if heavy scoring is found, the drum must be renewed. It is usual to find a lip on the drum's inboard edge which consists of a mixture of rust and brake dust. This should be scraped away to leave a smooth surface which can be polished with fine (120 to 150 grade) emery paper. If, however, the lip is due to the friction surface being recessed by excessive wear, then the drum must be renewed.

8 If the drum is thought to be excessively worn or oval, its internal diameter must be measured at several points by using an internal micrometer. Take measurements in pairs, the second at right angles to the first, and compare the two to check for signs of ovality. Provided that it does not enlarge the drum to beyond the specified maximum diameter, it may be possible to have the drum refinished by skimming or grinding but if this is not possible, the drums on both sides must be renewed.

Refitting

9 Refitting is the reverse of the removal procedure, noting the following:

  a) On fitting a new brake drum, use a

17.4c Brake drum can be drawn off hub by using two 8 mm bolts

suitable solvent to remove any preservative coating that may have been applied to its interior.
b) If the existing drum is to be refitted, use a clean wire brush to remove all traces of dirt, brake dust and corrosion from the mating surfaces of the drum and the hub flange.
c) Align the marks made on removal (where applicable).
d) Tighten the drum retaining screws and the roadwheel nuts to their specified torque wrench settings.

18 Rear wheel cylinder – removal, overhaul and refitting

Note: *Before attempting to overhaul a rear wheel cylinder, check the price and availability of individual components and the price of a new or reconditioned unit, as overhaul may not be viable on economic grounds alone.*

Removal

1 Remove the brake shoes.
2 Minimise fluid loss by removing the master cylinder reservoir cap and then tightening it down onto a piece of polythene to obtain an airtight seal (taking care not to damage the sender unit), or by using a brake hose clamp, a G-clamp or a similar tool to clamp the flexible hose.
3 Wipe away all traces of dirt around the brake pipe union at the rear of the wheel cylinder and unscrew the union nut. Carefully ease the pipe out of the wheel cylinder and plug or tape over its end to prevent dirt entry **(see illustration)**.
4 Unscrew the two wheel cylinder retaining bolts from the rear of the backplate and remove the cylinder, noting the rubber sealing ring which is fitted between the cylinder and backplate.

Overhaul

5 Remove the wheel cylinder from the vehicle and clean it thoroughly.
6 Mount the wheel cylinder in a soft-jawed vice and remove the rubber protective caps. Extract the piston assemblies.
7 Thoroughly clean all components using only methylated spirit, isopropyl alcohol or clean hydraulic fluid as a cleaning medium. Dry the components immediately using compressed air or a clean, lint-free cloth.
Caution: Never use mineral-based solvents such as petrol or paraffin which will attack the hydraulic system's rubber components.
8 Check all components and renew any that are worn or damaged. Check particularly the cylinder bore and pistons. The complete assembly must be renewed if these are scratched, worn or corroded. If there is any doubt about the condition of the assembly or of any of its components, renew it. Remove the bleed screw and check that the fluid entry port and bleed screw passages are clear.

9 If the assembly is fit for further use, obtain a repair kit. Renew the rubber protective caps, dust caps and seals disturbed on dismantling, these should never be re-used. Renew also any other items included in the repair kit.
10 On reassembly, soak the pistons and the new seals in clean hydraulic fluid. Smear clean fluid on the cylinder bore surface.
11 Fit the new seals to their pistons using only the fingers to manipulate them into the grooves. Ensure that all components are refitted in the correct order and the right way round.
12 Insert the pistons into the bore using a twisting motion to avoid trapping the seal lips. Apply a smear of rubber lubricant to each piston before fitting the new rubber protective caps.

Refitting

13 Fit a new sealing ring to the rear of the wheel cylinder and place the cylinder in position on the backplate.
14 Refit the wheel cylinder retaining bolts and tighten them to the specified torque.
15 Tighten the brake pipe union nut and, if necessary, remove the clamp from the brake hose.
16 Refit the brake shoes.
17 Bleed the hydraulic braking system. If precautions were taken to minimise fluid loss, it should only be necessary to bleed the relevant rear brake. On completion, check that both footbrake and handbrake function correctly before taking the vehicle on the road.

19 Rear brake pads – inspection

Refer to Chapter 1A or 1B.

20 Rear brake pads – renewal

 Warning: Renew both sets of rear brake pads at the same time. Never renew the pads on only one wheel as uneven braking may result.

18.3 Wheel cylinder retaining bolts (A) and brake pipe union nut (B)

Removal

1 Chock the front wheels then jack up the rear of the vehicle and support on axle stands (see *Jacking and Vehicle Support*). Remove the rear roadwheels.
2 Undo the two bolts securing the caliper shield in position and remove the shield from the rear of the caliper.
3 Remove both caliper guide pin bolts whilst, if necessary, using a slim open-ended spanner to prevent the guide pins from rotating. Lift the caliper away from the disc, noting the upper pad spring which is fitted to the roof of the caliper. Tie the caliper to the suspension strut using a piece of wire to avoid straining the hydraulic hose **(see illustration)**.
4 Remove the brake pads from the caliper mounting bracket whilst noting the correct fitted positions of the brake pads, pad retainer springs and pad shims.
5 Inspect the pads as described for the front brake pads and, if necessary, renew as a complete axle set.

Fitting

6 Fit the pad retainer springs to the caliper mounting bracket.
7 Apply a thin smear of Molykote M77 compound to the sides and back of each pad's metal backing and to those surfaces of the caliper body and mounting bracket which bear on the pads. In the absence of the specified lubricant, a good quality high-temperature brake grease (silicone- or PBC/Poly Butyl Cuprysil-based) or anti-seize compound may be used. Fit the shims to the back of both pads, noting that the smaller shim must be fitted to the piston side pad, and apply a thin smear of lubricant to the back of each shim.
Caution: Do not allow lubricant to foul the friction material.
8 Install the brake pads in the caliper mounting bracket, ensuring that the friction material is against the disc and the pad with the smaller shim attached is fitted on the inside.
9 If new pads have been fitted, it will be necessary to retract the piston fully into the caliper bore by rotating it in a clockwise direction. This can be achieved by using a suitable pair of circlip pliers as a peg spanner or by fabricating a peg spanner for the task. Provided that the master cylinder reservoir has not been overfilled with hydraulic fluid, there should be no spillage, but keep a careful watch on the fluid level while retracting the piston. If the fluid level rises above the MAX level line at any time, the surplus should be syphoned off or ejected via a plastic tube connected to the bleed screw.
10 Ensure the upper pad spring is still in position in the caliper then slide the caliper into position in its mounting bracket. When fitting the caliper, ensure that the lug on the rear of the piston side pad is located in one of the piston slots. Refit the caliper guide pin

20.3 Rear brake caliper components

1	Handbrake lever retaining nut	8	Bleed screw	16	Spring cover
2	Washer	9	Pushrod	17	Circlip
3	Return spring	10	O-ring	18	Piston seal
4	Handbrake operating lever	11	Adjusting bolt piston	19	Circlip
5	Dust seal	12	Adjusting bolt	20	Thrustwasher
6	Guide pin bolt	13	Bearing	21	Spring
7	Caliper body	14	Spring seat	22	Adjuster nut
		15	Spring	23	Piston

24	Dust seal	32	Guide pin
25	Pad spring	33	Handbrake cable mounting bracket
26	Inner pad shim	34	Cam washer
27	Brake pads	35	Pin
28	Outer pad shim	36	Bolt
29	Pad spring	37	Handbrake mechanism cam
30	Caliper mounting bracket		
31	Gaiter		

bolts and tighten them to the specified torque setting.

11 Depress the footbrake to bring the piston into contact with the pads then check that the lug on the piston side pad is located in one of the piston slots. If necessary, remove the caliper and adjust the piston position as described above. Refit the shield to the rear of the caliper.

12 Repeat the above procedure on the remaining rear brake caliper.

13 Once both calipers have been done, repeatedly depress the brake pedal until normal (non-assisted) pedal operation returns, then repeatedly apply the handbrake to set handbrake adjustment. Check the operation of the handbrake and, if necessary, adjust the cable as described in Chapter 1A or 1B.

14 Refit the roadwheels, then lower the vehicle to the ground and tighten the roadwheel nuts to the specified torque.

15 Check the hydraulic fluid level (see *Weekly checks*).

21 Rear brake caliper – removal, overhaul and refitting

Removal

1 Chock the front wheels, then jack up the rear of the vehicle and support on axle stands (see *Jacking and Vehicle Support*). Remove the rear wheel.

2 Undo the two bolts securing the caliper shield in position and remove the shield from the rear of the caliper.

3 Extract the spring clip and clevis pin securing the handbrake cable to the caliper handbrake lever, then remove the clip securing the outer cable to its mounting bracket and detach the handbrake cable from the caliper.

4 Minimise fluid loss by removing the master cylinder reservoir cap and then tightening it down onto a piece of polythene to obtain an airtight seal (taking care not to damage the sender unit), or by using a brake hose clamp or similar tool to seal off the flexible hose. *Caution: Do not use a G-clamp on the brake hose, as the edges of the jaws may pinch the hose internally and cause it to fail.*

 HAYNES HiNT *If a proprietary brake hose clamp is not available, fit two old sockets over the jaws of a pair of mole grips then use them to clamp the brake hose. The rounded edges of the socket will prevent the jaws damaging the inside of the hose.*

5 Clean the area around the hose union, then undo the brake hose union bolt and disconnect the hose from the caliper. Plug the end of the hose and the caliper orifice to prevent dirt entering the hydraulic system. Discard the sealing washers as they must be renewed whenever disturbed.

6 Remove both the caliper guide pin bolts whilst, if necessary, using a slim open-ended spanner to prevent the guide pins from rotating, then lift the caliper away from the disc, noting the upper pad spring which is fitted to the roof of the caliper. Note that the brake pads need not be disturbed and can be left in position in the caliper mounting bracket.

Overhaul

7 With the caliper on the bench, wipe away all traces of dust and dirt.

⚠️ *Warning: Avoid inhaling the dust as it is injurious to health.*

8 Using a small screwdriver, carefully prise out the dust seal from the caliper bore.

9 Remove the piston from the caliper bore by rotating it in an anti-clockwise direction. This can be achieved using a suitable pair of circlip pliers as a peg spanner or by fabricating a peg spanner for the task. Once the piston turns freely but does not come out any further, then it can be withdrawn by hand, or if necessary, pushed out by applying compressed air to the union bolt hole. Only low pressure should be required such as is generated by a foot pump; place a block of wood at the end of the piston, to prevent it striking the caliper as it is ejected from the bore.

10 With the piston removed, extract the circlip from inside the piston and withdraw the thrustwasher, spring and adjuster nut.

11 Remove the piston (fluid) seal, taking great care not to scratch the caliper bore.

12 Extract the circlip from the caliper bore and withdraw the spring cover, spring, spring seat, bearing and adjusting bolt. Now remove the adjusting bolt piston, noting the O-ring fitted to the rear of the piston, and withdraw the small pushrod.

13 Slacken and remove the handbrake lever retaining nut and washer and remove the return spring, lever and dust seal. Withdraw the handbrake mechanism cam from the caliper and remove the cam washer.

14 Withdraw the guide pins from the caliper mounting bracket and remove the guide pin gaiters.

15 Inspect all the caliper components as described for the front brake caliper and renew as necessary.

16 On reassembly ensure that all components are absolutely clean and dry.

17 Apply a good quality high-temperature brake grease (silicone- or PBC/Poly Butyl Cuprysil-based) or anti-seize compound to the handbrake mechanism cam and refit the cam washer and cam to the caliper. Fit the dust seal, lever, return spring and washer and tighten the handbrake lever retaining nut securely.

18 Fit a new O-ring to the adjusting bolt piston then insert the small pushrod into the rear of the piston and install the adjusting bolt

piston assembly in the caliper bore. Operate the handbrake lever and check that the piston is free to move smoothly then refit the adjusting bolt, followed by the bearing and spring seat. Fit the spring, so that its tapered end is innermost, then install the spring cover. Secure all the above components in position with the circlip, ensuring that it is correctly seated in the groove in the caliper bore.

19 Locate the adjusting nut with the cutout on the inside of the caliper piston and refit the spring, thrustwasher and circlip. Ensure the circlip is correctly located in its groove.

20 Soak the piston and the new piston fluid seal in clean hydraulic fluid. Smear clean fluid on the cylinder bore surface.

21 Fit the new piston fluid seal into the cylinder bore groove by hand (do not use any tools), then refit the piston assembly. Turn the piston in a clockwise direction, using the method employed on dismantling, until it is fully retracted into the caliper bore.

22 Fit the piston dust seal to the caliper ensuring that it is correctly located in the caliper and also the groove on the piston.

23 Apply the grease supplied in the repair kit, or a good quality high-temperature brake grease (silicone- or PBC/Poly Butyl Cuprysil-based) or anti-seize compound to the guide pins and fit the new gaiters. Fit the guide pins to the caliper mounting bracket, ensuring that the gaiters are correctly located in the grooves on both the guide pin and mounting bracket.

Refitting

24 Ensure the upper pad spring is still in position in the caliper then slide the caliper into position in its mounting bracket. When fitting the caliper, ensure that the lug on the rear of the piston side pad is located in the centre of the caliper piston at the point where the two piston slots cross. Refit the caliper guide pin bolts and tighten them to the specified torque setting.

25 Position a new sealing washer on each side of the hose union and refit the brake hose union bolt. Ensure that the brake hose union is correctly positioned between the lugs on the caliper then tighten the union bolt to the specified torque setting.

26 Remove the brake hose clamp, where fitted, and bleed the hydraulic system. Providing the precautions described were taken to minimise brake fluid loss, it should only be necessary to bleed the relevant rear brake.

27 Refit the handbrake cable outer to its mounting bracket and secure it in position with the retaining clip. Ensure the return spring is located in the groove in the operating lever then refit the handbrake cable-to-lever clevis pin and secure it in position with the spring clip.

28 Depress the brake pedal several times until normal (non-assisted) operation returns then check and, if necessary, adjust the handbrake cable as described in Chapter 1A or 1B.

23.3 Handbrake lever switch (A), mounting bolts (B) and adjusting nut (C)

29 Refit the shield to the rear of the caliper and tighten its retaining bolts securely.

30 Refit the roadwheel, then lower the vehicle to the ground and tighten the roadwheel nuts to the specified torque.

31 Check the hydraulic fluid level (see *Weekly checks*).

22 Rear brake disc – inspection, removal and refitting

Note: *If either rear brake disc requires renewal, both should be renewed at the same time to ensure even and consistent braking.*

Inspection

1 Chock the front wheels, then jack up the rear of the vehicle and support on axle stands (see *Jacking and Vehicle Support*). Remove the appropriate rear roadwheel.

2 Inspect the disc as described for the front brake disc.

Removal

3 Undo the two caliper shield retaining bolts and remove the shield from the rear of the caliper.

4 Undo the two bolts securing the caliper mounting bracket to the trailing arm assembly and slide the caliper assembly off the disc. Using a piece of wire or string, tie the caliper to the coils of the rear suspension strut to avoid placing any strain on the hydraulic brake hose.

5 Use chalk or paint to mark the relationship of the disc to the hub, then remove the two screws securing the brake disc to the hub and remove the disc. If the disc is a tight fit on the hub, it can be drawn off by screwing two bolts into the jacking holes provided.

Refitting

6 Refitting is the reverse of the removal procedure, noting the following:

a) *Ensure that the mating surfaces of the disc and hub are clean and flat.*
b) *Align (if applicable) the marks made on removal.*

c) *If a new disc has been fitted, use a suitable solvent to wipe any preservative coating from the disc before refitting the caliper.*
d) *Tighten the disc retaining screws, caliper bracket bolts and roadwheel nuts to their specified torque wrench settings.*

23 Handbrake lever – removal and refitting

Removal

1 With the vehicle parked on level ground, chock the roadwheels so that the vehicle cannot move.

2 From inside the vehicle, prise out the cover from the top of the rear centre console section to gain access to the two retaining screws. Undo the two screws and remove the rear console section.

3 Remove the handbrake lever rubber gaiter and disconnect the wiring connector from the lever warning lamp switch **(see illustration)**.

4 Slacken and remove the handbrake cable adjusting nut from the rear of the lever and

24.4 Handbrake cable adjusting nut (A), equaliser plate (B) and cable outer retaining plate bolts (C)

23.4 Handbrake mechanism layout

1 Handbrake lever	3 Compensator	6 Rear disc brake
2 Intermediate rod	4 Rear cables	7 Rear drum brake
	5 Adjusting nut	

undo the bolts securing the handbrake lever assembly to the floorpan **(see illustration)**.

5 Lift the handbrake assembly out of position, noting the spring which is fitted to the lever adjusting rod.

Refitting

6 Refitting is a reverse of the removal procedure. Prior to refitting the handbrake lever rubber gaiter, adjust the handbrake cable as described in Chapter 1A or 1B.

24 Handbrake cables – removal and refitting

Removal

1 Firmly chock the front wheels then jack up the rear of the vehicle and support it on axle stands (see *Jacking and Vehicle Support*). The handbrake cable consists of two sections (right- and left-hand), which are linked to the lever assembly by an equaliser plate. Each section can be removed individually.

2 From inside the vehicle, prise out the cover from the top of the rear centre console section to gain access to the two retaining screws. Undo the two screws and remove the rear console section.

3 Slacken and remove the handbrake cable adjusting nut from the rear of the lever and disconnect the equaliser plate, noting the spring which is fitted to the lever adjusting rod.

4 Undo the two bolts securing the cable outer retaining plate to the floorpan **(see illustration)**. Remove the retaining plate then detach the relevant cable inner from the equaliser plate and release the cable grommet from the floorpan.

5 On models equipped with rear disc brakes, working from underneath the vehicle, remove

24.6 Using a ring spanner to compress cable outer retaining tangs

the two brake caliper shield retaining bolts and remove the shield from the caliper. Extract the spring clip and clevis pin securing the handbrake cable to the caliper handbrake lever then remove the clip securing the cable outer to its mounting bracket and detach the handbrake cable from the caliper.

6 On models equipped with rear drum brakes, remove the relevant rear brake drum. Remove the trailing shoe retainer spring and pin, using a pair of pliers to press in the retainer clip until it can be rotated through 90° and released. Ease the trailing shoe out of the lower pivot point to release the tension of the return spring, then disconnect the lower return spring from both shoes. Disconnect the handbrake cable from the trailing shoe then use a ring spanner to compress the handbrake cable retaining tangs and withdraw the cable from the rear of the backplate **(see illustration)**.

7 On all models, release the main silencer from its three rubber mountings and carefully lower the tailpipe section to gain access to the heat shield. Undo the three heat shield retaining bolts and remove the shield from the vehicle underbody.

8 Work along the length of the cable section and remove all bolts securing the cable outer to the vehicle underbody and trailing arm. Once free, withdraw the cable from underneath the vehicle and, if necessary, repeat the procedure for the remaining cable section.

Refitting

9 Refitting is a reversal of the removal sequence noting the following:

25.4 Stop-lamp switch wiring connector (A) and locknut (B)

a) Lubricate all exposed linkages and cable pivots with a good quality multi-purpose grease.
b) Ensure the cable outer grommet is correctly located in the floorpan and that all retaining bolts are tightened to the specified torque.
c) On models with rear drum brakes, relocate the trailing shoe and refit the brake drum.
d) Prior to refitting the rear centre console section, adjust the handbrake cable as described in Chapter 1A or 1B.

25 Stop-lamp switch – removal, refitting and adjustment

Removal

1 Working inside the vehicle, undo the five screws and remove the right-hand lower facia panel.
2 Remove the screws and lower the fuse panel away from its mounting bracket.
3 Disconnect the wiring connector from the stop-lamp switch **(see illustration 25.4)**.
4 Slacken the stop-lamp switch locknut and unscrew the switch from the pedal bracket **(see illustration)**.

Refitting and adjustment

5 Screw the switch back into position in the mounting bracket.
6 Connect an ohmmeter across the stop-lamp switch terminals and screw the switch in until an open circuit is present between the switch terminals. Depress the pedal and check that continuity exists between the switch terminals as soon as the pedal is depressed. If necessary, reposition the switch until it operates as specified.
7 Once the stop-lamp switch is correctly adjusted, hold the switch stationary and tighten the locknut securely.
8 Connect the wiring connector to the switch and refit the fuse panel lower facia panel.

26 Anti-lock Braking System (ABS) – component removal and refitting

 Warning: After any work on the ABS system or components, system operation must be checked by and MG Rover dealer using special diagnostic equipment.

ABS hydraulic modulator

1 Disconnect the battery earth lead.
2 Apply the handbrake, chock the rear roadwheels, then jack up the front of the car and support it on axle stands (see *Jacking and Vehicle Support*)
3 If necessary, refer to Section 6 – connect a bleed tube to the bleed screw on the front

right-hand caliper. Place the other end of the tube in a container. Open the bleed screw and pump the brake pedal to expel fluid from the master cylinder. Tighten the bleed screw.
4 Repeat the above operation at the left-hand caliper.
5 Pull the clip outwards, and disconnect the multi-plug from the modulator ECU.
6 Clean around the pipe connections, and position cloths under the modulator to absorb fluid spills.
7 Disconnect four pipes from the top of the modulator, and two pipes from the front of the modulator **(see illustration)**.
Caution: Make a note of how the six pipes are connected to the modulator. Plug the connections immediately after disconnection.
8 Slacken two nuts securing the modulator to the mounting bracket. Release the lower bush from the mounting bracket spigot, and remove the modulator.
Caution: do not attempt to dismantle the modulator – special equipment is needed.
9 Refitting is a reversal of the removal procedure, noting:
  Use a torque wrench with suitable adapters to tighten mounting nuts and pipe connections to the specified torque.
  Ensure that the six pipes are correctly connected as noted before removal.
  Bleed the brake system – see Section 6.
  Have the operation of the ABS system tested by an MG Rover dealer.

Front wheel sensor

10 Chock the rear wheels, firmly apply the handbrake, jack up the front of the vehicle and support on axle stands (see *Jacking and Vehicle Support*). Remove the appropriate front roadwheel.
11 From inside the engine compartment, disconnect the relevant sensor wiring connector and displace the sensor wiring grommet.
12 From underneath the vehicle, pull the sensor wiring lead through the wing valance then undo the sensor lead bracket retaining bolts and remove the brackets.
13 Slacken and remove the two bolts securing the sensor unit to the wheel hub then remove the sensor and lead assembly.

26.7 Disconnect six pipes from modulator

14 Refitting is the reverse of the removal procedure, noting the following:

a) *Ensure that the sensor and hub sealing faces are clean then refit the sensor and tighten its retaining bolts to the specified torque.*

b) *Ensure the sensor wiring is correctly routed and all bracket retaining bolts are tightened to the specified torque.*

Rear wheel sensor

Models with disc brakes

15 Chock the front wheels then jack up the rear of the vehicle and support it on axle stands (see *Jacking and Vehicle Support*). Remove the appropriate roadwheel.

16 Trace the wiring back from the sensor to the wiring connector then free the connector from its retaining clips and disconnect it.

17 Undo the sensor lead bracket retaining bolts and remove the brackets.

18 Slacken and remove the bolt securing the strap to the sensor cover then undo the sensor cover retaining bolts and remove the cover.

19 Undo the two screws securing the sensor to the rear hub assembly and remove it from the vehicle, along with the shim which is fitted behind it.

20 Refitting is the reverse of the removal procedure, noting the following:

a) *Ensure the sensor and hub sealing faces are clean, then install the sensor and shim and tighten the sensor retaining screws to the specified torque.*

b) *Refit the sensor cover, cover strap retaining bolt and sensor lead brackets, then tighten all retaining bolts to the specified torque.*

c) *Reconnect the sensor lead wiring connector and refit the connector to its retaining clip.*

Models with drum brakes

21 With reference to Sections 16 and 17, remove the relevant brake drum and both brake shoes from the backplate.

22 Work along the length of the ABS sensor wiring and release it from the clips on the rear suspension components. Locate the wiring connector, to the rear of the axle beam mounting. Prise the connector from its retaining clip and unplug it.

23 Slacken and withdraw the two mounting bolts, then lift the sensor and adapter assembly from the brake backplate.

24 Prise the sensor wiring grommet from the backplate, then withdraw the sensor and adapter assembly through the backplate aperture.

25 Loosen the lockscrew and slide sensor body from the adapter.

26 Fit the new sensor to the adapter, then pass the assembly through the backplate aperture and press the wiring grommet into place. Fit and tighten the two retaining bolts to the specified torque.

27 Loosen the adapter lockscrew, then using a feeler blade, adjust the position of the sensor in the adapter so that the clearance between the tip of the sensor and the reluctor ring is as listed in the Specifications. On completion, tighten the adapter lockscrew.

28 The remainder of the refitting procedure is a reversal of removal, noting the following points:

a) *Ensure that the sensor wiring connector is securely refitted.*

b) *Press the sensor wiring and connector firmly into their retaining clips.*

c) *Refit the brake shoes and drum with reference to Sections 16 and 17 respectively.*

Reluctor rings

29 The reluctor rings are not available as separate items. The front rings are available only as an integral part of the outer constant velocity joint assembly and the rear rings are available only as an integral part of the rear hub.

Relays

30 Both the solenoid relay and return pump relay are located in the modulator block assembly. To gain access to them, undo the relay cover retaining screw and lift off the cover. Either relay can then be simply pulled out of position. Refer to Chapter 12 for further information on relays.

27 Brake servo vacuum pump (diesel models) – removal and refitting

Removal

1 Disconnect the battery negative cable and position it away from the terminal.

2 Raise the front of the car, support it securely on axle stands (see *Jacking and Vehicle Support*) and remove the right-hand front roadwheel.

3 Remove the fixings and lower the undertray away from the underside of the engine compartment.

4 Remove the auxiliary drivebelt with reference to Chapter 10, Section 22.

5 Position a trolley jack under the engine and place a wooden block in the jack head. Raise the jack so that it is just supporting the weight of the engine.

6 Refer to Chapter 2B and remove the right-hand engine mounting bracket.

7 Unplug the multiway wiring connector from the rear of the alternator, then remove the nut and disconnect the main battery cable from the alternator stud terminal.

8 Release the clip and disconnect the vacuum hose from the pump port.

9 Slacken the clip and disconnect the vacuum pump oil return hose from the sump pipe.

Caution: Be prepared for some oil spillage; position a drain container under the union and pad the surrounding area with absorbent rags.

10 Undo the union and disconnect the vacuum pump oil supply pipe from the cylinder block. Again, be prepared for some oil spillage **(see illustration)**.

11 Lift the right-hand end of the engine slightly, by raising the trolley jack to gain access to the alternator mounting bolts. Slacken and withdraw the bolts and remove the alternator from its mounting bracket **(see illustrations)**.

12 Remove the alternator from the engine bay.

13 Remove the four securing bolts and

27.10 Vacuum pump oil supply pipe (A) and return hose (B)

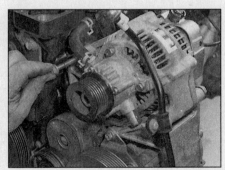

27.11a Alternator/vacuum pump upper mounting bolt

27.11b Alternator/vacuum pump upper mounting nut and bolt (arrowed)

27.13 Remove the four securing bolts (arrowed) and detach the vacuum pump from the front of the alternator

detach the vacuum pump from the front of the alternator **(see illustration)**.

Refitting

14 Refitting is a reversal of removal, noting the following points:

a) *Ensure that the vacuum pump-to-alternator bolts are tightened to the specified torque.*

b) *Tighten the alternator mounting bolts to the specified torque (see Chapter 5A).*

c) *Ensure that all oil supply and return unions are clean before reconnection, and tighten the union nuts securely.*

d) *Refit the right-hand engine mountings with reference to Chapter 2B.*

e) *Refit the auxiliary drivebelt with reference to Chapter 10.*

Chapter 10
Suspension and steering

Contents

Degrees of difficulty

Easy, suitable for novice with little experience	Fairly easy, suitable for beginner with some experience	Fairly difficult, suitable for competent DIY mechanic	Difficult, suitable for experienced DIY mechanic 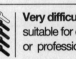	Very difficult, suitable for expert DIY or professional

Specifications

Front suspension

Type	Fully independent, MacPherson struts, with dampers and coil springs. Anti-roll bar fitted
Front coil springs:	
Total coils:	
R25	5.5
MG ZR	4.5
Wire diameter:	
R25	13.95 mm ± 0.05 mm
MG ZR	14.341 mm ± 0.05 mm
Nominal height to wheel arch from hub centre – at unladen weight:	
R25	386 mm ± 10 mm
MG ZR	366 mm ± 10 mm

Rear suspension

Type	Independent, MacPherson type struts, with dampers and coil springs, attached to beam axle with trailing arms
Rear coil springs:	
Total coils:	
R25	8.4
MG ZR	8.0
Wire diameter:	
R25	10.50 mm ± 0.05 mm
MG ZR	11.24 mm ± 0.05 mm
Nominal height to wheel arch from hub centre – at unladen weight:	
R25	386 mm ± 10 mm
MG ZR	366 mm ± 10 mm

Steering

Type	Power-assisted rack and pinion, linear ratio system, positive centre feel
Turns lock to lock:	
R25	3.0
MG ZR	2.8

Wheel alignment and steering angles – unladen condition

Front:
  R25:
    Camber angle . . . .   -0.33° ± 0.75°
    Castor angle . . . .   1.70° ± 1°
    King pin inclination . . . .   12.12°
    Wheel alignment – total . . . .   0° ± 0.25°
  MG ZR:
    Camber angle . . . .   -0.66° ± 0.75°
    Castor angle . . . .   2.20° ± 1°
    King pin inclination . . . .   12.40°
    Wheel alignment – total . . . .   0° ± 0.25°
  Rear (all models):
    Camber angle . . . .   -0.33° ± 0.75°
    Thrust angle . . . .   0° ± 0.1°
    Wheel alignment – total . . . .   0.27° ± 0.25°

Roadwheels

Steel . . . .   5.5J x R14
Alloy . . . .   5.5J x R14 (rough terrain RTS type), 6.0 x R15, 6.5 x R16, 7.0 x R17
Spare:
  Full size (steel) . . . .   6.0J x R15, 5.5J x R14
  Space saver (steel) . . . .   3.5 x R15
Caution: The space saver spare wheel is for temporary use only. When in use, max. road speed is 50 mph (80 km/h). Only one space saver wheel may be fitted at any one time.

Tyres

Type . . . .   Tubeless, steel braced radial
Wheel size:
  5.5J x 14 steel wheel 175/65 R14 82T
  5.5J x 14 alloy wheel 185/55 R14 86T
  6.0J x 15 alloy wheel 185/55 R15 82H
  6.5J x 16 alloy wheel 205/45 R16 83V, 205/50 R16 87H
  7.0J x 17 alloy wheel 205/45 R17 84V
  3.5 x 15 space saver wheel t125/80 R15 95M
Tyre pressures . . . .   See end of *Weekly checks* on page 0•18

Torque wrench settings

	Nm	lbf ft
Rear suspension		
Beam axle pivot bush bolt	100	74
Beam axle-to-body bolts	100	74
Damper mounting plate nuts**	38	28
Damper-to-beam axle bolt**	80	59
Damper-to-mounting plate self-locking nut	29	21
Hub shaft nut*	185	137
Stub axle-to-beam axle bolts	45	33
Steering		
Steering arm balljoint nut	45	33
Steering column lower clamp bolt/nut	22	16
Steering column universal joint bolts	28	21
Steering column upper bracket bolts/nuts	15	11
Steering pipe clip	9	7
Steering rack clamp bolts	38	28
Steering rack feed pipe union	37	27
Steering rack return pipe union	28	21
Steering wheel nut*	50	37
Track rod end locknut	45	33
Petrol engines:		
Power steering pump drivebelt tensioner bolts	25	18
Power steering pump outlet hose union	20	15
Power steering pump pulley bolts	9	7
Power steering pump-to-mounting bracket nuts and bolts	25	18
Diesel engines:		
High pressure hose union to power steering pump	20	15
Power steering pump oil feed flange bolts	10	7
Power steering pump pulley bolts*	10	7
Power steering pump-to-coolant pump bolts	25	18
Power steering pump-to-mounting bracket bolts	25	18

Torque wrench settings (continued)

	Nm	lbf ft
Front suspension		
Anti-roll bar clamp-to-rear beam bolts	22	16
Anti-roll bar link-to-lower arm bolt	60	44
Anti-roll bar-to-link bolt	45	33
Beam-to-body bolts	100	74
Damper nut	40	30
Damper top mounting nuts**	30	22
Damper-to-hub clamp bolt**	80	59
Lower arm balljoint nut	55	41
Lower arm-to-rear beam pivot bolt **	60	44
Tie-rod-to-front beam nut	45	33
Tie-rod-to-lower arm bolts	80	59
Roadwheels		
Roadwheel nuts	110	81

* Fit new nuts/bolts
** Tighten with vehicle weight on suspension

1.1 Front suspension components

1 Rubber cover
2 Self-locking nut
3 Washer
4 Strut upper mounting nut
5 Upper mounting plate
6 Bearing
7 Upper spring seat
8 Dust cover
9 Coil spring
10 Washer
11 Rubber damper stop
12 Strut
13 Strut lower clamp bolt
14 Tie bar
15 Bolt – tie bar to lower arm
16 Nut – tie bar to subframe
17 Flanged washer
18 Mounting bush
19 Spacer
20 Driveshaft retaining nut
21 Brake disc
22 Disc retaining screw
23 Hub
24 Disc shield
25 Bolt
26 Circlip
27 Hub bearing
28 Swivel hub
29 Driveshaft
30 Suspension lower arm
31 Balljoint retaining nut
32 Lower arm pivot bush
33 Lower arm pivot bolt
34 Anti-roll bar connecting link
35 Bolt
36 Nut
37 Bolt – anti-roll bar connecting
   link to lower arm
38 Anti-roll bar
39 Mounting rubber
40 Mounting clamp
41 Bolt
42 Split pin
43 Track rod balljoint

H29783

1.2 Rear suspension components (model with drum brakes shown – with disc brakes similar)

1 Beam axle
2 Stub axle
3 Brake shoe and backplate assembly
4 Hub and bearing assembly
5 Spacer
6 Hub nut
7 Dust cap
8 Brake drum
9 Anti-roll bar
10 Anti-roll bar collar
11 Beam axle pivot bush
12 Beam axle pivot mounting bracket
13 Beam axle pivot mounting bolt

H29821

1 General information and precautions

General information

The independent front suspension is of the MacPherson strut type, incorporating coil springs and integral telescopic shock absorbers **(see illustration 1.1 on previous page)**. The MacPherson struts are located by transverse suspension lower arms, which utilise rubber inner mounting bushes and incorporate a balljoint at the outer ends, and forward-facing longitudinal tie bars. Both suspension lower arms are connected to an anti-roll bar via a short drop link. The front swivel hubs, which carry the wheel bearings, brake calipers and the hub/disc assemblies, are bolted to the MacPherson struts and connected to the lower arms via the balljoints.

The rear suspension is of the torsion beam type, utilising tubular steel trailing arms linked via a single twist beam axle **(see illustration 1.2)**. The roadwheel stub axles are bolted to the ends of the trailing arms. Each trailing arm is mounted on the vehicle underbody at an angle by means of a large rubber bush, which incorporates a combination of voids and steel interleaving. This construction allows the entire trailing arm and torsion beam assembly to rotate about one mounting slightly during cornering; the amount of rotation is governed by the degree to which the rear of the vehicle rolls. The net effect is that the rear wheels tend to steer in phase with the front wheels during hard cornering, thus improving the vehicle's grip and handling. The rear suspension struts incorporate coil springs and integral telescopic shock absorbers and are mounted onto the rear lower lateral link via a rubber mounting bush.

H44650

1.3 Steering wheel components

1 Airbag module
2 Steering wheel
3 Self locking nut
4 Torx bolt
5 Screw – self-tapping
6 Rotary coupler
7 Screw
8 Cancel cam – indicator switch
9 Lighting, indicators and wiper switch
10 Shear bolt
11 Bracket – steering lock/starter switch assembly
12 Steering lock assembly
13 Shroud – upper
14 Shroud – lower
15 Screw

1.4 Steering column components

1 Cover – steering joint
2 Clip – joint cover
3 Screw
4 Retainer collar – steering column
5 Lower clamp – upper half
6 Bolt – lower clamp
7 Bolt and lock-washer
8 Universal joint
9 Bolt
10 Lower clamp – upper half
11 Steering column assembly

H44649

To provide driver protection in a frontal collision, the steering wheel is an energy absorbing design, and an air bag is installed behind the padded centre cover **(see illustration 1.3)**.

The steering column has a two-piece collapsible upper section, and a solid lower shaft, with a universal joint at each end. The lower joint is attached to the steering rack input shaft **(see illustration 1.4)**. In an impact, the column mountings are deigned to absorb energy by deforming and/or moving. At the lower end, the securing clamp allows the column to slide under impact load. Welded to the upper end of the column is a claw. Attached to the body, in line with the claw, is an energy absorbing plate. In an impact, the column will move forward, and the claw will contact the plate, which absorbs energy as it deforms.

Column rake/steering wheel height is adjustable.

The steering gear is a rack and pinion design, with integral power assistance **(see illustration 1.6)**. The rack unit is attached to the engine compartment bulkhead, via the suspension rear beam. Steering effort is

1.6 Steering rack components

Note: On some models the pipe connections are on the upper part of the rack

1 Track rod end balljoint
2 Collar
3 Bush
4 Steering gear
5 Fluid pipes
6 Mounting rubber
7 Clamp
8 Left-hand mounting bolt
9 Right-hand mounting bolt
10 Washer
11 Bush

H29788

2.8 Release track rod ball pin

2.11 Removing the swivel hub assembly

transmitted to the steering arms via track rods with adjustable balljoints at the steering arms. Power assistance is provided by hydraulic fluid pressurised by a roller vane pump, belt driven from the crankshaft pulley. The direction of fluid flow – to one end of the rack or the other – is controlled by a flow control valve, which is rotated when the steering wheel is turned. The amount of power assistance provided is dependent on how far the control valve is opened and, in turn, this is dependent on the steering effort required to turn the front roadwheels. During low speed manoeuvres, when steering effort is high, the valve opening will be greater to provide more power assistance. At high speed, when steering movements are small and forces are low, the valve may not open at all, or may open slightly. With no valve opening, the rack responds as a unit with no power assistance, and provides 'positive centre feel' for stable driving.

Precautions

The driveshaft and hub nuts are tightened to a very high torque – ensure the car is securely supported when loosening and tightening them.

A number of precautions must be observed when working on the steering components of vehicles equipped with a Supplementary Restraint System (SRS); these are listed in Chapter 12.

3.2 Press out the drive flange

2 Front swivel hub assembly – removal and refitting

Note: *The following new parts are needed – hub to driveshaft nut, track rod balljoint nut, split pin for the suspension lower arm nut.*

Removal

1 Chock the rear wheels, firmly apply the handbrake then jack up the front of the vehicle and support it on axle stands (see *Jacking and Vehicle Support*). Remove the appropriate front roadwheel.
2 Using a hammer and suitable chisel-nosed tool, tap up the staking securing the driveshaft retaining nut to the groove in the CV joint (refer to Chapter 8 for details).
3 Have an assistant firmly depress the footbrake then, using a socket and extension bar, slacken and remove the driveshaft retaining nut. Discard the nut; a new nut must be obtained for reassembly.
4 Remove the securing bolt and detach the brake hose mounting bracket from the base of the suspension strut. If the hub bearings are to be disturbed, remove the brake disc. If not, undo the two bolts securing the caliper mounting bracket to the hub and slide the caliper off the disc. Tie the caliper to the suspension strut to avoid placing any strain on the brake hose.
5 On models equipped with ABS, remove the front wheel sensor.
6 Slacken and remove the bolt and washer securing the anti-roll bar drop link to the suspension lower arm and undo the two bolts securing the tie bar to the lower arm.
7 Slacken the self-locking nut securing the track rod balljoint to the steering arm, until it is flush with the end of the ball pin threads.
Caution: Take care not to damage the balljoint rubber boot.
8 Using a suitable taper joint separator, release the ball pin from the steering arm. Remove the nut, and disconnect the track rod end **(see illustration)**.
9 Remove and discard the split pin from the castellated nut securing the suspension lower arm to the hub.

Caution: Take care not to damage the balljoint rubber boot.
10 Slacken the nut until it is flush with the end of the ball pin threads. Using a suitable taper joint separator, break the joint. Remove the nut, and disconnect the suspension arm.
11 Remove the clamp bolt securing the front hub to the suspension strut. Release the hub from the strut **(see illustration)**. Pull the hub outwards to release it from the driveshaft. Tie-up the driveshaft to prevent strain on the driveshaft joint.

Refitting

12 Refitting is a reversal of the removal procedure, noting:
 Ensure that the lug on the base of the suspension strut engages correctly with the slot on the hub assembly clamp.
 Use a torque wrench to tighten all nuts and bolts to the specified torque.
 After tightening the new driveshaft nut, stake it securely into the driveshaft using a suitable punch.
 Use a new self-locking nut to secure the track rod balljoint.
 Use a new split pin to secure the suspension lower arm castellated nut.
 Have the front wheel alignment checked by an MG Rover dealer or specialist.

3 Front hub bearings – removal and refitting

Note: *The front hub bearing is a sealed, pre-adjusted and pre-lubricated, double-row roller type, and is intended to last the vehicle's entire service life without maintenance or attention. Do not attempt to remove the bearing unless absolutely necessary, as it will probably be damaged during the removal operation. Never overtighten the driveshaft nut beyond the specified torque wrench setting in an attempt to 'adjust' the bearing.*
Note: *A press will be required to dismantle and rebuild the hub assembly. If such a tool is not available, a large bench vice and suitable spacers (such as large sockets) will serve as an adequate substitute. The service tool numbers for the special Rover mandrels are given in the accompanying illustrations. The bearing's inner races are an interference fit on the hub. If the outboard inner race remains on the hub when it is pressed out of the hub carrier, a proprietary knife-edged bearing puller will be required to remove it.*

Removal

Note: *The following new parts are needed – bearing kit containing bearing and circlip.*
1 Remove the swivel hub assembly – see Section 2. Remove the brake disc shield.
2 Press out the drive flange from the hub **(see illustration). Note:** *Part of the bearing inner track will remain on the drive flange.*

3.5 Press out bearing from hub

3.8 Press hub onto bearing

3.10 Press the drive flange into the hub

3 Clamp the drive flange securely in a vice and, using a suitable bearing puller, remove the bearing inner track from the drive flange.

4 Remove and discard the circlip securing the bearing in the front hub.

5 Position the swivel hub under a press and using suitable spacers – such as large sockets – press the bearing from the hub. Discard the bearing **(see illustration)**.

Refitting

6 Clean the drive flange and swivel hub. Check for cracks or other damage – renew any damaged component. Polish away any burrs or raised edges.

7 Check the condition of the roadwheel studs. Renew any with damaged or worn threads.

8 Position the new bearing on a suitable mandrel which supports the bearing. Locate the swivel hub on the bearing, and carefully press the hub onto the bearing **(see illustration)**.

9 Fit the new circlip.

10 Fully supporting the bearing inner race, press the drive flange into the hub **(see illustration)**.

11 Fit the brake disc shield.

12 Fit the swivel hub assembly – see Section 2.

---

4 Front suspension strut –
removal, overhaul and refitting

Caution: If renewing the strut damper during overhaul, both the left- and right-hand dampers should be renewed as a pair, to preserve the handling characteristics of the vehicle.

Note: *Before attempting to dismantle the front suspension strut, a suitable tool to hold the coil spring in compression must be obtained. Adjustable coil spring compressors are readily available and are recommended for this operation. Any attempt to dismantle the strut without such a tool is likely to result in damage or personal injury. In addition, a suitable crow's-foot adapter will be needed to allow the strut top mounting nut to be tightened to the correct torque during reassembly.*

Removal

1 Chock the rear wheels, firmly apply the handbrake, then jack up the front of the vehicle and support on axle stands (see *Jacking and Vehicle Support*). Remove the appropriate roadwheel.

2 Slacken and remove the bolt and washer securing the anti-roll bar drop link to the

suspension lower arm (see Section 6 for details).

3 Undo the bolt securing the brake hose retaining clamp to the strut, then remove the clamp and free the flexible hose **(see illustration)**.

4 Slacken the swivel hub-to-suspension strut clamp bolt, then insert a stout pry bar between the clamp bolt flanges at the rear of the swivel hub. Use the bar to prise the flanges apart slightly, so that the base of the strut is released from the swivel hub.

5 Carefully ease the swivel hub assembly off the lower end of the strut by pressing down on the suspension lower arm and pivoting the top of the swivel hub towards you. Avoid straining the driveshaft CV joint as you do this.

6 Working in the engine compartment, remove the strut rubber dust cover. Use chalk or a marker pen to mark the relative positions of the suspension strut upper mounting and bodywork **(see illustration)**.

7 Support the strut inside the wheelarch, then undo the three upper mounting nuts – DO NOT slacken or remove the strut centre nut at this stage. Lower the strut assembly away from the bodywork and out of the wheelarch. Note the seal which is fitted between the upper mounting plate and vehicle body **(see illustration)**.

4.3 Removing the bolt securing the brake hose to suspension strut

4.6 Remove the rubber cover and strut upper mounting nuts (arrowed)

4.7 Removing a front suspension strut

4.9 Compress the coil spring with a suitable pair of spring compressors . . .

4.10 . . . and remove the upper mounting nut whilst retaining the piston with an Allen key

4.21 Align the suspension strut lug with the slot in the swivel hub (arrowed)

Caution: *Do not attempt to slacken or remove the strut centre nut until the coil spring is compressed using suitable compressors.*

Overhaul

8 With the strut removed from the vehicle, clean away all external dirt then mount it upright in a bench vice, with the lower end of the strut clamped in the vice jaws.

9 Fit the spring compressor and compress the coil spring until all tension is relieved from the upper mounting plate **(see illustration)**.

10 Slacken the upper mounting retaining nut with a ring spanner; counterhold the damper rod, using a suitable Allen key or hex bit, as the nut is unscrewed – do not allow the rod to rotate inside the damper, as this may damage the piston seal **(see illustration)**.

11 Remove the nut and upper cup washer, followed by the mounting plate/bearing, upper spring seat and lower cup washer. Slide the bump stop rubber off the damper piston rod, then lift off the coil spring together with the piston dust cover and separate the two components. Make a careful note of the order of removal to aid reassembly.

12 With the strut assembly completely dismantled, examine all components for wear, damage or corrosion, and check the mounting plate/bearing for smoothness of rotation. Renew any component displaying signs of deterioration.

13 Examine the damper for signs of fluid leakage. Check the piston rod for signs of pitting along its entire length and check the strut body for signs of damage or corrosion. Test the operation of the strut, while holding it in an upright position, by moving the piston through several full-length strokes; the resistance felt should be smooth and continuous. Now operate the piston rod through short strokes of 50 to 100 mm. If fluid has leaked from the damper, the piston will have an amount of undamped 'freeplay' at the end of its travel. If this is the case, or if there are any visible signs of wear, damage or corrosion, renewal of the strut will be necessary.

14 If any doubt exists about the condition of the coil spring, carefully remove the spring compressors and check the spring for

distortion, cracking or excessive corrosion. Since no minimum free length is specified by Rover, the only way to check the tension of the spring is to compare it to a new component. Renew the spring if it is damaged or distorted or there is any doubt as to its condition.

15 Inspect all other components for signs of damage or deterioration and renew any that are suspect.

16 If new damper strut insert is being fitted, prime the damper (with reference to the manufacturer's instructions) by operating the piston rod through several full-length strokes.

17 Pass the compressed coil spring over the top of the damper piston rod and place it in position on the lower spring seat, ensuring that the end of the spring is correctly located in the lower spring seat recess. Fit the damper dust cover over the top of the coil spring.

18 Slide the bump stop rubber over the end of the damper piston rod. Fit the lower cup washer, followed by the upper spring seat, the mounting plate/bearing and the upper cup washer. Ensure that the upper end of the coil spring is correctly located in the recess in the upper spring seat, then fit the new damper rod top nut and tighten it to the specified torque setting. Note that you will need to fit a crow's-foot adapter to the torque wrench to allow the damper rod nut to be tightened to the correct torque. Counterhold the damper rod, using a suitable Allen key or hex bit, as the nut is tightened. Remove the spring compressor.

Caution: *Do not allow the rod to rotate*

5.2 Remove the anti-roll bar-to-drop link bolts

inside the damper, as this may damage the piston seal.

Refitting

19 Manoeuvre the strut assembly into position under the wheel arch, passing the three mounting plate studs through the holes in the suspension turret. Use the markings made during removal to ensure that the strut to bodywork alignment is correct.

20 Fit the three top mounting nuts loosely – do not tighten them at this stage.

21 Engage the lower end of the strut with the hub carrier, ensuring that the locating lug at the base of the strut slots between the clamp bolt flanges at the rear of the swivel hub **(see illustration)**. Insert the clamp bolt, then fit the nut finger-tight.

22 Refit the brake hydraulic line bracket to the base of the strut and tighten the securing bolt.

23 Refit the anti-roll bar drop link to the suspension lower arm, with reference to Section 6.

24 Refit the roadwheel, lower the vehicle to the ground and tighten the roadwheel nuts to the specified torque.

25 Tighten the three strut upper mounting nuts to the specified torque, then press the dust cover into position. Tighten the damper-to-hub clamp bolts to the specified torque.

26 Have the front wheel alignment checked (and if necessary, adjusted) by a Rover dealer or a tyre specialist at the earliest opportunity.

---

5 Anti-roll bars –
removal and refitting

Front anti-roll bar

Removal

1 Chock the rear wheels, firmly apply the handbrake then jack up the front of the vehicle and support it on axle stands (see *Jacking and Vehicle Support*).

2 Slacken and remove the nuts and washers securing each end of the anti-roll bar to the drop links and remove the bolts **(see illustration)**.

5.3 Correct position of the anti-roll bar mounting bush split (arrowed)

3 Mark the location of the clamp bushes on the bar to aid refitting, then undo the mounting clamp retaining bolts. Lower the clamps away from the anti-roll bar. Make a note of the fitted position of the rubber bush splits to ensure that they are positioned correctly on refitting **(see illustration)**. Manoeuvre the anti-roll bar away from the underside of the vehicle.

4 Carefully examine the anti-roll bar components for signs of wear, damage or deterioration, paying particular attention to the mounting rubbers. Renew worn components as necessary.

Refitting

5 Manoeuvre the anti-roll bar into position under the vehicle and refit the drop link bolts. Refit the washers and tighten the nuts, finger-tight only.

6 Smear the bore of the bush with rubber grease, then lever the bar down and slide the bushes into position on the anti-roll bar. Ensure that the bush splits are facing the rear of the vehicle, then align them with the marks made during removal.

7 Refit the anti-roll bar mounting clamps and tighten the retaining bolts to the specified torque setting, then tighten the anti-roll bar-to-drop link bolts to the specified torque.

8 Lower the car to the ground, then rock it from side to side to settle the anti-roll bar in its mountings.

Rear anti-roll bar

Removal

9 Chock the front wheels, then jack up the rear of the vehicle and support it on axle stands (see *Jacking and Vehicle Support*).

10 Remove the nuts and washers securing each end of the anti-roll bar to the rear axle assembly **(see illustration)**.

11 Pull the anti-roll bar towards the front of the vehicle to release it from the beam axle. Manoeuvre the anti-roll bar away from the underside of the vehicle.

12 Carefully examine the anti-roll bar components for signs of wear, damage or deterioration, paying particular attention to the mounting rubbers and tubular collar. Renew worn components as necessary.

Refitting

13 Fit the tubular collars into the mounting holes at the base of the trailing arms.

14 Fit the washers to the anti-roll bar, then manoeuvre the anti-roll bar into position under the vehicle. Apply a light coating of grease to the anti-roll bar spigots and pass the spigots through the spacers. Refit the washers, then fit the retaining nuts and tighten them securely.

15 Lower the car to the ground, then rock it from side to side to settle the anti-roll bar in its mountings.

6 Front anti-roll bar drop link – removal and refitting

Removal

1 Chock the rear wheels, firmly apply the handbrake, jack up the front of the vehicle and support on axle stands (see *Jacking and Vehicle Support*). Remove the appropriate front roadwheel.

2 From underneath the vehicle, remove the bolt and washer securing the drop link to the suspension lower arm **(see illustration)**.

3 Remove the nut and washer securing the drop link to the anti-roll bar, then withdraw the bolt and remove the drop link from under the vehicle.

Refitting

4 Refitting is the reverse of the removal sequence. Tighten both the drop link bolts to the specified torque setting.

7 Front suspension tie bar – removal and refitting

Removal

1 Chock the rear wheels, firmly apply the handbrake, jack up the front of the vehicle and support on axle stands (see *Jacking and Vehicle Support*). Remove the appropriate front roadwheel.

7.2 Tie bar retaining nut is accessed from front of subframe

5.10 Remove the nuts (arrowed) and washers securing each end of the anti-roll bar to the rear axle assembly

6.2 Anti-roll bar drop link

2 Undo the nut securing the front of the tie bar to the front suspension beam then remove the flanged washer and mounting bush, noting the direction the flange faces **(see illustration)**.

3 Undo the two bolts securing the tie bar to the suspension lower arm, then remove the rod from the vehicle and slide the spacer, mounting bush and flanged washer off the tie bar **(see illustration)**.

4 Examine all the components for signs of wear or damage, paying particular attention to the mounting bushes and tie bar threads. Renew components as necessary **(see illustration)**.

Refitting

5 Slide the flange washer, mounting bush and spacer onto the tie bar threads. Ensure that

7.3 Tie bar-to-suspension lower arm bolts (arrowed)

7.4 Renew tie bar mounting bushes (arrowed) if damaged

7.5 Fit flange washer, spacer and mounting bush onto tie bar . . .

7.6 . . . then refit tie bar to subframe and install second mounting bush and flange washer

the flange of the washer is facing away from the mounting bush and that the rounded surface of the bush is facing the washer **(see illustration)**.

6 Refit the tie bar to the front suspension beam and fit the second mounting bush and flanged washer. Ensure the flat surface of the mounting bush is facing the subframe and that the flange of the washer is facing away from the mounting bush, then refit the tie bar nut, tightening it finger-tight **(see illustration)**.

7 Refit the tie bar-to-suspension lower arm bolts and tighten them to the specified torque, then tighten the tie bar retaining nut to the specified torque setting.

8 Refit the roadwheel, then lower the vehicle to the ground and tighten the roadwheel nuts to the specified torque.

9 Have the front wheel alignment checked (and if necessary, adjusted) by a Rover dealer or a tyre specialist at the earliest opportunity.

8 Front suspension lower arm – removal and refitting

Note: *The lower arm balljoint is an integral part of the arm, and cannot be renewed separately. Renewal of the arm inner bush requires special tools and should normally be done by an MG Rover dealer.*

Removal

1 Chock the rear wheels, jack up the front of the vehicle and support it securely on axle stands (see *Jacking and Vehicle Support*). Remove the front roadwheels.

2 Remove the bolts and washers securing the anti-roll bar drop link to the suspension lower arm. Remove the two bolts securing the tie bar to the suspension lower arm.

3 Remove and discard the split pin from the castellated nut securing the suspension lower arm ball pin to the hub.

4 Slacken the nut until it is flush with the end of the ball pin threads. Using a suitable taper joint separator, break the joint. Remove the nut, and disconnect the suspension arm **(see illustration)**.

Caution: Take care not to damage the balljoint rubber boot.

5 Remove the through-bolt securing the lower arm to the suspension rear beam, and remove the arm **(see illustration)**.

6 If the inner bush is damaged, and the special tools are available, renew the bush **(see illustration)**.

Refitting

7 Refitting is a reversal of the removal procedure, noting:

Use a torque wrench to tighten all nuts and bolts to the specified torque.

Fit a new split pin to the castellated nut.

Have the front wheel alignment checked (and if necessary, adjusted) by a Rover dealer or a tyre specialist at the earliest opportunity.

Caution: To ensure that the arm inner bush is not in stress when the vehicle is at normal ride height, do not finally tighten the bush through-bolt until the roadwheels

8.4 Disconnect the lower arm ball pin

8.5 Remove the through-bolt

8.6 Renew lower arm bush

A Removing old bush   *B Fitting new bush*

9.3a Remove the tie bar securing nut . . .

9.3b . . . washers . . .

9.3c . . . and bushes

are on the ground, and the suspension has been settled by moving the front end of the vehicle up and down.

9 Front suspension front beam – removal and refitting

Removal

1 Chock the rear wheels, firmly apply the handbrake, jack up the front of the vehicle and support on axle stands (see *Jacking and Vehicle Support*). Remove both front roadwheels to improve access.

2 On diesel-engined models, remove the screws and lower the undertray away from the engine compartment.

3 With reference to Section 7, remove the nuts, bushes and cupped washers from the ends of both tie bars **(see illustrations)**.

4 Slacken and withdraw the four securing bolts (two at either end of the beam), then lower the beam away from the underside of the vehicle **(see illustrations)**.

Refitting

5 Refitting is a reversal of removal, noting the following points:

a) *Thoroughly clean the mating surface between the suspension beam and the vehicle's bodywork.*

b) *Tighten the suspension beam securing bolts to the specified torque.*

c) *Refit the tie bars to the front suspension beam with reference to Section 7.*

d) *Have the front wheel alignment checked (and if necessary, adjusted) by a Rover dealer or a tyre specialist at the earliest opportunity.*

10 Front suspension rear beam – removal and refitting

Removal

1 Chock the rear wheels and apply the handbrake. Jack up the front of the vehicle, and support securely on axle stands (see *Jacking*

9.4a Slacken and withdraw the four securing bolts . . .

and Vehicle Support). Remove both front roadwheels.

2 Remove the exhaust front pipe – see Chapter 4A or 4B.

3 Remove the steering rack – see Section 21.

4 Remove two through-bolts securing the suspension lower arms the rear beam **(see illustration 8.5)**.

5 Remove two through-bolts securing the drop links to the anti-roll bar.

6 Remove the bolt securing the power steering pipe to the rear beam.

7 Remove the bolt securing the clutch cable bracket to the rear beam.

8 On petrol-engine models, release the evaporative canister vent hose from the rear beam.

9 Slacken four bolts – two at each side – securing the beam to the body. Lower the beam slightly to gain access to the bolt securing the power steering pipe to the beam, and remove the bolt.

10 Position a trolley jack to just take the weight of the beam. Remove the four beam attachment bolts **(see illustration)**.

11 Disengage the lower arms from the beam, and lower the beam.

Refitting

12 Place the beam on the trolley jack, and raise into position. Screw in the four beam securing bolts a few turns.

13 Engage the suspension lower arms, and fit the through-bolts. Screw on the nuts a few turns.

14 Locate the power steering pipe on the beam, and fit and tighten the securing bolt.

15 Use a torque wrench to tighten the four

9.4b . . . then lower the beam away from the underside of the vehicle

beam attachment bolts to the specified torque.

16 Fit the evaporative canister vent hose to the beam.

17 Locate the clutch cable on the beam, and secure with the bolt.

18 Locate the power steering pipe on the beam, and secure with the bolt.

19 Fit the bolts securing the anti-roll bar drop-links. Use a torque wrench to tighten the bolts to the specified torque.

20 Fit the steering rack – see Section 21.

21 Fit the exhaust front pipe – see Chapter 4A or 4B.

22 Fit the roadwheels and nuts, and tighten the nuts to secure the wheels. Remove the stands, and lower the vehicle to the ground.

23 Use a torque wrench to tighten the roadwheel nuts to the specified torque.

24 Use a torque wrench to tighten the suspension lower arm bolts to the specified torque.

10.10 Remove beam attachment bolts

11.5a Removing the hub and bearing assembly from the stub axle

11 Rear hub and bearings – removal and refitting

Note: *The bearing is a sealed, pre-adjusted and pre-lubricated, double-row tapered-roller type and is intended to last the vehicle's entire service life without maintenance or attention. Never overtighten the hub nut beyond the specified torque wrench setting in an attempt to 'adjust' the bearings.*

Note: *The bearing is an integral part of the hub and cannot be purchased separately. If renewal of the bearing is necessary, the complete hub assembly must be renewed as a unit. The only component which is available separately are roadwheel studs.*

Removal

1 Chock the front wheels, then jack up the rear of the vehicle and support it on axle stands (see *Jacking and Vehicle Support*). Remove the appropriate rear roadwheel.

2 Prise out the cap from the centre of the hub assembly and, using a hammer and suitable chisel-nosed tool, tap up the staking securing the hub retaining nut to the groove in the stub axle.

3 Using a socket and extension bar, slacken and remove the hub retaining nut, followed by the washer. **Note:** *The **left hand** hub nut has a **left-handed** thread.*

4 Remove the brake drum or caliper and disc, as applicable. On models with drum brakes and ABS, also remove both brake shoes.

5 Once the brake drum/disc has been removed, the hub assembly can be pulled off the stub axle **(see illustrations)**. If necessary, the hub can be drawn off the stub axle using a three-legged puller. Discard the nut, noting that a new hub retaining nut must be obtained for reassembly.

6 Check that there is no sign of free play in the hub bearing and that the bearing inner race rotates smoothly and easily without any sign of roughness. If there is any sign of wear or damage to the hub assembly or bearing, the complete hub assembly must be renewed as a unit.

7 Check the condition of the roadwheel studs in the hub flange. If any are sheared off,

stretched or have damaged threads, they can be pressed out of the hub providing that its flange is fully supported from the opposite side. On refitting, support the hub flange using the same method employed during removal, pressing in the new stud until it seats fully.

Refitting

8 Prior to refitting the hub, inspect the stub axle for signs of wear or scoring and, if necessary, renew it.

9 Apply a thin smear of grease to the hub bearing seal and refit the hub assembly. Refit the toothed washer, ensuring that its tooth locates with the groove in the stub axle. Install the new hub nut and tighten it to the specified torque.

10 Check that the hub rotates smoothly, then stake the hub retaining nut fully into the stub axle groove. Refit the hub centre cap.

11 On models with drum brakes and ABS, refer to Chapter 9, Section 26, and set the clearance between the hub rotor and the wheel sensor. On completion, refit the brake shoes.

12 Refit the brake drum or disc and caliper (as applicable) with reference to Chapter 9.

13 Refit the roadwheel, then lower the vehicle to the ground and tighten the roadwheel nuts to the specified torque.

14 Check the operation of the braking system thoroughly before using the vehicle on the road. On models with ABS, the operation of the ABS system should be verified by a Rover dealer using the appropriate diagnostic equipment.

12 Rear stub axle – removal and refitting

Models with rear drum brakes

Removal

1 Chock the front wheels, jack up the rear of the vehicle, support it securely on axle stands

H29784

11.5b Rear hub and bearing components

1 Dust cap	4 Hub and
2 Hub nut	bearing
3 Washer	assembly

(see *Jacking and Vehicle Support*) and remove the appropriate rear roadwheel. Carry out the following preliminary operations:

a) *Remove the brake drum and shoes (Chapter 9)*

b) *Remove the rear hub from the stub axle (Section 11)*

2 Undo the bolts securing the handbrake cable to the beam axle assembly, then use a ring spanner to compress the handbrake cable retaining clip and withdraw the cable from the brake backplate.

3 Clamp the flexible section of the brake hose leading to the wheel cylinder, using a proprietary brake hose clamp. Slacken the union and disconnect the brake pipe from the wheel cylinder (see Chapter 9). Plug the end of the brake pipe to minimise fluid loss and to prevent the ingress of dirt.

4 Release the ABS wheel sensor connector from the securing clip on the underside of the car. Unplug the connector and release the remainder of the harness from the clips on the beam axle assembly.

5 Slacken and withdraw the four stub axle securing bolts, then lift the stub axle and backplate away from the beam axle.

6 Examine the stub axle spindle and mounting plate for signs of wear or damage such as scoring or cracking. If damaged, the stub axle must be renewed.

Refitting

7 Unbolt the backplate from the existing stub axle and transfer it, together with the wheel cylinder and ABS wheel sensor (where applicable), to the new stub axle. Tighten the retaining bolts securely.

8 Offer the stub axle up to the beam axle mounting plate, then insert the securing bolts and tighten them to the specified torque.

9 Reconnect the brake pipe to the rear of the wheel cylinder and tighten the union to the specified torque (see Chapter 9).

10 Reconnect the ABS wheel sensor wiring, and fit the connector body and wiring harness into the securing clips.

11 Refit the hub, with reference to Section 11, then tighten the hub retaining nut to the specified torque.

12 Check that the hub rotates smoothly, then stake the hub retaining nut fully into the stub axle groove. Refit the hub centre cap.

13 On models with ABS, refer to Chapter 9, Section 26, and set the wheel sensor to reluctor ring clearance using a feeler blade.

14 Refit the handbrake cable, brake shoes and brake drum, with reference to Chapter 9, then bleed the braking system.

15 Refit the roadwheel, then lower the vehicle to the ground and tighten the roadwheel nuts to the specified torque.

16 Check the operation of the braking system thoroughly before using the vehicle on the road. On models with ABS, the operation of the ABS system should be verified by a Rover dealer using the appropriate diagnostic equipment.

Models with rear disc brakes

Removal

17 Jack up the rear of the vehicle, support it securely on axle stands (see *Jacking and Vehicle Support*) and remove the appropriate rear roadwheel. Carry out the following preliminary operations:

a) *Remove the brake caliper (Chapter 9)*
b) *Remove the brake disc (Chapter 9)*
c) *Remove the rear hub from the stub axle (Section 11)*
d) *Remove the ABS wheel sensor (Chapter 9)*

18 Slacken and withdraw the four stub axle securing bolts, then lift the stub axle and backplate away from the beam axle.

Refitting

19 Examine the stub axle spindle and mounting plate for signs of wear or damage such as scoring or cracking. If damaged, the stub axle must be renewed.

20 If a new stub axle is to be fitted, unbolt the ABS wheel sensor mounting bracket and the brake backplate from the existing stub axle and transfer it to the new one. Tighten the retaining bolts securely.

21 Offer the stub axle up to the beam axle mounting plate, then insert the securing bolts and tighten them to the specified torque.

22 Refit the hub with reference to Section 11 and tighten the hub retaining nut to the specified torque. Check that the hub rotates smoothly, then stake the hub retaining nut fully into the stub axle groove. Refit the hub centre cap.

23 Refit the brake disc and caliper with reference to Chapter 9.

24 Refit the ABS wheel sensor with reference to Chapter 9.

25 Refit the roadwheel, then lower the vehicle to the ground and tighten the roadwheel nuts to the specified torque.

26 Check the operation of the braking system thoroughly before using the vehicle on the road. On models with ABS, the operation of the ABS system should be verified by a Rover dealer using the appropriate diagnostic equipment.

---

13 Rear suspension strut –
removal, overhaul and refitting

Caution: If renewing the strut damper during overhaul, both the left- and right-hand dampers should be renewed as a pair, to preserve the handling characteristics of the vehicle.

Removal

1 Chock the front wheels, then jack up the rear of the vehicle and support it on axle stands (see *Jacking and Vehicle Support*). Remove the appropriate rear roadwheel.

2 Position a trolley jack directly under the

13.3 Support the trailing arm, then slacken and remove the strut lower mounting bolt

13.4b . . . and lower trim securing screws . . .

strut lower mounting bolt and raise the jack head until it is just supporting the trailing arm.

3 Slacken and remove the strut lower mounting bolt **(see illustration)**. If the bolt is difficult to remove, relieve the strain on it by adjusting the height of the trailing arm using the trolley jack.

4 Open the tailgate, then remove the trim securing screws and fold the carpet panel away from the side of the load space. Lift the rubber cover from the strut upper mounting **(see illustrations)**.

5 Use chalk or a marker pen to mark the position of the suspension strut upper mounting in relation to the bodywork. Slacken and remove the two strut upper mounting nuts. DO NOT slacken the damper rod nut, at the centre of the strut **(see illustration)**.

6 Lower the trolley jack and manoeuvre the strut out from under the wheel arch, noting

13.4a Remove the upper . . .

13.4c . . . and fold the carpet panel away from the side of the load space . . .

the seal (where applicable) fitted between the upper mounting plate and vehicle body **(see illustration)**.

Overhaul

Note: *Before attempting to dismantle the rear suspension strut, a suitable tool to hold the coil spring in compression must be obtained. Adjustable coil spring compressors are readily available and are recommended for this operation. Any attempt to dismantle the strut without such a tool is likely to result in damage or personal injury.*

7 With the strut removed from the vehicle, clean away all external dirt. If desired, the strut can be mounted upright in the jaws of a bench vice.

8 Fit the spring compressor and compress the coil spring until all tension is relieved from the upper mounting plate **(see illustration)**.

13.4d . . . then lift the rubber cover from the strut upper mounting

13.5 Remove the two strut upper mounting nuts (arrowed) – do not slacken the centre nut

13.6 Remove the strut from the wheelarch

13.8 Fit the spring compressor and compress the spring until all tension is relieved from the upper mounting plate

13.9 Slacken the damper rod nut with a spanner, using an Allen key to prevent the rod from rotating

9 Slacken the damper rod nut with a spanner, using an Allen key to prevent the damper rod from rotating as the nut is slackened **(see illustration)**.

10 Remove the nut and washer followed by the upper spring seat/mounting plate assembly, noting the correct fitted position of the mounting rubber. Remove the coil spring

and lower spring seat rubber. Lift the dust seal and cover off the damper and slide the bump stop plate and rubber bump stop off the damper piston **(see illustrations)**.

11 With the strut assembly completely dismantled, examine all components for wear, damage or corrosion. Renew any component displaying signs of deterioration **(see illustration)**.

12 Examine the damper for signs of fluid leakage. Check the piston rod for signs of pitting along its entire length and check the strut body for signs of damage or corrosion. Test the operation of the strut, while holding it in an upright position, by moving the piston through several full-length strokes; the resistance felt should be smooth and continuous. Now operate the piston rod through short strokes of 50 to 100 mm. If fluid has leaked from the damper, the piston will

13.10a Remove the nut . . .

13.10b . . . and washer (noting its orientation) . . .

13.10c . . . followed by the upper spring seat/mounting plate assembly . . .

13.10d . . . then remove the coil spring . . .

13.10e . . . and the lower spring seat rubber . . .

13.10f . . . lift the dust seal and cover off the damper . . .

13.10g . . . and slide the bump stop plate . . .

13.10h . . . and rubber bump stop off the damper piston

have an amount of undamped 'freeplay' at the end of its travel. If this is the case, or if there are any visible signs of wear, damage or corrosion, renewal of the strut will be necessary.

13 If any doubt exists about the condition of the coil spring, carefully remove the spring compressors and check the spring for distortion, cracking or excessive corrosion. Since no minimum free length is specified by Rover, the only way to check the tension of the spring is to compare it to a new component. Renew the spring if it is damaged or distorted or there is any doubt as to its condition.

14 Inspect all other components for signs of damage or deterioration and renew any that are suspect.

15 If new damper strut insert is being fitted, prime the damper (with reference to the manufacturer's instructions) by operating the piston rod through several full-length strokes.

16 Slide the bump stop rubber, bump stop plate and dust cover over the end of the damper piston rod.

17 Place the lower spring seat rubber in position and orientate it such that the orientation peg fits into the hole in the spring seat. Pass the compressed coil spring over the top of the damper piston rod and place it in position on the lower spring seat, ensuring that the end of the spring is correctly located in the lower spring seat recess **(see illustrations)**.

18 Fit the upper spring seat rubber followed by the upper spring seat/mounting plate, ensuring that the upper end of the coil spring is correctly located in the corresponding mounting plate recess and that the mounting plate studs are vertical. Fit the washer (with the lip facing upwards) and then fit the new damper rod nut.

19 Tighten the damper rod nut securely. Note that you will need to fit a crow's-foot adapter to the torque wrench, to allow the damper rod nut to be tightened to the correct torque. Counterhold the damper rod, using a suitable Allen key or hex bit, as the nut is tightened. *Caution: Do not allow the rod to rotate inside the damper, as this may damage the piston seal.*

Refitting

20 Ensure the rubber seal (where applicable) is in position between the upper mounting plate and the bodywork then refit the suspension strut, using the alignment marks made during removal (where necessary). Refit the strut upper mounting nuts, but do not tighten them to the final torque setting at this stage.

21 Raise the trailing arm using the trolley jack, as described in the *Removal* procedure. Align the trailing arm mounting hole with the strut lower mounting bush, then insert the lower mounting bolt. Fit the nut but do not tighten it to the final torque setting at this stage.

13.11 Rear suspension strut components

1 Rubber cap	7 Coil spring
2 Damper rod nut	8 Dust seal and cover
3 Washer	9 Bump stop plate
4 Strut upper mounting nuts	10 Bump stop rubber
5 Upper spring seat/mounting plate	11 Lower spring seat rubber
assembly	12 Damper unit
6 Upper spring seat rubber	13 Strut lower mounting bolt

22 Refit the roadwheel, then lower the vehicle to the ground and tighten the roadwheel nuts to the specified torque.

23 With the vehicle standing on its wheels, rock the vehicle to settle the suspension components in position then tighten the strut lower mounting bolt to the specified torque. Finally, tighten both strut upper mounting nuts to the specified torque and refit the protective plastic cap.

14 Rear suspension beam axle – removal and refitting

Removal

1 Chock the front wheels, jack up the rear of the vehicle and support it securely on axle stands (see *Jacking and Vehicle Support*).

13.17a Position the lower spring seat rubber such that its orientation peg fits into the hole in the spring seat (arrowed) . . .

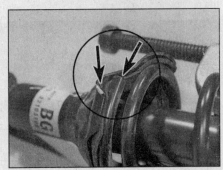

13.17b . . . and place the compressed coil spring in position (lower spring seat recess arrowed)

14.6 Remove the beam axle pivot mounting bolt (arrowed)

2 With reference to Chapter 9, carry out the following:

a) *Disconnect the handbrake cables from the rear brake drums/calipers (as applicable).*

b) *On models with disc brakes, remove the brake calipers (together with their mounting brackets) from the stub axles.*

c) *On models with drum brakes, slacken the unions and disconnect the brake pipes from the rear of both wheel cylinders.*

3 Withdraw the metal clips and detach the brake hose unions from the mounting brackets on both trailing arms. Where applicable, release the ABS wheel sensor wiring harness from the retaining clips on each trailing arm.

4 Unscrew the retaining bolts and release both handbrake cable mounting brackets from the beam axle mountings.

5 Using the information given in Section 13, position a trolley jack under each trailing arm then slacken and withdraw both rear strut lower mounting bolts, to separate the rear struts from the beam axle. On completion, carefully lower the beam axle trailing arms to the ground.

6 Reposition the trolley jack so that it now supports the centre of the leading edge of the beam axle assembly. Slacken and withdraw both pivot mounting bolts **(see illustration)**. Check that nothing remains connected to the beam axle assembly, then carefully lower it to the ground.

7 If a new beam axle assembly is to be fitted, remove the stub axle assemblies (as described in Section 12) and transfer them to the new beam axle.

Refitting

8 Position the axle assembly under the car on a trolley jack, then lift the assembly up to its mountings by raising the trolley jack.

9 Insert the beam axle pivot mounting bolts, but do not tighten them at this stage.

10 Reposition the trolley jack, then raise the rear of the beam axle using the jack so that the trailing arms engage with the suspension strut lower bushes. Insert the suspension strut lower mounting bolts, but do not tighten them at this stage.

11 Tighten the beam axle pivot mounting bolts to the specified torque.

12 Refit the handbrake cable mounting brackets to the beam axle mountings and tighten the bolts securely.

13 Press the brake hose union grommets into the brackets on the beam axle and fit the metal retaining clips. Similarly, press the ABS wiring grommets into the brackets on the beam axle.

14 Refer to Chapter 9 and carry out the following:

a) *Refit the brake calipers and mounting brackets (models with rear disc brakes).*

b) *Refit the brake pipes to the rear of the wheel cylinder and tighten the union to the specified torque (models with rear disc brakes).*

c) *Refit the handbrake cables.*

15 Refit the roadwheel, then lower the vehicle to the ground and tighten the roadwheel nuts to the specified torque.

16 With the vehicle standing on its wheels, rock the vehicle to settle the suspension components in position then tighten the suspension strut lower mounting bolts to the specified torque (see Section 13).

17 Refer to Chapter 9 and bleed the brake hydraulic system. On completion, adjust the operation of the handbrake.

15 Rear suspension beam axle bush renewal – general information

Bush renewal is best left to a Rover dealer, as a press, special bush removal/refitting mandrel, extraction tool and support are required (Rover Service Tool Numbers 18G 1756/3,

18G 1756/12 and IG 1756/5 respectively). While the old bush can be extracted using a strong bench vice and suitable selection of sockets, it is unlikely that new bushes can be installed successfully without the specially-shaped mandrel.

16 Steering wheel – removal and refitting

Removal

1 Remove the ignition key and wait at least ten minutes to allow the SRS system backup circuit to fully discharge. Disconnect BOTH battery leads, earth lead first, to avoid accidental detonation of the airbag.

2 Remove the airbag unit from the centre of the steering wheel (see Chapter 12).

3 With further reference to Chapter 12, detach the horn button (and, where applicable, the remote audio control button) wiring multiplug from the rotary coupler **(see illustration)**.

4 Set the steering in the straight-ahead position and, using a socket, unscrew the steering wheel retaining nut until its top is flush with the end of the column shaft. Do not use the steering column lock to brace the steering wheel as this may damage it.

5 Mark the steering wheel and steering column shaft in relation to each other then lift the steering wheel off the column splines. If it is tight, tap it up near the centre, using the palm of your hand, to release it from the shaft splines.

6 Remove and discard the steering wheel retaining nut. A new self-locking nut must be obtained for reassembly.

7 Remove the steering wheel from the column **(see illustration)**. Tape the inner and outer sections of the rotary coupler together, so that the coupler's alignment with the steering column shaft is preserved.

Caution: Do not allow the rotary coupler to rotate until the steering wheel is refitted.

Refitting

8 Refit the steering wheel by reversing the removal procedure, noting the following **(see illustrations)**:

16.3 Detach the horn button and remote audio control button wiring multiplug from the rotary coupler

16.7 Remove the steering wheel from the steering column

16.8a Fit a new self-locking steering wheel nut . . .

16.8b . . . and tighten it to the specified torque

a) Before refitting, check that the steering column splines are clean.

b) Enter the cut-outs on the lower surface of the wheel with the direction indicator cancelling cam tabs and align the marks made on dismantling. This should leave the wheel in the same position as before removal.

c) Ensure that the rotary coupler wiring is reconnected and take care to ensure that wiring harness is not trapped beneath the steering wheel.

d) Fit a new wheel retaining nut and tighten it to the specified torque wrench setting.

e) Refit the driver's airbag unit with reference to Chapter 12.

f) When reconnecting the battery leads, fit the negative lead last.

17 Steering column – removal and refitting

Removal

1 Remove the ignition key and wait at least ten minutes to allow the SRS system backup circuit to fully discharge. Disconnect both battery leads, earth lead first, to avoid accidental detonation of the airbag.

2 Set the steering in the straight-ahead position then lock the steering column in its lowest position.

3 Remove the airbag unit (see Chapter 12).

4 Remove the steering wheel, with reference to Section 16.

5 Release the stud fasteners and remove the fusebox cover panel from the underside of the facia **(see illustration)**.

6 Slacken and withdraw the three screws, then remove the lower part of the plastic shroud from the underside of the steering column. Carefully disengage the upper part of the steering column shroud from the lower edge of the instrument panel and lift it out over the combination switch stalks **(see illustrations)**.

7 Refer to Chapter 12 and remove the SRS rotary coupler from the steering column. Place a strip of masking tape around the rotary coupler to preserve its alignment.

8 Remove the steering column combination switch, together with the direction indicator cancelling cam (see Chapter 12).

9 On later models, follow the wiring harness

17.5 Remove the fusebox cover panel from the underside of the facia

from the ignition switch sensor coil to the multi-way connector and unplug it.

10 Trace the ignition switch wiring harness back to the fusebox and main wiring harness, then unplug the two multi-way wiring connectors. Release the ties securing the wiring harness to the steering column **(see illustrations)**.

11 Pull back the driver's footwell carpet and remove the two plastic clips securing the lower column cover to the floor. Remove the two retaining clips from the upper end of the cover and withdraw the cover **(see illustrations)**.

12 Using a hammer and punch, white paint or similar, mark the exact relationship between the steering column shaft and shaft-to-steering gear universal joint, then slacken and remove the pinch-bolt securing the joint to the column shaft **(see illustration)**.

13 Undo the nut and bolt securing the lower steering column mounting clamp to the swivel bracket and remove the clamp **(see illustration)**.

17.6a Remove the securing screws . . .

17.6b . . . and remove the lower . . .

17.6c . . . and upper sections of the steering column shroud

17.10a Unplug the steering column wiring from the main harness connector. . .

17.10b . . . and the fusebox

17.11a Remove the two plastic clips (arrowed) securing the lower column cover to the floor

17.11b . . . the two metal spring clips . . .

17.11c . . . and withdraw the lower column cover

17.12 Remove the pinch-bolt (arrowed) from the steering column shaft-to-steering gear universal joint

17.13 Lower steering column mounting clamp-to-swivel bracket bolt (arrowed)

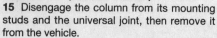

14 Slacken and remove the two nuts and two bolts securing the upper mounting assembly to the vehicle **(see illustrations)**.
15 Disengage the column from its mounting studs and the universal joint, then remove it from the vehicle.

Refitting

16 Before refitting the steering column, closely examine the upper mounting assembly for damage or misalignment.
17 Align the marks made on dismantling and engage the steering column shaft splines with those of the universal joint.
18 Locate the upper mounting bracket assembly over its mounting studs and refit the upper mounting nuts and bolts. Refit the lower mounting clamp and tighten its retaining nut and bolt to the specified torque setting, then tighten the upper mounting nuts and bolts to their specified torque setting.
19 Refit the universal joint to steering column pinch-bolt and tighten it to the specified torque. Refit the universal joint cover and secure it in position with the clips and studs.
20 Reconnect the combination switch and ignition switch multiplugs, then secure the wiring harness to the steering column.
21 Refit the steering column combination switch, direction indicator cancelling cam and SRS rotary coupler (see Chapter 12). Reconnect the ignition switch sensor coil wiring.
22 Refit the steering column shroud panels and fusebox cover, securing them in place with the screws and stud fixings.
23 Refit the steering wheel (Section 16) then refit the airbag unit, see Chapter 12.

17.14a Remove the steering column mounting nuts from the studs (arrowed) . . .

18 Steering column shrouds – removal and refitting

Removal

1 Disconnect the battery earth lead.
2 Remove the steering wheel – see Section 16.
3 Remove the keys from the starter switch.
4 Release three turnbuckles, and remove the fusebox cover.
5 Remove three screws securing the lower half of the shroud to the steering column **(see illustration 17.6a)**.

19.7 Remove the clamp bolts

17.14b . . . then remove the two mounting bolts (arrowed)

6 Remove the upper and lower halves of the shroud.

Refitting

7 Refitting is a reversal of the removal procedure.

19 Steering lock/ignition switch – removal and refitting

 Warning: *Before attempting removal of the steering lock/ignition switch, carefully read the precautions about the SRS system in Chapter 12.*
Note: *The lock, and lock shield are each secured by two shear-head bolts. Ensure that new bolts are supplied with the new lock and shield.*

Removal

1 Remove the steering column shrouds – see Section 18.
2 Remove the ignition switch transponder – see Chapter 12.
3 Centre punch the two shear-head bolts securing the lock shield. Drill off the heads using a 5 mm drill.
4 Remove the lower half of the lock shield.
5 Disconnect the multi-plugs, and remove the upper half of the lock shield.
6 Disconnect the starter switch multi-plugs from the fusebox, and main harness.
7 Remove the nut and bolt securing the lower column clamp to the pivot bracket, and remove the clamp **(see illustration)**.

19.9 Drill off the shear bolt heads

8 Remove two flange nuts and two bolts securing the column upper bracket, and lower the steering column.
Caution: If the lock is to be refitted, take care when drilling not to damage the lock body.
9 Centre punch the two shear-head bolts securing the lock to the column. Drill off the heads using a 5 mm drill **(see illustration)**.
10 Remove the lock and bracket.

Refitting

11 Fit the lock to the steering column, and loosely fit the two shear-head bolts.
12 Insert the starter key, and check that the key turns freely, and the lock operates correctly.
13 Tighten the shear bolts until the head shear off.
14 Locate the upper half of the lock shield on the lock barrel, and connect the two multi-plugs.
Caution: Ensure that the harness is routed around the upper half of the lock shield towards the front of the vehicle.
15 Fit the lower half of the lock shield. Fit two shear bolts, and tighten them until the heads shear off.
16 Lift up the column and fit the top bracket over the studs. Loosely fit the nuts and bolts.
17 Fit the lower clamp. Use a torque wrench to tighten the nut and bolt to the specified torque.
18 Use a torque wrench to tighten the top bracket nuts and bolts to the specified torque.
19 Connect the starter switch multi-plugs to the fusebox and main harness.
20 Fit the transponder.
21 Fit the steering column shrouds – see Section 18.

21.3 Remove joint bolts

20 Steering gear rubber gaiters – renewal

1 Remove the track rod balljoint (see Section 25) and unscrew the locknut from the track rod end.
2 Using a pair of pliers, release the outer steering gear gaiter retaining clip and slide it off the track rod end. Remove the inner gaiter retaining clip by cutting it, then slide the gaiter off the end of the track rod **(see illustration)**.
3 Thoroughly clean the track rod and the steering gear housing, using fine abrasive paper to polish off any corrosion, burrs or sharp edges which might damage the new gaiter's sealing lips on fitting. Repair kits which consist of new gaiters and retaining clips are available from Rover dealers.
4 Fit the new rubber gaiter, ensuring that it is correctly seated in the grooves in the steering gear housing and track rod.
5 Check that the gaiter is not twisted or dented then secure it in position using new retaining clips.
6 Refit the locknut and balljoint onto the track rod end.
7 Have the front wheel alignment checked (and if necessary, adjusted) by a Rover dealer or a tyre specialist at the earliest opportunity.

21 Steering gear – removal and refitting

Note: *The following new parts are needed – O-rings for power steering pipes, self-locking nuts for track rod ends, roll-pin for gearchange linkage (1.8 engine only).*

Removal

1 Set the front roadwheels at the straight ahead position, and remove the ignition key from the steering lock.
2 Working inside the vehicle, remove the two bolts and clip securing the plastic shroud around the lower section of the steering column.
3 Mark the relative position of the universal joint and steering rack pinion. Remove the

21.6 Remove steady bar body bracket

20.2 Track rod end assembly

1 Track rod end	4 Gaiter
2 Locknut	5 Clip
3 Clip	6 Track rod

two pinch-bolts from the universal joint, and slide the joint up the column until it is free from the pinion **(see illustration)**.
4 Chock the rear wheels and apply the handbrake. Jack up the front of the vehicle, and support securely on axle stands (see *Jacking and Vehicle Support*). Remove both front roadwheels.
5 Remove the exhaust front pipe – see Chapter 4A or 4B.
6 Remove the bolt securing the engine lower steady bar to the body bracket. Fold the bar down, and remove four bolts securing the steady bar bracket to the body. Remove the steady bar bracket **(see illustration)**.
7 On the left-hand and right-hand track rod ends, slacken the ball pin nuts until they are flush with the end of the ball pin threads. Using a suitable taper joint separator, release the ball pin from the steering arm. Remove the nuts, and disconnect the track rod ends **(see illustration 2.8)**
Caution: Take care not to damage the balljoint rubber boot.

1.4 and 1.6 petrol engine models

8 Using a large flat-blade screwdriver, carefully lever off three gearchange rod balljoints from the levers on the pivot bracket attached to the body **(see illustration)**.

21.8 Lever off gearchange rod balljoints

21.10 Disconnect gearchange steady bar

21.11 Drive out the roll-pin

21.15 Remove beam securing bolts

21.16 Disconnect power steering pipes

21.17 Remove rack clamp bolts

21.18 Remove rack flange bolts

9 Remove three bolts securing the gearchange link bracket to the body, and remove the bracket. Tie the linkage clear of the work area.

1.8 petrol engine models

10 Remove the bolt and disconnect the gearchange steady bar from the gearbox, and collect two washers **(see illustration)**.
11 Remove the clip securing the selector rod roll-pin. Using a suitable punch, drive out and discard the roll-pin **(see illustration)**.
12 Release the selector rod from the selector shaft.

All models

13 Release the plastic clip securing the power steering pipe to the top of the suspension beam.
14 With assistance, support the beam and rack assembly.

22.3 Release belt tension

15 Remove four bolts – two each side – securing the suspension beam to the body. Lower the jack to gain access to the power steering pipes attached to the rack pinion housing **(see illustration)**.
16 Position a container under the pipes to collect fluid spill. Disconnect the pipes, and remove and discard O-rings. Plug the ends of the pipes and the rack connections **(see illustration)**.
17 Remove two bolts securing the steering rack clamp. Remove the clamp and rubber bush **(see illustration)**.
18 Remove the two flange bolts securing the rack to the rear beam. Manoeuvre the rack towards the left-hand side, and remove the rack from the beam. Remove the rack-to-body aperture seal **(see illustration)**.

Refitting

19 Ensure that the aperture seal is correctly fitted to the rack.
20 With assistance, manoeuvre the rack into the beam. Align the rack, and loosely fit the two flange bolts securing the rack to the beam. Fit the rack clamp and rubber bush. Loosely fit the two bolts.
21 Tighten the two flange bolts, and two clamp bolts securely.
22 Remove the plugs from the power steering pipes and connections. Fit new O-ring to the ends of the pipes. Connect and tighten the pipes.
23 With assistance, raise the beam and rack assembly, and loosely fit four securing bolts.
24 Inside the vehicle, check that the universal

joint is free. Slide the joint down over the pinion splines.
25 Use a torque wrench to tighten the four beam securing bolts to the specified torque.
26 The remaining refitting is a reversal of the removal procedure, noting:
Use a torque wrench to tighten all nuts and bolts to the specified torque.
Use new self-locking nuts to secure the track rod end balljoints.
1.8 engine only, fit a new roll-pin securing selector rod to selector shaft, and fit the retaining clip.
Top-up and bleed the power steering system – see Section 24.
Have the front wheel alignment checked by an MG Rover dealer or specialist.

22 Power steering drivebelt – removal and refitting

Petrol models

Removal

1 Disconnect the battery earth lead.
2 Chock the rear wheels and apply the handbrake. Jack up the front of the vehicle, and support securely on axle stands (see *Jacking and Vehicle Support*). Remove the right-hand front roadwheel.
3 Fit a 13 mm spanner to the hexagon on the belt tensioner, and rotate fully clockwise to release belt tension **(see illustration)**.

22.4 Drivebelt arrangement

1	Drivebelt	3	4mm diameter
2	13mm spanner		rod

22.5 Remove belt

22.9 Check indicator position

22.15 Tensioner pulley bolt (arrowed) – diesel models with automatic tensioner (engine removed for clarity)

22.16 Using the spanner, hold the tensioner in the 'slackened' position, then release the drivebelt from the pulleys

4 Lock the tensioner in this position by fitting a 3 mm diameter locking pin through the centre of the hexagon and into the backplate **(see illustration)**.

5 Release the belt from the pulleys and tensioner, and remove the belt **(see illustration)**.

Refitting

6 Clean the pulleys and tensioner.

7 Fit the belt over the crankshaft pulley, and over the pump pulley.

8 Use the 13 mm spanner to relieve tension on the locking pin, and remove the pin. Release the spanner, and allow the tension pulley to rest on the belt.

9 Ensure that the indicator marking on the tensioner falls within the 'gauge' recessed into the tensioner backplate **(see illustration)**.

10 Fit the roadwheel and tighten the nuts to secure the wheel. Remove the stands, and lower the vehicle to the ground.

11 Use a torque wrench to tighten the roadwheel nuts to the specified torque.

12 Connect the battery earth lead.

Diesel models

Removal

13 Disconnect the battery negative cable and position it away from the terminal.

14 Chock the front wheels, raise the front of the vehicle and support it securely on axle stands (see *Jacking and Vehicle Support*). Remove the right-hand front roadwheel, then undo the screws and remove the plastic wheel arch liner.

15 Working through the right-hand wheel arch, fit a 15mm spanner to the tensioner pulley bolt and use it to rotate the whole tensioner assembly clockwise, so that the tension on the drivebelt is relieved **(see illustration)**.

16 Hold the tension pulley in this position and release the drivebelt from the power steering pump, crankshaft and air conditioning compressor (or idler pulley) **(see illustration)**.

17 Slowly release the tensioner and remove the drivebelt from the engine compartment.

Refitting

18 Fit a spanner to the tensioner pulley bolt (as described in *Removal*) and use it rotate the whole tensioner assembly clockwise to the limit of its travel.

19 Whilst holding the tensioner in the fully-rotated position, pass the drivebelt over the crankshaft, power steering pump, alternator (and where applicable, air conditioning compressor) pulleys, ensuring that the 'vee' pattern on the drive surface of the belt engages correctly with the grooves on each of the pulleys.

20 Manoeuvre the flat surface of the belt

23.3 Remove pulley securing bolts

under the tensioner pulley. Using the ring spanner, slowly release the tensioner assembly, until it contacts the drivebelt.

21 Using a spanner on the crankshaft pulley bolt, turn the crankshaft through one revolution to allow the belt tension to be evenly distributed and check that the belt is correctly engaged with both pulleys.

22 Check that the indicator marking on the tensioner assembly falls within the 'gauge' recessed into the tensioner backplate **(refer to illustration 22.9)**. If the indicator falls outside of the gauge markings, the wrong belt may have been fitted – check with your parts supplier before proceeding. Note that the recessed gauge is also used to indicate drivebelt wear – see Chapter 1B for details.

---

23 Power steering pump –
removal and refitting

Petrol models

Removal

1 Disconnect the battery earth lead.

2 Chock the rear wheels and apply the handbrake. Jack up the front of the vehicle, and support securely on axle stands (see *Jacking and Vehicle Support*). Remove the right-hand front roadwheel.

3 Slacken three bolts securing the pump drive pulley to the pump drive flange **(see illustration)**.

23.9 Remove pump securing bolts

4 Release the pump drivebelt from the pulley.
5 Remove three pulley bolts, and remove the pulley.
6 Position a container under the pump to collect fluid spill.
Caution: To prevent component damage, use two spanners when slackening or tightening unions.
7 Slacken the clip securing the fluid inlet hose to the pump, and disconnect the hose – plug the hose and connection.
8 Remove the bolt securing the fluid outlet hose clamp to the bracket. Slacken the union and disconnect the hose – plug the hose and connection.
9 Remove the bolt securing the pump to the mounting bracket. Remove two through-bolts securing the pump to the mounting bracket, and remove the pump **(see illustration)**. Remove the fluid container.

Refitting

10 To ease refitting of the pump, push back the two bolt distance pieces in the pump bracket, so that they do not protrude into the inside of the bracket.
11 Locate the pump in the bracket, align the bolt holes and fit the bolts and nuts. Use a torque wrench to tighten the bolts to the specified torque.

23.26 Remove pump securing bolts

12 Remove the plugs from the fluid outlet pipe and connection, and remove and discard the O-ring from the hose.
13 Lubricate and fit a new O-ring to the outlet hose. Connect the outlet hose to the pump, and tighten the union.
14 Align the outlet hose clamp on the bracket, and fit and tighten the bolt.
15 Remove the plugs from the fluid inlet pipe and connection. Connect the hose to the pump and secure with the clip.
16 Clean the pump pulley mating faces. Fit the pulley and align the bolt holes. Fit and loosely tighten the bolts.
17 Fit the pump drivebelt – see Section 22.
18 Use a torque wrench to tighten the pulley bolts to the specified torque.
19 Refit the roadwheel, and tighten the nuts to secure the wheel.
20 remove the axle stands, and lower the vehicle to the ground. Use a torque wrench to tighten the roadwheel nuts to the specified torque.
21 Connect the battery earth lead.
22 Top-up and bleed the power steering system – see Section 24.

Diesel models

Removal

23 Disconnect the battery earth lead.
24 Remove the coolant pump housing – see Chapter 3.
25 Remove and discard three Torx head bolts securing the power steering pump pulley to the drive flange, and remove the pulley.
26 Remove five bolts securing the power steering pump to the coolant pump housing, and move the mounting bracket aside **(see illustration)**.
27 Remove the power steering pump from the coolant pump housing.
28 Remove two bolts securing the fluid inlet flange to the power steering pump. Remove and discard the O-ring, and tie the hose clear of the work area.

Refitting

29 Clean the mating faces of the fluid inlet flange and power steering pump. Lubricate and fit a new O-ring to the flange. Align the flange on the power steering pump and fit the two bolts. Use a torque wrench to tighten the bolts to the specified torque.
30 Fit the power steering pump to the coolant pump housing.
31 Locate the power steering pump mounting bracket and fit the five bolts. Use a torque wrench to tighten the bolts to the specified torque.
32 Fit the power steering pump pulley to the drive flange and align the bolt holes. Fit three new Torx head bolts. Restrain the pulley, and use a torque wrench to tighten the bolts to the specified torque.
33 Fit the coolant pump housing – see Chapter 3.
34 Connect the battery earth lead.

24 Power steering system – bleeding

Caution: Do not hold the steering at full lock for more than a few seconds. Overheating and excess pressure may damage the pump.

1 Remove the fluid reservoir cap, and top-up with new fluid (see *Lubricants and fluids*).
2 Prevent the engine from starting by removing the fuel pump fuse – see *Wiring diagrams*.
3 Crank the engine for approx. 5 seconds to prime the pump.
4 Refit the fuel pump fuse, and check that the fluid level is between MIN and MAX markings on the reservoir.
5 Start the engine and allow it to idle for approximately 30 seconds with the front wheels pointing in the straight-ahead position. After 30 seconds, turn the steering onto full lock in one direction, hold it there for a few seconds, then turn it onto full lock in the opposite direction and hold it there for a few seconds. Return the front wheels to the straight-ahead position. Repeat this procedure until air bubbles cease to appear in the fluid reservoir.
6 If, when turning the steering, an abnormal noise is heard from the fluid lines, it indicates that there is still air in the system. Check this by turning the wheels to the straight-ahead position and switching off the engine. If the fluid level in the reservoir rises, then air is present in the system and further bleeding is necessary.
7 Once all traces of air have been removed from the power steering hydraulic system, turn the engine off and allow the system to cool. Once cool, check that the fluid level is up to the MAX mark on the power steering fluid reservoir. Top-up if necessary.

25 Track rod balljoint – removal and refitting

Note: *The following new parts are needed – self-locking nut for track rod balljoint.*

Removal

1 Apply the handbrake, then jack up the front of the vehicle and support it on axle stands (see *Jacking and Vehicle Support*). Remove the appropriate front roadwheel.
2 If the balljoint is to be re-used, use a straight-edge and a scriber, or similar, to mark its relationship to the track rod.
3 Holding the balljoint, unscrew its locknut by one quarter of a turn only.
4 Slacken the ball pin nut until it is flush with the end of the ball pin threads. Using a suitable taper joint separator, release the ball pin from the steering arm. Remove and discard the nut, and disconnect the track rod end **(see illustration 2.8)**.

Caution: Take care not to damage the balljoint rubber boot.

5 Unscrew the balljoint from the track rod, counting the exact number of turns necessary to do so. If the locknut is to be removed, mark its position on the track rod and count the number of turns required to remove it so that it can be returned exactly to its original position on reassembly.

6 Carefully clean the balljoint and the threads. Renew the balljoint if its movement is sloppy or too stiff, if it is excessively worn, or if it is damaged in any way. Carefully check the stud taper and threads. No grease leakage should be visible.

Refitting

7 If necessary, screw the locknut onto the track rod by the number of turns noted on removal. This should align the locknut with the mark made on dismantling.

8 Screw the balljoint onto the track rod by the number of turns noted on removal. This should bring the balljoint to within a quarter of a turn from the locknut, with the alignment marks that were made (if applicable) on removal lined up.

9 Fit the ball pin to the steering arm and fit a new self-locking nut. Use a torque wrench to tighten the nut to the specified torque.

10 Fit the roadwheel and tighten the nuts to secure the wheel. Remove the stands and lower the vehicle to the ground. Use a torque wrench to tighten the roadwheel nuts to the specified torque.

11 Have the front wheel alignment checked by an MG Rover dealer or specialist.

26 Wheel alignment and steering angles

1 A vehicle's steering and suspension geometry is defined in four basic settings. All angles are expressed in degrees and the steering axis is defined as an imaginary line drawn through the centres of the front suspension upper and lower balljoints, extended where necessary to contact the ground **(see illustration)**.

Camber

2 Camber is the angle between each roadwheel and a vertical line drawn through its centre and tyre contact patch when viewed from the front or rear of the vehicle. Positive camber is when the roadwheels are tilted outwards from the vertical at the top. Negative camber is when they are tilted inwards.

3 Camber is not adjustable and given for reference only. While it can be checked using a camber checking gauge, if the figure obtained is significantly different from that specified, then the vehicle must be taken for careful checking by a professional, as the fault can only be caused by wear or damage to the body or suspension components.

Castor

4 Castor is the angle between the steering axis and a vertical line drawn through each roadwheel's centre and tyre contact patch when viewed from the side of the vehicle. Positive castor is when the steering axis is tilted so that it contacts the ground ahead of the vertical. Negative castor is when it contacts the ground behind the vertical.

5 Castor is not adjustable and is given for reference only. While it can be checked using a castor checking gauge, if the figure obtained is significantly different from that specified, then the vehicle must be taken for careful checking by a professional, as the fault can only be caused by wear or damage to the body or suspension components.

Steering axis inclination/SAI

6 Also known as kingpin inclination/KPI, this is the angle between the steering axis and a vertical line drawn through each roadwheel's centre and tyre contact patch when viewed from the front or rear of the vehicle.

7 SAI/KPI is not adjustable and is given for reference only.

Toe

8 Toe is the difference, viewed from above, between lines drawn through the roadwheel centres and the vehicle's centre-line. Toe-in is when the roadwheels point inwards, towards each other at the front. Toe-out is when they splay outwards from each other at the front.

9 At the front, toe setting is adjusted by screwing the track rods in or out of their balljoints to alter the effective length of the track rod assemblies.

10 At the rear, toe setting is adjusted by slackening the bolts securing the beam axle assembly mounting brackets and moving the brackets in relation to the chassis.

Toe-out on turns

11 Also known as turning angles or Ackermann angles, this is the difference, viewed from above, between the angles of rotation of the inside and outside front roadwheels when they have been turned through a given angle.

12 Toe-out on turns is set in production and is not adjustable as such, but can be upset by altering the length of the track rods unequally. It is essential, therefore, to ensure that the track rod lengths are exactly the same and that they are turned by the same amount whenever the toe setting is altered.

Checking and adjustment

13 Due to the special measuring equipment necessary to check wheel alignment and the skill required to use it properly, checking and adjustment of the aforementioned settings is best left to a Rover dealer or similar expert. Note that most tyre-fitting shops now possess sophisticated checking equipment.

26.1 Wheel alignment and steering angles

Notes

Chapter 11
Bodywork and fittings

Contents

Degrees of difficulty

Easy, suitable for novice with little experience	**Fairly easy,** suitable for beginner with some experience	**Fairly difficult,** suitable for competent DIY mechanic	**Difficult,** suitable for experienced DIY mechanic	**Very difficult,** suitable for expert DIY or professional

Specifications

Torque wrench settings

	Nm	lbf ft
Bonnet hinge bolts	9	7
Bonnet locking platform support bracket bolts	9	7
Bonnet lock-to-body bolts	10	7
Bonnet release handle bolts	10	7
Door glass channel bolts	8	6
Door glass regulator roller guide	8	6
Door glass regulator-to-door bolts	9	7
Door glass motor-to-regulator screws	7	5
Door glass-to-regulator bolts	9	7
Door latch-to-door screws	6	4
Door lock motor screws	7	5
Door lock striker-to-body screws	18	13
Door lock-to-outside handle bolt	9	7
Door outside handle bolts	9	7
Facia mounting bolts	9	7
Facia rail bolts:		
M6	10	7
M8	20	15
Facia support panel-to-body bolts	20	15
Front bumper armature to body	10	7
Front door glass rear channel bolts	8	6
Rear bumper-to-body bolts	6	4
Rear door upper rear glass channel nuts	8	6

Torque wrench settings (continued)

	Nm	lbf ft
Seats and seat belts:		
Centre rear seat belt reel-to-seat frame bolt	50	37
Front seat belt floor guide-to-sill bolt	50	37
Front seat belt lower anchorage bolt	50	37
Front seat belt pretensioner-to-seat bolt	30	22
Front seat belt reel-to-B-post bolt	50	37
Front seat belt runner-to-floor bolts	34	25
Outer rear seat belt lower anchorage bolt	50	37
Outer rear seat belt reel locating bolt	10	7
Outer rear seat belt reel-to-squab bolt	50	37
Outer rear seat belt stalk-to-floor bolt	50	37
Outer rear seat belt upper anchorage bolt	50	37
Rear seat cushion-to-floor bolts	10	7
Tailgate hinges-to-body bolts	22	16
Tailgate latch-to-tailgate screws	7	5
Tailgate lock motor screws	9	7
Tailgate lock striker-to-body screws	9	7
Undertray bolts and nuts	10	7

1 General information

The vehicle bodyshell is made of pressed-steel sections in three and five-door hatchback versions. Most components are welded together but some use is made of structural adhesives. The front wings are bolted on.

The bonnet, door, tailgate and some other vulnerable panels are made of zinc-coated metal. Once assembled, the entire body is given an eight-stage pretreatment process including a high-pressure wash before painting. The first coat of primer is applied by cathodic electro-deposition, followed by four coats of paint and two of lacquer. An anti-stone chip coating (finished in matt black, where exposed) is applied to the outer faces of the sills and the corresponding surfaces of the front and rear wings. A PVC coating is applied to the underbody, followed by a coating of protective wax. All chassis members, box-sections and sills are injected with liquid cavity wax.

Several of the body cavities are filled with 'expand-in-place' foam. This process features a two-part liquid silicon foam and hardener mix which is injected into the cavities after the body has been painted and wax treated. The foam improves the noise insulation of the vehicle and is flame retardant. The foam is also hydrophobic, that is, it repels water.

Extensive use is made of plastic materials, mainly on the interior but also in exterior components such as the wheel arch liners to improve the body's resistance to corrosion.

2 Minor body damage – repair

Minor scratches

If the scratch is very superficial, and does not penetrate to the metal of the bodywork, repair is very simple. Lightly rub the area of the scratch with a paintwork renovator, or a very fine cutting paste, to remove loose paint from the scratch, and to clear the surrounding bodywork of wax polish. Rinse the area with clean water.

Apply touch-up paint to the scratch using a fine paint brush; continue to apply fine layers of paint until the surface of the paint in the scratch is level with the surrounding paintwork. Allow the new paint at least two weeks to harden, then blend it into the surrounding paintwork by rubbing the scratch area with a paintwork renovator or a very fine cutting paste. Finally, apply wax polish.

Where the scratch has penetrated right through to the metal of the bodywork, causing the metal to rust, a different repair technique is required. Remove any loose rust from the bottom of the scratch with a penknife, then apply rust-inhibiting paint to prevent the formation of rust in the future. Using a rubber or nylon applicator, fill the scratch with bodystopper paste. If required, this paste can be mixed with cellulose thinners to provide a very thin paste which is ideal for filling narrow scratches. Before the stopper-paste in the scratch hardens, wrap a piece of smooth cotton rag around the top of a finger. Dip the finger in cellulose thinners, and quickly sweep it across the surface of the stopper-paste in the scratch; this will ensure that the surface of the stopper-paste is slightly hollowed. The scratch can now be painted over as described earlier in this Section.

Dents

When deep denting of the vehicle's bodywork has taken place, the first task is to pull the dent out, until the affected bodywork almost attains its original shape. There is little point in trying to restore the original shape completely, as the metal in the damaged area will have stretched on impact, and cannot be reshaped fully to its original contour. It is better to bring the level of the dent up to a point which is about 3 mm below the level of the surrounding bodywork. In cases where the dent is very shallow anyway, it is not worth trying to pull it out at all. If the underside of the dent is accessible, it can be hammered out gently from behind, using a mallet with a wooden or plastic head. Whilst doing this, hold a suitable block of wood firmly against the outside of the panel, to absorb the impact from the hammer blows and thus prevent a large area of the bodywork from being 'belled-out'.

Should the dent be in a section of the bodywork which has a double skin, or some other factor making it inaccessible from behind, a different technique is called for. Drill several small holes through the metal inside the area – particularly in the deeper section. Then screw long self-tapping screws into the holes, just sufficiently for them to gain a good purchase in the metal. Now the dent can be pulled out by pulling on the protruding heads of the screws with a pair of pliers.

The next stage of the repair is the removal of the paint from the damaged area, and from an inch or so of the surrounding 'sound' bodywork. This is accomplished most easily by using a wire brush or abrasive pad on a power drill, although it can be done just as effectively by hand, using sheets of abrasive paper. To complete the preparation for filling, score the surface of the bare metal with a screwdriver or the tang of a file, or alternatively, drill small holes in the affected area. This will provide a really good 'key' for the filler paste.

To complete the repair, see the Section on filling and respraying.

Rust holes or gashes

Remove all paint from the affected area, and from an inch or so of the surrounding 'sound' bodywork, using an abrasive pad or a wire brush on a power drill. If these are not available, a few sheets of abrasive paper will do the job most effectively. With the paint removed, you will be able to judge the severity of the corrosion, and therefore decide whether to renew the whole panel (if this is possible) or to repair the affected area. New body panels are not as expensive as most people think, and it is often quicker and more satisfactory to fit a new panel than to attempt to repair large areas of corrosion.

Remove all fittings from the affected area, except those which will act as a guide to the original shape of the damaged bodywork (eg headlight shells etc). Then, using tin snips or a hacksaw blade, remove all loose metal and any other metal badly affected by corrosion. Hammer the edges of the hole inwards, in order to create a slight depression for the filler paste.

Wire-brush the affected area to remove the powdery rust from the surface of the remaining metal. Paint the affected area with rust-inhibiting paint, if the back of the rusted area is accessible, treat this also.

Before filling can take place, it will be necessary to block the hole in some way. This can be achieved by the use of aluminium or plastic mesh, or aluminium tape.

Aluminium or plastic mesh, or glass-fibre matting, is probably the best material to use for a large hole. Cut a piece to the approximate size and shape of the hole to be filled, then position it in the hole so that its edges are below the level of the surrounding bodywork. It can be retained in position by several blobs of filler paste around its periphery.

Aluminium tape should be used for small or very narrow holes. Pull a piece off the roll, trim it to the approximate size and shape required, then pull off the backing paper (if used) and stick the tape over the hole; it can be overlapped if the thickness of one piece is insufficient. Burnish down the edges of the tape with the handle of a screwdriver or similar, to ensure that the tape is securely attached to the metal underneath.

Filling and respraying

Before using this Section, see the Sections on dent, deep scratch, rust holes and gash repairs.

Many types of bodyfiller are available, but generally speaking, those proprietary kits which contain a tin of filler paste and a tube of resin hardener are best for this type of repair. A wide, flexible plastic or nylon applicator will be found invaluable for imparting a smooth and well-contoured finish to the surface of the filler.

Mix up a little filler on a clean piece of card or board – measure the hardener carefully (follow the maker's instructions on the pack), otherwise the filler will set too rapidly or too slowly. Using the applicator, apply the filler paste to the prepared area; draw the applicator across the surface of the filler to achieve the correct contour and to level the surface. As soon as a contour that approximates to the correct one is achieved, stop working the paste – if you carry on too long, the paste will become sticky and begin to 'pick-up' on the applicator. Continue to add thin layers of filler paste at 20-minute intervals, until the level of the filler is just proud of the surrounding bodywork.

Once the filler has hardened, the excess can be removed using a metal plane or file. From then on, progressively-finer grades of abrasive paper should be used, starting with a 40-grade production paper, and finishing with a 400-grade wet-and-dry paper. Always wrap the abrasive paper around a flat rubber, cork, or wooden block – otherwise the surface of the filler will not be completely flat. During the smoothing of the filler surface, the wet-and-dry paper should be periodically rinsed in water. This will ensure that a very smooth finish is imparted to the filler at the final stage.

At this stage, the 'dent' should be surrounded by a ring of bare metal, which in turn should be encircled by the finely 'feathered' edge of the good paintwork. Rinse the repair area with clean water, until all of the dust produced by the rubbing-down operation has gone.

Spray the whole area with a light coat of primer – this will show up any imperfections in the surface of the filler. Repair these imperfections with fresh filler paste or bodystopper, and once more smooth the surface with abrasive paper. Repeat this spray-and-repair procedure until you are satisfied that the surface of the filler, and the feathered edge of the paintwork, are perfect. Clean the repair area with clean water, and allow to dry fully. If bodystopper is used, it can be mixed with cellulose thinners to form a really thin paste which is ideal for filling small holes.

The repair area is now ready for final spraying. Paint spraying must be carried out in a warm, dry, windless and dust-free atmosphere. This condition can be created artificially if you have access to a large indoor working area, but if you are forced to work in the open, you will have to pick your day very carefully. If you are working indoors, dousing the floor in the work area with water will help to settle the dust which would otherwise be in the atmosphere. If the repair area is confined to one body panel, mask off the surrounding panels; this will help to minimise the effects of a slight mis-match in paint colours. Bodywork fittings (eg chrome strips, door handles etc) will also need to be masked off. Use genuine masking tape, and several thicknesses of newspaper, for the masking operations.

Before commencing to spray, agitate the aerosol can thoroughly, then spray a test area (an old tin, or similar) until the technique is mastered. Cover the repair area with a thick coat of primer; the thickness should be built up using several thin layers of paint, rather than one thick one. Using 400-grade wet-and-dry paper, rub down the surface of the primer until it is really smooth. While doing this, the work area should be thoroughly doused with water, and the wet-and-dry paper periodically rinsed in water. Allow to dry before spraying on more paint.

Spray on the top coat, again building up the thickness by using several thin layers of paint. Start spraying at one edge of the repair area, and then, using a side-to-side motion, work until the whole repair area and about 2 inches of the surrounding original paintwork is covered. Remove all masking material 10 to 15 minutes after spraying on the final coat of paint.

Allow the new paint at least two weeks to harden, then, using a paintwork renovator, or a very fine cutting paste, blend the edges of the paint into the existing paintwork. Finally, apply wax polish.

3 Plastic components – repair

With the use of more and more plastic body components by the vehicle manufacturers (eg bumpers. spoilers, and in some cases major body panels), rectification of more serious damage to such items has become a matter of either entrusting repair work to a specialist in this field, or renewing complete components. Repair of such damage by the DIY owner is not really feasible, owing to the cost of the equipment and materials required for effecting such repairs. The basic technique involves making a groove along the line of the crack in the plastic, using a rotary burr in a power drill. The damaged part is then welded back together, using a hot-air gun to heat up and fuse a plastic filler rod into the groove. Any excess plastic is then removed, and the area rubbed down to a smooth finish. It is important that a filler rod of the correct plastic is used, as body components can be made of a variety of different types (eg polycarbonate, ABS, polypropylene).

6.1a Remove the nut and bolt (arrowed) on each side . . .

6.1b . . . and the two bolts (arrowed) in the centre, securing the bumper to the bonnet lock platform

6.2 Remove the three bolts (arrowed) securing the bumper lower edge to the body

Damage of a less serious nature (abrasions, minor cracks etc) can be repaired by the DIY owner using a two-part epoxy filler repair material. Once mixed in equal proportions, this is used in similar fashion to the bodywork filler used on metal panels. The filler is usually cured in twenty to thirty minutes, ready for sanding and painting.

If the owner is renewing a complete component himself, or if he has repaired it with epoxy filler, he will be left with the problem of finding a suitable paint for finishing which is compatible with the type of plastic used. At one time, the use of a universal paint was not possible, owing to the complex range of plastics encountered in body component applications. Standard paints, generally speaking, will not bond to plastic or rubber satisfactorily. However, it is now possible to obtain a plastic body parts finishing kit which consists of a preprimer treatment, a primer and coloured top coat. Full instructions are normally supplied with a kit, but basically, the method of use is to first apply the preprimer to the component concerned, and allow it to dry for up to 30 minutes. Then the primer is applied, and left to dry for about an hour before finally applying the special-coloured top coat. The result is a correctly-coloured component, where the paint will flex with the plastic or rubber, a property that standard paint does not normally possess.

4 Major body damage – repair

Note: *Where serious damage has occurred to a vehicle, any repair is best left to a professional or a Rover agent with specialist equipment.*

Where serious damage has occurred, or large areas need renewal due to neglect, it means that complete new panels will need welding in. This is best left to professionals. If the damage is due to impact, it will also be necessary to check completely the alignment of the bodyshell. This can only be carried out accurately by a Rover dealer using special jigs. If the body is left misaligned, it is primarily dangerous as the vehicle will not handle properly and secondly, uneven stresses will be imposed on the steering, suspension and possibly transmission, causing abnormal wear or complete failure, particularly to items such as the tyres.

5 Body exterior trim panels – renewal

The exterior body and door trim strips are held in position with a special adhesive tape.

Removal requires the trim to be heated, to soften the adhesive, and then cut away from the door surface. Due to the high risk of damage to the vehicle's paintwork during this operation, it is recommended that work is entrusted to a Rover dealer.

6 Bumpers – removal and refitting

Front bumper

Removal

1 Remove the nut and bolt each side, and the two bolts in the centre, securing the bumper to the bonnet lock platform **(see illustrations)**.

2 Remove the three bolts securing the bumper lower edge to the body **(see illustration)**.

3 Remove the three screws each side securing the bumper to the wheel arch liners **(see illustration)**.

4 Ease the wheel arch liners away from the bumper then reach up and undo the two nuts each side securing the bumper to the front wings **(see illustrations)**.

5 With the help of an assistant, release the bumper from the front wings and body **(see**

6.3 Remove the three screws (arrowed) each side, securing the bumper to the wheel arch liners

6.4a Ease the wheel arch liners away from the bumper . . .

6.4b . . . then reach up and undo the two nuts (arrowed) each side, securing the bumper to the front wings

6.5 With the help of an assistant, release the bumper from the front wings and body

6.7a Remove the fixings securing the upper edge of the bumper to the bodywork by first undoing the centre screw . . .

6.7b . . . then prising out the plug beneath

illustration). When sufficient clearance exists, disconnect the direction indicator and, where fitted, the front foglamp wiring connectors, then remove the bumper from the car.

Refitting

6 Refitting is a reversal of the removal procedure.

Rear bumper

Removal

7 Open the tailgate, then remove the five screw plug fixings, securing the upper edge of the bumper to the bodywork. This kind of fixing is removed by first undoing the screw, then prising out the plug beneath using a forked implement **(see illustrations)**.

6.8 Remove the screws that secure the lower edge of the bumper to the wheel arch liners

8 Working at the lower corners of the bumper assembly, remove the two screws (one each side) that secure the bumper to the wheel arch liners **(see illustration)**.

9 Pull the wheel arch liners away from the bodywork slightly, then unscrew the bolts securing the upper corners of the bumper assembly to the bodywork **(see illustration)**.

10 Undo the screw securing the centre of the lower edge of the bumper to the bodywork **(see illustration)**.

11 With the help of an assistant, carefully pull the bumper assembly away from the car, ensuring that the edges of the assembly do not scratch the bodywork **(see illustration)**. On later models, when sufficient clearance exists, disconnect the wiring connectors at the number plate lamps.

Refitting

12 Refitting is a reverse of the removal sequence. Ensure that the bumper mounting nuts and bolts are tightened to their specified torque setting.

7 Radiator grille – removal and refitting

Removal

1 Remove two screw/rivets securing the front grille to the upper panel.

2 Release the grille from the retaining pegs and remove the grille.

Refitting

3 Refitting is a reversal of the removal procedure.

8 Bonnet – removal, refitting and adjustment

Removal

1 Open the bonnet and have an assistant support it. Mark the outline of each bonnet hinge to use as a guide when refitting.

2 Disconnect the windscreen washer supply pipe from the T-piece, and catch any fluid that spills out in a suitable container **(see illustration)**.

3 On models with heated washer jets, unplug the electrical wiring from the jets at the multiway connectors, then remove the bonnet sound insulation panel and release the washer jet wiring harness from the clips.

4 Undo the bonnet retaining bolts and, with the help of an assistant, carefully lift the bonnet away from the engine compartment. Note any shims which may be fitted between

6.9 Unscrew the bolts securing the upper corners of the bumper assembly to the bodywork

6.10 Undo the screw securing the centre of the lower edge of the bumper to the bodywork

6.11 Carefully pull the bumper assembly away from the rear of the car

8.2 Disconnect the windscreen washer supply pipe from the T-piece

the bonnet and hinge **(see illustration)**. Store the bonnet out of the way in a safe place.

Refitting and adjustment

5 Offer up the bonnet to the vehicle, position the shims (where fitted) between the bonnet and hinges, then fit and finger-tighten the retaining bolts, aligning the hinges with the marks made on removal (where applicable).

6 Reconnect the windscreen washer supply pipe. On models with heated washer jets, secure the harness to the bonnet with the securing clips, then refit the sound insulation panel.

7 Close the bonnet so that only the safety catch engages and check for the alignment of the bonnet by observing the gap between each edge of the bonnet and the surrounding body panels. If necessary, slacken the hinge bolts and realign the bonnet to suit. Once the bonnet is correctly aligned, tighten the hinge bolts to the specified torque.

8 Check that the bonnet height is correct as compared with that of the front wings. If necessary, adjust by slackening the locknut and rotating the relevant bonnet rubber stop, to alter its height.

9 Once the bonnet is correctly aligned, check that the bonnet fastens and releases in a satisfactory manner. If adjustment is necessary, remove the plastic lock cover then slacken the bonnet lock retaining bolts and adjust the position of the lock to suit. Once the lock is operating correctly, tighten its retaining bolts to the specified torque and refit the lock cover.

9.5a Slacken and withdraw the securing bolts . . .

8.4 Undo the bonnet retaining bolts

9 Bonnet release cable – removal and refitting

Removal

1 Refer to Section 10 and remove the bonnet lock assembly.

2 Refer to Section 6 and remove the nuts that secure the upper edge of the bumper assembly to the lock mounting platform. Carefully prise the edge of the bumper away from the mounting platform, then free the bonnet release cable from its securing clips as they become accessible. Withdraw the cable from the mounting platform.

3 Work along the length of the cable and release it from any remaining retaining clips in the engine compartment.

4 Release the securing studs and remove the cover from the fusebox, located on the underside of the driver's side of the facia. Release the clips and lower the felt panel from the space above the driver's footwell.

5 Slacken and withdraw the securing bolts, then detach the bonnet release knob mounting bracket from the bodywork. Remove the cable from the mounting bracket **(see illustrations)**.

6 Release the cable sealing grommet from the bulkhead. Pull the cable through from inside the vehicle and remove it from the vehicle.

Refitting

7 Refitting is a reversal of removal. Ensure

9.5b . . . then detach the bonnet release knob mounting bracket from the bodywork

that the cable is routed correctly and is not kinked or twisted. Refit the lock mechanism with reference to Section 10, then check that the operation of the release cable is satisfactory before securing the bumper in place.

10 Bonnet lock – removal, refitting and adjustment

Removal

1 Remove the front grille – see Section 7.

2 Pull out the press-stud from the bottom of the plastic lock cover.

3 To aid correct refitting, mark the position of the lock on the upper panel.

4 Remove three bolts securing the lock to the upper panel. Release the lock cable and remove the lock.

Refitting

5 Refitting is a reversal of the removal procedure noting:

Align the lock with the marks made before removal.

Use a torque wrench to tighten the lock bolts to the specified torque.

Close and open the bonnet to check lock operation. If necessary, adjust the lock position.

Fit the front grille – see Section 7.

11 Door lock, lock cylinder and handles – removal and refitting

Removal

Front door lock mechanism

1 Disconnect the battery negative cable and position it away from the terminal. Refer to the relevant sub-Section and remove the exterior door handle.

2 Release the clip and detach the outside door handle control rod from the lock mechanism. Where applicable, detach the lock cylinder control rod from the lock mechanism in the same manner.

3 Refer to the relevant sub-Section and remove the interior door handle. Detach the control rod from the rear of the handle assembly.

4 Slacken and remove the bolts that secure the window glass rear guide channel to the door. Remove the guide channel from the door to give access to the lock mechanism **(see illustrations)**.

5 Undo the lock mechanism securing screws and detach the mechanism from the door. On models with central locking, unplug the wiring harness from the lock mechanism at the multiway connector **(see illustrations)**.

11.4a Remove the bolts that secure the window glass rear guide channel to the door . . .

11.4b . . . and the guide channel from the door to give access to the lock mechanism

11.5a Undo the lock mechanism securing screws and detach the mechanism from the door . . .

11.5b . . . and unplug the wiring harness at the multiway connector (models with central locking)

11.6a Release the interior handle and locking knob control rods from the lock mechanism . . .

11.6b . . . then manoeuvre the lock mechanism from the door, guiding the remaining control rods through the aperture

6 Release the interior handle and locking knob control rods from the lock mechanism, then manoeuvre the lock mechanism from the door, guiding the remaining control rods through the aperture **(see illustrations)**.

Rear door lock mechanism

7 Disconnect the battery negative cable and position it away from the terminal. Refer to the relevant sub-Section and remove the exterior door handle.

8 Release the clip and detach the interior door handle control rod from the lock mechanism. Detach the locking knob control rod from the lock mechanism in the same manner **(see illustration)**.

9 On models with central locking, release the wiring harness from the securing clip, then unplug the harness from the lock mechanism at the multiway connector **(see illustration)**.

10 Undo the lock mechanism securing screws and detach the mechanism from the door **(see illustration)**.

11 Manoeuvre the lock mechanism from the door **(see illustration)**.

Front door lock cylinder

12 Ensure the window glass is fully up then remove the door inner trim panel and waterproof membrane. Disconnect the battery negative cable and position it away from the terminal.

13 Slacken and withdraw the lock cylinder retaining bolt.

14 Release the clip and detach the lock mechanism control rod from the lever at the rear of the lock cylinder.

15 Manoeuvre the lock cylinder from the door.

Interior door handle

16 Remove the inner trim panel and the waterproof membrane.

11.8 Detach the interior door handle and locking knob control rods (arrowed) from the lock mechanism

11.10 Undo the lock mechanism securing screws . . .

17 Undo the screws securing the interior handle to the door, then disconnect the handle from its operating rod and remove it from the vehicle **(see illustration)**.

11.9 On models with central locking, unplug the harness from the lock mechanism at the multiway connector

11.11 . . . and manoeuvre the lock mechanism from the door

11.17 Interior door handle securing screws (arrowed)

11.19 Front door exterior handle securing bolts (one hidden from view)

11.20 Release the clips and disconnect the lock mechanism control rod from the handle

11.22a Undo the two retaining bolts and withdraw the handle from the door . . .

11.22b . . . release the clip and disconnect the lock mechanism control rod (arrowed) from the handle

Front door exterior handle

18 Remove the inner trim panel and partially peel back the waterproof membrane, to gain access to the rear of the exterior handle retaining bolts. Ensure that the window glass is fully raised. Disconnect the battery negative cable and position it away from the terminal.
19 Undo the two retaining bolts and detach the handle from the door **(see illustration)**.
20 Release the clips and disconnect the lock mechanism control rod from the handle **(see illustration)**.

Rear door exterior handle

21 Remove the inner trim panel and partially peel back the waterproof membrane, to gain access to the rear of the exterior handle retaining bolts.
22 Undo the two retaining bolts and withdraw the handle from the door. Release the clip and

disconnect the lock mechanism control rod from the handle **(see illustrations)**.
23 Remove the handle from the door aperture.

Refitting

24 Refitting is the reverse of the removal sequence, noting the following:
a) *Tighten all retaining bolts to the specified torque settings.*
b) *Ensure that all operating rods are securely held in position by the retaining clips.*
c) *Apply grease to all lock and operating rod pivot points.*
d) *Before fitting the inner trim panel, thoroughly check the operation of all the door lock handles and, where necessary, the central locking system. Ensure that the water membrane is securely stuck to the door.*

12 Doors –
removal, refitting and adjustment

Note: *If there is insufficient slack in the wiring to be able to withdraw the wiring connectors from the door panel, then it will be necessary to remove the inner trim panel and peel back the waterproof membrane to gain further access.*

Removal

1 Open the door and peel back the wiring gaiter, or displace the wiring grommet from the front edge of the door panel. Carefully withdraw the wiring from the door until the wiring connector(s) emerge. Disconnect the block connector(s) and tape the door side of the connectors to the door frame to prevent them falling back into the door panel **(see illustration)**.
2 Mark the outline position of each door hinge to use as a guide when refitting.
3 Remove the retaining clip (where fitted) and extract the pin securing the door check link to the door pillar **(see illustration)**.
4 Have an assistant support the door and undo the nuts which secure the upper and lower hinges to the door, then remove the door from the vehicle.
5 If necessary, the hinges can now be unbolted and removed from the door pillar, having first marked the position of the hinge on the pillar. To gain access to the front door hinge bolts, it will first be necessary to remove the wheel arch liner.

Refitting and adjustment

6 The door is refitted by a reversal of the removal procedure. Align the hinges with the marks made on removal and tighten the bolts securely.
7 On completion, shut the door carefully and check that the door is correctly aligned with all surrounding bodywork with an equal clearance all around. If necessary, adjustment can be made by slackening the hinge bolts and moving the door. Once the door is positioned correctly, tighten the hinge bolts securely.

12.1 Unplug the door wiring from the block connectors

12.3 Extract the pin (arrowed) securing the door check link to the door pillar

8 With the door correctly aligned, check that it closes easily, is flush with the adjacent panels and does not rattle when closed. If not, slacken the door striker retaining screws and reposition the striker. Once door operation is satisfactory, tighten the striker retaining screws securely.

13 Door inner trim panel – removal and refitting

Removal

Front door

1 Carefully prise the centre escutcheon from the door handle outer escutcheon – it is held by three clips.
2 Carefully prise the outer escutcheon from the door – it is held by four clips.
3 Carefully prise the escutcheon from the door pull handle.
4 Remove three screws securing the door pull to the door, and remove the door pull.
5 On models with manually-operated windows, remove the spring clip from behind the window regulator handle, by hooking it out with a screwdriver or a piece of bent wire. Remove the handle and escutcheon **(see illustrations)**.
6 Remove screw covers and two screws securing the trim panel to the door – one screw at top outer edge, and one screw at lower inner edge.
7 Working around the edge of the panel, carefully pull the panel away from the door to release six clips securing the panel to the door.
8 As the panel is removed from the door, ensure that it is raised to release the door locking button. Disconnect the multi-plug from the tweeter, and remove the panel.

Rear door

9 Carefully prise the escutcheon from the door pull handle.
10 Remove three screws securing the door pull to the door, and remove the door pull.
11 Carefully prise the centre escutcheon from the door handle outer escutcheon – it is held by three clips.
12 Carefully prise the outer escutcheon from the door – it is held by four clips.
13 On models with manually-operated windows, remove the spring clip from behind the window regulator handle, by hooking it out with a screwdriver or a piece of bent wire. Remove the handle and escutcheon.
14 Remove the screw cover and one screw securing the trim panel to the door.
15 Working around the edge of the panel, carefully pull the panel away from the door to release six clips securing the panel to the door.
16 As the panel is removed from the door, ensure that it is raised to release the door locking button – note that the button trim may need to be prised out to release the button.

13.5a Remove the regulator handle horseshoe clip (arrowed) by hooking it out with a screwdriver . . .

17 On models with electrically-operated windows, disconnect the multi-plug from the window switch.

Refitting

18 Refitting is a reversal of the removal procedure, noting:
On models with manually-operated windows, first fit the spring clip to the regulator, then push the regulator onto the spindle.

14 Door window glass and regulator – removal and refitting

Front door glass and regulator

Removal

1 Remove the front door inner trim panel and waterproof membrane (see Section 13).
2 On models equipped with electrically-operated windows, temporarily reconnect the window switch wiring connector(s) and position the glass so that access can be gained to both glass retaining bolts via the cutaway in the door panel.
3 On models equipped with manually-operated windows, temporarily refit the regulator handle and position the glass so that its retaining bolts can be accessed through the cutaway in the door.
4 Undo the two bolts securing the window glass to the regulator, then lift up the glass and manoeuvre it out of the door **(see illustrations)**.

14.4b . . . then lift up the glass and manoeuvre it out of the door

13.5b . . . then pull the handle off the spindle

5 On models with electric windows, unplug the wiring connector from the regulator motor and release the wiring harness from its securing clips **(see illustration)**.
6 Mark the position of the two regulator roller guide retaining bolts, in relation to the door. Slacken and withdraw all six regulator assembly retaining bolts, then manoeuvre the assembly out through the door panel aperture **(see illustrations)**.
7 The window regulator motor can be removed as follows: mark the relationship between the regulator and the geared segment using a marker pen or similar, then undo the three securing screws and withdraw the motor from the regulator.

Refitting

8 Apply a small amount of general purpose grease to the motor gear, then refit the motor to the regulator assembly using the alignment

14.4a Undo the two bolts securing the window glass to the regulator . . .

14.5 On models with electric windows, unplug the wiring connector from the regulator motor

14.6a Slacken and withdraw the regulator assembly retaining bolts . . .

14.6b . . . then manoeuvre the assembly out through the door panel aperture

14.17a Slacken the securing bolts and detach the glass from the regulator . . .

14.17b . . . manoeuvre the glass to the bottom of the door aperture and allow it to rest on the padding

14.18 Carefully peel the rubber seal at the top of the window aperture away from the rear glass channel

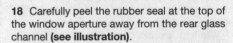

14.19 Slacken and remove the securing nuts (arrowed) and detach the rear glass channel from the door

marks made during removal. Insert the securing screws and tighten them to the specified torque.

9 Lubricate the regulator joints and pivot points using a multi-purpose grease.

10 Refit the regulator to the door panel and lightly tighten its retaining bolts. Position the roller guide according to the alignment marks made during removal, then tighten the retaining bolts to the specified torque.

11 On models with electric windows, reconnect the wiring harness multiway plug.

12 Install the window glass and tighten the glass-to-regulator bolts to the specified torque.

13 Operate the regulator mechanism a few times to check that the window travels up-and-down smoothly.

14 Refit the waterproof membrane to the door ensuring that it is securely stuck down around the edges. The remainder of refitting is a reversal of the removal procedure.

Rear door glass and regulator

Removal

15 Remove the rear door inner trim panel and waterproof membrane.

16 Temporarily refit the regulator handle and position the window glass such that its retaining bolts can be accessed through the cutaway in the door panel.

17 Line the bottom of the door aperture with a thick wad of rags or newspapers, to act as padding. Slacken the securing bolts and detach the glass from the regulator. Manoeuvre the glass to the bottom of the door aperture and allow it to rest on the padding (see illustrations).

18 Carefully peel the rubber seal at the top of the window aperture away from the rear glass channel (see illustration).

19 Slacken and remove the securing nuts and detach the rear glass channel from the door (see illustration).

20 Manoeuvre the glass panel past the regulator and lift it out of the door aperture (see illustration).

21 Undo the four regulator securing bolts and manoeuvre the regulator assembly from the door (see illustrations).

Refitting

22 Refitting is a reversal of removal. Before the door inner trim panel is refitted, operate the regulator mechanism a few times to check that the window travels up-and-down smoothly, before tightening the glass channel securing nuts to their specified torque.

14.20 Manoeuvre the glass panel past the regulator and lift it out of the door aperture

14.21a Undo the four regulator securing bolts . . .

14.21b . . . and manoeuvre the regulator assembly from the door

15 Exterior mirror – removal and refitting

Mirror glass

Removal

1 Place a hand on the mirror glass and push down on the inside edge.

2 Keeping the glass pushed down, slide it away from the mirror housing.

3 Lift the glass away from the housing, ensuring that the damper blade stays with the mirror.

4 On models with electric mirrors, disconnect two Lucar connectors from the glass, and remove the glass.

Refitting

5 Refitting is a reversal of the removal procedure

Manual mirror assembly

Removal

6 Remove the door interior trim panel – see Section 13.

7 Carefully prise off the trim panel from the corner panel at the back of the mirror, and remove the escutcheon.

8 Remove three Torx head bolts securing the mirror to the corner panel, and remove the mirror.

Refitting

9 Refitting is a reversal of the removal procedure.

Electric mirror assembly

Removal

10 Disconnect the battery earth lead.

11 Remove the door interior trim panel – see Section 13.

12 Disconnect the multi-plug from the mirror.

13 Carefully prise off the trim panel from the corner panel at the back of the mirror, and remove the escutcheon.

14 Remove three Torx head bolts securing the mirror to the corner panel, and remove the mirror.

Refitting

15 Refitting is a reversal of the removal procedure.

16 Tailgate – removal, refitting and adjustment

Removal

1 Open the tailgate and undo the screws (two each side) securing both tailgate side trim panels in place.

2 Using a large, flat-bladed screwdriver, work around the outside of each side trim panel

16.3 Displace the grommet from the tailgate and withdraw the wiring

and carefully prise it away from the tailgate, to free the retaining clips. Once all the retaining clips have been freed, remove the side trim panels. Prise the upper trim panel away from the tailgate in the same manner.

3 Disconnect the two wiring block connectors, situated on the right-hand side of the tailgate, which connect the tailgate electrical components to the main wiring loom. Tie a piece of string around the wiring side of the block connector, then displace the grommet from the upper right-hand corner of the tailgate and withdraw the wiring (see illustration). Once free, untie the string from the end of the wiring and leave it in place in the tailgate. The string can then be used to draw the wiring back into position when refitting.

4 Disconnect the washer hose from the tailgate grommet.

5 Mark the positions of the hinges on the tailgate.

6 Have an assistant support the tailgate then raise the spring clips and pull the support struts off their balljoint studs on the tailgate (see Section 17). Undo the four hinge retaining bolts and remove the tailgate from the vehicle, noting the positions of any shims which may be fitted between the hinge and tailgate (see illustration).

Refitting and adjustment

7 Offer up the tailgate, positioning any shims necessary between the hinge and tailgate. Refit the hinge bolts. Press the support struts firmly onto the balljoint mountings and clip the spring clips back into position. Align the hinges with the marks made on removal, or centralise the hinges, and tighten the retaining bolts securely.

8 Tie the string around the end of the tailgate wiring and draw the wiring back into position. Untie the string, then reconnect the wiring harness plugs and relocate the grommet in the tailgate.

9 Renew any broken retaining clips, then refit the upper and side trim panels to the tailgate. Ensure both side panels are securely clipped in position then refit and tighten the retaining screws. Reconnect the washer hose to the tailgate grommet.

10 On completion, shut the tailgate and check that it is correctly aligned with the

16.6 Tailgate hinge retaining bolts (arrowed)

surrounding bodywork. If adjustment is necessary, slacken the hinge bolts and reposition the tailgate as necessary. Once alignment is correct, tighten the hinge bolts to the specified torque.

11 If correct alignment is not possible by repositioning the tailgate, it will be necessary to alter the hinge-to-body position. To do this, release the rubber tailgate sealing strip from the top edge of the body aperture and extract the stud fixings securing the headlining in position. Peel the sealant away from the joint between the hinge and the bodywork. Slacken the hinge bolts and reposition the tailgate to suit (see illustration). On completion, tighten the hinge retaining bolts to the specified torque. Finally, relocate the headlining and tailgate sealing strip, then apply a bead of silicone sealant to the joint between the hinge and bodywork.

12 Adjust the height of the tailgate by screwing the rubber stop in or out, as necessary, then check that the tailgate closes easily and does not rattle when closed. If adjustment is necessary, slacken the tailgate striker retaining screws and reposition the striker. Once the tailgate operation is satisfactory, tighten the striker retaining bolts securely.

17 Tailgate support strut – removal and refitting

Removal

1 Support the tailgate in the open position by

16.11 Slacken the bolts and reposition the tailgate hinges to achieve correct tailgate-to-body alignment

17.2 Raise the balljoint spring clip and pull the support strut off the tailgate mounting

18.2 Removing the interior trim panel from the tailgate

18.3 On models with central locking, disconnect the motor link rod (arrowed) from the lock mechanism lever

using a stout piece of wood, or with the help of an assistant.

2 Raise the spring clip and pull the support strut off its balljoint mounting on the tailgate **(see illustration)**. The strut may extend

suddenly when released from its upper mounting, so keep it compressed by hand and allow the spring pressure to release slowly.

3 Detach the lower of the strut from the

bodywork mounting in a similar manner, then remove the strut from the vehicle.

Refitting

4 Refitting is the reverse sequence of removal. Ensure that the strut is pressed firmly onto each of its balljoints and the spring clips are correctly positioned.

18.4a Slacken and withdraw the securing screws . . .

18.4b . . . then lift the lock assembly from the tailgate

18 Tailgate lock and lock cylinder – removal and refitting

Tailgate lock

Removal

1 Open the tailgate and undo the two screws securing the tailgate inner trim panel to the tailgate, then carefully prise out the screw retaining plugs.

2 Using a large flat-bladed screwdriver, work around the outside of the trim panel and carefully prise it away from the tailgate to free all the retaining clips **(see illustration)**. Once all the clips have been freed, remove the trim panel.

3 Disconnect the release cable from the latch mechanism then, on models with central locking, disconnect the motor link rod from the lock mechanism lever **(see illustration)**.

4 Slacken and withdraw the securing screws, then lift the lock assembly from the tailgate **(see illustrations)**.

5 Where applicable, unplug the wiring at the connector, then remove the two retaining screws and withdraw the lock motor from the tailgate **(see illustrations)**.

Refitting

6 Refitting is a reverse of the removal sequence.

18.5a Unplug the lock motor wiring at the connector . . .

18.5b . . . then remove the two retaining screws and withdraw the lock motor from the tailgate

Tailgate latch

Removal

7 Open the tailgate and remove the lower trim panel, as described in the previous sub-Section.

8 Unclip the moulded cover from the latch mechanism, then slacken and remove the latch retaining bolts **(see illustrations)**.

18.8a Unclip the moulded cover from the latch mechanism . . .

18.8b . . . then slacken and remove the latch retaining bolts

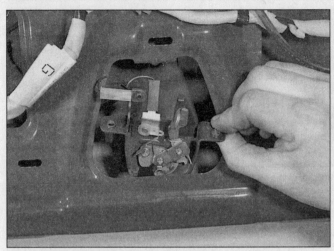

18.9 Lift the latch mechanism away from the tailgate

18.10 Unplug the switch wiring from the latch at the connectors

9 Lift the latch mechanism away from the tailgate, then detach the release cable from the operating lever **(see illustration)**.

10 Unplug the switch wiring from the latch at the connectors, then remove the latch from the vehicle **(see illustration)**.

Refitting

11 Refitting is a reverse of the removal procedure.

19 Quarterlight glass – removal and refitting

Removal

5-door models

1 Refer to Section 14 and remove the rear door window glass.

2 Pull the quarterlight from the door, together with the sealing strip **(see illustration)**.

3-door models

3 Remove the rear window parcel shelf, then remove the rear seat back and cushion, as described in Section 22.

4 Refer to Section 24 and unbolt the relevant rear passenger lower seat belt anchorage from the floorpan. Unclip the seat belt aperture trim from the parcel shelf support panel.

5 At the underside of the parcel shelf support panel, disconnect the wiring from the luggage compartment light and the rear speakers.

6 Remove the screws and stud fixings, then disengage the clip at the front of the parcel shelf support panel and lift it away from the bodywork.

7 Open the front door, then prise enough of the rubber seal away from the rear of the door aperture to reveal the edge of the rear quarter lower trim panel.

8 Open the quarterlight and prise the rubber seal away from the lower edge of the quarterlight aperture, to reveal the upper edge of the rear quarter lower trim panel.

9 Remove the three screws securing the rear quarter lower trim panel in position, then carefully prise the panel away from the body with a suitable forked instrument, to release the remaining press-stud fixings. Once all the fixings have been released, remove the trim panel from the vehicle.

10 Extract the screw-stud fixing and remove the door B-pillar trim panel. Similarly, extract the screw stud fixing and remove the tailgate D-pillar trim panel. Prise the alarm system volumetric sensor from the B-pillar trim panel and unplug the wiring from it at the connector.

11 Refer to Section 24 and unbolt the front seat belt upper mounting from the anchorage. Note that the securing bolt must be renewed.

12 Open the tailgate and prise the rubber seal away from the side of the tailgate aperture to reveal the rear edge of the rear quarter upper trim panel.

13 Working around the edge of the rear quarter upper trim panel, use a suitable forked instrument to release all of the press-stud fixings in turn and then detach the trim panel from the bodywork.

14 Mark the position of the quarterlight rear catch on the body, then remove the three hinge retaining screws.

15 Support the window glass, undo the two

19.2 Pull the quarterlight from the door, together with the sealing strip (5-door model)

front hinge retaining nuts, then release the glass from the clip at its leading edge and remove it from the vehicle.

Refitting

5-door models

16 Refitting is a reversal of removal.

3-door models

17 Refitting is a reverse of the removal sequence, noting the following:
a) Align the rear window catch with the marks made on dismantling and lightly tighten the retaining screws.
b) Close the window and check that it is correctly aligned with the surrounding bodywork. Adjust, if necessary, by repositioning the hinge, then tighten all the hinge retaining screws securely.
c) Where possible, renew any broken trim panel retaining clips.
d) Tighten the new seat belt upper mounting nut to the specified torque, with reference to the relevant Section in this Chapter.
e) On completion, ensure all trim panels are securely retained and the door/window/tailgate seals are correctly located.

20 Windscreen and tailgate glass – general information

These areas of glass are bonded directly the body aperture. The process of removing and refitting areas of glass that are secured in this manner can be difficult, messy and time-consuming, particularly for the inexperienced. Without plenty of practice, it is very difficult to obtain a secure, waterproof fit. Furthermore, the task carries a high risk of breakage; this applies especially to the laminated glass windscreen. In view of this, owners are strongly advised to have work of this nature carried out by one of the many specialist windscreen fitters.

21.2a Unscrew the circular access cover in the panel in the headlining, between the sun visors . . .

21 Sunroof – repair

1 An electrically-operated sunroof is available as an option (or standard fit) on all models. Due to the complexity of the sunroof mechanism, considerable expertise is needed to repair or replace sunroof components successfully. Removal of the sunroof requires the headlining to be removed, which is a complex and tedious operation and not a task to be undertaken lightly. Any problems with the sunroof should therefore be referred to a Rover dealer.

2 If the sunroof motor fails to operate, first check the relevant fuse. If the fault cannot be traced and rectified, then the sunroof can be opened and closed manually by using a suitable cranked screwdriver. Use a

22.2 Remove the Torx bolts securing the rear of the seat runners to the floor

22.4 Unplug the wiring from the seat belt pretensioner at the multiway connector

21.2b . . . and insert the wrench into the drive spindle. Rotate the key to move the sunroof to the required position

screwdriver or coin to unscrew the circular access cover in the panel in the headlining, situated between the sun visors, and insert the wrench into the drive spindle. Rotate the key to move the sunroof to the required position (see illustrations). A suitable wrench is supplied with the vehicle and should be in the luggage compartment where it is stowed next to the wheel trim remover.

22 Seats – removal and refitting

Front seats

 Warning: All models are fitted with front seat belt pretensioners. Before removing the front seat(s),

22.3 Undo the Torx bolts securing the front of the seat runners to the floor

22.7a Press down on the rear seat cushion to expose the securing bolts . . .

read the Supplementary Restraint System (SRS) safety information given in Chapter 12. Failure to observe the precautions could result in accidental detonation of the seat belt pretensioners.

Removal

1 Remove the ignition key and wait **AT LEAST TEN MINUTES** to allow the system backup circuit to fully discharge. Disconnect **BOTH** battery leads (negative lead first) from the battery and position them well away from the battery terminals. Failure to observe this procedure could cause accidental detonation of the airbag and/or seat belt pretensioners.

2 Slide the seat fully forwards, then slacken and remove the two Torx bolts securing the rear of the seat runners to the floor (**see illustration**).

3 Slide the seat fully rearwards, then undo the two Torx bolts securing the front of the seat runners to the floor (**see illustration**).

4 Where applicable, reach underneath the seat and unplug the wiring from the seat belt pretensioner at the multiway connector (**see illustration**).

5 Lift the seat, together with its runners, away from the floorpan and remove it from the vehicle.

Refitting

6 Refitting is a reversal of removal.

Rear seat cushion

Removal

7 Press down the rear edge of the cushion to expose the three cushion securing bolts. Slacken and withdraw the bolts, then pivot the cushion forward and unhook the leading edge from the floorpan (**see illustrations**).

Refitting

8 Refitting is a reversal of removal.

Rear seat back

Removal

9 Remove the rear seat cushion, as described in the previous sub-Section.

10 Refer to Section 24 and unbolt each of the rear seat belt lower anchorage brackets from the floorpan.

22.7b . . . pivot the cushion forward and unhook the leading edge from the floorpan

22.11a Rotate the centre hinge clamp bolt clockwise . . .

22.11b . . . until the hinge pin can be withdrawn from the bracket

22.12 Release the pins from the outer seat back hinges (arrowed)

11 Working at the rear of the seat back, rotate the centre hinge clamp bolt clockwise, until the hinge pin can be withdrawn from the bracket **(see illustrations)**. There is no need to remove the clamp bolt completely.

12 Release the pins from the outer seat back hinges and then lift the seat back out of the vehicle **(see illustration)**.

Refitting

13 Refitting is a reversal of removal. Tighten the seat belt lower anchorage bracket bolts to the correct torque.

23 Interior trim – removal and refitting

Interior trim panels

1 The interior trim panels are secured either by screws or by various types of trim fasteners, usually studs or clips.

2 Check that there are no other panels overlapping the one to be removed. Usually there is a sequence that has to be followed that will become obvious on close inspection.

3 Remove all obvious fasteners, such as screws. If the panel will not come free then it is held by hidden clips or fasteners. These are usually situated around the edge of the panel and can be prised up to release them. Note, however, that they can break quite easily, so care should be exercised. The best way of releasing such clips in the absence of the correct type of tool, is to use a large flat-bladed screwdriver. Pad the screwdriver blade by wrapping insulating tape around it, to avoid scratching paintwork. Note that in many cases, rubber sealing strips (such as those fitted to door or tailgate apertures) may need to be prised back when releasing a panel.

4 When removing a panel, never use excessive force or the panel may be damaged. Always check carefully that all fasteners have been removed or released before attempting to withdraw a panel.

5 When refitting a panel, secure the fasteners by pressing them firmly into place and ensure that all disturbed components are correctly secured to prevent rattles. Use a suitable trim

adhesive (a Rover dealer should be able to recommend a proprietary product) on reassembly.

HAYNES HINT *If adhesives were found at any point on removal, use white spirit to remove all traces of old adhesive, then wash off all traces of spirit using soapy water.*

Carpets

6 The passenger compartment floor carpet is in one piece and is secured at its edges by screws or clips, usually the same fasteners used to secure the various adjoining trim panels.

7 Carpet removal and refitting is reasonably straightforward but very time-consuming due to the fact that all adjoining trim panels must be removed first, as must components such as the seats, the centre console and seat belt lower anchorages.

Headlining

8 The headlining is clipped to the roof and can be withdrawn once all fittings such as the grab handles, sun visors, sunroof (if fitted), windscreen and rear quarterlights and related trim panels have been removed and the door, tailgate and sunroof aperture sealing strips have been prised clear.

9 Note that headlining removal and refitting requires considerable skill and experience if it is to be carried out without damage and is therefore best entrusted to an expert.

24.1a Carefully prise the rubber seal from the rear edge of the front door aperture . . .

24 Seat belts – removal and refitting

Removal

⚠️ *Warning: All models are fitted with front seat belt pre-tensioners. Before disturbing the front seat belt(s), read the Supplementary Restraint System (SRS) safety information given in Chapter 12. Failure to observe the precautions could result in accidental detonation of the seat belt pretensioners.*

Note: *All seat belt fasteners must be renewed.*

Front seat belt – 5-door models

1 Carefully prise the rubber seal from the rear edge of the front door aperture, then release the clips and remove the B-pillar lower trim panel **(see illustrations)**.

2 Remove the bolt cover at the belt upper mounting, undo the seat belt retaining bolt and detach the belt **(see illustrations)**.

3 Remove the cap from the seat belt lower mounting bolt then undo the Torx bolt and detach the belt from the bodywork **(see illustration)**.

4 Undo the bolt securing the inertia reel unit to the base of the door B-pillar and remove the reel and seat belt assembly from the vehicle **(see illustration)**.

Front seat belt – 3-door models

5 Remove the rear window parcel shelf, then

24.1b . . . then release the clips and remove the B-pillar lower trim panel

24.2a Remove the bolt cover at the belt upper mounting . . .

24.2b . . . and undo the seat belt retaining bolt and detach the belt

24.3 Undo the Torx bolt and detach the seat belt lower mounting from the bodywork

24.4 Undo the bolt securing the inertia reel unit to the base of the door B-pillar

24.19a Slacken and withdraw the screws . . .

24.19b . . . and remove the rear parcel shelf support panel (5-door model)

remove the rear seat back and cushion, as described in Section 22. Unclip the rear side seat belt aperture trim from the parcel shelf support panel.

6 At the underside of the parcel shelf support panel, disconnect the wiring from the luggage compartment light and the rear speakers.

7 Remove the screws and stud fixings, then disengage the clip at the front of the parcel shelf support panel and lift it away from the bodywork.

8 Open the front door, then prise enough of the rubber seal away from the rear of the door aperture to reveal the edge of the rear quarter lower trim panel.

9 Open the rear quarterlight and prise the rubber seal away from the lower edge of the quarterlight aperture, to reveal the upper edge of the rear quarter lower trim panel.

10 Remove the three screws securing the rear quarter lower trim panel in position, then

carefully prise the panel away from the body with a suitable forked instrument to release the remaining press-stud fixings. Once all the fixings have been released, remove the trim panel from the vehicle.

11 Remove the bolt cover at the belt upper mounting, then undo the seat belt retaining bolt and detach the belt from the door B-pillar.

12 Unbolt the front of the seat belt lower guide rail from the bodywork. Slide the seat belt off the end of the guide rail.

13 Undo the bolt securing the inertia reel unit to the base of the door B-pillar, then remove the reel and seat belt assembly from the vehicle.

Front seat belt stalk and pretensioner

14 Refer to the information given in Chapter 12.

Rear seat side belt – 3-door models

15 Remove the rear quarter lower trim panel, as described in paragraphs 5 to 10.

16 Unbolt the seat belt lower anchorage bracket from the bodywork.

17 Slacken and withdraw the securing bolt and detach the seat belt stalk from the bodywork.

18 Undo the two securing bolts and remove the inertia reel unit from the seat back support bracket. Remove the seat belt assembly from the vehicle.

Rear seat side belt – 5-door models

19 Remove the rear parcel shelf support panel, as described in paragraphs 5 to 7 (see illustrations).

20 Open the rear door and prise the rubber seal away from the rear of the door aperture to expose the front edge of the rear quarter lower trim panel (see illustration).

21 Remove the securing screws and lift the rear quarter lower trim panel away from the bodywork (see illustration).

24.20 Prise the rubber seal away from the rear of the door aperture

24.21 Remove the securing screws and lift the rear quarter lower trim panel away from the bodywork

24.22 Unbolt the seat belt lower anchorage bracket from the bodywork

24.23 Withdraw the securing bolt and detach the seat belt stalk from the bodywork

22 Unbolt the seat belt lower anchorage bracket from the bodywork **(see illustration)**.
23 Slacken and withdraw the securing bolt and detach the seat belt stalk from the bodywork **(see illustration)**.
24 Undo the two securing bolts and remove the inertia reel unit from the seat back support bracket. Remove the seat belt assembly from the vehicle **(see illustrations)**.

Rear seat centre belt

25 Refer to Section 22 and remove the rear seat cushion.
26 Unbolt the seat belt lower anchorage bracket from the bodywork **(see illustration)**.
27 Slacken and withdraw the securing bolt and detach the seat belt stalk from the bodywork.
28 Open the tailgate and remove the parcel shelf.

25.1 Unclip the rear ashtray from its housing

25.2b . . . slacken and remove the two exposed securing screws

24.24a Inertia reel unit upper . . .

24.26 Unbolt the seat belt lower anchorage bracket from the bodywork

29 Undo the screws and lift off the seat belt inertia reel cover panel **(see illustration)**. Slacken and remove the securing nut then withdraw the inertia reel unit from the seat back.

25.2a Carefully prise up and remove the cover panel from the front edge of the console . . .

25.3 Lift the console up over the handbrake lever and remove it from the vehicle

24.24b . . . and lower mounting bolts

24.29 Remove the screws and lift off the seat belt inertia reel cover panel

Refitting

30 Refitting is a reversal of the removal procedure, noting:
Renew all seat belt fasteners.
Use a torque wrench to tighten all nuts and bolts to the specified torque.
Renew any damaged trim panel clips.

25 Rear console (pre-2004 models) – removal and refitting

Removal

1 Unclip the rear ashtray from its housing **(see illustration)**.
2 Carefully prise up and remove the cover panel from the front edge of the console. Slacken and remove the two exposed securing screws beneath **(see illustrations)**.
3 Lift the console up over the handbrake lever and remove it from the vehicle **(see illustration)**.

Refitting

4 Refitting is a reversal of removal.

26 Centre console – removal and refitting

Removal (pre-2004 models)

1 Disconnect the battery earth lead.
2 Remove the rear console – see Section 25.

26.12 Lift up and release the cup holder from the front of the centre console

26.13a Carefully prise free the window lift switches . . .

26.13b . . . and disconnect the wiring connectors

3 Remove the radio – see Chapter 12.
4 Release the gearchange lever gaiter from the base of the knob, and unscrew the knob from the lever.
5 On models with electric windows, release the window switch panel, disconnect the multi-plugs and remove the switch panel.
6 Remove four screws securing the console to the facia, and pull the console away from the facia, releasing the clips from the adjacent heater control panel.
7 To ensure correct reconnection, mark the plugs, then disconnect the multi-plugs from the bank of switches at the top of the console.
8 Disconnect the Lucar connector and multi-plug from the cigar lighter.
9 Ensuring that nothing remains connected, remove the console.

Refitting (pre-2004 models)

10 Refitting is a reversal of the removal procedure, noting:
11 Before fitting the console, fit the gear lever gaiter to the knob as follows.

Inside the gearchange knob, squeeze the two tangs together and separate the halves of the knob. Turn the gaiter inside out and remove the rubber ring. Ensuring that it is the right way round, fit the lower half of the knob into the top edge of the gaiter and fit the rubber ring around the gaiter and knob lower half.

Turn the gaiter the right way out, and ensure that the lower half of the knob is correctly aligned.

When the console is installed, screw the upper half of the knob onto the gear lever

until it is correctly aligned. Pull the lower section of the knob up over the upper section, until the locking tangs engage.

Removal (2004 onward models)

12 Lift up and release the cup holder from the front of the centre console **(see illustration)**.
13 Using a small screwdriver, carefully prise free the window lift switches from the front of the centre console. Disconnect the wiring connectors and remove the switches **(see illustrations)**.
14 Release the clips and disengage the gear lever gaiter retaining ring from the centre console **(see illustration)**.
15 Undo the two screws at the front, adjacent to the gear lever, and the two screws at the rear, adjacent to the handbrake lever, securing the centre console to the floor **(see illustration)**.
16 Release the handbrake lever gaiter from the centre console **(see illustration)**.
17 Lift the console up at the rear and slide it away from the facia to disengage the locating lugs. Once free, feed the gear lever gaiter and retaining ring through the console opening, then disconnect the cigarette lighter wiring connector **(see illustrations)**.
18 Lift the console over the handbrake lever and remove it from the car.

Refitting (2004 onward models)

19 Refitting is a reversal of the removal procedure.

26.14 Release the clips and disengage the gear lever gaiter retaining ring from the centre console

26.15 Centre console rear retaining screws (arrowed)

26.16 Release the handbrake lever gaiter from the centre console

26.17a Feed the gear lever gaiter and retaining ring through the console opening . . .

26.17b . . . then disconnect the cigarette lighter wiring connector

27.3 Remove the lower cover panel from the passenger's side of the facia

27.4a Remove the two securing screws . . .

27.4b . . . and withdraw the glovebox from the facia

27.8 Unplug the facia wiring harness from the fusebox at the two multiway connectors

27.9 Slacken and remove the exposed facia securing nut (arrowed)

27.10a Prise the cover panels from the ends of the facia assembly . . .

27 Facia – removal and refitting

> ⚠ **Warning: All models are fitted with a Supplementary Restraint System (SRS). Before disturbing the facia components, read the SRS safety information given in Chapter 12.**

Removal

1 Disconnect both battery cables from the terminals (negative first).
2 Refer to Section 26 and remove the centre console.
3 Release the stud fixings, then remove the lower cover panel from the passenger's side of the facia **(see illustration)**.
4 Remove the two securing screws and withdraw the glovebox from the facia **(see illustrations)**.

5 Where applicable, remove the passenger airbag unit as described in Chapter 12.
6 Refer to Chapter 3 and remove the heater control panel.
7 Refer to Chapter 10 and remove the steering column.
8 Unplug the facia wiring harness from the fusebox at the two multiway connectors **(see illustration)**.
9 On pre-2004 models, carefully prise the trim panel from the clock display. On 2004 onward models, remove the clock as described in Chapter 12. With the trim panel or clock removed, where applicable, slacken and remove the exposed facia securing nut **(see illustration)**.
10 Open the front doors and prise the cover panels from the ends of the facia assembly, then slacken and remove the exposed facia securing bolts **(see illustrations)**.
11 Remove the bolts securing the lower edge

27.10b . . . then slacken and remove the exposed facia securing bolts

of the facia to the mounting brackets at the base of the door A-pillars **(see illustrations)**.
12 Where fitted, remove the two bolts securing the centre, lower edge of the facia to the mounting bracket at the top of the transmission linkage tunnel **(see illustration)**.

27.11a Remove the bolts securing the lower edge of the facia to the mounting brackets on the right-hand side . . .

27.11b . . . and the left-hand side

27.12 Remove the two bolts securing the centre, lower edge of the facia to its mounting bracket

27.13 Withdraw the facia assembly from the bulkhead and lift it out of the vehicle

Alternatively, undo the two screws above the heater control panel aperture, and the two screws at the lower centre of the facia.

13 Carefully manoeuvre the facia assembly away from the bulkhead. Disconnect the heater/ventilation ducts from the rear of their respective vents as they become accessible. Release the remaining sections of the wiring harness from any retaining clips. With the front seats fully rearward, lift the facia assembly out of the vehicle **(see illustration)**.

Refitting

14 Offer up the facia, reconnect the heater/ventilation ducting and secure the wiring harness in position with the retaining clips.

15 Manoeuvre the facia into position on the bulkhead then refit and tighten the facia mounting bolts, nuts and screws.

16 The remainder of the refitting procedure is a reversal of removal, noting the following:

a) Refit the steering column with reference to Chapter 10.

b) Ensure that all SRS component wiring (including the control unit earth lead) is properly located and securely reconnected – refer to Chapter 12 for guidance and observe the safety precautions given.

c) Refit the heater control panel with reference to Chapter 3.

d) On completion, reconnect the battery and check that all electrical components and switches function correctly.

28 Vehicle exterior and interior – maintenance and inspection

Vehicle exterior

The general condition of a vehicle's bodywork is the one thing that significantly affects its value. Maintenance is easy but needs to be regular. Neglect, particularly after minor damage, can lead quickly to further deterioration and costly repair bills. It is important also to keep watch on those parts of the vehicle not immediately visible, for instance the underbody, inside all the wheelarches and the lower part of the engine compartment.

The basic maintenance routine for the bodywork is washing – preferably with a lot of water, from a hose. This will remove all the loose solids which may have stuck to the vehicle. It is important to flush these off in such a way as to prevent grit from scratching the finish. The wheelarches and underbody need washing in the same way to remove any accumulated mud which will retain moisture and tend to encourage rust, particularly in winter when it is essential that any salt (from that put down on the roads) is washed off. Paradoxically enough, the best time to clean the underbody and wheelarches is in wet weather when the mud is thoroughly wet and soft. In very wet weather the underbody is usually cleaned automatically of large accumulations; this is therefore a good time for inspection.

If the vehicle is very dirty, especially underneath or in the engine compartment, it is tempting to use one of the pressure washers or steam cleaners available on garage forecourts. Whilst these are quick and effective, especially for the removal of the accumulation of oily grime which sometimes is allowed to become thick in certain areas, their usage does have some disadvantages. If caked-on dirt is simply blasted off the paintwork, its finish soon becomes scratched and dull and the pressure can allow water to penetrate door and window seals and the lock mechanisms. If the full force of such a jet is directed at the vehicle's underbody, the wax-based protective coating can easily be damaged and water (with whatever cleaning solvent is used) could be forced into crevices or components that it would not normally reach. Similarly, if such equipment is used to clean the engine compartment, water can be forced into the components of the fuel and electrical systems and the protective coating can be removed that is applied to many small components during manufacture; this may therefore actually promote corrosion (especially inside electrical connectors) and initiate engine problems or other electrical faults. Also, if the jet is pointed directly at any of the oil seals, water can be forced past the seal lips and into the engine or transmission. Great care is required, therefore, if such equipment is used and, in general, regular cleaning by such methods should be avoided.

A much better solution in the long term is just to flush away as much loose dirt as possible using a hose alone, even if this leaves the engine compartment looking dirty. If an oil leak has developed, or if any other accumulation of oil or grease is to be removed, there are one or two excellent grease solvents available, which can be brush applied. The dirt can then be simply hosed off. Take care to replace the wax-based protective coat, if this was affected by the solvent.

Normal washing of the bodywork is best carried out using cold or warm water with a proprietary car shampoo. Tar spots can be removed by using white spirit, followed by soapy water to remove all traces of spirit. Try to keep water out of the bonnet air intakes and check afterwards that the heater air inlet box drain tube is clear so that any water has drained out of the box.

After washing the paintwork, wipe off with a chamois leather to give an unspotted clear finish. A coat of clear protective wax polish will give added protection against chemical pollutants in the air. If the paintwork sheen has dulled or oxidised, use a cleaner/polisher combination to restore the brilliance of the shine. This requires a little effort, but such dulling is usually caused because regular washing has been neglected. Care needs to be taken with metallic paintwork, as special non-abrasive cleaner/polisher is required to avoid damage to the finish.

Brightwork should be treated in the same way as paintwork.

Windscreens and windows can be kept clear of the smeary film which often appears, by the use of proprietary glass cleaner. Never use any form of wax or other body or chromium polish on glass.

Vehicle interior

Mats and carpets should be brushed or vacuum cleaned regularly to keep them free of grit. If they are badly stained remove them from the vehicle for scrubbing or sponging and make quite sure they are dry before refitting.

Where leather upholstery is fitted it should be cleaned only if necessary, using either a mild soap (such as saddle soap) or a proprietary leather cleaner; do not use strong soaps, detergents or chemical cleaners. If the leather is very stained, seek the advice of a Rover dealer. Fabric-trimmed seats and interior trim panels can be kept clean by wiping with a damp cloth and a suitable cleaner. If they do become stained (which can be more apparent on light-coloured upholstery) use a little liquid detergent and a soft nail brush to scour the grime out of the grain of the material. Do not forget to keep the headlining clean in the same way as the (fabric) upholstery.

When using liquid cleaners of any sort inside the vehicle, do not over-wet the surfaces being cleaned. Excessive damp could get into the seams and padded interior causing stains, offensive odours or even rot. If the inside of the vehicle gets wet accidentally it is worthwhile taking some trouble to dry it out properly, particularly where carpets are involved. Do not leave oil or electric heaters inside the vehicle for this purpose.

Do not allow the airbag unit in the centre of the steering wheel to become flooded with detergents or water and do not clean with petrol or furniture cream and polishes. Clean the unit sparingly with a damp cloth and upholstery cleaner. Failure to observe these precautions may result in the airbag inflating, with the subsequent risk of personal injury.

Chapter 12
Body electrical systems

Contents

Degrees of difficulty

Easy, suitable for novice with little experience	**Fairly easy,** suitable for beginner with some experience	**Fairly difficult,** suitable for competent DIY mechanic	**Difficult,** suitable for experienced DIY mechanic	**Very difficult,** suitable for expert DIY or professional

Specifications

Fuses .... See Wiring diagrams

Bulbs

	Fitting	Wattage
Direction indicator lamps	Bayonet	21
Direction indicator side repeater lamps	Capless	5
Front foglamps	H1	55
Glovebox lamp	Festoon	5
Headlamp dipped beam bulb	H7	55
Headlamp main beam bulb	H1 or H7	55
High-level brake lamp	Capless	3
Instrument panel illumination lamps	Integral with holder	14V, 3.4W
Interior lamp	Festoon	10
Luggage compartment lamp	Bayonet	10
Number plate lamps	Festoon	5
Rear foglamps	Bayonet	21
Reversing lamps	Bayonet	21
Sidelamps	Capless	5
Stop-lamps	Bayonet	21
Tail lamps	Bayonet	10

Torque wrench settings

	Nm	lbf ft
Airbag control unit screws	9	7
Driver's airbag screws	9	7
Passenger's airbag screws	9	7
Seat belt pretensioner bolts	30	22
Tailgate wiper motor bolts	8	6
Vehicle speed sensor bolt	9	7
Windscreen wiper linkage assembly bolts	10	7
Windscreen wiper motor mounting bracket bolts	10	7
Windscreen wiper motor-to-bracket bolts	5	4
Wiper arm spindle nut	10	7

1 General information and precautions

General information

The electrical system is of the 12 volt negative earth type and comprises a 12 volt battery, an alternator with integral voltage regulator, a starter motor and related electrical accessories, components and wiring. The battery is of the maintenance-free (sealed for life) type and is charged by the alternator, which is belt-driven from a crankshaft-mounted pulley.

While some repair procedures are given, the usual course of action is to renew a defective component. The owner whose interest extends beyond mere component renewal should obtain a copy of the *Automotive Electrical & Electronic Systems Manual*, available from the publishers of this Manual.

Precautions

It is necessary to take extra care when working on the electrical system to avoid the risk of personal injury and to avoid damage to components. In addition to the precautions given in *Safety first!* at the beginning of this Manual, observe the following when working on the system:

a) *Always remove rings, watches, etc, before working on the electrical system. Even with the battery disconnected, capacitive discharge could occur if a component's live terminal is earthed through a metal object. This could cause a shock or nasty burn.*

b) *Do not reverse the battery connections. Components such as the alternator, fuel injection/ignition system ECU, or any other having semi-conductor circuitry could be irreparably damaged.*

c) *If the engine is being started using jump leads and a slave battery, connect the batteries positive-to-positive and negative-to-negative. This also applies when connecting a battery charger.*

d) *Never disconnect the battery terminals, the alternator, any electrical wiring or any test instruments when the engine is running.*

e) *Do not allow the engine to turn the alternator when the alternator is not connected.*

f) *Never test for alternator output by 'flashing' the output lead to earth.*

g) *Always ensure that the battery negative lead is disconnected when working on the electrical system.*

Electronic Control Units (ECUs) contain semiconductor components that are sensitive to static electricity. Once the multiway harness connector has been unplugged, the exposed ECU connector pins can freely conduct stray static electricity to these

components, damaging or even destroying them – the damage will be invisible and may not manifest itself immediately. Expensive repairs can be avoided by observing the following basic handling rules:

a) *Handle a disconnected ECU by its case only; do not allow fingers or tools to come into contact with the pins.*

b) *When carrying an ECU around, 'ground' yourself from time to time, by touching a metal object such as an unpainted water pipe, this will discharge any potentially damaging static that may have built up during normal activity.*

c) *Do not leave the ECU unplugged from its connector for any longer than is absolutely necessary.*

d) *Never use an ohmmeter of the type incorporating a hand-cranked generator for sensor or actuator testing.*

e) *Before using electric-arc welding equipment on the vehicle, disconnect the battery, alternator and the engine management system ECU.*

A number of additional precautions must be observed when working on vehicles equipped with a Supplementary Restraint System (SRS); these are as follows:

a) *When cleaning the interior of the vehicle, do not allow the airbag or seat belt pretensioner units to become flooded with detergents or water, and do not clean with petrol or furniture cream and polishes. Clean the unit sparingly with a damp cloth and upholstery cleaner.*

b) *Before working on any part of the system, remove the ignition key and wait at least ten minutes to allow the system backup circuit to fully discharge. Disconnect both battery leads, earth lead first, to avoid accidental detonation of the airbag or seat belt pretensioner components.*

c) *Make no attempt to splice into any of the electric cables in the SRS wiring harness as this may affect the operation of the SRS. Never fit electronic equipment such as mobile telephones, radios, etc, into the harness and ensure that the harness is routed so that it cannot be trapped.*

d) *Avoid hammering or causing any harsh vibration at the front of the vehicle, particularly in the engine bay, as this may trigger the crash sensors and activate the SRS.*

e) *Do not use ohmmeters, continuity testers or any other device capable of supplying current on any of the SRS components, as this may cause accidental detonation.*

f) *Always use new replacement parts. Never fit parts that are from another vehicle or show signs of damage through being dropped or improperly handled.*

g) *Airbags are classed as pyrotechnical devices and must be stored and handled according to the relevant laws in the country concerned. In general, do not leave these components disconnected from their electrical cabling any longer*

than is absolutely necessary as in this state they are unstable and the risk of accidental detonation is introduced. Rest a disconnected airbag unit with the pad surface facing upwards and never rest anything on the pad. Store it on a secure flat surface, away from flammable materials, high heat sources, oils, grease, detergents or water, and never leave it unattended.

h) *The SRS indicator light should extinguish 3 seconds after the ignition switch is turned to position II. If this is not the case, check the electrical system connections as soon as possible.*

i) *The SRS control unit and slip-ring are non-serviceable components and no attempt should be made to carry out repairs or modifications to them.*

j) *Only use the recommended special bolts when fitting the airbag assembly. Do not use any other type of bolt.*

k) *Never invert the airbag unit.*

l) *Renew the airbag unit and slip-ring every 15 years, regardless of condition.*

m) *Return disused airbag and seat belt pretensioner units to your Rover dealer for safe disposal. Do not endanger others by careless disposal.*

2 Electrical fault finding – general information

A typical electrical circuit consists of an electrical component, any switches, relays, motors, fuses, fusible links or circuit breakers related to that component, and the wiring and connectors that link the component to both the battery and the chassis. To help you pinpoint an electrical circuit problem, wiring diagrams are included at the end of this Chapter.

Before tackling any troublesome electrical circuit, first study the appropriate wiring diagrams to get a complete understanding of what components are included in that individual circuit. Trouble spots can be identified by noting if other components related to the circuit are operating properly. If several components or circuits fail at one time, then the problem is probably in a fuse or earth connection, because several circuits are often routed through the same fuse and earth connections.

Electrical problems usually stem from simple causes, such as loose or corroded connections, a blown fuse, a melted fusible link or a faulty relay. Inspect the condition of all fuses, wires and connections in a problem circuit before testing the components. Use the diagrams to note which terminal connections will need to be checked in order to pinpoint the trouble spot.

The basic tools needed for electrical fault finding include a circuit tester or voltmeter (a 12 volt bulb with a set of test leads can also be used), a continuity tester, a battery and set of test leads, and a jumper wire, preferably with a circuit breaker incorporated, which can be used to bypass electrical components. Before attempting to locate a problem with test instruments, use the wiring diagram to decide where to make the connections.

General

Electrical fault finding is simple if you keep in mind that all electrical circuits are basically electricity flowing from the battery, through the wires, switches, relays, fuses and fusible links to each electrical component (light bulb, motor, etc) and to earth, from which it is passed back to the battery. Any electrical problem is an interruption or restriction in the flow of electricity to and from the battery.

Voltage checks

Voltage checks should be performed if a circuit is not functioning properly. Connect one lead of a circuit tester to either the negative battery terminal or a known good earth. Connect the other lead to a connector in the circuit being tested, preferably nearest to the battery or fuse. If the bulb of the tester lights then voltage is present, which means that the part of the circuit between the connector and the battery is problem free. Continue checking the rest of the circuit in the same fashion. When you reach a point at which no voltage is present, the problem lies between that point and the last test point with voltage. Most problems can be traced to a loose connection. Bear in mind that some circuits are only live when the ignition switch is switched to a particular position.

Finding a short circuit

One method of finding a short circuit is to remove the fuse and connect a test light or voltmeter to the fuse terminals with all the relevant electrical components switched off. There should be no voltage present in the circuit. Move the wiring from side to side while watching the test light. If the bulb lights up, there is a short to earth somewhere in that area, probably where the insulation has rubbed through. The same test can be performed on each component in the circuit, even a switch.

Earth check

On vehicles with a negative-earth electrical system, current is supplied by the battery to electrical components via the wiring harness and is returned to the battery via common earth points on the vehicle's bodywork. Performing an earth check tests whether a component has a good earth point.

Disconnect the battery and connect one lead of a self-powered test light, known as a continuity tester, to a known good earth point. Connect the other lead to the wire or earth connection being tested. If the bulb lights up, the earth is good. If not, the earth is faulty.

If an earth connection is thought to be

faulty, dismantle the connection and clean back to bare metal both the bodyshell and the wire terminal or the component's earth connection mating surface. Be careful to remove all traces of dirt and corrosion, then use a knife to trim away any paint, so that a clean metal-to-metal joint is made. On reassembly, tighten the joint fasteners securely; if a wire terminal is being refitted, use serrated washers between the terminal and the bodyshell to ensure a clean and secure connection. When the connection is remade, prevent the onset of corrosion in the future by applying a coat of petroleum jelly or silicone-based grease or by spraying on a proprietary ignition sealer or a water dispersant lubricant at regular intervals.

Continuity check

A continuity check is necessary to determine if there are any breaks in a circuit. With the circuit off (ie: no power in the circuit), a self-powered continuity tester can be used to check the circuit. Connect the test leads to both ends of the circuit, or to the positive end and a good earth. If the test light comes on, the circuit is passing current properly. If the light does not come on, there is a break somewhere in the circuit. The same procedure can be used to test a switch, by connecting the continuity tester to the switch terminals. With the switch turned on, the test light should come on.

Finding an open circuit

When checking for possible open circuits, it is often difficult to locate them by sight because oxidation or terminal misalignment may be hidden by the connectors. Merely moving a connector on a sensor or in the wiring harness may correct the open circuit condition. Remember this when an open circuit is indicated when fault finding in a circuit. Intermittent problems may also be caused by oxidized or loose connections. Bear in mind that a circuit carrying a heavy load (ie, passing a lot of current) may 'break down' under load. For example, a poor connection in the wiring supplying a starter motor may not be detectable with a simple continuity tester, but under cranking conditions the volt drop caused by the poor

connection may be severe enough to prevent the starter motor turning properly. If you have doubts about the condition of a particular wiring connection, it's best to separate it and clean the connection surfaces (as described in *Earth check*) to be on the safe side.

3 Fuses, fusible links and relays – location and renewal

Fuses

1 Fuses are located in an engine bay fusebox, or a fusebox under the steering column. The passenger compartment box contains only blade fuses. Three different types of fuse are fitted to the engine compartment fusebox:
Blade fuse – small pull-out male fuse, used to protect circuits from 5 A to 30 A.
J-case fuse – small square-shaped pull out female fuse, used to protect circuits from 30 A to 60A.
Bolt-down fuse – also know as fusible links, used to protect circuits from 40 A to 250 A.
2 Access to the main fusebox is gained by removing the plastic cover panel. Symbols on the reverse of the lid/cover indicate the circuits protected by the fuses and a number of spare fuses are supplied, together with plastic extractor to remove and fit them **(see illustrations)**.
3 The fuse protecting the Supplementary Restraint System (SRS) circuit is located on the side of the main fusebox and is indicated by a yellow plastic collar.
Caution: Under no circumstances should this fuse be removed as this may cause accidental inflation of the airbag. Refer to your Rover dealer if you think renewal of this fuse may be necessary.
4 To remove a fuse, first switch off the circuit concerned (or the ignition), then fit the tweezers and pull the fuse out of its terminals. Slide the fuse sideways from the tweezers. The wire within the fuse is clearly visible. If the fuse is blown, the wire will be broken or melted **(see illustrations)**.
5 Always renew a fuse with one of an

3.2a Release the fixings by turning them through a quarter of a turn . . .

3.2b . . . remove the plastic cover panel

3.4a Withdraw the integral plastic extractor from its slot . . .

3.4b . . . and use it to remove the fuse

3.5 Push the new fuse firmly into place

identical rating **(see illustration)**. The fuse rating is stamped on top of the fuse. Fuses are also colour-coded for easy recognition.

Warning: Never use a fuse with a different rating from the original or substitute anything else in its place – it could cause a fire in the wiring harness.

6 If a new fuse blows immediately, find the cause before renewing it again. A short to earth as a result of faulty insulation is the most likely cause. Where a fuse protects more than one circuit, try to isolate the defect by switching on each circuit in turn (if possible) until the fuse blows again.

7 If any of the spare fuses are used, always renew it so that a spare of each rating is available.

Fusible links

8 The fusible links are located in the rear of the fusebox, situated on the left-hand side of the engine compartment. Unclip the lid to gain access to them. All links are numbered on the rear of the fusebox lid.

9 To remove a fusible link, first ensure that the circuit concerned is switched off then prise off the plastic cover. Slacken the two link retaining screws then lift the fusible link out of the fusebox. The wire within the fusible link is clearly visible. If the fuse is blown, it will be broken or melted. A blown fusible link indicates a serious wiring or system fault which must be diagnosed before the link is renewed.

10 Always renew a fusible link with one of an identical rating. Never use a link with a different rating from the original or substitute anything else. On refitting, tighten the link retaining screws securely and refit the link cover.

Relays

11 Refer to the relevant wiring diagram for relay locations and wiring connections.

12 If a circuit or system controlled by a relay develops a fault and the relay is suspect, operate the system. If the relay is functioning, it should be possible to hear it click as it is energised. If this is the case, the fault lies with the components or wiring of the system. If the relay is not being energised, then either the relay is not receiving a main supply or a switching voltage, or the relay itself is faulty. Testing is by the substitution of a known good unit but be careful as some relays are identical in appearance, but perform different functions and have different electrical specifications.

13 To renew a relay, ensure that the ignition switch is off, then pull the unit from the socket and press in a new one. Note that heavy duty relays may be secured to their bases with one or more screws.

4 Switches – removal and refitting

Note: *Disconnect the battery negative lead before removing any switch and after refitting the switch, reconnect the lead.*

Ignition switch

1 Refer to Chapter 10 for details of steering lock/ignition switch removal and refitting.

Steering column switch

2 Remove the ignition key and wait at least ten minutes to allow the SRS system backup circuit to fully discharge. Disconnect both battery leads, earth lead first, to avoid accidental detonation of the airbag.

3 Set the steering in the straight-ahead position then lock the steering column in its lowest position.

4 Remove the driver's airbag unit, as described in Section 14.

5 Remove the steering wheel, as described in Chapter 10.

6 Remove the airbag rotary coupler, as described in Section 14.

7 Withdraw the indicator cancelling cam from the steering column **(see illustration)**.

8 To remove the complete combination switch assembly, slacken and remove the two retaining screws and slide the switch off the steering column **(see illustration)**.

4.7 Withdraw the indicator cancelling cam from the steering column

4.8 Remove the two retaining screws and slide the switch off the steering column

4.9a Disconnect the multiplugs from the combination switch . . .

4.9b . . . followed by the SRS wiring connector

4.14a Prise the switch unit out using a suitable flat-bladed screwdriver . . .

4.14b . . . and unplug the wiring connector from the rear of the switch

4.17 Unplug the wiring connector from the electric window switch unit

9 Disconnect the multiplugs from the combination switch, followed by the SRS wiring connector **(see illustrations)**.

10 Each individual switch can be removed by unscrewing its two retaining screws and sliding the switch out of the housing.

11 Refitting is the reverse of the removal procedure.

12 Upon completion of refitting the airbag unit, reconnect both battery leads, negative lead last, and turn the ignition switch to the II position. Check the condition of the system by observing the SRS warning light located in the steering wheel centre pad. The light should stay illuminated for 3 seconds whilst the system performs a self-diagnosis test. If the test is satisfactory, the light will extinguish. If the test is unsatisfactory, the light will remain on or fail to illuminate at all, denoting that the system must be serviced as soon as possible.

Instrument panel and facia switches

13 Ensure that the ignition switch and the switch to be removed are both in the off position.

14 Taking great care not to scratch or damage the switch or its surround, prise the switch unit out using a suitable flat-bladed screwdriver; pad the blade with insulating tape to prevent damage. Withdraw the switch until the connector plug appears then unplug the wiring connector and remove the switch **(see illustrations)**. Tie a piece of string to the wiring connector to prevent it from falling behind the facia panel.

15 On refitting, connect the wiring connector to the switch and press the switch into position until the retaining clips click into place.

Window switches

16 On pre-2004 models, carefully prise the switch panel from the base of the centre console. On 2004 onward models, using a small screwdriver, carefully prise the relevant window switch from the front of the centre console.

17 Disconnect the wiring connector from the relevant switch **(see illustration)**.

18 On pre-2004 models, undo the retaining screws and detach the relevant switch unit from the panel.

19 Refitting is a reversal of removal.

Courtesy lamp switches

20 With the door open, undo the screw securing the switch to the body. Pull out the switch and tie a piece of string to the wiring to prevent it dropping into the body.

21 Disconnect the wiring from the switch and remove it from the vehicle.

22 Refitting is a reverse of removal.

Handbrake warning switch

23 On pre-2004 models, remove the rear console as described in Chapter 11. On 2004 onward models, remove the centre console as described in Chapter 11.

24 Unplug the wiring connector from the handbrake lever switch, then slacken and remove the retaining screw and remove the switch from the handbrake lever quadrant **(see illustration)**.

25 Refitting is a reverse of the removal procedure.

Horn push switch

26 Remove the driver's airbag unit from the steering wheel, as described in Section 14.

27 Detach the earth wire from the steering wheel **(see illustration 4.30)**.

28 Unplug the multiway connector from the steering wheel rotary coupler **(see illustration 4.30)**.

29 Remove each horn button by carefully using the flat blade of a small screwdriver to lever it from position. Pad the blade of the screwdriver with insulation tape to prevent damage.

4.24 Handbrake warning lamp switch retaining screw (A) and wiring connector (B)

30 Unplug the two electrical connectors from the button and remove it **(see illustration)**.

31 Refitting is the reversal of removal, noting the following:

a) Take care to ensure that wiring is not trapped between mating surfaces.

b) Refit the airbag unit as described in Section 14 and carry out the system check.

c) Test the horn after refitting each button.

Ignition switch transponder

32 Remove the lower half of the steering column cowl – see Chapter 10.

33 Remove the transponder from the ignition switch, and disconnect the transponder multiplug.

34 Refitting is a reversal of the removal procedure.

---

5 Bulbs (exterior lamps) – renewal

General

1 Whenever a bulb is to be renewed, note the following:

a) Disconnect the battery negative lead before starting work.

H29508

4.30 Disconnect the earth wire (A) and rotary coupler connector (B), then lever out the switch and unplug the contact wiring (C)

5.2 Remove the circular cover on the back of the headlamp

5.3 Disconnect the wiring multiplug from the relevant headlamp bulb

5.4a Unhook the wire retaining clip . . .

b) Remember that if the lamp has just been in use, the bulb may be extremely hot.

c) Always check the bulb contacts and holder, ensuring that there is clean metal-to-metal contact between the bulb and its live contacts and earth. Clean off any corrosion or dirt before fitting a new bulb.

d) Wherever bayonet-type bulbs are fitted, ensure that the live contacts bear firmly against the bulb contact.

e) Always ensure that the new bulb is of the correct rating and that it is completely clean before fitting. This applies particularly to headlamp bulbs.

Headlamp

Note: *The inboard headlamps contain the main beam headlamp and on pre-2004*

models, the sidelamp. The outboard headlamps contain the dipped beam headlamp and on 2004 onward models, the sidelamp. To ensure correct location, the inboard headlamp flange has a flat on one side. The flange of the outboard bulb has a square tab which must be aligned vertically in the bulbholder. The bulbs are not interchangeable and must be fitted correctly.

Caution: Do not touch the glass of any bulb. Halogen headlamp bulbs may shatter if contaminated with grease or perspiration. If necessary, clean the glass with methylated spirits.

2 Working in the engine bay, turn the circular cover on the back of the headlamp one eighth of a turn anti-clockwise and remove the cover **(see illustration)**.

3 Disconnect the wiring multiplug from the relevant headlamp bulb **(see illustration)**.

4 Unhook the wire retaining clip and turn it away from the bulb, then remove the bulb from the headlamp **(see illustrations)**.

5 Refitting is a reversal of the removal procedure. When fitting the circular cover, ensure that the lug on the outer rim is aligned with the large cut-out in the lower part of the headlamp body.

Sidelamp

6 The sidelamp bulbholder is adjacent to the inboard headlamp bulb (pre-2004 models), or outboard headlamp bulb (2004 onward models). With the circular cover removed from the headlamp, remove the bulbholder from the headlamp unit, and remove the bulb from the bulbholder **(see illustration)**.

Front direction indicator

Pre-2004 models

7 Using a small flat-blade screwdriver, carefully insert the blade in the gap between the inboard end of the lens and bumper, so that the blade fits behind the retaining spring.

8 Carefully move the blade to compress the spring, and remove the lamp unit from the bumper.

9 Turn the bulbholder one quarter turn anti-clockwise and remove it from the lamp unit.

10 Push and turn the bulb to remove it from the holder.

11 Refitting is a reversal of the removal procedure. When fitting the lamp unit, insert the outboard end first, then carefully locate the inboard end. Push the unit in until the retaining spring clicks into position.

2004 onward models

12 Using a small flat-blade screwdriver, carefully insert the blade in the gap between the direction indicator lens and the plastic surround. Gently lever off the surround and remove it from the bumper **(see illustrations)**.

13 Undo the two retaining screws and

5.4b . . . then remove the bulb from the headlamp

5.6 Remove the bulbholder from the headlamp unit, and remove the bulb from the bulbholder

5.12a Insert the blade of a small screwdriver in the gap between the direction indicator lens and the plastic surround . . .

5.12b . . . gently lever off the surround and remove it from the bumper

5.13 Undo the two screws (arrowed) and withdraw the direction indicator lamp unit

5.14 Turn the bulbholder one quarter turn anti-clockwise and remove it from the lamp unit

5.17a Push the lamp unit towards the right to free its retaining clips . . .

5.17b . . . then withdraw it from the wing

5.18a Pull the bulbholder out of the lamp unit . . .

5.18b . . . then pull the capless (push-fit) bulb from its holder

withdraw the direction indicator lamp unit from the bumper (see illustration).

14 Turn the bulbholder one quarter turn anti-clockwise and remove it from the lamp unit (see illustration).

5.21 Depress the catch at the centre of the unit and withdraw the bulb panel from the lens unit

5.22 Rear lamp cluster bulb removal

15 Push and turn the bulb to remove it from the holder.

16 Refitting is a reversal of the removal procedure.

Direction indicator side repeater

17 Push the lamp unit towards the right to free its retaining clips, then withdraw it from the front wing (see illustrations).

18 Pull the bulbholder out of the lamp unit, then pull the capless bulb from the holder (see illustrations).

19 Refitting is a reversal of the removal procedure.

Rear lamp cluster

20 From inside the luggage compartment release the two stud fixings, or single stud fixing and retaining screw, and remove the trim panel from the rear of the relevant lamp cluster.

5.24 Undo the two mounting screws and remove the combined number plate lamp lens and bulbholder

21 Depress the catch at the centre of the unit and withdraw the bulb panel from the lens unit (see illustration).

22 The relevant bulb can then be removed from the panel. All the bulbs are a bayonet fit in the panel and can be removed by pressing them in slightly and twisting in an anti-clockwise direction (see illustration).

23 Refitting is a reversal of the removal procedure.

Number plate lamps

Pre-2004 models

24 Undo the two mounting screws and remove the combined number plate lamp lens and bulbholder from the tailgate (see illustration).

25 The festoon bulb can be pulled from the terminal clips (see illustration).

5.25 The festoon-type bulb can be pulled from the terminal clips

5.27 Carefully prise the lens from the number plate lamp unit

5.28 Pull the capless number plate lamp bulb from the bulbholder

5.39 Drill through the indents (arrowed) on the spoiler for access to the high-level brake lamp securing screws

26 Refitting is a reversal of the removal procedure.

2004 onward models

27 Insert a small screwdriver in the slot on the side on the lens and carefully prise the lens from the lamp unit **(see illustration)**.
28 Pull the capless bulb from the bulbholder **(see illustration)**.
29 Refitting is a reversal of the removal procedure.

Front foglamps

30 Using a flat-bladed screwdriver, carefully lever off the foglamp surround panel.
31 Slacken and remove the three foglamp retaining screws, then withdraw the lamp unit from the bumper.
32 Rotate the bulbholder one quarter turn anti-clockwise and withdraw it from the rear of the lamp unit.
33 The bulb is a push-fit in the holder. When handling a new bulb, use a tissue or clean cloth to avoid touching the glass with the fingers. Moisture and grease from the skin can cause blackening and rapid failure of halogen bulbs.

 HAYNES HiNT *If the glass of a foglamp bulb is accidentally touched, wipe it clean using methylated spirit before fitting it.*

34 Refitting is a reversal of the removal procedure.

High-level brake lamp

35 Disconnect the battery earth lead.

36 From inside the tailgate, remove the two screws securing the side trim panels and remove the panels.
37 Remove the upper trim panel.
38 Undo the two nuts and two bolts securing the rear spoiler to the tailgate and withdraw the spoiler. Disconnect the high-level brake lamp wiring connector and remove the spoiler from the tailgate.
39 To gain access to the lamp securing screws, locate the two marked indents on the spoiler and drill through them with a 10 mm drill bit **(see illustration)**.
40 Using a long magnetic screwdriver, undo the two lamp securing screws and remove the unit.
41 Refitting is a reversal of the removal procedure.

6 Bulbs (interior lamps) – renewal

General

1 Refer to the information given in Section 5.

Courtesy lamps

2 Carefully prise the lens off the lamp unit then remove the festoon bulb from its terminal clips **(see illustrations)**.
3 Fit the new bulb using a reversal of the removal procedure. Check the tension of the spring contacts and if necessary, bend them so that they firmly contact the bulb end caps.

Glovebox lamp

4 Open up the glovebox and then, using a

flat-bladed screwdriver, carefully prise the lamp unit from the facia.
5 Release the festoon bulb from its contacts and remove it from the light unit.
6 Fit the new bulb using a reversal of the removal procedure. Check the tension of the spring contacts and, if necessary, bend them so that they firmly grip the bulb end caps.

Luggage compartment lamp

7 Slide the lamp unit/bulbholder to the left and release it from the parcel shelf support panel.
8 The bulb is a bayonet fit and can be removed by pressing it in and twisting anti-clockwise.
9 Refitting is a reverse of the removal procedure.

Instrument panel illumination and warning lamps

10 Remove the instrument panel, as described in Section 10.
11 Twist the relevant bulbholder anti-clockwise and withdraw it from the rear of the panel. The bulbs are a push-fit in the holders **(see illustrations)**.
12 Refitting is the reverse of the removal procedure. Be very careful to ensure that the new bulbs are of the same rating as those removed. This is especially important in the case of the ignition/battery charging warning lamp.

Heater control illumination

13 Working as described in Chapter 3, remove the heater control panel from the facia.
14 Detach the knobs from the heater controls.

6.2a Carefully prise the lens off the lamp unit . . .

6.2b . . . then remove the festoon bulb from its terminal clips

6.11a Twist the relevant bulbholder anti-clockwise and withdraw it from the rear of the instrument panel

6.11b The bulbs are a push-fit in the holders

6.19 Unscrew the capped bulb from the side of the switch body

6.21a Unscrew the capped bulb at the rear of the clock body . . .

6.21b . . . and remove it

15 Remove the two securing screws, then release the clips and detach the faceplate from the front of the control panel.

16 Twist the relevant bulbholder anti-clockwise and withdraw it from the rear of the face plate.

17 Refitting is the reverse of the removal procedure. Be very careful to ensure that the new bulbs are of the same rating as those removed.

Switch illumination bulbs

18 All of the facia panel switches are fitted with illuminating bulbs. Some are also fitted with a bulb to show when the circuit concerned is operating.

19 Remove the relevant switch (see Section 4), then unscrew the capped bulb from the side of the switch body **(see illustration)**.

Clock illumination bulb

20 Remove the clock unit as described in Section 11.

21 Unscrew the capped bulb from the rear of the clock body and remove it **(see illustrations)**.

<table>
<tr><td>**7**</td><td>**Exterior lamp units –**
removal and refitting</td></tr>
</table>

Note: *Disconnect the battery negative lead before removing any lamp unit, and reconnect the lead after refitting the lamp.*

Headlamp

1 Remove the front bumper – see Chapter 11.

2 To ensure that the headlamp unit is correctly located during refitting, mark the bonnet lock platform around the bolt hole tabs. Undo and remove the three bolts securing the headlamp unit to the bonnet lock platform and inner wing **(see illustrations)**.

3 Disconnect the multiplugs from the headlamp and headlamp levelling motor.

4 Refitting is a reversal of the removal procedure, noting:

If a new headlamp unit is being fitted, transfer the bulbs and holders to the new unit. Also transfer the headlamp levelling motor – see Section 15.

Before tightening the securing bolts, align

the marks made on the bonnet locking platform.

Have the headlamp beam alignment checked (Section 8).

Front direction indicator

5 The procedure for removing the lamp unit is covered in Section 5 under bulb renewal.

Direction indicator side repeater

6 Push the lamp unit towards the right to free its retaining clips then withdraw it from the wing (refer to the illustrations in Section 5 for greater detail).

7 Pull the bulbholder out and remove the lamp from the vehicle. Recover the O-ring seal.

8 Refitting is a reverse of the removal procedure.

Rear lamp cluster

9 Open the tailgate, then release the two-

piece stud fixings and move the carpet trim to one side, to gain access to the rear of the lamp cluster.

10 Unplug the wiring from the lamp cluster at the multiway connector **(see illustration)**.

7.2a Mark the bonnet lock platform around the headlamp unit bolt hole tabs

7.2c . . . and lower retaining bolt (arrowed)

7.2b Undo the headlamp upper retaining bolts (arrowed) . . .

7.10 Unplug the wiring from the lamp cluster at the multiway connector

7.11a Undo the three nuts securing the lamp unit to the body . . .

7.11b . . . and remove the unit from the vehicle

7.13 Carefully prise the number plate lamp unit from its location using a small screwdriver

11 Undo the three nuts securing the lamp unit to the body and remove the unit from the vehicle. Note the sealing material which is fitted between the lamp unit and body **(see illustrations)**.

12 Refitting is a reversal of the removal procedure. The sealing material must be renewed if damaged.

Number plate lamps

13 On pre-2004 models, undo the two mounting screws and remove the number plate lamp lens/bulbholder and seal. On 2004 onward models, carefully prise the lamp unit from its location using a small screwdriver **(see illustration)**.

14 Withdraw the lamp unit until the wiring connector appears then disconnect the connector and remove the unit from the vehicle.

15 Refitting is the reverse of the removal procedure. The seal must be renewed if damaged.

Front foglamps

16 Carefully unclip the surround panel from the front of the foglamp unit.

17 Remove the three screws and withdraw the foglamp from the valence. Unplug the wiring connector as it becomes accessible.

18 Refitting is a reversal of removal. Check the foglamp beam alignment and adjust if necessary to avoid dazzling other road users.

8 Headlamp beam alignment – general information

Accurate adjustment of the headlight beam is only possible using optical beam-setting equipment, and this work should therefore be carried out by a Rover dealer or service station with the necessary facilities. In an emergency, however, the following procedure will provide an acceptable light pattern.

Position the car on a level surface with tyres correctly inflated, approximately 10 metres in front of, and at right-angles to, a wall or garage door.

Draw a horizontal line on the wall or door at headlamp centre height. Draw a vertical line

corresponding to the centre line of the car, then measure off a point either side of this, on the horizontal line, corresponding with the headlamp centres.

Switch on the main beam and check that the areas of maximum illumination coincide with the headlamp centre marks on the wall. If not, turn the adjustment screws located on the rear and upper surfaces of the headlight unit (depending on model) to adjust the beam horizontally, and vertically. On models with electric headlight adjustment, make sure that the control is set at its basic setting before making the adjustment.

Have the headlamp beam alignment checked accurately at the earliest opportunity.

9 Dim-dip headlamp system – operation

This system comprises the dim-dip unit (mounted behind the right-hand lower facia panel) and a resistor (situated behind the left-hand headlamp assembly).

The dim-dip unit is supplied with current from the sidelamp circuit and energised by a feed from the ignition switch. When energised, the unit allows battery voltage to pass through the resistor to the headlamp dipped-beam circuits. This lights the headlamps with approximately one-sixth of their normal power so that the vehicle cannot be driven using sidelamps alone.

10 Instrument panel – removal and refitting

Removal

1 Disconnect the battery earth lead.

2 Release the clamp, and lower the steering column as far as possible.

3 Remove the four shroud retaining screws – peel back the rubber around the column shroud to gain access to the lower screws.

4 Remove the rubber finisher from the

instrument panel. Release two clips securing the instrument panel shroud to the facia, and remove the shroud.

5 Remove four screws securing the panel to the facia, and withdraw the panel to gain access to the multiplugs.

6 Disconnect three multiplugs from the back of the panel, and remove the panel.

Refitting

7 Refitting is a reversal of the removal procedure, noting:

Ensure that the multiplugs are securely connected.

Check the operation of the instruments and lamps.

11 Clock – removal and refitting

Removal

Pre-2004 models

1 Disconnect the battery negative lead.

2 Using a suitable flat-bladed instrument, carefully release the clips at the base of the clock mounting trim strip from the facia. Withdraw the trim from the facia **(see illustrations)**

3 Undo the two clock retaining screws and remove the clock from the facia. Disconnect the wiring connector from the rear of the clock. Tie a piece of string to the wiring

11.2a Using a flat-bladed instrument, release the clips at the base of the clock mounting trim

11.2b . . . and remove the clock trim from the facia

11.3a Undo the two clock retaining screws . . .

11.3b . . . then remove the clock from the facia and unplug the wiring connector

connector to prevent it falling back inside the facia **(see illustrations)**.

2004 onward models

4 Disconnect the battery negative lead.
5 Carefully pull the switch panel surround from the centre of the facia to release the seven retaining clips **(see illustration)**. Suitably identify the wiring connectors and disconnect them from the rear of the panel switches.
6 Pull out the lower edge of the clock surround/vent panel to release the internal clips, then disengage the panel at the top. Disconnect the wiring connector from the rear of the clock, then remove the clock surround/vent panel from the facia **(see illustrations)**.
7 Undo the two retaining screws and remove the clock from the surround/vent panel **(see illustration)**.

Refitting

8 Refitting is a reversal of the removal procedure.

---

12 Multi-function unit – operation, removal and refitting

Operation

Note: *Not all features are fitted to all models.*
1 The MFU is attached to the rear of the passenger compartment fusebox, and controls the following:

Front wipers intermittent wipe and programmed wash/wipe.
Rear wipers intermittent wipe, programmed wash/wipe and reverse gear operation.

Interior lamp delay/fader.
Lights ON alarm.
Heated rear window timer.
Dim-dip headlamp control.
Rear foglamp latch control.
Engine immobilisation sounder.
Electric window time-out delay.
The MFU also contains integral electronic relays for horn, front wipers, and rear foglamp control.

Removal

2 Disconnect the battery negative terminal.
3 Undo the quick-release screw fixings and remove the right-hand lower facia panel.
4 Remove the two fusebox retaining nuts then partially withdraw the fusebox until the upper wiring block connector(s) can be disconnected.
5 Carefully turn the fusebox assembly around and unplug both multiway connectors from the MFU. Release the MFU from the rear of the fusebox and remove it from the vehicle.

Refitting

6 Refitting is a reversal of the removal procedure. Ensure that all wiring connectors are correctly refitted. On completion, reconnect the battery terminal and check that all electrical circuits function correctly.

---

13 Supplementary Restraint System (SRS) – operation

The Supplementary Restraint System (SRS) components comprise: a driver's airbag (mounted at the centre of the steering wheel), a front seat passenger's airbag (mounted above the glovebox in the facia), a diagnostic control unit located behind the facia, two seat belt pretensioner units (one per front seat), an instrument panel-mounted warning light, a steering wheel rotary coupler and a dedicated wiring harness. System operation is as follows:

If the vehicle suffers a direct or oblique frontal impact of sufficient force, a sensor inside the diagnostic control unit triggers the SRS. A secondary sensor (fitted to discriminate between an actual crash and false triggering) confirms the impact and a

11.5 Carefully pull the switch panel surround from the centre of the facia

11.6a Pull out the clock surround/vent panel to release the internal clips . . .

11.6b . . . then disconnect the clock wiring connector

11.7 Undo the two retaining screws (arrowed) and remove the clock from the surround/vent panel

14.2 Remove the two airbag unit retaining screws accessed from behind the steering wheel

detonation current, supplied from the battery or a backup circuit, activates the airbag(s) and seat belt pretensioners.

Explosive materials in the airbag(s) rapidly produce large volumes of inert gas, causing the airbags to inflate fully within 30 milliseconds. As the driver (or passenger) is thrown forward, airbag deflates progressively through built-in vents, cushioning the impact and reducing the risk of injury from contact with the steering wheel, facia or windscreen. The total time from impact to complete airbag inflation is approximately one tenth of a second.

At the same time, explosive materials in the seat belt pretensioners produce gas which causes the retraction of a piston mechanism, connected to the seat belt stalk. This the effect of taking up all the slack in the seat belts, pulling the occupants back into their seats. Their forward movement towards the facia, windscreen, steering wheel and column is greatly reduced and this helps to minimise the risk of impact injuries.

At vehicle start-up, a warning light located in the instrument panel will illuminate when the system electrical circuits are activated by turning the ignition switch to position II and will stay illuminated for a short period of time whilst the system performs a self-diagnostic

test. If this test is satisfactory, the light will extinguish. If the test is unsatisfactory, the light will remain on or fail to illuminate at all indicating that the system must be serviced as soon as possible.

---

14 Supplementary Restraint System (SRS) – component removal and refitting

Note: *For safety reasons, owners are strongly advised against attempting to diagnose problems with the SRS using standard workshop equipment. The information in this Section is therefore limited to those components in the SRS which must be removed to gain access to other components on the vehicle. Read carefully the precautions given in Section 1 of this Chapter before commencing work on any part of the system.*
Note: *All SRS system wiring can be identified by its yellow, or yellow and black insulation.*

Driver's airbag unit

Removal

1 Remove the ignition key and wait **AT LEAST TEN MINUTES** to allow the system backup circuit to fully discharge. Disconnect **BOTH** battery leads (negative lead last) from the battery and position them well away from the battery terminals. Failure to observe this procedure could cause accidental detonation of the airbag and/or seat belt pretensioners.
2 Remove the two airbag unit retaining screws which are accessed from behind the steering wheel **(see illustration)**.
3 Carefully release the airbag unit from the steering wheel **(see illustration)** and withdraw it just enough to gain access to its wiring behind. Do not allow the unit to hang from its wiring.
4 Unplug the wiring connector from the rear of the airbag unit **(see illustration)** and

carefully remove the unit from the vehicle, placing it in safe storage.

Refitting

5 Refit the airbag unit by reversing the removal procedure, noting the following:
a) *The cable connector must face upper-most when refitted to the airbag unit.*
b) *Observe the specified torque wrench setting when tightening the airbag retaining screws (Torx type) and take care not to cross-thread them. Note that special screws are used to secure the airbag in place – do substitute them for any other kind of screw.*
c) *Reconnect both battery leads, negative lead last, and turn the ignition switch to the II position. Check the condition of the system by observing the SRS warning light located in the steering wheel centre pad. The light should stay illuminated for 3 seconds whilst the system performs a self-diagnosis test. If the test is satisfactory, the light will extinguish. If the test is unsatisfactory, the light will remain on or fail to illuminate at all, denoting that the system must be serviced as soon as possible.*

Passenger airbag unit

Removal

6 Remove the ignition key and wait **AT LEAST TEN MINUTES** to allow the system backup circuit to fully discharge. Disconnect **BOTH** battery leads (negative lead first) from the battery and position them well away from the battery terminals. Failure to observe this procedure could cause accidental detonation of the airbag and/or seat belt pretensioners.
7 Refer to Chapter 11, Section 27, and remove the glovebox.
8 Remove the two screws that secure the airbag unit to its support panel.
9 Withdraw the airbag unit from the facia slightly. Unplug the two multiway wiring connectors from the unit as they become accessible.

14.3 Carefully release the airbag unit from the steering wheel

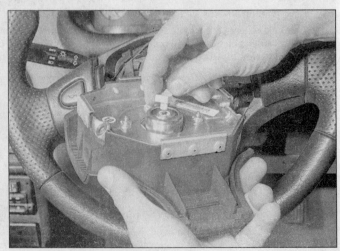

14.4 Unplug the wiring connector from the rear of the airbag unit

10 Carefully remove the passenger airbag unit from the vehicle, placing it in safe storage.

Refitting

11 Refit the airbag unit by reversing the removal procedure, noting the following:
  a) *Observe the specified torque wrench setting when tightening the airbag retaining screws (Torx type) and take care not to cross-thread them. Note that special screws are used to secure the airbag in place – do substitute them for any other kind of screw.*
  b) *Reconnect both battery leads, negative lead last, and turn the ignition switch to the II position. Check the condition of the system by observing the SRS warning light located in the steering wheel centre pad. The light should stay illuminated for 3 seconds whilst the system performs a self-diagnosis test. If the test is satisfactory, the light will extinguish. If the test is unsatisfactory, the light will remain on or fail to illuminate at all, denoting that the system must be serviced as soon as possible.*

Airbag control unit

Removal

12 Remove the ignition key, and wait **AT LEAST TEN MINUTES** to allow the system back-up circuit to discharge.
13 Disconnect **BOTH** battery leads, earth lead first.
14 Press down on the rear edge of the rear seat cushion to expose three cushion securing bolts, and remove the bolts.
15 Pivot the cushion forwards and unhook the front edge from the floor, and remove the cushion.
16 Remove the control unit cover, and disconnect the multiplug.
17 Remove the Torx bolt securing the earth lead to the body.
18 Remove and discard three Torx bolts securing the control unit to the floor, and remove the unit.

Refitting

19 Refitting is a reversal of the removal procedure, noting:
Caution: ensure that the control unit and bracket mating faces are clean and free from burrs.
20 An incorrectly mounted unit can cause system failure or incorrect operation.
  Ensure that the electrical leads are not trapped or strained in any way.
  Use a torque wrench to tighten three new Torx bolts to the specified torque.
  Reconnect the battery positive lead followed by the negative lead.
  Check the system. Turn the ignition switch to position II. The SRS warning lamp should come on for approx. three seconds whilst a self-diagnosis test takes place. If no fault is detected the lamp will go out.
21 If the lamp does not go out, or does not come on at all, there is a system fault which must be repaired by an MG Rover dealer.

Steering wheel rotary coupler

Removal

22 Set the steering in the straight-ahead position.
23 Remove the ignition key and wait **AT LEAST TEN MINUTES** to allow the system backup circuit to fully discharge. Disconnect **BOTH** battery leads (negative lead first) from the battery and position them well away from the battery terminals. Failure to observe this procedure could cause accidental detonation of the airbag and/or seat belt pretensioners.
24 Remove the driver's airbag unit as described earlier in this Section.
25 Unplug the wiring from the rotary coupler at the multiway connector.
26 With reference to Chapter 10, remove the steering wheel, followed by the steering column upper and lower shroud panels.
27 Apply a length of self-adhesive tape to the rotary coupler, to prevent rotation after removal **(see illustration 14.28b)**.

28 Remove the four screws securing the rotary coupler to the column switch assembly and remove the unit from the vehicle **(see illustrations)**.

Refitting

29 Refit the rotary coupler by reversing the removal procedure, noting the following:
  a) *Remove the self-adhesive tape after securing the rotary coupler in place with its retaining screws.*
  b) *Take care to ensure that wiring harness is not trapped between mating surfaces.*
  c) *Refit the steering wheel and column shroud panels with reference to Chapter 10.*
  d) *Refit the driver's airbag unit, as described earlier in this Section.*
  e) *Reconnect both battery leads, negative lead last, and turn the ignition switch to the II position. Check the condition of the system by observing the SRS warning light located in the steering wheel centre pad. The light should stay illuminated for 3 seconds whilst the system performs a self-diagnosis test. If the test is satisfactory, the light will extinguish. If the test is unsatisfactory, the light will remain on or fail to illuminate at all, denoting that the system must be serviced as soon as possible.*

Seat belt pretensioners

Removal

30 Remove the ignition key and wait **AT LEAST TEN MINUTES** to allow the system backup circuit to fully discharge. Disconnect **BOTH** battery leads (negative lead first) from the battery and position them well away from the battery terminals. Failure to observe this procedure could cause accidental detonation of the airbag and/or seat belt pretensioners.
31 Refer to Chapter 11 and remove the relevant front seat.
32 Release the pretensioner wiring harness from the clip on the underside of the seat cushion.

14.28a Remove the four screws (arrowed) securing the rotary coupler . . .

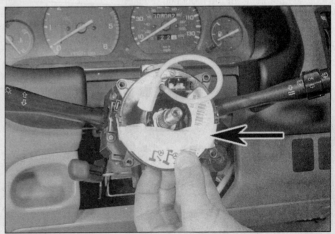

14.28b . . . and remove the coupler from the column switch assembly. Self-adhesive tape (arrowed) applied to the coupler to prevent rotation

33 Slacken and withdraw the securing bolt, then remove the pretensioner unit from the seat **(see illustration)**.

Refitting

34 Refitting is a reversal of removal. Tighten the pretensioner securing bolt to the specified torque wrench setting.

15 Headlamp-levelling motor – removal and refitting

Removal

1 Remove the headlamp unit – see Section 7.
2 Remove the headlamp bulb circular access cover.
3 Using an Allen key, turn the adjuster clockwise to fully extend the motor link rod.
4 Turn the motor 45° to release from the headlamp unit. Lift the motor to release the link rod balljoint from the pin at the back of the headlamp, and remove the motor.

Refitting

5 Refitting is a reversal of the removal procedure, noting:
  Ensure that the motor link rod is fully extended by turning with an Allen key.
  Ensure that the link rod fits correctly over the headlamp pin.

16 Horn – removal and refitting

Removal

1 Disconnect the battery negative cable and position it away from the terminal.
2 Remove the front bumper, as described in Chapter 11.
3 Disconnect the horn wiring connectors and unbolt the horn(s) from the mounting bracket **(see illustration)**.

Refitting

4 Refitting is a reversal of the removal procedure.

14.33 Seat belt pretensioner unit securing bolt (arrowed)

17 Windscreen/tailgate washer system components – removal and refitting

1 The windscreen washer reservoir is situated at the front right-hand corner of the engine compartment, with the washer system pump being mounted on the side of the reservoir. The reservoir is also used to supply the tailgate washer system via a second pump.

Fluid reservoir and pumps

Removal

2 Refer to Chapter 11 and remove the front bumper. Position a container underneath the reservoir to catch any spilt washer fluid.
3 Unplug the wiring connectors from the pumps, then disconnect the plastic tubing from the reservoir.
4 Slacken and remove the screw securing the filler neck to the bodywork. Extract the filler neck from the top of the reservoir.
5 Undo the three screws and remove the reservoir from the bodywork **(see illustration)**.
6 Empty the reservoir of any remaining fluid then if required, carefully separate the pumps from the reservoir and recover the rubber seals.

Refitting

7 Refitting is a reversal of removal. Lubricate the pump seals with soapy water before fitting them to the reservoir **(see illustration)**. Ensure that the washer tubes are not trapped

16.3 Horn mounting bolt (arrowed)

when refitting the reservoir and note that the pump wiring connectors are colour-coded to aid correct reconnection.

Windscreen washer jets

Removal

8 Open the bonnet and disconnect the windscreen washer supply pipe from the underside of the relevant jet. Catch any fluid that spills out in a suitable container.
9 On models with heated washer jets, unplug the electrical wiring from the jet at the multiway connectors.
10 Depress the catch at the side of the jet body and carefully prise it from the bonnet aperture.

Refitting

11 Refitting is a reversal of removal. To adjust the aim of the jet, carefully push a pin into the spherical insert at the centre of the jet and swivel it to alter the direction of the jet of washer fluid.

Tailgate washer jet

Removal

12 The tailgate washer jet is located at the end of the tailgate wiper arm spindle.
13 Flip up the protective plastic cap (which contains the jet and its seal) and pull it off the wiper arm spindle **(see illustration)**.

Refitting

14 Refitting is a reversal of removal. If trouble is experienced at any time with the flow to the tailgate washer, check that the non-return

17.5 Washer fluid reservoir mounting screws (arrowed)

17.7 Ensure that the washer pump seals (arrowed) are securely seated

17.13 Flip up the protective plastic cap and pull it off the wiper arm spindle

18.4 Slacken and withdraw the motor mounting bracket bolts

18.5a Pull the motor and bracket assembly away from the bulkhead to gain access to the linkage nut (arrowed) . . .

18.5b . . . undo the nut and detach the wiper linkage from the motor spindle

valve is not blocked. The valve is fitted in the tube next to the reservoir and should allow fluid to pass only outwards to the jet.

18 Windscreen wiper motor and linkage – removal and refitting

Windscreen wiper motor

Removal

1 Operate the wiper motor then switch it off so that the wiper blades return to the rest position.
2 Stick a piece of masking tape on the windscreen alongside the edge of each wiper blade to use as an alignment aid on refitting, then open the bonnet.
3 Disconnect the battery negative cable and position it away from the terminal.

4 Slacken and withdraw the motor mounting bracket bolts **(see illustration)**. Recover the mounting rubbers, if they are loose.
5 Pull the motor and bracket assembly away from the bulkhead slightly, to gain access to the linkage, then undo the nut (recover the washer) and detach the wiper linkage from the motor spindle **(see illustrations)**.
6 Release the wiring harness from the clip on the wiper motor mounting bracket. Unplug the wiring connector from the wiper motor harness **(see illustration)**.
7 Remove the motor and bracket assembly from the engine compartment. If required, the motor can be separated from the bracket after removing the three securing screws.

Refitting

8 Refitting is a reversal of removal. Tighten

the linkage-to-motor spindle nut to the specified torque.

Wiper linkage

Removal

9 Slacken and remove the wiper arm spindle nuts and pull the arms off their spindles (see Section 19). If necessary, the arms can be levered off their spindles by using a large flat-bladed screwdriver.
10 Carefully prise out the seven trim caps from the ventilation grille to gain access to the grille retaining screws. Slacken and remove all the retaining screws then release the eight retaining clips situated along the front edge of the grille and remove the grille from the vehicle **(see illustrations)**.
11 With reference to the previous sub-Section, disconnect the linkage from the wiper motor spindle **(see illustration)**.

18.6 Unplug the wiring connector from the wiper motor harness

18.10a Carefully prise out the seven trim caps from the ventilation grille . . .

18.10b . . . slacken and remove all the retaining screws . . .

18.10c . . . then release the eight retaining clips situated along the front edge of the grille . . .

18.10d . . . and remove the grille from the vehicle

18.11 Remove the nut (arrowed) and disconnect the linkage from the wiper motor spindle

18.12 Wiper linkage securing bolts (left-hand side shown)

19.3a Remove the plastic cap/washer jet from the spindle nut . . .

19.3b . . . and slacken the nut with a ring spanner, then remove it from the spindle (tailgate wiper)

19.3c Removing the wiper spindle nut (windscreen wiper)

19.4a Removing the windscreen wiper arm

19.4b Removing the tailgate wiper arm

12 Slacken and remove the six securing bolts, then remove the linkage assembly from the bulkhead **(see illustration)**.

Refitting

13 Refitting is a reversal of removal.

19 Windscreen/tailgate wiper arms – removal and refitting

Removal

1 Operate the wiper motor then switch it off so that the wiper blades return to the rest position.

2 Stick a piece of masking tape on the windscreen alongside the edge of each wiper blade to use as an alignment aid on refitting, then open the bonnet.

3 Where applicable, remove the plastic cap from the spindle nut. Slacken the nut with a ring spanner, then remove it from the spindle. Note that on the tailgate wiper arm, the washer jet is integrated into the wiper arm spindle **(see illustrations)**.

4 Lift the wiper arm from the spindle **(see illustrations)**.

Refitting

5 Refitting is a reversal of removal, tightening the spindle nut to the specified torque. Align the wiper arm so that the edge of the wiper lies on the alignment mark made during removal. Operate the wipers, then switch them off and check that the wiper arm stops in the correct rest position on the screen.

20 Tailgate wiper motor – removal and refitting

Removal

1 Operate the tailgate wiper motor, then switch it off so that the wiper blade returns to the rest position.

2 Stick a piece of masking tape alongside the edge of the wiper blade to use as an alignment aid on refitting.

3 Prise off the spindle nut cover/washer jet then undo the wiper arm spindle nut and pull the arm off its spindle – see the previous sub-Section for details. If necessary, the arm can be levered off using a large flat-bladed screwdriver.

4 Prise off the spindle nut cover, then undo the spindle retaining nut and remove the washer and rubber seal **(see illustrations)**.

5 Open up the tailgate and undo the two screws securing the tailgate lower trim panel **(see illustration)**.

20.4a Prise off the spindle nut cover . . .

20.4b . . . then undo the spindle retaining nut . . .

20.4c . . . and remove the washer . . .

20.4d . . . and rubber seal

20.5 Undo the two screws securing the tailgate lower trim panel

20.7a Disconnect the washer fluid supply pipe – be prepared for a small amount of fluid spillage . . .

20.7b . . . and unplug the wiring connector from the wiper motor

20.8a Undo the securing bolts . . .

20.8b . . . and remove the motor from the tailgate

6 Using a large flat-bladed screwdriver (pad the blade with insulating tape to prevent damage), work around the outside of the trim panel and carefully prise it away from the tailgate to release the press stud fixings. Remove the trim panel from the tailgate when all of the fixings have been released.

7 Disconnect the washer fluid supply pipe, then unplug the wiring connector from the wiper motor – be prepared for a small amount of fluid spillage **(see illustrations)**.

8 Undo the bolts securing the wiper motor to the tailgate. Remove the motor from the tailgate, noting the motor mounting rubbers and the washer and rubber seal fitted to the wiper spindle **(see illustrations)**.

Refitting

9 Refitting is a reverse of the removal procedure, noting the following:

a) Examine the wiper motor mounting

21.3a Removing the radio/cassette unit using the special extraction tools . . .

rubbers and spindle seals for signs of damage and deterioration, and renew if necessary.

b) Tighten the wiper motor mounting bolts to the specified torque.

c) Ensure the wiper arm spindle is clean, then align the wiper blade with the tape fitted on removal and press the arm firmly onto the spindle. Tighten the wiper arm spindle nut to the specified torque and refit the nut cover.

21 Radio/cassette player – removal and refitting

Note: *The following removal and refitting procedure is for the range of radio/cassette units which Rover fit as standard equipment. Removal and refitting procedures of non-standard units may differ slightly.*

Removal

1 Referring to the instructions supplied with the radio/cassette unit, temporarily de-activate the security code.

2 Disconnect the battery negative lead.

3 To remove the unit, two standard DIN extraction tools are required. These are two U-shaped rods which are inserted into the four small holes in the front of the unit to release the unit retaining clips. The tools may possibly be obtained from a Rover dealer or any audio accessory outlet, or can be made out of 3.0 mm wire rod, such as a welding rod.

Using the tools, push back the clamps on the left and right-hand sides, withdraw the unit and disconnect the wiring plugs and aerial **(see illustrations)**.

Refitting

4 Refitting is the reverse of the removal procedure. On completion, connect the battery negative terminal and reactivate the unit by entering the security code.

22 Speakers – removal and refitting

Removal

Front door-mounted woofer

1 Remove the front door inner trim panel, as described in Chapter 11.

21.3b . . . and disconnecting the aerial co-axial cable from the rear of the unit

22.2a Undo the three speaker retaining screws then withdraw the speaker from the front door . . .

2 Undo the three speaker retaining screws then withdraw the speaker. Disconnect the speaker wiring connectors and remove the speaker from the door **(see illustrations)**.

Front door-mounted tweeter

3 Remove the door interior trim panel – see Chapter 11.
4 Rotate the tweeter and remove it from the trim panel.

Rear speaker

5 Disconnect the wiring from the speaker at the multiway connector **(see illustration)**.
6 Undo the four speaker retaining screws, then detach the speaker from the underside of the parcel shelf support panel and remove it from the vehicle **(see illustration)**.

Refitting

7 Refitting is a reverse of the removal procedure.

23 Radio aerial and co-axial cable – removal and refitting

Removal

Note: *The aerial whip can be unscrewed from the aerial base and renewed as separate item.*
1 Remove the radio/cassette player and unplug the co-axial cable from the rear of the unit.

22.5 Disconnect the wiring from the rear speaker at the connectors

22.2b . . . and disconnect the speaker wiring connectors

2 Refer to Chapter 11, Section 27, and remove the glovebox from the facia. Reach inside the facia and release the co-axial cable from the clips on the heater/blower unit.
3 Release the rubber sealing strip from the passenger's door aperture, then unclip the trim panel from the A-pillar.
4 Slacken and withdraw the securing screws and remove all four sun visor hinge brackets from the roof.
5 Carefully prise out the press stud fixings that secure the front edge of the headlining to the roof.
6 On models fitted with a sunroof, unclip the sunroof switch trim panel from the headlining.
7 Lower the headlining away from the roof slightly to gain access to the underside of the aerial base.
8 On models fitted with a sunroof, remove the two securing screws and detach the sunroof switch assembly from the roof. Allow the assembly to rest on the headlining.
9 Remove the plastic cap from the stud terminal on the underside of the aerial base, then remove the nut and disconnect the co-axial cable from the aerial base. Remove the aerial base from the roof and recover the seal.
10 Trace the aerial lead back along its length and free it from any remaining retaining clips or ties. Tie a long piece of string around the aerial end plug (radio end).
11 Carefully pull the aerial lead out through the roof aperture until the end plug appears. Untie the string and leave it in position in the vehicle.

22.6 Undo the retaining screws, then detach the speaker from the parcel shelf support panel (panel removed)

Refitting

12 Securely tie the string around the aerial lead plug and fit the rubber seal to the aerial.
13 From inside the vehicle, gently pull the string through the facia and out of the radio aperture, whilst feeding the aerial lead in through the roof aperture. When the aerial lead plug emerges on the inside of the vehicle, untie the string.
14 The remainder of the refitting procedure is a reversal of the removal procedure. Ensure that the co-axial cable is retained by its securing clips, so that it does not interfere with the operation of the heater controls.

24 Battery Back-up Sounder (BBUS) – operation, removal and refitting

Operation

1 The BBUS is fitted to ensure that, if the vehicle main battery is disconnected or tampered with, an audible alarm will still sound if the alarm system is triggered, or if an incorrect disarming sequence is detected. Internal rechargeable batteries power the alarm.

Removal

Note: *The following new parts are needed – two shear-head bolts to secure the sounder shield.*
2 Remove the windscreen wiper arms – see Section 19.
3 Remove seven screw covers and screws along the upper edge of the air intake scuttle panel.
4 Release eight studs securing the lower edge of the panel to the body.
5 Release the panel from the bonnet hinges and A-pillar finishers, and remove the panel.
6 Centre punch the two shear-head bolts securing the sounder shield to the bracket. Using a 5 mm drill, drill out the two bolts.
7 Release and disconnect the multiplug from the sounder.
8 Remove the nut and bolt securing the sounder bracket to the bulkhead, and remove the sounder and bracket.
9 Note the fitted position of the sounder in relation to the bracket. Remove the nut and remove the sounder from the bracket.

Refitting

10 Refitting is a reversal of the removal procedure, noting:
   Ensure that the sounder is correctly aligned in relation to the bracket, and that the location notches correctly locate.
   Ensuring that the fitting tag is correctly located, position the sounder and bracket on the bulkhead, and secure with the nut and bolt.
Fit the shield and two new shear-head bolts. Tighten the bolts until the heads shear off.

Rover 25/MG ZR typical wiring diagrams

Diagram 1

Key to symbols

Bulb		Item no.	2
Flashing bulb		Single speed pump/motor	M
Switch			
Multiple contact switch (ganged)		Gauge/meter	
Fuse/fusible link and current rating	F5 30A	Earth point & location	E4
Resistor		Diode	
Variable resistor		Light emitting diode (LED)	
Variable resistor		Solenoid actuator	
Wire splice or soldered joint		Heating element	
Connecting wires		Plug & socket contact	

Wire colour & cross sectional area (brown with yellow tracer 0.5 mm²) — N/Y 0.5

Dashed outline denotes part of a larger item, containing in this case an electronic or solid state device. e.g. connector no. 595, pin 9.

C595/9

Key to circuits

Diagram 1	Information for wiring diagrams.
Diagram 2	Starting, charging, engine cooling fan, cigar lighter & horn.
Diagram 3	Head, side, tail & number plate lights, direction indicators & hazard warning lights.
Diagram 4	Stop & reversing lights, lights-on warning buzzer & foglights.
Diagram 5	Headlight levelling, heater blower & interior lighting.
Diagram 6	Front wash/wipe, heated washer jets, heated rear window & clock.
Diagram 7	Rear wash/wipe, supplementary restraint & anti-lock braking systems.
Diagram 8	Sunroof, audio system, diagnostic socket & retracting mirrors.
Diagram 9	Electric mirrors, central locking & parking distance sensor.
Diagram 10	Electric windows & instrument cluster.

Earth locations

E1	Beneath rear seat	E8	Behind LH side of fascia
E2	Front of LH inner wing	E9	RH side of luggage compartment
E3	LH side of bonnet lock platform		
E4	LH side of bonnet lock platform	E10	RH side of luggage compartment
E5	Front of LH inner wing		
E6	LHD - Front of LH inner wing	E11	Centre rear of engine
	RHD - Behind RH side of fascia	E12	On front of gearbox
E7	LHD - Behind LH side of fascia		
	RHD - Behind RH side of fascia		

Engine compartment fuses

Fuse	Rating	Circuit protected
F1	10A	Engine management, speedometer & auto. trans.
F2	20A	Engine management, fuel pump
F3	10A	Glow plug relay
F4	10A	Air conditioning relay, glow plug relay
F5	15A	Alarm, central locking
F6	15A	Front fog lights
F7	15A	Hazard warning lights
F8	15A	Engine management
F9	10A	Air conditioning
F10	20A	Fuel cut-off switch

Passenger compartment fuses

Fuse	Rating	Circuit protected
F1	10A	Hazard warning switch, clock, instrument cluster, auto. trans.
F2	10A	ABS
F3	10A	Interior light, luggage compartment light, clock, audio system, instruments, diagnostic socket
F4	10A	RH headlight main beam, main beam warning light
F5	10A	LH headlight main beam
F6	25A	Sunroof
F7	5A	Safety restraint system
F8	10A	LH tail light, LH sidelight, headlight levelling, front foglights, switch lighting
F9	20A	Cigar lighter, multi-function unit
F10	10A	LH headlight
F11	10A	RH headlight
F12	15A	RH side & tail light, headlight levelling, number plate light
F13	15A	Front wash/wipe
F14	10A	Engine cooling fan, engine man., alarm/immobiliser
F15	15A	Rear wash/wipe, heated washer jets, air conditioning, parking distance sensor
F16	10A	Stop & reversing lights
F17	10A	Audio system, lights-on warning, multi-function unit
F18	7.5A	Electric mirrors
F19	20A	Heater blower
F20	10A	Ignition switch
F21	20A	RH front electric window
F22	20A	LH front electric window
F23	-	Not fitted
F24	15A	Multifunction unit, horn
F25	10A	Daytime running lights (Scandinavian vehicles only)
F26	20A	Power wash relay (Scandinavian vehicles only)
F27	10A	RH heated seat
F28	10A	LH heated seat
F29	10A	Daytime running lights (Scandinavian vehicles only)
F30	-	Not fitted
F31	15A	Rear RH electric window
F32	15A	Rear LH electric window

Engine fusebox   Passenger fusebox

H32846

Wire colours

B Black   **P** Purple
G Green   **R** Red
K Pink   **S** Slate
Lg Light green   **U** Blue
N Brown   **W** White
O Orange   **Y** Yellow

Key to items

1 Battery
2 Starter motor
3 Alternator
4 Ignition switch
5 Engine fusebox
   a = starter relay
   b = engine management relay
   c = engine cooling fan relay
6 Passenger fusebox
7 Satellite fusebox
8 Horn
9 Multifunction unit
   a = horn relay
10 Horn switch
11 Rotary coupler
12 Common earth connector
13 Cigar lighter
14 Engine cooling fan

Diagram 2

H32847

Starting & charging system

Term Pos	Aux	IN 1	IGN 2B	IN 2	IGN 1	IGN 2A	Crank
Lock							
Aux							
On							
Crank							
Term	7	3	6	1	5	2	4

C632/1   FL3   C571/3
40A
C826/1
FL1   FL7
150A   40A
a
87a
30
85
86
87
C576/1
C576/7
C572/1
C575/6   C578/8
N/P 4.0
W/R 1.0
W/R 2.0
W/R 1.0
B/R 0.5
N 15.0
N/R 3.0
F20
10A
C595/9
C595/10
7
R 10.0
R 40.0
N/Y 0.75
N/Y 0.75
B 25.0
1
2
5

C584/16
C581/6
6
N/Y 0.5

See diagram 10
Instrument cluster
(alternator warning light)

N 15.0   C183/1   'K' series
N/Y 0.75   C185/1   (without A/C)
3

N 15.0   C1720/1   'K' series
N/Y 0.75   C850/1   (with A/C)
3

N 15.0   C183/1   'L' series
N/Y 1.0   C53/1
3

Automatic transmission
(Engine management
control unit)

Manual transmission
(Alarm control unit)

CVT
(CVT switch)

Horn

C632/1   FL4   C574/2
40A
5
N 4.0
C595/1   F24
C595/2   15A
7
R 10.0
a
87a   C16/3
30
85   C62/6
86
87   C16/8
9
P/N 1.0
P/B 0.5
C82/4
C1254/4
11
R 0.5
8
1
2
P/Y 1.0
B 2.5
E5
B 25.0
1
10
B 0.5   R 0.5
10
B 0.5   R 0.5

Engine cooling fan

Engine management
control unit

C632/1   FL8   C574/1
20A
5
R 10.0
b
87a
30
85
86
87
C576/9
c
87a
30
85
86
87
C574/3
C575/10
C570/4
S/U 0.5
W/K 0.5
U/P 2.5
B 25.0
1
U 2.5
P/U 2.5
'K' series
B 4.0   4 M 3   14
B 3.0   2 M 1   14
'L' series
E4

Cigar lighter

C632/1   FL4   C574/2
40A
5
R 10.0
N 4.0
See diagram 5
Interior lighting feed B
C587/1   F9
C584/6   20A
6
C74/1
C89/2
C89/1
R/B 0.5
U 1.0
B 2.0
13
2 1
12
B 2.0
B 25.0
1
E5

Wire colours

B	Black	P	Purple
G	Green	R	Red
K	Pink	S	Slate
Lg	Light green	U	Blue
N	Brown	W	White
O	Orange	Y	Yellow

Key to items

1 Battery
4 Ignition switch
5 Engine fusebox
6 Passenger fusebox
  a = hazard warning relay
12 Common earth connector
17 Number plate light
18 LH rear light unit
  a = tail light
  b = direction indicator

19 RH rear light unit
  (as item 18)
20 Light switch
  a = headlight flasher
  b = dip/main beam
  c = side/headlight
21 LH headlight unit
  a = side light
  b = dip beam
  c = main beam

22 RH headlight unit
  (as item 21)
24 Hazard warning switch
25 Direction indicator switch
26 LH front direction indicator
27 RH front direction indicator
28 LH indicator side repeater
29 RH indicator side repeater

Diagram 3

H32848

Head, side, tail & number plate lights

Direction indicators & hazard warning lights

Term Pos	Aux	IN 1	IGN 2B	IN 2	IGN 1	IGN 2A	Crank
Lock							
Aux	●	●——●					
On	●	●——●		●——●——●			
Crank				●——●		●——●	
Term	7	3	6	1	5	2	4

Wire colours

B	Black	**P**	Purple
G	Green	**R**	Red
K	Pink	**S**	Slate
Lg	Light green	**U**	Blue
N	Brown	**W**	White
O	Orange	**Y**	Yellow

Key to items

1 Battery
4 Ignition switch
5 Engine fusebox
  d = front foglight relay
6 Passenger fusebox
7 Satellite fusebox
9 Multifunction unit
12 Common earth connector

18 LH rear light unit
  c = reversing light
  d = stop light
  e = foglight
19 RH rear light unit
  (as item 18)
20 Light switch
  c = side/headlight

32 High level brake light
33 Stop light switch
34 Reversing light (manual)
35 Starter inhibitor/reversing light switch (auto.)
36 LH front foglight
37 RH front foglight
38 Front foglight switch
39 Rear foglight switch

Diagram 4

H32849

Wire colours

B	Black	P	Purple
G	Green	R	Red
K	Pink	S	Slate
Lg	Light green	U	Blue
N	Brown	W	White
O	Orange	Y	Yellow

Key to items

1 Battery
4 Ignition switch
5 Engine fusebox
6 Passenger fusebox
7 Satellite fusebox
9 Multifunction unit
12 Common earth connector
20 Light switch
   c = side/headlight
42 Headlight levelling switch
43 LH headlight levelling motor
44 RH headlight levelling motor
45 Glovebox light
46 Glovebox light switch
47 Interior light
48 Luggage compartment light
49 Luggage compartment light switch
50 LH front door switch
51 LH rear door switch
52 RH front door switch
53 RH rear door switch
54 Heater blower motor
55 Heater blower switch
56 Heater blower resistor
57 Heater switch illumination

Diagram 5

H32850

Headlight levelling

Interior Lighting

Heater blower

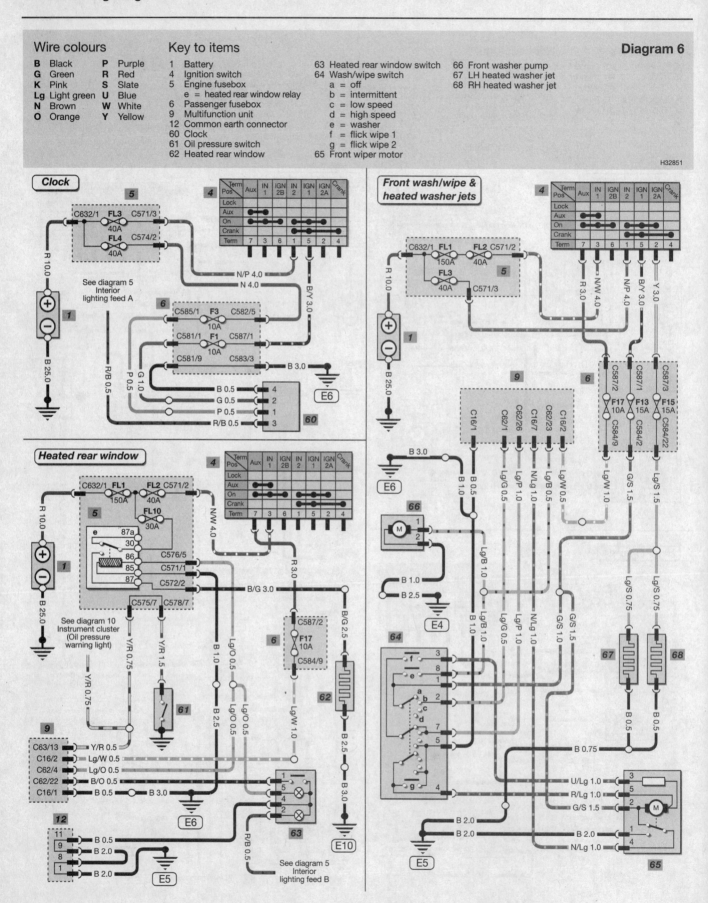

Wire colours

B	Black	P	Purple
G	Green	R	Red
K	Pink	S	Slate
Lg	Light green	U	Blue
N	Brown	W	White
O	Orange	Y	Yellow

Key to items

1 Battery
4 Ignition switch
5 Engine fusebox
   e = heated rear window relay
6 Passenger fusebox
9 Multifunction unit
12 Common earth connector
60 Clock
61 Oil pressure switch
62 Heated rear window

63 Heated rear window switch
64 Wash/wipe switch
   a = off
   b = intermittent
   c = low speed
   d = high speed
   e = washer
   f = flick wipe 1
   g = flick wipe 2
65 Front wiper motor

66 Front washer pump
67 LH heated washer jet
68 RH heated washer jet

Diagram 6

H32851

Wire colours

B	Black	**P**	Purple
G	Green	**R**	Red
K	Pink	**S**	Slate
Lg	Light green	**U**	Blue
N	Brown	**W**	White
O	Orange	**Y**	Yellow

Key to items

1 Battery
4 Ignition switch
5 Engine fusebox
6 Passenger fusebox
7 Satellite fusebox
9 Multifunction unit
11 Rotary coupler
64 Wash/wipe switch
  b = intermittent

70 Rear washer pump
71 Rear wiper relay
72 Rear wiper switch
  a = wiper
  b = washer
73 Rear wiper motor
74 SRS control unit
75 LH seat belt pretensioner
76 RH seat belt pretensioner

77 Driver's airbag
78 Passenger's airbag
79 ABS control unit
80 LH front wheel sensor
81 RH front wheel sensor
82 LH rear wheel sensor
83 RH rear wheel sensor

Diagram 7

H32852

Rear wash/wipe

Term Pos	Aux	IN 1	IGN 2B	IN 2	IGN 1	IGN 2A	Crank
Lock							
Aux	●	●	●				
On	●	●	●	●	●		
Crank				●	●	●	●
Term	7	3	6	1	5	2	4

Supplementary restraint system

Term Pos	Aux	IN 1	IGN 2B	IN 2	IGN 1	IGN 2A	Crank
Lock							
Aux	●	●	●				
On	●	●	●	●	●		
Crank				●	●	●	●
Term	7	3	6	1	5	2	4

See diagram 10
Instrument cluster
SRS warning light

See diagram 8
Diagnostic socket

ABS

Term Pos	Aux	IN 1	IGN 2B	IN 2	IGN 1	IGN 2A	Crank
Lock							
Aux	●	●	●				
On	●	●	●	●	●		
Crank				●	●	●	●
Term	7	3	6	1	5	2	4

See diagram 10
Instrument cluster
(ABS warning light)

See diagram 4
Stop light switch

Engine management

See diagram 8
Diagnostic socket

See diagram 4
Reversing light switch

Wire colours

B	Black	**P**	Purple
G	Green	**R**	Red
K	Pink	**S**	Slate
Lg	Light green	**U**	Blue
N	Brown	**W**	White
O	Orange	**Y**	Yellow

Key to items

1 Battery
4 Ignition switch
5 Engine fusebox
6 Passenger fusebox
7 Satellite fusebox
9 Multifunction unit
11 Rotary coupler
85 Sunroof relay

86 Sunroof motor
87 Sunroof switch
  a = open
  b = close
88 Diagnostic socket
89 LH front speaker
90 LH front tweeter
91 LH rear speaker

92 RH front speaker
93 RH front tweeter
94 RH rear speaker
95 Remote audio controls
  a = volume -
  b = volume +
  c = search -
  d = search +

96 CD/tuner unit
97 Mirror retraction control unit
98 Mirror control switch
  a = mirror retraction switch
99 Driver's door mirror assembly
  a = mirror retraction motor
100 Passenger's door mirror assembly
  a = mirror retraction motor

Diagram 8

H32853

Sunroof

Audio system

Diagnostic socket

Retracting mirrors

Wire colours

B	Black	P	Purple
G	Green	R	Red
K	Pink	S	Slate
Lg	Light green	U	Blue
N	Brown	W	White
O	Orange	Y	Yellow

Key to items

1 Battery
4 Ignition switch
5 Engine fusebox
6 Passenger fusebox
12 Common earth connector
98 Mirror control switch
   b = up/down switch
   c = right/left switch
   d = driver/passenger switch
99 Driver's door mirror assembly
   b = vertical adjustment
   c = horizontal adjustment
   d = heating element

100 Passenger's door mirror assembly
   b = vertical adjustment
   c = horizontal adjustment
   d = heating element
101 Alarm/immobiliser control unit
102 LH front door lock
103 RH front door lock
104 LH rear door lock
105 RH rear door lock
106 Tailgate lock
107 Parking distance control unit
108 Audible warning device
109 LH outer sensor

110 LH inner sensor
111 RH inner sensor
112 RH outer sensor

Diagram 9

H32854

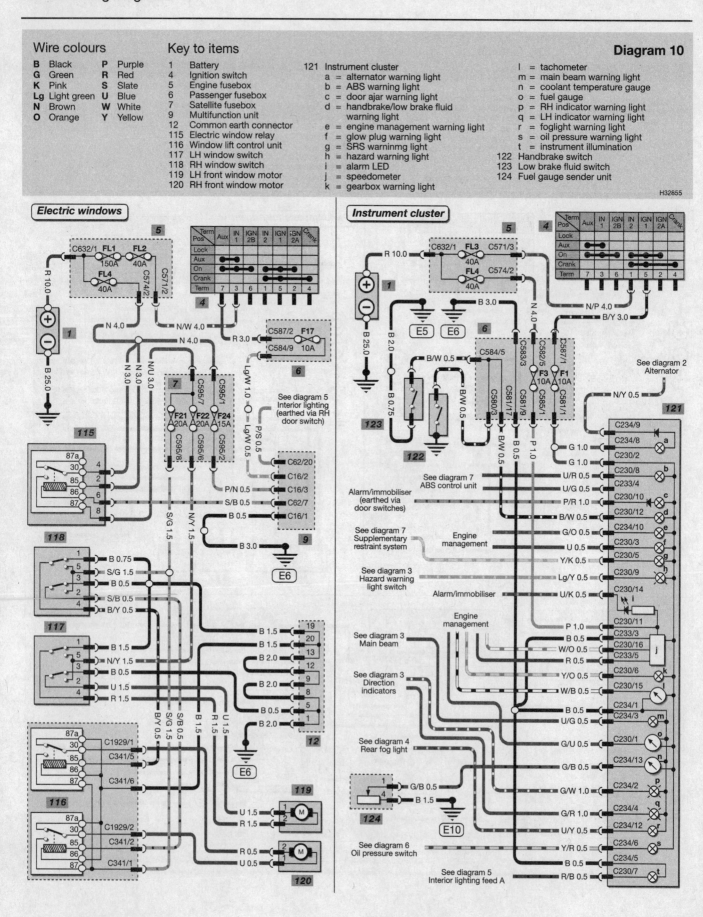

Wire colours

B	Black	P	Purple
G	Green	R	Red
K	Pink	S	Slate
Lg	Light green	U	Blue
N	Brown	W	White
O	Orange	Y	Yellow

Key to items

1 Battery
4 Ignition switch
5 Engine fusebox
6 Passenger fusebox
7 Satellite fusebox
9 Multifunction unit
12 Common earth connector
115 Electric window relay
116 Window lift control unit
117 LH window switch
118 RH window switch
119 LH front window motor
120 RH front window motor

121 Instrument cluster
a = alternator warning light
b = ABS warning light
c = door ajar warning light
d = handbrake/low brake fluid warning light
e = engine management warning light
f = glow plug warning light
g = SRS warninmg light
h = hazard warning light
i = alarm LED
j = speedometer
k = gearbox warning light

l = tachometer
m = main beam warning light
n = coolant temperature gauge
o = fuel gauge
p = RH indicator warning light
q = LH indicator warning light
r = foglight warning light
s = oil pressure warning light
t = instrument illumination
122 Handbrake switch
123 Low brake fluid switch
124 Fuel gauge sender unit

Diagram 10

H32855

Dimensions and weights

Dimensions

	Rover 25	MG ZR
Overall length	3.990 m	4.011 m
Overall width – including mirrors	1.931 m	1.931 m
Overall width – excluding mirrors	1.688 m	1.688 m
Overall height – at kerb weight	1.419	1.400
Wheelbase	2.500 m	2.500 m
Ground clearance – between axles	135 mm	119 mm
Turning circle – kerb to kerb	11.21 m	11.64 m

Weights

Approx. unladen (fuel tank 90% full):
   1.1 litre petrol model . . . . .1020 – 1110 kg
   1.4 litre petrol model . . . . .1020 – 1135 kg
   1.6 litre petrol model . . . . .1030 – 1120 kg
   1.8 litre petrol model . . . . .1030 – 1135 kg
   Diesel model . . . . .1130 – 1230 kg
Maximum gross vehicle weight:
   1.1, 1.4 and 1.6 litre petrol models . . . . .1500 kg
   1.8 litre petrol model . . . . .1520 kg
   Diesel model . . . . .1600 kg
Maximum front axle load:
   1.1, 1.4, 1.6 litre petrol model . . . . .805 kg
   1.8 litre petrol model . . . . .830 kg
   Diesel model . . . . .915 kg

Maximum rear axle load (must not be exceeded) . . . . .750 kg
Towing weights:
   Maximum towing weight with braked trailer*:
      1.1 litre petrol model . . . . .700 kg
      All other models . . . . .1000 kg
   Maximum trailer weight – unbraked . . . . .500 kg
   Max. towing hitch downward load . . . . .70 kg
   Coupling device max. overhang:
      Fixed coupling . . . . .749 kg
      Removable coupling . . . . .779 kg
Max. roof rack load – including weight of rack . . . . .65 kg
Allows restart on 12 % (1 in 8) gradient with two occupants

Vehicle identification

Modifications are a continuing and unpubliscised process in vehicle manufacture, quite apart from major model changes. Spare parts manuals and lists are compiled upon a numerical basis, the individual vehicle identification numbers being essential to correct identification of the component concerned.

When ordering spare parts, always give as much information as possible. Quote the vehicle model, year of manufacture, body and engine numbers as appropriate.

The *vehicle identification plate* is situated on the passenger door pillar **(see illustration)**. It gives the VIN (vehicle identification number), vehicle weight information and paint and trim colour codes.

The *vehicle identification number* is repeated in the form of stamped numbers on the centre of the engine compartment bulkhead **(see illustration)**, and also on a plate below the lower left-hand corner of the windscreen.

The *body number* is stamped into a plate fixed to the left-hand side of the spare wheel well, in the luggage compartment.

The *engine number* on petrol engines is stamped on the front face of the cylinder block, next to the transmission casing **(see illustration)**. On diesel engines, the engine number is stamped on the upper front face of the cylinder block, at the centre.

The *Manual Transmission number* is stamped on label attached to the front face of the clutch housing.

Vehicle identification plate on passenger door pillar

Vehicle identification number on engine compartment bulkhead

Engine number (petrol engine) on front of cylinder block/crankcase

Radio/cassette Anti-theft system – precaution

The radio/cassette unit fitted as standard equipment by Rover is equipped with a built-in security code to deter thieves. If the power source to the unit is cut, the anti-theft system will activate. Even if the power source is immediately reconnected, the radio/cassette unit will not function until the correct security code has been entered. Therefore, if you do not know the correct security code for the unit, do not disconnect the battery negative lead, or remove the radio/cassette unit from the vehicle.

The procedure for reprogramming a unit that has been disconnected from its power supply varies from model to model. Consult the handbook supplied with the unit for specific details or refer to your Rover dealer.

Whenever servicing, repair or overhaul work is carried out on the car or its components, observe the following procedures and instructions. This will assist in carrying out the operation efficiently and to a professional standard of workmanship.

Joint mating faces and gaskets

When separating components at their mating faces, never insert screwdrivers or similar implements into the joint between the faces in order to prise them apart. This can cause severe damage which results in oil leaks, coolant leaks, etc upon reassembly. Separation is usually achieved by tapping along the joint with a soft-faced hammer in order to break the seal. However, note that this method may not be suitable where dowels are used for component location.

Where a gasket is used between the mating faces of two components, a new one must be fitted on reassembly; fit it dry unless otherwise stated in the repair procedure. Make sure that the mating faces are clean and dry, with all traces of old gasket removed. When cleaning a joint face, use a tool which is unlikely to score or damage the face, and remove any burrs or nicks with an oilstone or fine file.

Make sure that tapped holes are cleaned with a pipe cleaner, and keep them free of jointing compound, if this is being used, unless specifically instructed otherwise.

Ensure that all orifices, channels or pipes are clear, and blow through them, preferably using compressed air.

Oil seals

Oil seals can be removed by levering them out with a wide flat-bladed screwdriver or similar implement. Alternatively, a number of self-tapping screws may be screwed into the seal, and these used as a purchase for pliers or some similar device in order to pull the seal free.

Whenever an oil seal is removed from its working location, either individually or as part of an assembly, it should be renewed.

The very fine sealing lip of the seal is easily damaged, and will not seal if the surface it contacts is not completely clean and free from scratches, nicks or grooves. If the original sealing surface of the component cannot be restored, and the manufacturer has not made provision for slight relocation of the seal relative to the sealing surface, the component should be renewed.

Protect the lips of the seal from any surface which may damage them in the course of fitting. Use tape or a conical sleeve where possible. Lubricate the seal lips with oil before fitting and, on dual-lipped seals, fill the space between the lips with grease.

Unless otherwise stated, oil seals must be fitted with their sealing lips toward the lubricant to be sealed.

Use a tubular drift or block of wood of the appropriate size to install the seal and, if the seal housing is shouldered, drive the seal down to the shoulder. If the seal housing is unshouldered, the seal should be fitted with its face flush with the housing top face (unless otherwise instructed).

Screw threads and fastenings

Seized nuts, bolts and screws are quite a common occurrence where corrosion has set in, and the use of penetrating oil or releasing fluid will often overcome this problem if the offending item is soaked for a while before attempting to release it. The use of an impact driver may also provide a means of releasing such stubborn fastening devices, when used in conjunction with the appropriate screwdriver bit or socket. If none of these methods works, it may be necessary to resort to the careful application of heat, or the use of a hacksaw or nut splitter device.

Studs are usually removed by locking two nuts together on the threaded part, and then using a spanner on the lower nut to unscrew the stud. Studs or bolts which have broken off below the surface of the component in which they are mounted can sometimes be removed using a stud extractor. Always ensure that a blind tapped hole is completely free from oil, grease, water or other fluid before installing the bolt or stud. Failure to do this could cause the housing to crack due to the hydraulic action of the bolt or stud as it is screwed in.

When tightening a castellated nut to accept a split pin, tighten the nut to the specified torque, where applicable, and then tighten further to the next split pin hole. Never slacken the nut to align the split pin hole, unless stated in the repair procedure.

When checking or retightening a nut or bolt to a specified torque setting, slacken the nut or bolt by a quarter of a turn, and then retighten to the specified setting. However, this should not be attempted where angular tightening has been used.

For some screw fastenings, notably cylinder head bolts or nuts, torque wrench settings are no longer specified for the latter stages of tightening, "angle-tightening" being called up instead. Typically, a fairly low torque wrench setting will be applied to the bolts/nuts in the correct sequence, followed by one or more stages of tightening through specified angles.

Locknuts, locktabs and washers

Any fastening which will rotate against a component or housing during tightening should always have a washer between it and the relevant component or housing.

Spring or split washers should always be renewed when they are used to lock a critical component such as a big-end bearing retaining bolt or nut. Locktabs which are folded over to retain a nut or bolt should always be renewed.

Self-locking nuts can be re-used in non-critical areas, providing resistance can be felt when the locking portion passes over the bolt or stud thread. However, it should be noted that self-locking stiffnuts tend to lose their effectiveness after long periods of use, and should then be renewed as a matter of course.

Split pins must always be replaced with new ones of the correct size for the hole.

When thread-locking compound is found on the threads of a fastener which is to be re-used, it should be cleaned off with a wire brush and solvent, and fresh compound applied on reassembly.

Special tools

Some repair procedures in this manual entail the use of special tools such as a press, two or three-legged pullers, spring compressors, etc. Wherever possible, suitable readily-available alternatives to the manufacturer's special tools are described, and are shown in use. In some instances, where no alternative is possible, it has been necessary to resort to the use of a manufacturer's tool, and this has been done for reasons of safety as well as the efficient completion of the repair operation. Unless you are highly-skilled and have a thorough understanding of the procedures described, never attempt to bypass the use of any special tool when the procedure described specifies its use. Not only is there a very great risk of personal injury, but expensive damage could be caused to the components involved.

Environmental considerations

When disposing of used engine oil, brake fluid, antifreeze, etc, give due consideration to any detrimental environmental effects. Do not, for instance, pour any of the above liquids down drains into the general sewage system, or onto the ground to soak away. Many local council refuse tips provide a facility for waste oil disposal, as do some garages. If none of these facilities are available, consult your local Environmental Health Department, or the National Rivers Authority, for further advice.

With the universal tightening-up of legislation regarding the emission of environmentally-harmful substances from motor vehicles, most vehicles have tamperproof devices fitted to the main adjustment points of the fuel system. These devices are primarily designed to prevent unqualified persons from adjusting the fuel/air mixture, with the chance of a consequent increase in toxic emissions. If such devices are found during servicing or overhaul, they should, wherever possible, be renewed or refitted in accordance with the manufacturer's requirements or current legislation.

Note: It is antisocial and illegal to dump oil down the drain. To find the location of your local oil recycling bank, call this number free.

Spare parts are available from many sources, including maker's appointed garages, accessory shops, and motor factors. To be sure of obtaining the correct parts, it will sometimes be necessary to quote the vehicle identification number. If possible, it can also be useful to take the old parts along for positive identification. Items such as starter motors and alternators may be available under a service exchange scheme – any parts returned should be clean.

Our advice regarding spare parts is as follows.

Officially appointed garages

This is the best source of parts which are peculiar to your car, and which are not otherwise generally available (eg, badges, interior trim, certain body panels, etc). It is also the only place at which you should buy parts if the vehicle is still under warranty.

Accessory shops

These are very good places to buy materials and components needed for the maintenance of your car (oil, air and fuel filters, light bulbs, drivebelts, greases, brake pads, tough-up paint, etc). Components of this nature sold by a reputable shop are of the same standard as those used by the car manufacturer.

Besides components, these shops also sell tools and general accessories, usually have convenient opening hours, charge lower prices, and can often be found close to home. Some accessory shops have parts counters where components needed for almost any repair job can be purchased or ordered.

Motor factors

Good factors will stock all the more important components which wear out comparatively quickly, and can sometimes supply individual components needed for the overhaul of a larger assembly (eg, brake seals and hydraulic parts, bearing shells, pistons, valves). They may also handle work such as cylinder block reboring, crankshaft regrinding, etc.

Tyre and exhaust specialists

These outlets may be independent, or members of a local or national chain. They frequently offer competitive prices when compared with a main dealer or local garage, but it will pay to obtain several quotes before making a decision. When researching prices, also ask what 'extras' may be added – for instance fitting a new valve and balancing the wheel are both commonly charged on top of the price of a new tyre.

Other sources

Beware of parts or materials obtained from market stalls, car boot sales or similar outlets. Such items are not invariably sub-standard, but there is little chance of compensation if they do prove unsatisfactory. In the case of safety-critical components such as brake pads, there is the risk not only of financial loss, but also of an accident causing injury or death.

Second-hand components or assemblies obtained from a car breaker or 'scrapyard' can be a good buy in some circumstances, but this sort of purchase is best made by the experienced DIY mechanic.

Jacking and vehicle support

The jack supplied with the vehicle tool kit should only be used for changing the roadwheels – see *Wheel changing* at the front of this Manual.

When using the jack supplied with the vehicle, position it on firm ground and locate its head in the relevant vehicle jacking point **(see illustration)**.

On models fitted with side skirt/sill extension trim panels, the access panel must first be removed from the trim panel to gain access to jacking points 3, 4, 5 and 7.

When carrying out any other kind of work, raise the vehicle using a hydraulic (or trolley) jack, and always supplement this jack with axle stands positioned under the indicated points. Always use the recommended jacking and support points, and refer to the following instructions:

If the front of the vehicle is to be raised, firmly apply the handbrake and place the jack head under point 1. Jack the vehicle up and position the axle stands either on the sills at points 3 and 4, or the underbody longitudinal supports at points 6.

To raise the rear of the vehicle, chock the front wheels and place the jack head under point 2, the reinforced location pad immediately in front of the rear towing eye. The axle stands should be placed either on the sills at points 5 and 7 or the underbody longitudinal supports at points 8.

To raise the side of the vehicle, place the jack head under the sill at point 3 or 4 (as applicable) at the front, then jack up the vehicle and position an axle stand under the longitudinal support at point 6. Remove the jack and position it under point 5 or 7 (as applicable) then jack up the rear of the vehicle and position an axle stand under the longitudinal support at point 8.

Never work under, around or near a raised vehicle unless it is adequately supported in at least two places.

H29831

Jacking and support points

1 Front central jacking point
2 Rear central jacking point
3 Left-hand sill reinforced bracket – front
4 Right-hand sill reinforced bracket – front
5 Left-hand sill reinforced bracket – rear
6 Longitudinal members – front
7 Right-hand sill reinforced bracket – rear
8 Longitudinal members – rear

Introduction

A selection of good tools is a fundamental requirement for anyone contemplating the maintenance and repair of a motor vehicle. For the owner who does not possess any, their purchase will prove a considerable expense, offsetting some of the savings made by doing-it-yourself. However, provided that the tools purchased meet the relevant national safety standards and are of good quality, they will last for many years and prove an extremely worthwhile investment.

To help the average owner to decide which tools are needed to carry out the various tasks detailed in this manual, we have compiled three lists of tools under the following headings: *Maintenance and minor repair, Repair and overhaul*, and *Special*. Newcomers to practical mechanics should start off with the *Maintenance and minor repair* tool kit, and confine themselves to the simpler jobs around the vehicle. Then, as confidence and experience grow, more difficult tasks can be undertaken, with extra tools being purchased as, and when, they are needed. In this way, a *Maintenance and minor repair* tool kit can be built up into a *Repair and overhaul* tool kit over a considerable period of time, without any major cash outlays. The experienced do-it-yourselfer will have a tool kit good enough for most repair and overhaul procedures, and will add tools from the *Special* category when it is felt that the expense is justified by the amount of use to which these tools will be put.

Maintenance and minor repair tool kit

The tools given in this list should be considered as a minimum requirement if routine maintenance, servicing and minor repair operations are to be undertaken. We recommend the purchase of combination spanners (ring one end, open-ended the other); although more expensive than open-ended ones, they do give the advantages of both types of spanner.

☐ *Combination spanners:*
  Metric - 8 to 19 mm inclusive
☐ *Adjustable spanner - 35 mm jaw (approx.)*
☐ *Spark plug spanner (with rubber insert) - petrol models*
☐ *Spark plug gap adjustment tool - petrol models*
☐ *Set of feeler gauges*
☐ *Brake bleed nipple spanner*
☐ *Screwdrivers:*
  Flat blade - 100 mm long x 6 mm dia
  Cross blade - 100 mm long x 6 mm dia
  Torx - various sizes (not all vehicles)
☐ *Combination pliers*
☐ *Hacksaw (junior)*
☐ *Tyre pump*
☐ *Tyre pressure gauge*
☐ *Oil can*
☐ *Oil filter removal tool*
☐ *Fine emery cloth*
☐ *Wire brush (small)*
☐ *Funnel (medium size)*
☐ *Sump drain plug key (not all vehicles)*

Repair and overhaul tool kit

These tools are virtually essential for anyone undertaking any major repairs to a motor vehicle, and are additional to those given in the *Maintenance and minor repair* list. Included in this list is a comprehensive set of sockets. Although these are expensive, they will be found invaluable as they are so versatile - particularly if various drives are included in the set. We recommend the half-inch square-drive type, as this can be used with most proprietary torque wrenches.

The tools in this list will sometimes need to be supplemented by tools from the *Special* list:

☐ *Sockets (or box spanners) to cover range in previous list (including Torx sockets)*
☐ *Reversible ratchet drive (for use with sockets)*
☐ *Extension piece, 250 mm (for use with sockets)*
☐ *Universal joint (for use with sockets)*
☐ *Flexible handle or sliding T "breaker bar" (for use with sockets)*
☐ *Torque wrench (for use with sockets)*
☐ *Self-locking grips*
☐ *Ball pein hammer*
☐ *Soft-faced mallet (plastic or rubber)*
☐ *Screwdrivers:*
  Flat blade - long & sturdy, short (chubby), and narrow (electrician's) types
  Cross blade - long & sturdy, and short (chubby) types
☐ *Pliers:*
  Long-nosed
  Side cutters (electrician's)
  Circlip (internal and external)
☐ *Cold chisel - 25 mm*
☐ *Scriber*
☐ *Scraper*
☐ *Centre-punch*
☐ *Pin punch*
☐ *Hacksaw*
☐ *Brake hose clamp*
☐ *Brake/clutch bleeding kit*
☐ *Selection of twist drills*
☐ *Steel rule/straight-edge*
☐ *Allen keys (inc. splined/Torx type)*
☐ *Selection of files*
☐ *Wire brush*
☐ *Axle stands*
☐ *Jack (strong trolley or hydraulic type)*
☐ *Light with extension lead*
☐ *Universal electrical multi-meter*

Sockets and reversible ratchet drive

Brake bleeding kit

Torx key, socket and bit

Hose clamp

Angular-tightening gauge

Special tools

The tools in this list are those which are not used regularly, are expensive to buy, or which need to be used in accordance with their manufacturers' instructions. Unless relatively difficult mechanical jobs are undertaken frequently, it will not be economic to buy many of these tools. Where this is the case, you could consider clubbing together with friends (or joining a motorists' club) to make a joint purchase, or borrowing the tools against a deposit from a local garage or tool hire specialist. It is worth noting that many of the larger DIY superstores now carry a large range of special tools for hire at modest rates.

The following list contains only those tools and instruments freely available to the public, and not those special tools produced by the vehicle manufacturer specifically for its dealer network. You will find occasional references to these manufacturers' special tools in the text of this manual. Generally, an alternative method of doing the job without the vehicle manufacturers' special tool is given. However, sometimes there is no alternative to using them. Where this is the case and the relevant tool cannot be bought or borrowed, you will have to entrust the work to a dealer.

- ☐ Angular-tightening gauge
- ☐ Valve spring compressor
- ☐ Valve grinding tool
- ☐ Piston ring compressor
- ☐ Piston ring removal/installation tool
- ☐ Cylinder bore hone
- ☐ Balljoint separator
- ☐ Coil spring compressors (where applicable)
- ☐ Two/three-legged hub and bearing puller
- ☐ Impact screwdriver
- ☐ Micrometer and/or vernier calipers
- ☐ Dial gauge
- ☐ Stroboscopic timing light
- ☐ Dwell angle meter/tachometer
- ☐ Fault code reader
- ☐ Cylinder compression gauge
- ☐ Hand-operated vacuum pump and gauge
- ☐ Clutch plate alignment set
- ☐ Brake shoe steady spring cup removal tool
- ☐ Bush and bearing removal/installation set
- ☐ Stud extractors
- ☐ Tap and die set
- ☐ Lifting tackle
- ☐ Trolley jack

Buying tools

Reputable motor accessory shops and superstores often offer excellent quality tools at discount prices, so it pays to shop around.

Remember, you don't have to buy the most expensive items on the shelf, but it is always advisable to steer clear of the very cheap tools. Beware of 'bargains' offered on market stalls or at car boot sales. There are plenty of good tools around at reasonable prices, but always aim to purchase items which meet the relevant national safety standards. If in doubt, ask the proprietor or manager of the shop for advice before making a purchase.

Care and maintenance of tools

Having purchased a reasonable tool kit, it is necessary to keep the tools in a clean and serviceable condition. After use, always wipe off any dirt, grease and metal particles using a clean, dry cloth, before putting the tools away. Never leave them lying around after they have been used. A simple tool rack on the garage or workshop wall for items such as screwdrivers and pliers is a good idea. Store all normal spanners and sockets in a metal box. Any measuring instruments, gauges, meters, etc, must be carefully stored where they cannot be damaged or become rusty.

Take a little care when tools are used. Hammer heads inevitably become marked, and screwdrivers lose the keen edge on their blades from time to time. A little timely attention with emery cloth or a file will soon restore items like this to a good finish.

Working facilities

Not to be forgotten when discussing tools is the workshop itself. If anything more than routine maintenance is to be carried out, a suitable working area becomes essential.

It is appreciated that many an owner-mechanic is forced by circumstances to remove an engine or similar item without the benefit of a garage or workshop. Having done this, any repairs should always be done under the cover of a roof.

Wherever possible, any dismantling should be done on a clean, flat workbench or table at a suitable working height.

Any workbench needs a vice; one with a jaw opening of 100 mm is suitable for most jobs. As mentioned previously, some clean dry storage space is also required for tools, as well as for any lubricants, cleaning fluids, touch-up paints etc, which become necessary.

Another item which may be required, and which has a much more general usage, is an electric drill with a chuck capacity of at least 8 mm. This, together with a good range of twist drills, is virtually essential for fitting accessories.

Last, but not least, always keep a supply of old newspapers and clean, lint-free rags available, and try to keep any working area as clean as possible.

Micrometers

Dial test indicator ("dial gauge")

Strap wrench

Compression tester

Fault code reader

This is a guide to getting your vehicle through the MOT test. Obviously it will not be possible to examine the vehicle to the same standard as the professional MOT tester. However, working through the following checks will enable you to identify any problem areas before submitting the vehicle for the test.

It has only been possible to summarise the test requirements here, based on the regulations in force at the time of printing. Test standards are becoming increasingly stringent, although there are some exemptions for older vehicles.

An assistant will be needed to help carry out some of these checks.

The checks have been sub-divided into four categories, as follows:

1 Checks carried out **FROM THE DRIVER'S SEAT**

2 Checks carried out **WITH THE VEHICLE ON THE GROUND**

3 Checks carried out **WITH THE VEHICLE RAISED AND THE WHEELS FREE TO TURN**

4 Checks carried out on **YOUR VEHICLE'S EXHAUST EMISSION SYSTEM**

---

1 Checks carried out **FROM THE DRIVER'S SEAT**

Handbrake

☐ Test the operation of the handbrake. Excessive travel (too many clicks) indicates incorrect brake or cable adjustment.
☐ Check that the handbrake cannot be released by tapping the lever sideways. Check the security of the lever mountings.

Footbrake

☐ Depress the brake pedal and check that it does not creep down to the floor, indicating a master cylinder fault. Release the pedal, wait a few seconds, then depress it again. If the pedal travels nearly to the floor before firm resistance is felt, brake adjustment or repair is necessary. If the pedal feels spongy, there is air in the hydraulic system which must be removed by bleeding.

☐ Check that the brake pedal is secure and in good condition. Check also for signs of fluid leaks on the pedal, floor or carpets, which would indicate failed seals in the brake master cylinder.
☐ Check the servo unit (when applicable) by operating the brake pedal several times, then keeping the pedal depressed and starting the engine. As the engine starts, the pedal will move down slightly. If not, the vacuum hose or the servo itself may be faulty.

Steering wheel and column

☐ Examine the steering wheel for fractures or looseness of the hub, spokes or rim.
☐ Move the steering wheel from side to side and then up and down. Check that the steering wheel is not loose on the column, indicating wear or a loose retaining nut. Continue moving the steering wheel as before, but also turn it slightly from left to right.
☐ Check that the steering wheel is not loose on the column, and that there is no abnormal

movement of the steering wheel, indicating wear in the column support bearings or couplings.

Windscreen, mirrors and sunvisor

☐ The windscreen must be free of cracks or other significant damage within the driver's field of view. (Small stone chips are acceptable.) Rear view mirrors must be secure, intact, and capable of being adjusted.

☐ The driver's sunvisor must be capable of being stored in the "up" position.

Seat belts and seats

Note: *The following checks are applicable to all seat belts, front and rear.*

☐ Examine the webbing of all the belts (including rear belts if fitted) for cuts, serious fraying or deterioration. Fasten and unfasten each belt to check the buckles. If applicable, check the retracting mechanism. Check the security of all seat belt mountings accessible from inside the vehicle.

☐ Seat belts with pre-tensioners, once activated, have a "flag" or similar showing on the seat belt stalk. This, in itself, is not a reason for test failure.

☐ The front seats themselves must be securely attached and the backrests must lock in the upright position.

Doors

☐ Both front doors must be able to be opened and closed from outside and inside, and must latch securely when closed.

2 Checks carried out WITH THE VEHICLE ON THE GROUND

Vehicle identification

☐ Number plates must be in good condition, secure and legible, with letters and numbers correctly spaced – spacing at (A) should be at least twice that at (B).

☐ The VIN plate and/or homologation plate must be legible.

Electrical equipment

☐ Switch on the ignition and check the operation of the horn.

☐ Check the windscreen washers and wipers, examining the wiper blades; renew damaged or perished blades. Also check the operation of the stop-lights.

☐ Check the operation of the sidelights and number plate lights. The lenses and reflectors must be secure, clean and undamaged.

☐ Check the operation and alignment of the headlights. The headlight reflectors must not be tarnished and the lenses must be undamaged.

☐ Switch on the ignition and check the operation of the direction indicators (including the instrument panel tell-tale) and the hazard warning lights. Operation of the sidelights and stop-lights must not affect the indicators - if it does, the cause is usually a bad earth at the rear light cluster.

☐ Check the operation of the rear foglight(s), including the warning light on the instrument panel or in the switch.

☐ The ABS warning light must illuminate in accordance with the manufacturers' design. For most vehicles, the ABS warning light should illuminate when the ignition is switched on, and (if the system is operating properly) extinguish after a few seconds. Refer to the owner's handbook.

Footbrake

☐ Examine the master cylinder, brake pipes and servo unit for leaks, loose mountings, corrosion or other damage.

☐ The fluid reservoir must be secure and the fluid level must be between the upper (**A**) and lower (**B**) markings.

☐ Inspect both front brake flexible hoses for cracks or deterioration of the rubber. Turn the steering from lock to lock, and ensure that the hoses do not contact the wheel, tyre, or any part of the steering or suspension mechanism. With the brake pedal firmly depressed, check the hoses for bulges or leaks under pressure.

Steering and suspension

☐ Have your assistant turn the steering wheel from side to side slightly, up to the point where the steering gear just begins to transmit this movement to the roadwheels. Check for excessive free play between the steering wheel and the steering gear, indicating wear or insecurity of the steering column joints, the column-to-steering gear coupling, or the steering gear itself.

☐ Have your assistant turn the steering wheel more vigorously in each direction, so that the roadwheels just begin to turn. As this is done, examine all the steering joints, linkages, fittings and attachments. Renew any component that shows signs of wear or damage. On vehicles with power steering, check the security and condition of the steering pump, drivebelt and hoses.

☐ Check that the vehicle is standing level, and at approximately the correct ride height.

Shock absorbers

☐ Depress each corner of the vehicle in turn, then release it. The vehicle should rise and then settle in its normal position. If the vehicle continues to rise and fall, the shock absorber is defective. A shock absorber which has seized will also cause the vehicle to fail.

Exhaust system

☐ Start the engine. With your assistant holding a rag over the tailpipe, check the entire system for leaks. Repair or renew leaking sections.

3 Checks carried out **WITH THE VEHICLE RAISED AND THE WHEELS FREE TO TURN**

Jack up the front and rear of the vehicle, and securely support it on axle stands. Position the stands clear of the suspension assemblies. Ensure that the wheels are clear of the ground and that the steering can be turned from lock to lock.

Steering mechanism

☐ Have your assistant turn the steering from lock to lock. Check that the steering turns smoothly, and that no part of the steering mechanism, including a wheel or tyre, fouls any brake hose or pipe or any part of the body structure.

☐ Examine the steering rack rubber gaiters for damage or insecurity of the retaining clips. If power steering is fitted, check for signs of damage or leakage of the fluid hoses, pipes or connections. Also check for excessive stiffness or binding of the steering, a missing split pin or locking device, or severe corrosion of the body structure within 30 cm of any steering component attachment point.

Front and rear suspension and wheel bearings

☐ Starting at the front right-hand side, grasp the roadwheel at the 3 o'clock and 9 o'clock positions and rock gently but firmly. Check for free play or insecurity at the wheel bearings, suspension balljoints, or suspension mountings, pivots and attachments.

☐ Now grasp the wheel at the 12 o'clock and 6 o'clock positions and repeat the previous inspection. Spin the wheel, and check for roughness or tightness of the front wheel bearing.

☐ If excess free play is suspected at a component pivot point, this can be confirmed by using a large screwdriver or similar tool and levering between the mounting and the component attachment. This will confirm whether the wear is in the pivot bush, its retaining bolt, or in the mounting itself (the bolt holes can often become elongated).

☐ Carry out all the above checks at the other front wheel, and then at both rear wheels.

Springs and shock absorbers

☐ Examine the suspension struts (when applicable) for serious fluid leakage, corrosion, or damage to the casing. Also check the security of the mounting points.

☐ If coil springs are fitted, check that the spring ends locate in their seats, and that the spring is not corroded, cracked or broken.

☐ If leaf springs are fitted, check that all leaves are intact, that the axle is securely attached to each spring, and that there is no deterioration of the spring eye mountings, bushes, and shackles.

☐ The same general checks apply to vehicles fitted with other suspension types, such as torsion bars, hydraulic displacer units, etc. Ensure that all mountings and attachments are secure, that there are no signs of excessive wear, corrosion or damage, and (on hydraulic types) that there are no fluid leaks or damaged pipes.

☐ Inspect the shock absorbers for signs of serious fluid leakage. Check for wear of the mounting bushes or attachments, or damage to the body of the unit.

Driveshafts (fwd vehicles only)

☐ Rotate each front wheel in turn and inspect the constant velocity joint gaiters for splits or damage. Also check that each driveshaft is straight and undamaged.

Braking system

☐ If possible without dismantling, check brake pad wear and disc condition. Ensure that the friction lining material has not worn excessively, (A) and that the discs are not fractured, pitted, scored or badly worn (B).

☐ Examine all the rigid brake pipes underneath the vehicle, and the flexible hose(s) at the rear. Look for corrosion, chafing or insecurity of the pipes, and for signs of bulging under pressure, chafing, splits or deterioration of the flexible hoses.

☐ Look for signs of fluid leaks at the brake calipers or on the brake backplates. Repair or renew leaking components.

☐ Slowly spin each wheel, while your assistant depresses and releases the footbrake. Ensure that each brake is operating and does not bind when the pedal is released.

☐ Examine the handbrake mechanism, checking for frayed or broken cables, excessive corrosion, or wear or insecurity of the linkage. Check that the mechanism works on each relevant wheel, and releases fully, without binding.

☐ It is not possible to test brake efficiency without special equipment, but a road test can be carried out later to check that the vehicle pulls up in a straight line.

Fuel and exhaust systems

☐ Inspect the fuel tank (including the filler cap), fuel pipes, hoses and unions. All components must be secure and free from leaks.

☐ Examine the exhaust system over its entire length, checking for any damaged, broken or missing mountings, security of the retaining clamps and rust or corrosion.

Wheels and tyres

☐ Examine the sidewalls and tread area of each tyre in turn. Check for cuts, tears, lumps, bulges, separation of the tread, and exposure of the ply or cord due to wear or damage. Check that the tyre bead is correctly seated on the wheel rim, that the valve is sound and properly seated, and that the wheel is not distorted or damaged.

☐ Check that the tyres are of the correct size for the vehicle, that they are of the same size

and type on each axle, and that the pressures are correct.

☐ Check the tyre tread depth. The legal minimum at the time of writing is 1.6 mm over at least three-quarters of the tread width. Abnormal tread wear may indicate incorrect front wheel alignment.

Body corrosion

☐ Check the condition of the entire vehicle structure for signs of corrosion in load-bearing areas. (These include chassis box sections, side sills, cross-members, pillars, and all suspension, steering, braking system and seat belt mountings and anchorages.) Any corrosion which has seriously reduced the thickness of a load-bearing area is likely to cause the vehicle to fail. In this case professional repairs are likely to be needed.

☐ Damage or corrosion which causes sharp or otherwise dangerous edges to be exposed will also cause the vehicle to fail.

4 Checks carried out on **YOUR VEHICLE'S EXHAUST EMISSION SYSTEM**

Petrol models

☐ The engine should be warmed up, and running well (ignition system in good order, air filter element clean, etc).

☐ Before testing, run the engine at around 2500 rpm for 20 seconds. Let the engine drop to idle, and watch for smoke from the exhaust. If the idle speed is too high, or if dense blue or black smoke emerges for more than 5 seconds, the vehicle will fail. Typically, blue smoke signifies oil burning (engine wear); black smoke means unburnt fuel (dirty air cleaner element, or other fuel system fault).

☐ An exhaust gas analyser for measuring carbon monoxide (CO) and hydrocarbons (HC) is now needed. If one cannot be hired or borrowed, have a local garage perform the check.

CO emissions (mixture)

☐ The MOT tester has access to the CO limits for all vehicles. The CO level is measured at idle speed, and at 'fast idle' (2500 to 3000 rpm). The following limits are given as a general guide:

At idle speed – Less than 0.5% CO
At 'fast idle' – Less than 0.3% CO
Lambda reading – 0.97 to 1.03

☐ If the CO level is too high, this may point to poor maintenance, a fuel injection system problem, faulty lambda (oxygen) sensor or catalytic converter. Try an injector cleaning treatment, and check the vehicle's ECU for fault codes.

HC emissions

☐ The MOT tester has access to HC limits for all vehicles. The HC level is measured at 'fast idle' (2500 to 3000 rpm). The following limits are given as a general guide:

At 'fast idle' – Less then 200 ppm

☐ Excessive HC emissions are typically caused by oil being burnt (worn engine), or by a blocked crankcase ventilation system ('breather'). If the engine oil is old and thin, an oil change may help. If the engine is running badly, check the vehicle's ECU for fault codes.

Diesel models

☐ The only emission test for diesel engines is measuring exhaust smoke density, using a calibrated smoke meter. The test involves accelerating the engine at least 3 times to its maximum unloaded speed.

Note: *On engines with a timing belt, it is VITAL that the belt is in good condition before the test is carried out.*

☐ With the engine warmed up, it is first purged by running at around 2500 rpm for 20 seconds. A governor check is then carried out, by slowly accelerating the engine to its maximum speed. After this, the smoke meter is connected, and the engine is accelerated quickly to maximum speed three times. If the smoke density is less than the limits given below, the vehicle will pass:

Non-turbo vehicles: 2.5m-1
Turbocharged vehicles: 3.0m-1

☐ If excess smoke is produced, try fitting a new air cleaner element, or using an injector cleaning treatment. If the engine is running badly, where applicable, check the vehicle's ECU for fault codes. Also check the vehicle's EGR system, where applicable. At high mileages, the injectors may require professional attention.

Engine

- [ ] Engine fails to rotate when attempting to start
- [ ] Engine rotates, but will not start
- [ ] Engine difficult to start when cold
- [ ] Engine difficult to start when hot
- [ ] Starter motor noisy or excessively-rough in engagement
- [ ] Engine starts, but stops immediately
- [ ] Engine idles erratically
- [ ] Engine misfires at idle speed
- [ ] Engine misfires throughout the driving speed range
- [ ] Engine hesitates on acceleration
- [ ] Engine stalls
- [ ] Engine lacks power
- [ ] Engine backfires
- [ ] Oil pressure warning light illuminated with engine running
- [ ] Engine runs-on after switching off
- [ ] Engine noises

Cooling system

- [ ] Overheating
- [ ] Overcooling
- [ ] External coolant leakage
- [ ] Internal coolant leakage
- [ ] Corrosion

Fuel and exhaust systems

- [ ] Excessive fuel consumption
- [ ] Fuel leakage and/or fuel odour
- [ ] Excessive noise or fumes from the exhaust system

Clutch

- [ ] Pedal travels to floor – no pressure or very little resistance
- [ ] Clutch fails to disengage (unable to select gears)
- [ ] Clutch slips (engine speed increases, with no increase in vehicle speed)
- [ ] Judder as clutch is engaged
- [ ] Noise when depressing or releasing clutch pedal

Manual transmission

- [ ] Noisy in neutral with engine running
- [ ] Noisy in one particular gear
- [ ] Difficulty engaging gears
- [ ] Jumps out of gear
- [ ] Vibration
- [ ] Lubricant leaks

Driveshafts

- [ ] Vibration when accelerating or decelerating
- [ ] Clicking or knocking noise on turns (at slow speed on full-lock)

Braking system

- [ ] Vehicle pulls to one side under braking
- [ ] Noise (grinding or high-pitched squeal) when brakes applied
- [ ] Excessive brake pedal travel
- [ ] Brake pedal feels spongy when depressed
- [ ] Excessive brake pedal effort required to stop vehicle
- [ ] Judder felt through brake pedal or steering wheel when braking
- [ ] Pedal pulsates when braking hard
- [ ] Brakes binding
- [ ] Rear wheels locking under normal braking

Steering and suspension

- [ ] Vehicle pulls to one side
- [ ] Wheel wobble and vibration
- [ ] Excessive pitching and/or rolling around corners, or during braking
- [ ] Wandering or general instability
- [ ] Excessively-stiff steering
- [ ] Excessive play in steering
- [ ] Lack of power assistance
- [ ] Tyre wear excessive

Electrical system

- [ ] Battery will not hold a charge for more than a few days
- [ ] Ignition/no-charge warning light remains illuminated with engine running
- [ ] Ignition/no-charge warning light fails to come on
- [ ] Lights inoperative
- [ ] Instrument readings inaccurate or erratic
- [ ] Horn inoperative, or unsatisfactory in operation
- [ ] Windscreen/tailgate wipers inoperative, or unsatisfactory in operation
- [ ] Windscreen/tailgate washers inoperative, or unsatisfactory in operation
- [ ] Electric windows inoperative, or unsatisfactory in operation
- [ ] Central locking system inoperative, or unsatisfactory in operation

Introduction

The vehicle owner who does his or her own maintenance according to the recommended service schedules should not have to use this section of the manual very often. Modern component reliability is such that, provided those items subject to wear or deterioration are inspected or renewed at the specified intervals, sudden failure is comparatively rare. Faults do not usually just happen as a result of sudden failure, but develop over a period of time. Major mechanical failures in particular are usually preceded by characteristic symptoms over hundreds or even thousands of miles. Those components which do occasionally fail without warning are often small and easily carried in the vehicle.

With any fault-finding, the first step is to decide where to begin investigations. This may be obvious, but some detective work may be necessary. The owner who makes half a dozen haphazard adjustments or replacements may be successful in curing a fault (or its symptoms), but will be none the wiser if the fault recurs, and ultimately may have spent more time and money than was necessary. A calm and logical approach will be found to be more satisfactory in the long run. Always take into account any warning signs that may have been noticed in the period preceding the fault – power loss, high or low gauge readings, unusual smells, etc – and remember – failure of components such as fuses or spark plugs may only be pointers to some underlying fault.

The pages which follow provide an easy-reference guide to the more common problems which may occur during the operation of the vehicle. These problems and their possible causes are grouped under headings denoting various components or systems, such as Engine, Cooling system, etc. The general Chapter which deals with the problem is also shown in brackets; refer to the relevant part of that Chapter for system-specific information. Whatever the fault, certain basic principles apply. These are as follows:

Verify the fault. This is simply a matter of being sure that you know what the symptoms are before starting work. This is particularly important if you are investigating a fault for someone else, who may not have described it very accurately.

Don't overlook the obvious. For example, if the vehicle won't start, is there fuel in the tank? (Don't take anyone else's word on this particular point, and don't trust the fuel gauge either!) If an electrical fault is indicated, look for loose or broken wires before digging out the test gear.

Cure the disease, not the symptom. Substituting a flat battery with a fully-charged one will get you off the hard shoulder, but if the underlying cause is not attended to, the new battery will go the same way. Similarly, changing oil-fouled spark plugs for a new set will get you moving again, but remember that the reason for the fouling (if it wasn't simply an incorrect grade of plug) will have to be established and corrected.

Don't take anything for granted. Particularly, don't forget that a 'new' component may itself be defective (especially if it's been rattling around in the boot for months), and don't leave components out of a fault diagnosis sequence just because they are new or recently-fitted. When you do finally diagnose a difficult fault, you'll probably realise that all the evidence was there from the start.

Engine

Engine fails to rotate when attempting to start

- [ ] Battery terminal connections loose or corroded (see Weekly checks).
- [ ] Battery discharged or faulty (Chapter 5A).
- [ ] Broken, loose or disconnected wiring in the starting circuit (Chapter 5A).
- [ ] Defective starter solenoid or switch (Chapter 5A).
- [ ] Defective starter motor (Chapter 5A).
- [ ] Starter pinion or flywheel ring gear teeth loose or broken (Chapters 2 and 5A).
- [ ] Engine earth strap broken or disconnected (Chapter 5A).

Engine rotates, but will not start

- [ ] Fuel tank empty.
- [ ] Battery discharged (engine rotates slowly) (Chapter 5A).
- [ ] Battery terminal connections loose or corroded (see Weekly checks).
- [ ] Ignition components damp or damaged – petrol models (Chapters 1A and 5B).
- [ ] Broken, loose or disconnected wiring in the ignition circuit – petrol models (Chapters 1A and 5B).
- [ ] Worn, faulty or incorrectly-gapped spark plugs – petrol models (Chapter 1A).
- [ ] Preheating system faulty – diesel models (Chapter 5C).
- [ ] Fuel injection system faulty – petrol models (Chapter 4A).
- [ ] Stop solenoid faulty – diesel models (Chapter 4B).
- [ ] Air in fuel system – diesel models (Chapter 4B).
- [ ] Major mechanical failure (eg camshaft drive) (Chapter 2).

Engine difficult to start when cold

- [ ] Battery discharged (Chapter 5A).
- [ ] Battery terminal connections loose or corroded (see Weekly checks).
- [ ] Worn, faulty or incorrectly-gapped spark plugs – petrol models (Chapter 1A).
- [ ] Preheating system faulty – diesel models (Chapter 5C).
- [ ] Fuel injection system faulty – petrol models (Chapter 4A).
- [ ] Other ignition system fault – petrol models (Chapters 1A and 5B).
- [ ] Low cylinder compressions (Chapter 2).

Engine difficult to start when hot

- [ ] Air filter element dirty or clogged (Chapter 1).
- [ ] Fuel injection system faulty – petrol models (Chapter 4A).
- [ ] Low cylinder compressions (Chapter 2).

Starter motor noisy or excessively-rough in engagement

- [ ] Starter pinion or flywheel ring gear teeth loose or broken (Chapters 2 and 5A).
- [ ] Starter motor mounting bolts loose or missing (Chapter 5A).
- [ ] Starter motor internal components worn or damaged (Chapter 5A).

Engine starts, but stops immediately

- [ ] Loose or faulty electrical connections in the ignition circuit – petrol models (Chapters 1A and 5B).
- [ ] Vacuum leak at the throttle body or inlet manifold – petrol models (Chapter 4A).
- [ ] Blocked injector/fuel injection system fault – petrol models (Chapter 4A).

Engine idles erratically

- [ ] Air filter element clogged (Chapter 1).
- [ ] Vacuum leak at the throttle body, inlet manifold or associated hoses – petrol models (Chapter 4A).
- [ ] Worn, faulty or incorrectly-gapped spark plugs – petrol models (Chapter 1A).
- [ ] Uneven or low cylinder compressions (Chapter 2).
- [ ] Camshaft lobes worn (Chapter 2).
- [ ] Timing belt/chain incorrectly fitted (Chapter 2).
- [ ] Blocked injector/fuel injection system fault – petrol models (Chapter 4A).
- [ ] Faulty injector(s) – diesel models (Chapter 4B).

Engine misfires at idle speed

- [ ] Worn, faulty or incorrectly-gapped spark plugs – petrol models (Chapter 1A).
- [ ] Faulty spark plug HT leads – petrol models (Chapter 1A).
- [ ] Vacuum leak at the throttle body, inlet manifold or associated hoses – petrol models (Chapter 4A).
- [ ] Blocked injector/fuel injection system fault – petrol models (Chapter 4A).

- [ ] Faulty injector(s) – diesel models (Chapter 4B).
- [ ] Uneven or low cylinder compressions (Chapter 2).
- [ ] Disconnected, leaking, or perished crankcase ventilation hoses (Chapter 4C).

Engine misfires throughout the driving speed range

- [ ] Fuel filter choked (Chapter 1).
- [ ] Fuel pump faulty, or delivery pressure low – petrol models (Chapter 4A).
- [ ] Fuel tank vent blocked, or fuel pipes restricted (Chapter 4).
- [ ] Vacuum leak at the throttle body, inlet manifold or associated hoses – petrol models (Chapter 4A).
- [ ] Worn, faulty or incorrectly-gapped spark plugs – petrol models (Chapter 1A).
- [ ] Faulty spark plug HT leads – petrol models (Chapter 1A).
- [ ] Faulty injector(s) – diesel models (Chapter 4B).
- [ ] Faulty ignition coil – petrol models (Chapter 5B).
- [ ] Uneven or low cylinder compressions (Chapter 2).
- [ ] Blocked injector/fuel injection system fault – petrol models (Chapter 4A).

Engine hesitates on acceleration

- [ ] Worn, faulty or incorrectly-gapped spark plugs – petrol models (Chapter 1A).
- [ ] Vacuum leak at the throttle body, inlet manifold or associated hoses – petrol models (Chapter 4A).
- [ ] Blocked injector/fuel injection system fault – petrol models (Chapter 4A).
- [ ] Faulty injector(s) – diesel models (Chapter 4B).

Engine stalls

- [ ] Vacuum leak at the throttle body, inlet manifold or associated hoses – petrol models (Chapter 4A).
- [ ] Fuel filter choked (Chapter 1).
- [ ] Fuel pump faulty, or delivery pressure low – petrol models (Chapter 4A).
- [ ] Fuel tank vent blocked, or fuel pipes restricted (Chapter 4).
- [ ] Blocked injector/fuel injection system fault – petrol models (Chapter 4A).
- [ ] Faulty injector(s) – diesel models (Chapter 4B).

Engine (continued)

Engine lacks power

- [ ] Timing belt/chain incorrectly fitted or tensioned (Chapter 2).
- [ ] Fuel filter choked (Chapter 1).
- [ ] Fuel pump faulty, or delivery pressure low – petrol models (Chapter 4A).
- [ ] Uneven or low cylinder compressions (Chapter 2).
- [ ] Worn, faulty or incorrectly-gapped spark plugs – petrol models (Chapter 1A).
- [ ] Vacuum leak at the throttle body, inlet manifold or associated hoses – petrol models (Chapter 4A).
- [ ] Blocked injector/fuel injection system fault – petrol models (Chapter 4A).
- [ ] Faulty injector(s) – diesel models (Chapter 4B).
- [ ] Injection pump timing incorrect – diesel models (Chapter 4B).
- [ ] Air trapped in fuel system – diesel models (Chapter 4B).
- [ ] Brakes binding (Chapters 1 and 9).
- [ ] Clutch slipping (Chapter 6).

Engine backfires

- [ ] Timing belt/chain incorrectly fitted or tensioned (Chapter 2).
- [ ] Vacuum leak at the throttle body, inlet manifold or associated hoses – petrol models (Chapter 4A).
- [ ] Blocked injector/fuel injection system fault – petrol models (Chapter 4A).

Oil pressure warning light illuminated with engine running

- [ ] Low oil level, or incorrect oil grade (see Weekly checks).
- [ ] Faulty oil pressure sensor (Chapter 5A).
- [ ] Worn engine bearings and/or oil pump (Chapter 2).
- [ ] High engine operating temperature (Chapter 3).
- [ ] Oil pressure relief valve defective (Chapter 2).
- [ ] Oil pick-up strainer clogged (Chapter 2).

Engine runs-on after switching off

- [ ] Excessive carbon build-up in engine (Chapter 2).
- [ ] High engine operating temperature (Chapter 3).
- [ ] Fuel injection system faulty – petrol models (Chapter 4A).
- [ ] Faulty stop solenoid – diesel models (Chapter 4B).

Engine noises

Pre-ignition (pinking) or knocking during acceleration or under load

- [ ] Ignition timing incorrect/ignition system fault – petrol models (Chapters 1A and 5B).
- [ ] Incorrect grade of spark plug – petrol models (Chapter 1A).

- [ ] Incorrect grade of fuel (Chapter 4).
- [ ] Vacuum leak at the throttle body, inlet manifold or associated hoses – petrol models (Chapter 4A).
- [ ] Excessive carbon build-up in engine (Chapter 2).
- [ ] Blocked injector/injection system fault – petrol models (Chapter 4A).

Whistling or wheezing noises

- [ ] Leaking inlet manifold or throttle body gasket – petrol models (Chapter 4A).
- [ ] Leaking exhaust manifold gasket or pipe-to-manifold joint (Chapter 4).
- [ ] Leaking vacuum hose (Chapters 4, 5 and 9).
- [ ] Blowing cylinder head gasket (Chapter 2).

Tapping or rattling noises

- [ ] Worn valve gear or camshaft (Chapter 2).
- [ ] Ancillary component fault (coolant pump, alternator, etc) (Chapters 3, 5, etc).

Knocking or thumping noises

- [ ] Worn big-end bearings (regular heavy knocking, perhaps less under load) (Chapter 2).
- [ ] Worn main bearings (rumbling and knocking, perhaps worsening under load) (Chapter 2).
- [ ] Piston slap (most noticeable when cold) (Chapter 2).
- [ ] Ancillary component fault (coolant pump, alternator, etc) (Chapters 3, 5, etc).

Cooling system

Overheating

- [ ] Insufficient coolant in system (see Weekly checks).
- [ ] Thermostat faulty (Chapter 3).
- [ ] Radiator core blocked, or grille restricted (Chapter 3).
- [ ] Electric cooling fan or thermostatic switch faulty (Chapter 3).
- [ ] Inaccurate temperature gauge sender unit (Chapter 3).
- [ ] Airlock in cooling system (Chapter 3).
- [ ] Expansion tank pressure cap faulty (Chapter 3).

Overcooling

- [ ] Thermostat faulty (Chapter 3).
- [ ] Inaccurate temperature gauge sender unit (Chapter 3).

External coolant leakage

- [ ] Deteriorated or damaged hoses or hose clips (Chapter 1).
- [ ] Radiator core or heater matrix leaking (Chapter 3).
- [ ] Pressure cap faulty (Chapter 3).
- [ ] Coolant pump internal seal leaking (Chapter 3).

- [ ] Coolant pump-to-block seal leaking (Chapter 3).
- [ ] Boiling due to overheating (Chapter 3).
- [ ] Core plug leaking (Chapter 2).

Internal coolant leakage

- [ ] Leaking cylinder head gasket (Chapter 2).
- [ ] Cracked cylinder head or cylinder block (Chapter 2).

Corrosion

- [ ] Infrequent draining and flushing (Chapter 1).
- [ ] Incorrect coolant mixture or inappropriate coolant type (see Weekly checks).

Fuel and exhaust systems

Excessive fuel consumption

- [ ] Air filter element dirty or clogged (Chapter 1).
- [ ] Fuel injection system faulty – petrol models (Chapter 4A).
- [ ] Faulty injector(s) – diesel models (Chapter 4B).
- [ ] Ignition timing incorrect/ignition system

faulty – petrol models (Chapters 1A and 5B).
- [ ] Tyres under-inflated (see Weekly checks).

Fuel leakage and/or fuel odour

- [ ] Damaged or corroded fuel tank, pipes or connections (Chapter 4).

Excessive noise or fumes from the exhaust system

- [ ] Leaking exhaust system or manifold joints (Chapters 1 and 4).
- [ ] Leaking, corroded or damaged silencers or pipe (Chapters 1 and 4).
- [ ] Broken mountings causing body or suspension contact (Chapter 1).

Clutch

Pedal travels to floor – no pressure or very little resistance

☐ Broken clutch cable (Chapter 6).
☐ Broken clutch release bearing or arm (Chapter 6).
☐ Broken diaphragm spring in clutch pressure plate (Chapter 6).

Clutch fails to disengage (unable to select gears)

☐ Faulty clutch cable (Chapter 6).
☐ Clutch disc sticking on gearbox input shaft splines (Chapter 6).
☐ Clutch disc sticking to flywheel or pressure plate (Chapter 6).
☐ Faulty pressure plate assembly (Chapter 6).
☐ Clutch release mechanism worn or incorrectly assembled (Chapter 6).

Clutch slips (engine speed increases, with no increase in vehicle speed)

☐ Worn clutch cable (Chapter 6).
☐ Clutch disc linings excessively worn (Chapter 6).
☐ Clutch disc linings contaminated with oil or grease (Chapter 6).
☐ Faulty pressure plate or weak diaphragm spring (Chapter 6).

Judder as clutch is engaged

☐ Clutch disc linings contaminated with oil or grease (Chapter 6).
☐ Clutch disc linings excessively worn (Chapter 6).

☐ Faulty or distorted pressure plate or diaphragm spring (Chapter 6).
☐ Worn or loose engine or gearbox mountings (Chapter 2).
☐ Clutch disc hub or gearbox input shaft splines worn (Chapter 6).

Noise when depressing or releasing clutch pedal

☐ Worn clutch release bearing (Chapter 6).
☐ Worn clutch cable (Chapter 6)
☐ Worn or dry clutch pedal pivot (Chapter 6).
☐ Faulty pressure plate assembly (Chapter 6).
☐ Pressure plate diaphragm spring broken (Chapter 6).
☐ Broken clutch friction plate cushioning springs (Chapter 6).

Manual transmission

Noisy in neutral with engine running

☐ Input shaft bearings worn (noise apparent with clutch pedal released, but not when depressed) (Chapter 7).*
☐ Clutch release bearing worn (noise apparent with clutch pedal depressed, possibly less when released) (Chapter 6).

Noisy in one particular gear

☐ Worn, damaged or chipped gear teeth (Chapter 7).*

Difficulty engaging gears

☐ Clutch faulty (Chapter 6).
☐ Worn or damaged gear linkage (Chapter 7).
☐ Worn synchroniser units (Chapter 7).*

Jumps out of gear

☐ Worn or damaged gear linkage (Chapter 7).
☐ Worn synchroniser units (Chapter 7).*
☐ Worn selector forks (Chapter 7).*

Vibration

☐ Lack of oil (Chapter 1).
☐ Worn bearings (Chapter 7).*

Lubricant leaks

☐ Leaking oil seal (Chapter 7).
☐ Leaking housing joint (Chapter 7).*
☐ Leaking input shaft oil seal (Chapter 7).*

*Although the corrective action necessary to remedy the symptoms described is beyond the scope of the home mechanic, the above information should be helpful in isolating the cause of the condition, so that the owner can communicate clearly with a professional mechanic.

Driveshafts

Vibration when accelerating or decelerating

☐ Worn inner constant velocity joint (Chapter 8).
☐ Bent or distorted driveshaft (Chapter 8).

☐ Worn intermediate bearing (Chapter 8).

Clicking or knocking noise on turns (at slow speed on full-lock)

☐ Worn outer constant velocity joint (Chapter 8).

☐ Lack of constant velocity joint lubricant, possibly due to damaged gaiter (Chapter 8).

Braking system

Note: Before assuming that a brake problem exists, make sure that the tyres are in good condition and correctly inflated, that the front wheel alignment is correct, and that the vehicle is not loaded with weight in an unequal manner. Apart from checking the condition of all pipe and hose connections, any faults occurring on the anti-lock braking system should be referred to a Rover dealer for diagnosis.

Vehicle pulls to one side under braking

☐ Worn, defective, damaged or contaminated front or rear brake pads/shoes on one side (Chapters 1 and 9).
☐ Seized or partially-seized front or rear brake caliper/wheel cylinder piston (Chapter 9).

☐ A mixture of brake pad/shoe lining materials fitted between sides (Chapter 9).
☐ Brake caliper or rear brake backplate mounting bolts loose (Chapter 9).
☐ Worn or damaged steering or suspension components (Chapters 1 and 10).

Noise (grinding or high-pitched squeal) when brakes applied

☐ Brake pad/shoe friction lining material worn down to metal backing (Chapters 1 and 9).
☐ Excessive corrosion of brake disc or drum – may be apparent after the vehicle has been standing for some time (Chapters 1 and 9).
☐ Foreign object (stone chipping, etc) trapped between brake disc and shield (Chapters 1 and 9).

Excessive brake pedal travel

☐ Faulty rear drum brake self-adjust mechanism (Chapter 9).
☐ Faulty master cylinder (Chapter 9).
☐ Air in hydraulic system (Chapter 9).
☐ Faulty vacuum servo unit (Chapter 9).
☐ Faulty vacuum pump – diesel models (Chapter 9).

Brake pedal feels spongy when depressed

☐ Air in hydraulic system (Chapter 9).
☐ Deteriorated flexible rubber brake hoses (Chapters 1 and 9).
☐ Master cylinder mountings loose (Chapter 9).
☐ Faulty master cylinder (Chapter 9).

Braking system (continued)

Excessive brake pedal effort required to stop vehicle

- ☐ Faulty vacuum servo unit (Chapter 9).
- ☐ Disconnected, damaged or insecure brake servo vacuum hose (Chapters 1 and 9).
- ☐ Faulty vacuum pump – diesel models (Chapter 9).
- ☐ Primary or secondary hydraulic circuit failure (Chapter 9).
- ☐ Seized brake caliper or wheel cylinder piston(s) (Chapter 9).
- ☐ Brake pads/shoes incorrectly fitted (Chapter 9).
- ☐ Incorrect grade of brake pads/shoes fitted (Chapter 9).

- ☐ Brake pads/shoe linings contaminated (Chapter 9).

Judder felt through brake pedal or steering wheel when braking

- ☐ Excessive run-out or distortion of brake disc(s) or drum(s) (Chapter 9).
- ☐ Brake pad/shoe linings worn (Chapters 1 and 9).
- ☐ Brake caliper or rear brake backplate mounting bolts loose (Chapter 9).
- ☐ Wear in suspension or steering components or mountings (Chapters 1 and 10).

Pedal pulsates when braking hard

- ☐ Normal feature of ABS – no fault

Brakes binding

- ☐ Seized brake caliper/wheel cylinder piston(s) (Chapter 9).
- ☐ Incorrectly-adjusted handbrake mechanism (Chapter 9).
- ☐ Faulty master cylinder (Chapter 9).

Rear wheels locking under normal braking

- ☐ Rear brake pad/shoe linings contaminated (Chapters 1 and 9).
- ☐ Rear brake discs/drums warped (Chapters 1 and 9).

Steering and suspension

Note: *Before diagnosing suspension or steering faults, be sure that the trouble is not due to incorrect tyre pressures, mixtures of tyre types, or binding brakes.*

Vehicle pulls to one side

- ☐ Defective tyre (see Weekly checks).
- ☐ Excessive wear in suspension or steering components (Chapters 1 and 10).
- ☐ Incorrect front wheel alignment (Chapter 10).
- ☐ Accident damage to steering or suspension components (Chapters 1 and 10).

Wheel wobble and vibration

- ☐ Front roadwheels out of balance (vibration felt mainly through the steering wheel) (Chapter 10).
- ☐ Rear roadwheels out of balance (vibration felt throughout the vehicle) (Chapter 10).
- ☐ Roadwheels damaged or distorted (Chapter 10).
- ☐ Faulty or damaged tyre (see Weekly checks).
- ☐ Worn steering or suspension joints, bushes or components (Chapters 1 and 10).
- ☐ Wheel bolts loose (Chapter 1 and 10).

Excessive pitching and/or rolling around corners, or during braking

- ☐ Defective shock absorbers (Chapters 1 and 10).
- ☐ Broken or weak coil spring and/or suspension component (Chapters 1 and 10).
- ☐ Worn or damaged anti-roll bar or mountings (Chapter 10).

Wandering or general instability

- ☐ Incorrect front wheel alignment (Chapter 10).
- ☐ Worn steering or suspension joints, bushes or components (Chapters 1 and 10).
- ☐ Roadwheels out of balance (Chapter 10).
- ☐ Faulty or damaged tyre (see Weekly checks).
- ☐ Wheel bolts loose (Chapter 10).
- ☐ Defective shock absorbers (Chapters 1 and 10).

Excessively-stiff steering

- ☐ Seized track rod end balljoint or suspension balljoint (Chapters 1 and 10).
- ☐ Broken or incorrectly adjusted auxiliary drivebelt (Chapter 1).
- ☐ Incorrect front wheel alignment (Chapter 10).
- ☐ Steering gear damaged (Chapter 10).

Excessive play in steering

- ☐ Worn steering column universal joint(s) (Chapter 10).
- ☐ Worn steering track rod end balljoints (Chapters 1 and 10).
- ☐ Worn steering gear (Chapter 10).
- ☐ Worn steering or suspension joints, bushes or components (Chapters 1 and 10).

Lack of power assistance

- ☐ Broken or incorrectly-adjusted auxiliary drivebelt (Chapter 1).
- ☐ Incorrect power steering fluid level (see Weekly checks).
- ☐ Restriction in power steering fluid hoses (Chapter 10).

- ☐ Faulty power steering pump (Chapter 10).
- ☐ Faulty steering gear (Chapter 10).

Tyre wear excessive

Tyres worn on inside or outside edges

- ☐ Tyres under-inflated (wear on both edges) (see Weekly checks).
- ☐ Incorrect camber or castor angles (wear on one edge only) (Chapter 10).
- ☐ Worn steering or suspension joints, bushes or components (Chapters 1 and 10).
- ☐ Excessively-hard cornering.
- ☐ Accident damage.

Tyre treads exhibit feathered edges

- ☐ Incorrect toe setting (Chapter 10).

Tyres worn in centre of tread

- ☐ Tyres over-inflated (see Weekly checks).

Tyres worn on inside and outside edges

- ☐ Tyres under-inflated (see Weekly checks).
- ☐ Worn shock absorbers (Chapter 10).

Tyres worn unevenly

- ☐ Tyres/wheels out of balance (see Weekly checks).
- ☐ Excessive wheel or tyre run-out (Chapter 10).
- ☐ Worn shock absorbers (Chapters 1 and 10).
- ☐ Faulty tyre (see Weekly checks).

Electrical system

Note: *For problems associated with the starting system, refer to the faults listed under 'Engine' earlier in this Section.*

Battery will not hold a charge more than a few days

- ☐ Battery defective internally (Chapter 5A).
- ☐ Battery electrolyte level low – where applicable (see Weekly checks).
- ☐ Battery terminal connections loose or corroded (see Weekly checks).
- ☐ Auxiliary drivebelt worn – or incorrectly adjusted, where applicable (Chapter 1).
- ☐ Alternator not charging at correct output (Chapter 5A).
- ☐ Alternator or voltage regulator faulty (Chapter 5A).
- ☐ Short-circuit causing continual battery drain (Chapters 5 and 12).

Ignition/no-charge warning light remains illuminated with engine running

- ☐ Auxiliary drivebelt broken, worn, or incorrectly adjusted (Chapter 1).
- ☐ Internal fault in alternator or voltage regulator (Chapter 5A).
- ☐ Broken, disconnected, or loose wiring in charging circuit (Chapter 5A).

Ignition/no-charge warning light fails to come on

- ☐ Warning light bulb blown (Chapter 12).
- ☐ Broken, disconnected, or loose wiring in warning light circuit (Chapter 12).
- ☐ Alternator faulty (Chapter 5A).

Lights inoperative

- ☐ Bulb blown (Chapter 12).
- ☐ Corrosion of bulb or bulbholder contacts (Chapter 12).
- ☐ Blown fuse (Chapter 12).
- ☐ Faulty relay (Chapter 12).
- ☐ Broken, loose, or disconnected wiring (Chapter 12).
- ☐ Faulty switch (Chapter 12).

Instrument readings inaccurate or erratic

Instrument readings increase with engine speed

- ☐ Faulty voltage regulator (Chapter 12).

Fuel or temperature gauges give no reading

- ☐ Faulty gauge sender unit (Chapters 3 and 4).
- ☐ Wiring open-circuit (Chapter 12).
- ☐ Faulty gauge (Chapter 12).

Fuel or temperature gauges give continuous maximum reading

- ☐ Faulty gauge sender unit (Chapters 3 and 4).
- ☐ Wiring short-circuit (Chapter 12).
- ☐ Faulty gauge (Chapter 12).

Horn inoperative, or unsatisfactory in operation

Horn operates all the time

- ☐ Horn contacts permanently bridged or horn push stuck down (Chapter 12).

Horn fails to operate

- ☐ Blown fuse (Chapter 12).
- ☐ Cable or connections loose, broken or disconnected (Chapter 12).
- ☐ Faulty horn (Chapter 12).

Horn emits intermittent or unsatisfactory sound

- ☐ Cable connections loose (Chapter 12).
- ☐ Horn mountings loose (Chapter 12).
- ☐ Faulty horn (Chapter 12).

Windscreen/tailgate wipers inoperative, or unsatisfactory in operation

Wipers fail to operate, or operate very slowly

- ☐ Wiper blades stuck to screen, or linkage seized or binding (see Weekly checks and Chapter 12).
- ☐ Blown fuse (Chapter 12).
- ☐ Cable or connections loose, broken or disconnected (Chapter 12).
- ☐ Faulty relay (Chapter 12).
- ☐ Faulty wiper motor (Chapter 12).

Wiper blades sweep over too large or too small an area of the glass

- ☐ Wiper arms incorrectly positioned on spindles (Chapter 12).
- ☐ Excessive wear of wiper linkage (Chapter 12).
- ☐ Wiper motor or linkage mountings loose or insecure (Chapter 12).

Wiper blades fail to clean the glass effectively

- ☐ Wiper blade rubbers worn or perished (see Weekly checks).
- ☐ Wiper arm tension springs broken, or arm pivots seized (Chapter 12).
- ☐ Insufficient windscreen washer additive to adequately remove road film (see Weekly checks).

Windscreen/tailgate washers inoperative, or unsatisfactory in operation

One or more washer jets inoperative

- ☐ Blocked washer jet (Chapter 12).
- ☐ Disconnected, kinked or restricted fluid hose (Chapter 12).
- ☐ Insufficient fluid in washer reservoir (see Weekly checks).

Washer pump fails to operate

- ☐ Broken or disconnected wiring or connections (Chapter 12).
- ☐ Blown fuse (Chapter 12).
- ☐ Faulty washer switch (Chapter 12).
- ☐ Faulty washer pump (Chapter 12).

Washer pump runs for some time before fluid is emitted from jets

- ☐ Faulty one-way valve in fluid supply hose (Chapter 12).

Electric windows inoperative, or unsatisfactory in operation

Window glass will only move in one direction

- ☐ Faulty switch (Chapter 12).

Window glass slow to move

- ☐ Regulator seized or damaged, or in need of lubrication (Chapter 11).
- ☐ Door internal components or trim fouling regulator (Chapter 11).
- ☐ Faulty motor (Chapter 11).

Window glass fails to move

- ☐ Blown fuse (Chapter 12).
- ☐ Faulty relay (Chapter 12).
- ☐ Broken or disconnected wiring or connections (Chapter 12).
- ☐ Faulty motor (Chapter 12).

Central locking system inoperative, or unsatisfactory in operation

Complete system failure

- ☐ Blown fuse (Chapter 12).
- ☐ Faulty relay (Chapter 12).
- ☐ Broken or disconnected wiring or connections (Chapter 12).
- ☐ Faulty motor (Chapter 11).

Latch locks but will not unlock, or unlocks but will not lock

- ☐ Faulty switch (Chapter 12).
- ☐ Broken or disconnected latch operating rods or levers (Chapter 11).
- ☐ Faulty relay (Chapter 12).
- ☐ Faulty motor (Chapter 11).

One solenoid/motor fails to operate

- ☐ Broken or disconnected wiring or connections (Chapter 12).
- ☐ Faulty motor (Chapter 11).
- ☐ Broken, binding or disconnected lock operating rods or levers (Chapter 11).
- ☐ Fault in door lock (Chapter 11).

Note: *References throughout this index are in the form "Chapter number" • "Page number"*

Haynes Manuals – The Complete UK Car List

Title	Book No.
ALFA ROMEO Alfasud/Sprint (74 - 88) up to F *	0292
Alfa Romeo Alfetta (73 – 87) up to E *	0531
AUDI 80, 90 & Coupe Petrol (79 – Nov 88) up to F	0605
Audi 80, 90 & Coupe Petrol (Oct 86 – 90) D to H	1491
Audi 100 & A6 Petrol & Diesel (May 91 – May 97) H to P	3504
Audi A3 Petrol & Diesel (96 – May 03) P to 03	4253
Audi A3 Petrol & Diesel (June 03 – Mar 08) 03 to 08	4884
Audi A4 Petrol & Diesel (95 – 00) M to X	3575
Audi A4 Petrol & Diesel (01 – 04) X to 54	4609
Audi A4 Petrol & Diesel (Jan 05 – Feb 08) 54 to 57	4885
AUSTIN A35 & A40 (56 – 67) up to F *	0118
Mini (59 – 69) up to H *	0527
Mini (69 – 01) up to X	0646
Austin Healey 100/6 & 3000 (56 – 68) up to G *	0049
BEDFORD/Vauxhall Rascal & Suzuki Supercarry (86 – Oct 94) C to M	3015
BMW 1-Series 4-cyl Petrol & Diesel (04 – Aug 11) 54 to 11	4918
BMW 316, 320 & 320i (4-cyl)(75 – Feb 83) up to Y *	0276
BMW 3- & 5- Series Petrol (81 – 91) up to J	1948
BMW 3-Series Petrol (Apr 91 – 99) H to V	3210
BMW 3-Series Petrol (Sept 98 – 06) S to 56	4067
BMW 3-Series Petrol & Diesel (05 – Sept 08) 54 to 58	4782
BMW 5-Series 6-cyl Petrol (April 96 – Aug 03) N to 03	4151
BMW 5-Series Diesel (Sept 03 – 10) 53 to 10	4901
BMW 1500, 1502, 1600, 1602, 2000 & 2002 (59 – 77) up to S *	0240
CHRYSLER PT Cruiser Petrol (00-09) W to 09	4058
CITROEN 2CV, Ami & Dyane (67 – 90) up to H	0196
Citroen AX Petrol & Diesel (87- 97) D to P	3014
Citroen Berlingo & Peugeot Partner Petrol & Diesel (96 – 10) P to 60	4281
Citroen C1 Petrol (05 – 11) 05 to 11	4922
Citroen C2 Petrol & Diesel (03 – 10) 53 to 60	5635
Citroen C3 Petrol & Diesel (02 – 09) 51 to 59	4890
Citroen C4 Petrol & Diesel (04 – 10) 54 to 60	5576
Citroen C5 Petrol & Diesel (01 – 08) Y to 08	4745
Citroen C15 Van Petrol & Diesel (89 – Oct 98) F to S	3509
Citroen CX Petrol (75 – 88) up to F	0528
Citroen Saxo Petrol & Diesel (96 – 04) N to 54	3506
Citroen Xantia Petrol & Diesel (93 – 01) K to Y	3082
Citroen XM Petrol & Diesel (89 – 00) G to X	3451
Citroen Xsara Petrol & Diesel (97 – Sept 00) R to W	3751
Citroen Xsara Picasso Petrol & Diesel (00 – 02) W to 52	3944
Citroen Xsara Picasso (Mar 04 – 08) 04 to 58	4784
Citroen ZX Diesel (91 – 98) J to S	1922
Citroen ZX Petrol (91 – 98) H to S	1881
FIAT 126 (73 – 87) up to E *	0305
Fiat 500 (57 – 73) up to M *	0090
Fiat 500 & Panda (04 – 12) 53 to 61	5558
Fiat Bravo & Brava Petrol (95 – 00) N to W	3572
Fiat Cinquecento (93 – 98) K to R	3501
Fiat Grande Punto, Punto Evo & Punto Petrol (06 – 15) 55 to 15	5956
Fiat Panda (81 – 95) up to M	0793
Fiat Punto Petrol & Diesel (94 – Oct 99) L to V	3251
Fiat Punto Petrol (Oct 99 – July 03) V to 03	4066
Fiat Punto Petrol (03 – 07) 03 to 07	4746

Title	Book No.
Fiat Punto Petrol (Oct 99 – 07) V to 07	5634
Fiat X1/9 (74 – 89) up to G *	0273
FORD Anglia (59 – 68) up to G *	0001
Ford Capri II (& III) 1.6 & 2.0 (74 – 87) up to E *	0283
Ford Capri II (& III) 2.8 & 3.0 V6 (74 – 87) up to E	1309
Ford C-Max Petrol & Diesel (03 – 10) 53 to 60	4900
Ford Escort Mk I 1100 & 1300 (68 – 74) up to N *	0171
Ford Escort Mk I Mexico, RS 1600 & RS 2000 (70 – 74) up to N *	0139
Ford Escort Mk II Mexico, RS 1800 & RS 2000 (75 – 80) up to W *	0735
Ford Escort (75 – Aug 80) up to V *	0280
Ford Escort Petrol (Sept 80 – Sept 90) up to H	0686
Ford Escort & Orion Petrol (Sept 90 – 00) H to X	1737
Ford Escort & Orion Diesel (Sept 90 – 00) H to X	4081
Ford Fiesta Petrol (Feb 89 – Oct 95) F to N	1595
Ford Fiesta Petrol & Diesel (Oct 95 – Mar 02) N to 02	3397
Ford Fiesta Petrol & Diesel (Apr 02 – 08) 02 to 58	4170
Ford Fiesta Petrol & Diesel (08 – 11) 58 to 11	4907
Ford Focus Petrol & Diesel (98 – 01) S to Y	3759
Ford Focus Petrol & Diesel (Oct 01 – 05) 51 to 05	4167
Ford Focus Petrol (05 – 11) 54 to 61	4785
Ford Focus Diesel (05 – 11) 54 to 61	4807
Ford Focus Petrol & Diesel (11 – 14) 60 to 14	5632
Ford Fusion Petrol & Diesel (02 – 11) 02 to 61	5566
Ford Galaxy Petrol & Diesel (95 – Aug 00) M to W	3984
Ford Galaxy Petrol & Diesel (00 – 06) X to 06	5556
Ford Granada Petrol (Sept 77 – Feb 85) up to B *	0481
Ford Ka (96 – 08) P to 58	5567
Ford Ka Petrol (09 – 14) 58 to 14	5637
Ford Mondeo Petrol (93 – Sept 00) K to X	1923
Ford Mondeo Petrol & Diesel (Oct 00 – Jul 03) X to 03	3990
Ford Mondeo Petrol & Diesel (July 03 – 07) 03 to 56	4619
Ford Mondeo Petrol & Diesel (Apr 07 – 12) 07 to 61	5548
Ford Mondeo Diesel (93 – Sept 00) L to X	3465
Ford Transit Connect Diesel (02 – 11) 02 to 11	4903
Ford Transit Diesel (Feb 86 – 99) C to T	3019
Ford Transit Diesel (00 – Oct 06) X to 56	4775
Ford Transit Diesel (Nov 06 – 13) 56 to 63	5629
Ford 1.6 & 1.8 litre Diesel Engine (84 – 96) A to N	1172
HILLMAN Imp (63 – 76) up to R *	0022
HONDA Civic (Feb 84 – Oct 87) A to E	1226
Honda Civic (Nov 91 – 96) J to N	3199
Honda Civic Petrol (Mar 95 – 00) M to X	4050
Honda Civic Petrol & Diesel (01 – 05) X to 55	4611
Honda CR-V Petrol & Diesel (02 – 06) 51 to 56	4747
Honda Jazz (02 to 08) 51 to 58	4735
JAGUAR E-Type (61 – 72) up to L *	0140
Jaguar Mk I & II, 240 & 340 (55 – 69) up to H *	0098
Jaguar XJ6, XJ & Sovereign, Daimler Sovereign (68 – Oct 86) up to D	0242
Jaguar XJ6 & Sovereign (Oct 86 – Sept 94) D to M	3261
Jaguar XJ12, XJS & Sovereign, Daimler Double Six (72 – 88) up to F	0478
Jaguar X Type Petrol & Diesel (01 – 10) V to 60	5631
JEEP Cherokee Petrol (93 – 96) K to N	1943
LAND ROVER 90, 110 & Defender Diesel (83 – 07) up to 56	3017

Title	Book No.
Land Rover Discovery Petrol & Diesel (89 – 98) G to S	3016
Land Rover Discovery Diesel (Nov 98 – Jul 04) S to 04	4606
Land Rover Discovery Diesel (Aug 04 – Apr 09) 04 to 09	5562
Land Rover Freelander Petrol & Diesel (97 – Sept 03) R to 53	3929
Land Rover Freelander (97 – Oct 06) R to 56	5571
Land Rover Freelander Diesel (Nov 06 – 14) 56 to 64	5636
Land Rover Series II, IIA & III 4-cyl Petrol (58 – 85) up to C	0314
Land Rover Series II, IIA & III Petrol & Diesel (58 – 85) up to C	5568
MAZDA 323 (Mar 81 – Oct 89) up to G	1608
Mazda 323 (Oct 89 – 98) G to R	3455
Mazda B1600, B1800 & B2000 Pick-up Petrol (72 – 88) up to F	0267
Mazda MX-5 (89 – 05) G to 05	5565
Mazda RX-7 (79 – 85) up to C *	0460
MERCEDES-BENZ 190, 190E & 190D Petrol & Diesel (83 – 93) A to L	3450
Mercedes-Benz 200D, 240D, 240TD, 300D & 300TD 123 Series Diesel (Oct 76 – 85) up to C	1114
Mercedes-Benz 250 & 280 (68 – 72) up to L *	0346
Mercedes-Benz 250 & 280 123 Series Petrol (Oct 76 – 84) up to B *	0677
Mercedes-Benz 124 Series Petrol & Diesel (85 – Aug 93) C to K	3253
Mercedes-Benz A-Class Petrol & Diesel (98 – 04) S to 54	4748
Mercedes-Benz C-Class Petrol & Diesel (93 – Aug 00) L to W	3511
Mercedes-Benz C-Class (00 – 07) X to 07	4780
Mercedes-Benz E-Class Diesel (Jun 02 – Feb 10) 02 to 59	5710
Mercedes-Benz Sprinter Diesel (95 – Apr 06) M to 06	4902
MGA (55 – 62)	0475
MGB (62 – 80) up to W	0111
MGB 1962 to 1980 (special edition) *	4894
MG Midget & Austin-Healey Sprite (58 – 80) up to W *	0265
MINI Petrol (July 01 – 06) Y to 56	4273
MINI Petrol & Diesel (Nov 06 – 13) 56 to 13	4904
MITSUBISHI Shogun & L200 Pick-ups Petrol (83 – 94) up to M	1944
MORRIS Minor 1000 (56 – 71) up to K	0024
NISSAN Almera Petrol (95 – Feb 00) N to V	4053
Nissan Almera & Tino Petrol (Feb 00 – 07) V to 56	4612
Nissan Micra (83 – Jan 93) up to K	0931
Nissan Micra (93 – 02) K to 52	3254
Nissan Micra Petrol (03 – Oct 10) 52 to 60	4734
Nissan Primera Petrol (90 – Aug 99) H to T	1851
Nissan Qashqai Petrol & Diesel (07 – 12) 56 to 62	5610
OPEL Ascona & Manta (B-Series) (Sept 75 – 88) up to F *	0316
Opel Ascona Petrol (81 – 88)	3215
Opel Ascona Petrol (Oct 91 – Feb 98)	3156
Opel Corsa Petrol (83 – Mar 93)	3160
Opel Corsa Petrol (Mar 93 – 97)	3159
Opel Kadett Petrol (Oct 84 – Oct 91)	3196
Opel Omega & Senator Petrol (Nov 86 – 94)	3157
Opel Vectra Petrol (Oct 88 – Oct 95)	3158
PEUGEOT 106 Petrol & Diesel (91 – 04) J to 53)	1882
Peugeot 107 Petrol (05 – 11) 05 to 11	4923
Peugeot 205 Petrol (83 – 97) A to P	0932

* Classic reprint

Title	Book No.
Peugeot 206 Petrol & Diesel (98 – 01) S to X	3757
Peugeot 206 Petrol & Diesel (02 – 09) 51 to 59	4613
Peugeot 207 Petrol & Diesel (06 – July 09) 06 to 09	4787
Peugeot 306 Petrol & Diesel (93 – 02) K to 02	3073
Peugeot 307 Petrol & Diesel (01 – 08) Y to 58	4147
Peugeot 308 Petrol & Diesel (07 – 12) 07 to 12	5561
Peugeot 405 Diesel (88 – 97) E to P	3198
Peugeot 406 Petrol & Diesel (96 – Mar 99) N to T	3394
Peugeot 406 Petrol & Diesel (Mar 99 – 02) T to 52	3982
Peugeot 407 Diesel (04 -11) 53 to 11	5550
PORSCHE 911 (65 – 85) up to C	0264
Porsche 924 & 924 Turbo (76 – 85) up to C	0397
RANGE ROVER V8 Petrol (70 – Oct 92) up to K	0606
RELIANT Robin & Kitten (73 – 83) up to A *	0436
RENAULT 4 (61 – 86) up to D *	0072
Renault 5 Petrol (Feb 85 – 96) B to N	1219
Renault 19 Petrol (89 – 96) F to N	1646
Renault Clio Petrol (91 – May 98) H to R	1853
Renault Clio Petrol & Diesel (May 98 – May 01) R to Y	3906
Renault Clio Petrol & Diesel (June 01 – 05) Y to 55	4168
Renault Clio Petrol & Diesel (Oct 05 – May 09) 55 to 09	4788
Renault Espace Petrol & Diesel (85 – 96) C to N	3197
Renault Laguna Petrol & Diesel (94 – 00) L to W	3252
Renault Laguna Petrol & Diesel (Feb 01 – May 07) X to 07	4283
Renault Megane & Scenic Petrol & Diesel (96 – 99) N to T	3395
Renault Megane & Scenic Petrol & Diesel (Apr 99 – 02) T to 52	3916
Renault Megane Petrol & Diesel (Oct 02 – 08) 52 to 58	4284
Renault Megane Petrol & Diesel (Oct 08 – 14) 58 to 64	5955
Renault Scenic Petrol & Diesel (Sept 03 – 06) 53 to 06	4297
Renault Trafic Diesel (01 – 11) Y to 11	5551
ROVER 216 & 416 Petrol (89 – 96) G to N	1830
Rover 211, 214, 216, 218 & 220 Petrol & Diesel (Dec 95 – 99) N to V	3399
Rover 25 & MG ZR Petrol & Diesel (Oct 99 – 06) V to 06	4145
Rover 414, 416 & 420 Petrol & Diesel (May 95 – 99) M to V	3453
Rover 45 / MG ZS Petrol & Diesel (99 – 05) V to 55	4384
Rover 618, 620 & 623 Petrol (93 – 97) K to P	3257
Rover 75 / MG ZT Petrol & Diesel (99 – 06) S to 06	4292
Rover 820, 825 & 827 Petrol (86 – 95) D to N	1380
Rover 3500 (76 – 87) up to E *	0365
SAAB 95 & 96 (66 – 76) up to R *	0198
Saab 90, 99 & 900 (79 – Oct 93) up to L	0765
Saab 900 (Oct 93 – 98) L to R	3512
Saab 9000 4-cyl (85 – 98) C to S	1686
Saab 9-3 Petrol & Diesel (98 – Aug 02) R to 02	4614
Saab 9-3 Petrol & Diesel (92 – 07) 52 to 57	4749
Saab 9-3 Petrol & Diesel (07-on) 57 on	5569
Saab 9-5 4-cyl Petrol (97 – 05) R to 55	4156
Saab 9-5 (Sep 05 – Jun 10) 55 to 10	4891
SEAT Ibiza & Cordoba Petrol & Diesel (Oct 93 – Oct 99) L to V	3571
Seat Ibiza & Malaga Petrol (85 – 92) B to K	1609
Seat Ibiza Petrol & Diesel (May 02 – Apr 08) 02 to 08	4889
SKODA Fabia Petrol & Diesel (00 – 06) W to 06	4376

Title	Book No.
Skoda Felicia Petrol & Diesel (95 – 01) M to X	3505
Skoda Octavia Petrol (98 – April 04) R to 04	4285
Skoda Octavia Diesel (May 04 – 12) 04 to 61	5549
SUBARU 1600 & 1800 (Nov 79 – 90) up to H *	0995
SUNBEAM Alpine, Rapier & H120 (68 – 74) up to N *	0051
SUZUKI SJ Series, Samurai & Vitara 4-cyl Petrol (82 – 97) up to P	1942
Suzuki Supercarry & Bedford/Vauxhall Rascal (86 – Oct 94) C to M	3015
TOYOTA Avensis Petrol (98 – Jan 03) R to 52	4264
Toyota Aygo Petrol (05 – 11) 05 to 11	4921
Toyota Carina E Petrol (May 92 – 97) J to P	3256
Toyota Corolla (Sept 83 – Sept 87) A to E	1024
Toyota Corolla (Sept 87 – Aug 92) E to K	1683
Toyota Corolla Petrol (Aug 92 – 97) K to P	3259
Toyota Corolla Petrol (July 97 0 Feb 02) P to 51	4286
Toyota Corolla Petrol & Diesel (02 – Jan 07) 51 to 56	4791
Toyota Hi-Ace & Hi-Lux Petrol (69 – Oct 83) up to A	0304
Toyota RAV4 Petrol & Diesel (94 – 06) L to 55	4750
Toyota Yaris Petrol (99 – 05) T to 05	4265
TRIUMPH GT6 & Vitesse (62 0 74) up to N *	0112
Triumph Herald (59 – 71) up to K *	0010
Triumph Spitfire (62 – 81) up to X	0113
Triumph Stag (70 – 78) up to T *	0441
Triumph TR2, TR3, TR3A, TR4 & TR4A (52 – 67) up to F *	0028
Triumph TR5 & TR6 (67 – 75) up to P *	0031
Triumph TR7 (75 – 82) up to Y *	0322
VAUXHALL Astra Petrol (Oct 91 – Feb 98) J to R	1832
Vauxhall/Opel Astra & Zafira Petrol (Feb 98 – Apr 04) R to 04	3758
Vauxhall/Opel Astra & Zafira Diesel (Feb 98 – Apr 04) R to 04	3797
Vauxhall/Opel Astra Petrol (04 – 08)	4732
Vauxhall/Opel Astra Diesel (04 – 08)	4733
Vauxhall/Opel Astra Petrol & Diesel (Dec 09 – 13) 59 to 13	5578
Vauxhall/Opel Calibra (90 – 98) G to S	3502
Vauxhall Cavalier Petrol (Oct 88 0 95) F to N	1570
Vauxhall/Opel Corsa Diesel (Mar 93 – Oct 00) K to X	4087
Vauxhall Corsa Petrol (Mar 93 – 97) K to R	1985
Vauxhall/Opel Corsa Petrol (Apr 97 – Oct 00) P to X	3921
Vauxhall/Opel Corsa Petrol & Diesel (Oct 03 – Aug 06) 53 to 06	4617
Vauxhall/Opel Corsa Petrol & Diesel (Sept 06 – 10) 56 to 10	4886
Vauxhall/Opel Corsa Petrol & Diesel (00 – Aug 06) X to 06	5577
Vauxhall/Opel Frontera Petrol & Diesel (91 – Sept 98) J to S	3454
Vauxhall/Opel Insignia Petrol & Diesel (08 – 12) 08 to 61	5563
Vauxhall/Opel Meriva Petrol & Diesel (03 – May 10) 03 to 10	4893
Vauxhall/Opel Omega Petrol (94 – 99) L to T	3510
Vauxhall/Opel Vectra Petrol & Diesel (95 – Feb 99) N to S	3396
Vauxhall/Opel Vectra Petrol & Diesel (Mar 99 – May 02) T to 02	3930
Vauxhall/Opel Vectra Petrol & Diesel (June 02 – Sept 05) 02 to 55	4618

Title	Book No.
Vauxhall/Opel Vectra Petrol & Diesel (Oct 05 – Oct 08) 55 to 58	4887
Vauxhall/Opel Vivaro Diesel (01 – 11) Y to 11	5552
Vauxhall/Opel Zafira Petrol & Diesel (05 -09) 05 to 09	4792
Vauxhall/Opel 1.5, 1.6 & 1.7 litre Diesel Engine (82 – 96) up to N	1222
VW Beetle 1200 (54 – 77) up to S	0036
VW Beetle 1300 & 1500 (65 – 75) up to P	0039
VW 1302 & 1302S (70 – 72) up to L *	0110
VW Beetle 1303, 1303S & GT (72 – 75) up to P	0159
VW Beetle Petrol & Diesel (Apr 99 – 07) T to 57	3798
VW Golf & Jetta Mk 1 Petrol 1.1 & 1.3 (74 – 84) up to A	0716
VW Golf, Jetta & Scirocco Mk 1 Petrol 1.5, 1.6 & 1.8 (74 – 84) up to A	0726
VW Golf & Jetta Mk 1 Diesel (78 – 84) up to A	0451
VW Golf & Jetta Mk 2 Petrol (Mar 84 – Feb 92) A to J	1081
VW Golf & Vento Petrol & Diesel (Feb 92 – Mar 98) J to R	3097
VW Golf & Bora Petrol & Diesel (Apr 98 – 00) R to X	3727
VW Golf & Bora 4-cyl Petrol & Diesel (01 – 03) X to 53	4169
VW Golf & Jetta Petrol & Diesel (04 – 09) 53 to 09	4610
VW Golf Petrol & Diesel (09 – 12) 58 to 62	5633
VW LT Petrol Vans & Light Trucks (76 – 87) up to E	0637
VW Passat 4-cyl Petrol & Diesel (May 88 – 96) E to P	3498
VW Passat 4-cyl Petrol & Diesel (Dec 96 – Nov 00) P to X	3917
VW Passat Petrol & Diesel (Dec 00 – May 05) X to 05	4279
VW Passat Diesel (June 05 – 10) 05 to 60	4888
VW Polo Petrol (Nov 90 – Aug 94) H to L	3245
VW Polo Hatchback Petrol & Diesel (94 – 99) M to S	3500
VW Polo Hatchback Petrol (00 – Jan 02) V to 51	4150
VW Polo Petrol & Diesel (02 – Sep 09) 51 to 59	4608
VW Polo Petrol & Diesel (Oct 09 – Jul 14 (59 to 14)	5638
VW Transporter 1600 (68 – 79) up to V	0082
VW Transporter 1700, 1800 & 2000 (72 – 79) up to V *	0226
VW Transporter (air cooled) Petrol (79 – 82) up to Y *	0638
VW Transporter (water cooled) Petrol (82 – 90) up to H	3452
VW T4 Transporter Diesel (90 – 03) H to 03	5711
VW T5 Transporter Diesel (July 03 – 14) 03 to 64	5743
VW Type 3 (63 – 73) up to M *	0084
VOLVO 120 & 130 Series (& P1800) (61 – 73) up to M *	0203
Volvo 142, 144 & 145 (66 – 74) up to N *	0129
Volvo 240 Series Petrol (74 – 93) up to K	0270
Volvo 440, 460 & 480 Petrol (87 – 97) D to P	1691
Volvo 740 & 760 Petrol (82 – 91) up to J	1258
Volvo 850 Petrol (92 – 96) J to P	3260
Volvo 940 Petrol (90 – 98) H to R	3249
Volvo S40 & V40 Petrol (96 – Mar 04) N to 04	3569
Volvo S40 & V50 Petrol & Diesel (Mar 04 – Jun 07) 04 to 07	4731
Volvo S40 & V50 Diesel (July 07 - 13) 07 to 13	5684
Volvo S60 Petrol & Diesel (01 – 08) X to 09	4793
Volvo S70, V70 & C70 Petrol (96 – 99) P to V	3573
Volvo V70 / S80 Petrol & Diesel (98 – 07) S to 07	4263
Volvo V70 Diesel (June 07 – 12) 07 to 61	5557
Volvo XC60 / 90 Diesel (03 – 12) 52 to 62	5630

* Classic reprint

CL 07.06.15

Preserving Our Motoring Heritage

< The Model J Duesenberg Derham Tourster. Only eight of these magnificent cars were ever built – this is the only example to be found outside the United States of America

Almost every car you've ever loved, loathed or desired is gathered under one roof at the Haynes Motor Museum. Over 300 immaculately presented cars and motorbikes represent every aspect of our motoring heritage, from elegant reminders of bygone days, such as the superb Model J Duesenberg to curiosities like the bug-eyed BMW Isetta. There are also many old friends and flames. Perhaps you remember the 1959 Ford Popular that you did your courting in? The magnificent 'Red Collection' is a spectacle of classic sports cars including AC, Alfa Romeo, Austin Healey, Ferrari, Lamborghini, Maserati, MG, Riley, Porsche and Triumph.

A Perfect Day Out

Each and every vehicle at the Haynes Motor Museum has played its part in the history and culture of Motoring. Today, they make a wonderful spectacle and a great day out for all the family. Bring the kids, bring Mum and Dad, but above all bring your camera to capture those golden memories for ever. You will also find an impressive array of motoring memorabilia, a comfortable 70 seat video cinema and one of the most extensive transport book shops in Britain. The Pit Stop Cafe serves everything from a cup of tea to wholesome, home-made meals or, if you prefer, you can enjoy the large picnic area nestled in the beautiful rural surroundings of Somerset.

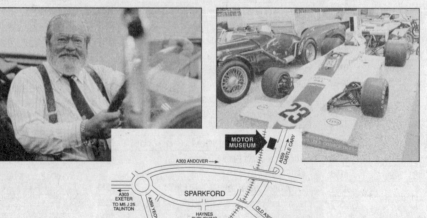

> John Haynes O.B.E., Founder and Chairman of the museum at the wheel of a Haynes Light 12.

< Graham Hill's Lola Cosworth Formula 1 car next to a 1934 Riley Sports.

The Museum is situated on the A359 Yeovil to Frome road at Sparkford, just off the A303 in Somerset. It is about 40 miles south of Bristol, and 25 minutes drive from the M5 intersection at Taunton.

Open 9.30am - 5.30pm (10.00am - 4.00pm Winter) 7 days a week, *except Christmas Day, Boxing Day and New Years Day*

Special rates available for schools, coach parties and outings Charitable Trust No. 292048